McGRAW-HILL PUBLICATIONS IN PSYCHOLOGY

J. F. DASHIELL, Ph.D., Consulting Editor

PSYCHOMETRIC METHODS

McGraw-Hill

Publications in Psychology

·

J. F. DASHIELL

CONSULTING EDITOR

Brown—PSYCHOLOGY AND THE SOCIAL ORDER

Davis—PSYCHOLOGY OF LEARNING

Franz and Gordon—PSYCHOLOGY

Franz and Gordon—PSYCHOLOGY WORK BOOK

Guilford—PSYCHOMETRIC METHODS

Lewin—A DYNAMIC THEORY OF PERSONALITY

Lewin—PRINCIPLES OF TOPOLOGICAL PSYCHOLOGY

Maier and Schneirla—PRINCIPLES OF ANIMAL PSYCHOLOGY

Metfessel—STUDENT'S GUIDE FOR DEMONSTRATIONS OF PSYCHOLOGICAL EXPERIMENTS

Pillsbury—AN ELEMENTARY PSYCHOLOGY OF THE ABNORMAL

Ruckmick—THE PSYCHOLOGY OF FEELING AND EMOTION

Terman and Miles—SEX AND PERSONALITY

Wallin—PERSONALITY MALADJUSTMENTS AND MENTAL HYGIENE

PSYCHOMETRIC METHODS

BY

J. P. GUILFORD

Professor of Psychology, University of Nebraska

FIRST EDITION

McGRAW-HILL BOOK COMPANY, Inc.

NEW YORK AND LONDON

1936

THE MAPLE PRESS COMPANY, YORK, PA.

PIONEERS IN
PSYCHOMETRIC METHODS

It is a pleasure to be able to present the portraits of twelve of those who have led the way in the building of a quantitative psychology. Without their devotion to the ideal of objective exactness in psychology this volume could not have been written. To them the book is appropriately dedicated.

Ernst Heinrich Weber

Gustav Theodor Fechner

Georg Elias Müller

F. M. Urban

Sir Francis Galton

J. McKeen Cattell

Edward Lee Thorndike

Louis Leon Thurstone

Alfred Binet

Truman L. Kelley

Lewis M. Terman

Charles E. Spearman

PREFACE

The primary aim of this volume is to teach the student of psychology how to deal effectively and intelligently with quantitative data. The typical student of statistical method is in his first year of graduate work and comes with the limited mathematical background of a single course in college algebra. Psychology has not yet reached the place where it can demand that all its graduate students shall have completed the equivalent of an undergraduate major in mathematics. The student must nevertheless become the master of certain statistical devices, must learn when to apply them and how to interpret the results. This can be accomplished, though with varying degrees of success, in a single intensive course. It is not possible to make a statistician of the average student, but he can be made to develop to some extent a sense of what is appropriate and what is not appropriate in the use of certain routine operations, and to grasp the meaning of what he does.

This volume is frankly concerned with applied statistics. There is a minimum of rationalizing of statistical processes and derivation of formulas. Statistical concepts are defined and their applications to concrete problems are discussed. References are made freely to secondary sources, since most primary sources in statistics are beyond the grasp of the average student.

A limited number of years of experience in assisting beginners in this field have led to certain convictions concerning the needs of the young investigator. It is one conviction of mine that experimental psychology is basic to all other fields, and that this is where the study of quantitative methods in psychology should naturally begin. In the past the student has typically been introduced to statistical methods in connection with problems in mental tests, and the student who is primarily concerned with experimental psychology rather than with educational psychology is left to apply what he can. On the other hand, if his only introduction to statistics has been in connection with purely experimental problems, his training

ix

is too often deficient in some of the more refined procedures better known to students of mental tests.

For these reasons, the presentation in this volume begins with statistical methods as applied to experimental psychology, in particular to the psychophysical methods. From this point of departure the student is conducted ultimately to methods of correlation and their applications to mental-test procedures. Since Titchener's *Quantitative Manuals* appeared, some thirty years ago, no book in English has been devoted primarily or in great detail to the psychophysical methods. Contributions to that field have modestly though persistently made their appearances since that time, and in very recent years interest in the methods has shown a distinct revival. It is time that the gains in that field should be consolidated. Although the various methods for scaling stimuli, such as paired comparisons, equal-appearing intervals, and order of merit, have been used for many years, their relationships to the psychophysical methods have only recently been demonstrated. They now demand a systematic treatment in book form.

Another conviction of the author is that in the use of correlational methods too much attention has been paid to the amount of correlation between variables and far too little to the types of relationship between them. For this reason, methods of correlation are introduced in connection with a study of functional relationships, nonlinear as well as linear, and in connection with the method of least squares. Recent advances in correlational methods have been numerous, particularly within the past ten years, and we have gained much knowledge of these methods from their many applications in the field of psychological tests. Detailed and critical work with mental tests, which in these days are being studied item by item, has revealed that mental tests and psychophysical methods have much in common. And so these two great wings of psychological measurement, which historically have been so long independent, can be brought with justification within the pages of a single book.

We are rapidly approaching a time when a common rationalzied basis can be elaborated for all the psychometric methods. The author has not attempted to attain the ideal here, but the common ground between the various methods is emphasized wherever possible. Last, but not least, the new subject of factor analysis has reached the stage of sufficient maturity that it can be given an established place in a book covering the field of mental measurement. The name "Psychometric Methods," too long restricted to clinical tests and the like, is surely broad enough to encompass appropriately all the topics just mentioned.

The historical tone of the volume will be evident to the reader. In a book primarily for graduate students this aspect of mental measurement surely deserves mention. It helps to serve at the same time a unifying and a pedagogical function. It is doubtful whether any technique can be fully appreciated and understood without knowing something of its evolution. The device of presenting each new method in connection with a concrete experimental problem is a purely pedagogical one. In this I have kept in mind the psychological truism that the individual "learns by doing." At the end of each chapter, lists of problems present data which may be employed by the student in lieu of data obtained experimentally by him. Chapters II, III, X, and XI are fundamental. Any of the other chapters could be omitted from a course on statistics, if desired, without serious inconvenience.

My indebtedness must be expressed first of all to the many pioneers and investigators in statistical methods and in the applications of those methods to the problems of psychology. To my teachers I owe much, particularly to Professor K. M. Dallenbach for his introduction to psychophysics. From my students I have also gained much; among these I mention George R. Thornton, Harold Dahms, and Robert C. Hall, who have read and checked the manuscript for errors. Professor L. L. Thurstone has very kindly read in manuscript form the chapters on Paired Comparisons and Factor Analysis and Professor E. A. Culler the chapter on the Constant Methods. Professor Harry Helson has read and criticized most of the chapters. Mrs. William W. Burke has improved the expression in many places. To all these I gladly render thanks and at the same time relieve them of any responsibility for errors that may still remain. To my wife, Ruth B. Guilford, I am most indebted for her continual help in the preparation of the manuscript and in its revision.

J. P. GUILFORD

EVANSTON, ILLINOIS,
August, 1936

CONTENTS

xiii

PART II.   PSYCHOLOGICAL SCALING METHODS

PSYCHOMETRIC METHODS

CHAPTER I

A GENERAL INTRODUCTION TO MENTAL MEASUREMENT

The great philosopher Kant once asserted that psychology could never rise to the dignity of a natural science because it is not possible to apply quantitative methods to its data. The *sine qua non* of a science, according to Kant, is measurement and the mathematical treatment of its data. Could Kant but glance at one of the contemporary journals of psychology, he would be amazed at the display of means, sigmas, critical ratios, coefficients of correlation, and other signs of statistical sophistication exhibited by those today called psychologists. If he were not impressed with the fact that psychology has at last become a science, he would at least be forced to conclude that psychologists as a group are expending an enormous amount of energy in maintaining a pretense that their work is science. Were his interests aroused sufficiently to examine some of the fruits of the many hours of labor at the calculating machine, he would be forced to realize that present-day methods, arduous as they are, carry us far beyond the armchair speculations of the psychologist of his day. Were he to question the motive that compels the modern investigator to phrase his conclusions in terms of probable errors and significance of differences, he would see in this urge an epitome of our struggle for objectivity. Objectivity is after all the touchstone of science, and quantitative methods are only a means to that end.

The Meaning of Measurement

Measurement Requires a Constant Unit.—We shall not attempt to formulate a short and comprehensive definition of measurement here. To state a formal definition invites controversy at the very outset. It should be sufficient for the sake of discussion to say that in making a measurement we assign numbers to phenomena and

1

those numbers may be added or subtracted.   Our general conception of measurement dates from the most primitive of examples, that of measuring linear extents.   This pencil, for example, is 15 cm. long and that one is 20 cm.   The latter is 5 cm. longer than the former. When placed end to end, they extend over a space of 35 cm.   Thus predictions can be made on the basis of this very elementary form of inference.   Such inferences are valid only if the centimeter unit is universally constant.   The constancy, and therefore the dependability of the unit, is the prime requirement of all measurement. Exact comparisons are impossible without constant units.   The use of the centimeter, the gram, and the second have placed the physical sciences in a rather enviable position in the minds of those in the biological and social sciences.   And yet it should be remembered that the greatest caution must be used in order to guarantee that those units shall be universally comparable.   The lengths of measuring rods and other devices change with variations in temperature and other conditions.   There is not a perfect centimeter, gram, or second to be found anywhere.   All measuring devices are merely approximations, some better and some worse.

An Absolute Zero Desirable but Not Essential.—Many measuring scales, in addition to having a constant unit, start at an absolute zero point: zero length, zero weight, or zero time.   Unfortunately, this cannot be true of many measuring scales, especially in psychology and the social sciences.   It has not always been true of some physical scales.   For many years the scale of temperatures lacked an absolute zero point.   When the temperature of water rose from 30 to 45°C. it could merely be said that there was an increase of 15°. One could not also say that the increase was 50 per cent, nor could one say that 60° is twice as warm as 30°.   Thus, although it is possible to make useful measurements with a scale that has no absolute zero point, the usefulness of those measurements is limited. Some psychological scales have been useful even when they lacked an absolute zero point and even when the units were probably not constant, for example, the mental-age scale for intelligence.

While a year is a year, to be sure, the increase of a year from age ten to eleven is now known not to be equivalent to an increase of a year from age four to five.   Even assuming that the mental-age year were a constant unit, because there is no absolute zero point in the mental-age scale, we cannot say that a mental age of ten is twice as great as a mental age of five.   Thanks to a rational solution of the problem by Thurstone, we now have something that approaches a scale for intelligence with an absolute zero point and equal units throughout the ages of developing intelligence (see page 440). The Binet age scale, despite its lack of an equal unit and an absolute zero, was practically useful, even as a scientific tool, just as the scale of physical temperature, without an absolute zero, was useful. Psychology has not been content to wait for perfect absolute scales before investigating its phenomena, desirable as such scales are. Neither has it been discouraged from its ambitious undertakings by warnings that it is dealing at times with pseudo measurements. Too often, it is true, the investigator is not fully aware of the type of measuring device he is using. But experience will show the alert investigator wherein his measuring devices are at fault and how he may correct them or make allowances for their defects.

All Measurements Are Indirect.—Many psychologists adopt the dictum of Thorndike that "Whatever exists at all, exists in some amount"[1] and they also adopt the corollary that whatever exists in amount can be measured: the quality of handwriting, the appreciation of a sunset, the attitude of an individual toward communism, or the strength of desire in a hungry rat. If an objection is raised that these very intangible qualities cannot be measured directly but only very indirectly, let it be said that as a matter of fact all measurements are indirect in one sense or another. Not even simple physical measurements are direct, as the philosophically naive individual is likely to maintain. The physical weight of an object is customarily determined by watching a pointer on a scale. No one could truthfully say that he 'saw' the weight. Evaluations of electrical potential, resistance, conduction, and other electrical and magnetic properties are also made indirectly by watching a pointer on a scale. The most direct measurement of all is that of visual extents, since a visual magnitude is evaluated on a visual scale. But by an irony of fate—irony for those who may hold that only physical measurements are direct—that very direct comparison is really a psychological affair. It depends upon the power of discrimination of the eye and brain. If there are any direct measurements at all, they are of this subjective type in which one sensory experience is compared with another or is evaluated directly with respect to some mental scale. Even this is indirect in the sense that one experience can

[1] E. L. Thorndike, "Seventeenth Year Book of the National Society for the Study of Education," Pt. II, p. 16, 1918.

be evaluated only by comparing it with another, either in perception or in retrospection.

The question of direct versus indirect measurement, when we are dealing with *objective* measurements, is a relative matter. It must be granted that, to measure such psychological attributes as appreciation of beauty, strength of leadership, or creative ability, we must depend upon secondary signs of these attributes. The secondary signs bear some functional relationship (in the mathematical sense) to the thing we wish to measure, just as the movement of a pointer on a scale is assumed to bear a functional relationship to the physical phenomenon under consideration. The functional relationship may be simpler and more dependable in the latter case than in the former and the type of relationship may be more obvious. That is the only logical difference. It is admittedly a difference of some practical consequence. But it is not a difference which leads to the conclusion that measurement is possible in the one case and impossible in the other.

Ordinal versus Cardinal Evaluations.—It is sometimes pointed out that the so-called measurements in psychology rest upon ordinal numbers rather than cardinal numbers. A score obtained by an individual in a mental test, for example, is an indicator, not of so many units of ability, but of a relative rank position of that individual among all the ranks possible for that test. There is much truth in this. It is obvious that, if the test items vary in difficulty from very easy to very difficult, the increase in one's test score which comes from solving one additional easy item does not indicate a gain in ability as great as that coming from the solving of one additional difficult item. The increments of ability between neighboring scores at the upper end of the scale are undoubtedly greater than those between neighboring scores at the lower end of the scale, even though both the higher and the lower increments are treated as unitary. It can be shown, however, that, when a test contains a very large number of items, the increments of difficulty become very small and approach equality.[1] The resulting series of scores may thus approach a status not unlike that in which cardinal numbers apply and the scores may be treated as if they actually were cardinal numbers. This is what mental testers have done, usually without being at all bothered about the logic of the situation. A still better escape from

[1] For the best empirical proof of this point, see E. Culler, Studies in psychometric theory, *J. Exper. Psychol.*, 1926, **9**, 271–279.

the charge that mental-test measurements are confined to ordinal evaluations is the recent proposal of Thurstone and others that we evaluate our test materials on an absolute scale with equal psychological units (see pages 440 *ff.*).

The charge that psychological measurements must be limited to the use of ordinal numbers is also directed toward the evaluation of sensory experience and of other perceptive and affective reactions. A bright light, it is said, is not the sum of a number of weak lights, nor is an intense pleasure the sum of two or more mild pleasures. To some extent this is true. But it is surely not true that we must be content to assign experiences merely to rank positions on the scale of intensity or some other scale. We can do more than that. If we know, for example, that a certain blue color is placed at a position on the scale of preference that is three units above that for a certain red, and that the red is in turn placed one unit above a green, then we may predict with some assurance that the red is four units higher in the scale of preference than the green. This is the type of result that we may now obtain in psychological measurement (see Chapter VII in particular). We must admit that we cannot make such statements as, "The red is three times as agreeable as the blue," or "This light is ten times as intense as that one." This implies the knowledge of an absolute zero. But, wherever it can be said that we have equal units, the prime requirement for measurement, we are no longer confined to the use of ordinal numbers.

A Brief History of Mental Measurement

The history of mental measurement shows development along two relatively independent lines. On the one hand is the psychophysical tradition, the forerunner of the first genuinely experimental psychology. On the other hand is the mental-test tradition, centering its interest upon individual differences. The former developed out of experimental physiology and the quantitative methods that grew up in connection with the natural sciences. It drew upon the ingenuity of those who had previously used similar quantitative and statistical methods in astronomy and physics. The mental-test tradition, inspired by the evolutionary biology of the nineteenth century and biology's interest in inherited traits, borrowed directly from those mathematicians who had indulged more or less seriously in problems of probability and the then embryonic statistical methods.   Both derived much, directly or indirectly, from a common source, the mathematics of probability.   We turn, therefore, to a synoptic account of the development of statistical method and of the psychophysical and the mental-test traditions.

The Origin of Statistical Methods.—It can be said that before the year 1600 no mathematical conceptions of probability were recognized.   Gamblers had speculated much concerning games of chance when it came time to consider their losses and gains, particularly their losses.   They had even attempted to interest mathematicians in their problems, though with small success.   Mathematicians were too busy with the newly discovered fields of analytical geometry and calculus to be bothered with problems of gambling.   The seventeenth century, however, saw the beginnings of serious interest in the mathematics of chance.   Bernoulli (1654–1705) published the first book to be entirely devoted to the subject.   De Moivre (1667–1754) may be credited with the discovery of the normal distribution curve at about 1733.   From that time on, interest was aroused among astronomers as well as mathematicians.   By 1812, Laplace (1749–1827) had written what is considered the greatest single work on probability.   In it he gave proof of the method of least squares (see page 297).   It was Gauss (1777–1855) who demonstrated the great practical value of the normal curve, showing how it applied to the distribution of measurements and to errors made in scientific observations.   It was he who devised the fundamental modes of computation of means, probable errors, and the like.   To this day one often sees the normal curve referred to as the *Gaussian curve*.

The application of the normal curve and elementary statistical methods to biological and social data must be attributed first to Quetelet (1796–1874), royal astronomer to the king of Belgium. He became the great promoter of statistical method on the continent of Europe.   He encouraged the keeping of records of the weather and of such social phenomena as births, deaths, marriages, diseases, and crimes.   He demonstrated the fact that the normal law of distribution applied to various types of anthropometric measurements when unselected populations are used.   So impressed was he with the normal distribution of populations that he is said to have remarked, "As if nature, in aiming at an ideal average man, *l'homme moyen*, missed the mark and thus created deviations on either side of the average" (1, p. 276).

The Mental-test Tradition.—The essential link between Quetelet and psychology lies in Sir Francis Galton (1822–1911), who, impressed by the former's work and fired by the ambition to unravel the problems of human heredity, undertook to measure individuals on a large scale. His anthropometric laboratory, which was set up at South Kensington in 1882, was equipped to make a variety of simple sensory and motor tests. Not finding the normal curve and its simpler applications adequate, he invented a number of additional statistical tools, among them the method of correlation, the use of standard scores (see page 86), the median (see page 40), and such psychological scaling methods as the order-of-merit and the rating-scale method (6). The remainder of mental-test history is more generally known. On the side of statistics, Karl Pearson heads the list of contributors. On the side of test development, the names of Cattell, Binet, Terman, Otis, Thorndike, Spearman, and Thurstone stand out from the crowd. Greater detail concerning the mental-test tradition will be given in a later chapter.

The Psychophysical Tradition.—The groundwork for psychophysics was laid long before Galton appeared on the scene with his simple psychological tests. Intensive differences in sensory experience had been a matter of common knowledge for centuries. The concept of an absolute threshold, or lower limit of sensation, had been suggested by Herbart[1] (1776–1841) many years before Fechner's announcement of a science of psychophysics. Weber (1795–1878) had also previously proposed his concept of the just noticeable difference (j.n.d.) and his law that the just noticeable increment in a stimulus is proportional to the stimulus. In terms of mathematical symbols,

$$\frac{\Delta R}{R} = K \text{ (a constant)}$$

in which ΔR is the just noticeable difference in the stimulus R, and K is a constant.[2]

Fechner saw in Weber's law the basis for his own famous psychophysical relationship, *i.e.*, the strength of the sensory process is

---

[1] It is interesting to note that Herbart, disregarding the teachings of Kant, made some very astute applications of mathematical logic to mental processes. He even suggested some rational equations which were intended to express the attracting and repelling forces existing between 'ideas' (1, pp. 247 f.).

[2] For further discussion of Weber's law and its applications see pages 113 ff.

proportional to the logarithm of the stimulus, or, in the familiar simple mathematical form,[1]

$$S = C \log R$$

where S = the intensity of the sensation.

R = the strength of the stimulus given in terms of the absolute threshold stimulus as the unit.

C = a constant multiplier depending upon the type of stimulus and the individual observer.

Once the logarithmic law had occurred to him, Fechner launched a program of research on a truly remarkable scale. He defined psychophysics as "an exact science of the functional relations of dependency between body and mind" (4, p. 8). This conception was sufficiently broad to include not only the measurement of sensory magnitudes but also the quantification of perception, feeling, action, and attention, in fact, any psychological process that could be correlated with stimuli. Fechner's own pioneer approach was confined largely to the study of sensation, although he did make a number of excursions into the field of aesthetic perception and so became the founder of experimental aesthetics. Of chief interest to us here is the fact that, in order to make the necessary measurements for this new 'exact' science of psychophysics, Fechner was compelled to adapt old or to invent new methods. To him belongs credit for laying the foundations for all the important psychophysical methods, the method of average error, the method of minimal changes (method of limits), and the constant method. From his work in aesthetics also came the idea of the methods of paired comparisons and of rank order. Much dispute arose immediately over his new psychophysics. There were rebuttals and counterrebuttals. Many of his fundamental assumptions have come through and remain standing today, although there is still considerable doubt as to the universal validity of his logarithmic law. The law could fall, however, and Fechner's place as the founder of a quantitative psychology would still be unquestioned.

Among the important critics of Fechner's psychophysics, who made many positive as well as negative contributions to theory and to method, mention should be made of Delboeuf, Wundt, and G. E. Müller. More recent contributors to psychophysical theory and

---

[1] This law will be treated at greater length in a later chapter (see pages 152 *ff.*)

method are Urban, Culler, and Thurstone. Details concerning
the development of the various psychophysical methods will be
presented in later chapters.

The Rapprochement of Psychophysical and Test Methods.—
It is unfortunate for psychology that mental measurement has had
to undergo a bifurcated type of development. Both psychophysics
and mental testing have rested upon the same fundamental statistical
devices. Each would have profited very much from acquaintance-
ship with the other. Each has gone very much its own way,
relatively unaware of the fundamental unity of all methods of
psychological measurement. The lack of a mutually helpful
relation between the two must be charged, along with other handi-
caps with which psychology has had to deal, to certain intolerances
that have accompanied diverging points of view. To the func-
tionalist, Fechner and his tedious techniques and boresome con-
troversies seemed utterly futile, as expressed in the oft-quoted
sentence of James, "Fechner's book was the starting point of a new
department of literature, which it would perhaps be impossible to
match for the qualities of thoroughness and subtlety, but of which,
in the humble opinion of the present writer, the proper psychological
outcome is just *nothing*."[1] James's neat and beguiling phrases have
succeeded all too often where cool facts would have failed to impress.
Different points of view in psychology divide along the lines of
human temperament. Many a staunch protagonist, instead of saying, "I believe you are on the wrong track and that your approach
is sterile," might more truthfully have said, "Your particular
problems have no personal appeal for me."

To be sure, some of those whose primary interests have been in
the problems of individual differences have been able to see value
in psychophysical techniques. They saw in Fechner's careful
methods the means of measuring individual differences in sensitivity
rather than a means of measuring sensations. The methods were
regarded as useful and valid; the interpretation of what was being
measured differed. It is now generally conceded that Fechner's
notion that he was measuring sensations was far too limited for a
comprehensive psychology. Cattell proposed the notion that in
psychophysical experiment we are measuring 'errors of observation.' This interpretation may do, so long as we are dealing with
normal adult human observers. But it breaks down when we are

[1] W. James, "Principles of Psychology," Vol. I, p. 534, 1890.

dealing with young children and with lower animals. In the latter cases Cattell's interpretation would still be adequate if we can assume attentive observation on the part of the organism. But when the 'judgment' of the organism is rendered by means of a conditioned response, then the term 'errors of observation' seems hardly suitable. In this discussion the writer is assuming that equivalent psychophysical methods are used; and they can be used with success whether the organism is adult or child, human or infrahuman.

In view of the facts just called to our attention, it is necessary for us to take a very broad, objective view of the psychophysical 'judgment.' If a dog can be trained to indicate by lifting his right foot when a stimulus is warmer for him and by lifting his left foot when it is colder, throughout a range of temperatures, we need only assume a psychological scale of discriminations that parallels a continuous change in the stimulus. It is immaterial, really, from the standpoint of methodology, whether we say we are measuring the dog's hypothetical temperature sensations, his errors of observation for temperature, his thermal sensitivity, or his power to discriminate temperatures. When the experiment is over, we have data by which we can relate certain physical differences on the one hand with certain proportions of reactions of a specified type on the other; laws of relationship can be discovered in this way. The fundamental psychological processes involved in psychophysical judgments, in adult or child or in lower animals, present a different problem—a problem of psychological analysis rather than of methodology. The interpretation of psychophysical judgments will thus vary according to the analysis of the experimental situation. The point of view adopted in this volume is made sufficiently broad to permit a wide application of quantitative methods.

The link between psychophysics and mental tests is really a very direct and intimate one. Let us again take the example of thermal discrimination. Let us assume that by following any one of the psychophysical methods we have determined the differential thresholds of a number of subjects. If we take the results as a measure of individual differences, we are *ipso facto* in the realm of tests. A discrimination of small differences in temperature is, to be sure, a simple sensory test, once the organism is well trained to give differential responses. Were the test new to the organism, as the lifted-weight problem is to the young child taking the Binet test, it involves learning ability or comprehension or what else you will.

The 'passing' of the test is in a general statistical sense equivalent to the simple correct discrimination of a difference. The proportion of successes made by a child for a series of such tests, similar in the powers demanded and equal in difficulty, is statistically comparable to the proportion of 'successes' in making psychophysical judgments. Thus, the treatment of test material offers problems very similar to those in the treatment of psychophysical judgments. In recent years we see more clearly the common ground existing in those two fields and a number of investigators have been instrumental in bridging the gap that has too long existed between them. It is one of the purposes of this volume to help point out the basic unity of the two fields and to assist in introducing the one to the other.

The Psychological Scaling Methods.—The psychological scaling methods, including the method of paired comparisons, ranking method (order of merit), rating scales, equal-appearing intervals, and their variations, have helped to find a common meeting ground for psychophysics and mental tests. Their chief purpose has been to evaluate stimulus objects on linear scales, such as a scale of affective values, or of belief, or of persuasiveness; quality of handwriting, of drawings, or of compositions; personality traits such as leadership, tactfulness, or sociability; and the like. In these cases there are no physical evaluations of the stimuli and so a complete psychophysical treatment is out of the question. Yet many of the scaling methods had their origin in psychophysics and of recent years Thurstone in particular has rationalized them on the basis of psychophysical theory.

The usefulness of the scaling methods in educational problems and especially in the systematic objective mode that they offer for deriving accurate judgments of individuals has endeared them to mental testers. The latter have depended much upon them for criteria against which to check the validity of their tests and have used them in lieu of tests in the estimation of traits, for which there are as yet no established tests. The scaling methods can therefore claim the joint parentage of psychophysics and mental testing. The former contributed their rational and mathematical bases and encouraged their application in experimental psychology, and the latter contributed much empirical information from their use in education and in the problems of individual differences.

SOME GENERAL SUGGESTIONS CONCERNING STATISTICAL METHOD

The beginner in the study of statistical method is also likely to be a beginner in original scientific research. It is not out of place, therefore, to offer here a few suggestions regarding scientific research in general, in the hope that they may prove useful. The importance of quantitative method and of a mastery of statistical tools cannot be overestimated. One cannot even read contemporary psychological literature intelligently and critically without having some substantial knowledge of statistical method. On the other hand, mere statistical manipulation and sophistication cannot take the place of scientific insights and the painstaking collection of data. We are given this warning in some very apt sentences of Thurstone.

Psychology has three defense mechanisms which frequently serve to hide the absence of ideas, namely, correlations and probable errors, unnecessary instrumentation, and verbiage, all of which help to make the obvious seem profound and scientific. What is needed in experimental psychology more than anything else is to formulate problems and investigations so as to reveal functional relations which should be rationalized whenever possible. This will advance psychology toward scientific respectability with more certainty than correlation coefficients, elaborate instrumentation, and discussion about points of view and the meaning of words.[1]

The last statements should not bring us to that cynical extreme which believes that one can prove anything by statistics. The sane attitude to take is to remember that statistical methods are merely helpful and significant tools and that the master craftsman remains the master of his tools; he never lets his tools become the master of him. If, too often, we find that figures fool, it is because too often fools figure. Statistical methods are not, and never can be, completely foolproof. It requires considerable common sense and scientific insight to decide when even the best statistics have led to a valid answer.

Steps in the Investigation of a Statistical Problem.—To be more specific, let us make a brief analysis of the important steps usually taken by the scientific investigator—a job analysis of the work of a scientist. These steps will be presented in the form of rules which those newly initiated into scientific method would do well to follow.

[1] L. L. Thurstone, "The Reliability and Validity of Tests," Edwards Brothers, Ann Arbor, preface, 1931.

1. The first requisite is the selection of a definite problem. Many a graduate student is faced with the necessity, probably for the first time, of "finding a problem." To the beginner problems do not "grow on bushes." He is likely to cast about in a rather hopeless manner, later to give up with a gesture of futility. This failure can be due to one of two things, either lack of background or lack of imagination. The former defect can be overcome by gaining broad experience in a field and the latter can be compensated for in various ways. The student who reads the literature with a critical, challenging attitude is likely to find an abundance of problems. The alert individual can see unsolved psychological questions on every hand in everyday life. Many writers in the literature end their accounts of previous investigations by suggesting new problems which were opened up by their work. Every hypothesis or theory mentioned in the literature, if it is a significant one, calls for crucial experimental tests.

2. Once a definite problem is realized, is it worth while? Here the beginner needs outside help. It is a question of evaluation. Problems that appear highly significant from one point of view or system of psychology seem trivial from another standpoint. The possible fruits, theoretical or practical, of a prospective investigation must be weighed if one would make the most valuable use of one's time. On the other hand, one cannot always tell beforehand whether a certain problem will lead unexpectedly to something important or whether it will take one into a blind alley or merely prove the obvious. Sometimes one merely follows a 'hunch' or unexplainable conviction that a certain question deserves an answer. Were all investigations that seem trivial at the start nipped in the bud, some of our greatest discoveries would never have been made. It is desirable, however, to think through and *beyond* any problem in order to see its many implications and ramifications.

3. Every problem should be clearly defined. This means having a clear-cut goal toward which to work. The mere casting about for data in the hope that something may come of it rarely leads to valuable results. Data collected with no particular end in view are usually found to be defective for one reason or another, since certain controls may be omitted or certain aspects of the phenomena be left unnoticed. To be sure, even if one has defined the problem as precisely as one can, it often happens that the early results require a shift in definition. It also happens that, after all the data have

been collected and inspected, one can see other problems that may be answered by the use of the same data. There is nothing in the above rule against shifting one's definition of the problem or against enlarging it as one goes along. It should be a general rule, however, to restrict one's problem at the start and to broaden it later, rather than to start with a too vague and comprehensive task and hope to bring it to a focus later.

4. Lay thorough and detailed plans at the beginning. This will naturally be partially accomplished by having a restricted, definite problem. Preliminary trial experiments may have to be carried out in order to test the feasibility of older techniques that one hopes to adapt. New techniques may have to be invented and given preliminary trials. Careful thought at this stage will save a great amount of useless labor later on.

5. Secure adequate data. No matter how well the problem is defined and how carefully the plans are laid, if the data are scanty or biased, the results are of little value. Here the question of sampling arises. If the investigation involves the use of populations, for example, a comparison of urban and rural children in spelling ability, naturally we cannot study all the children of a country, or of a single state, or even of a single community. We should have to select what seem to be representative children from both sources, matching them for age, *IQ*, years in school, and other factors that we wish to hold constant. An adequate number of subjects must be studied. The number will naturally vary with the type of problem.

If the data are to be obtained from an introspective study or from a questionnaire, the *quality* of the subjects must be considered as well as the number. It would be better to use the responses from a limited number of capable, cooperative, interested subjects than to include the careless, unreliable responses of a great many incompetent or uninterested individuals. If the problem is one in experimental psychology, in which relatively few individuals are typically employed as subjects, the normality or typicality of the subjects should be established. Here the problem of sampling has to do with the number of repetitions of the experiment needed to give reliable results. Statistical techniques will help us to decide how many individuals or how many repetitions of an experiment are necessary to render a dependable answer, but only if care has been taken to make the proper selection of cases.

6. Make preliminary surveys of the data. The data must be systematized and arranged in a form that can be surveyed as a whole. At this stage, one needs to "see the forest rather than the trees." A little ingenuity and experience will enable the investigator to cast the data in forms that help to do this. Perhaps all the data can be placed upon one large work sheet. They can be rearranged in different ways so as to give different total pictures. Graphic devices, charts and diagrams are often helpful at this stage. One should keep constantly in mind the original questions that one undertook to answer, as well as any new questions that have cropped up during the collection of data or, what is more likely, during these synoptic views.

7. Plan all statistical computations in advance. Statistical computations are means of summarizing data, of reducing to a few numbers what originally took many numbers to express. To select the most appropriate and fruitful statistical device to employ in any case requires sound statistical judgment, which can be acquired only by training and experience. No one should make such a fetish of his statistical tools that they are employed as a matter of ritual, as if something had to be done in the way of statistics. As an example of statistical ritual note the many writers who report coefficients of correlation between their new tests and some test of intelligence, regardless of whether or not there is any point in doing so. A systematic planning of all the calculations in advance saves work and leads to greater accuracy, since unnecessary duplications can be eliminated; at the same time one computation often serves as a numerical checking device for another.

8. Check all computations. In spite of the facts that statistical tables may be used and that the computations may be done with the aid of calculating machines, errors are bound to occur. The calculating should be conducted with the aid of all available checking devices applied at intervals along the way. The best possible check is to have two persons perform the computations independently from beginning to end.

9. Interpret the results with caution and reserve. Always remember that the samples which you have studied were a limited number out of a whole universe of cases which they represent. Your conclusions are valid only for your chosen samples and can be generalized to include the universe from which they came only if they are genuinely representative. By some trick of fate, unknown

to you, your cases may not be representative. Your statistical summaries will enable you to draw the proper inferences from the sampling that you did study. The kind of inferences that are legitimate will be explained in connection with every statistical device as it is presented in this volume.

10. Display your results to the best advantage. Make free use of summarizing tables. Your reader does not care to labor through lengthy and detailed tables, although he may want them available for reference, in an appendix, for example. Arrange your tables in a logical and orderly manner so that the point you are trying to show will stand out clearly. Make free use, also, of charts and diagrams, even if they duplicate the tables. In both graphs and tables all parts should be clearly labeled; a clear explanatory heading should be included and all symbols should be defined.

Errors in Computation.—The beginner in statistical calculation often asks the question, "How many decimal places shall I save in the answer?" Not many handbooks on statistics answer this practical question. Exceptions to this statement are the books of Holzinger (7) and Rietz (8). A few rules governing the accepted practice will be given here.

First of all it is necessary to point out a distinction that is made between *absolute* and *relative errors*. Any measurement is only approximately correct. Suppose that the true height of a certain infant is exactly 70 cm. Suppose that our first measurement of him is not 70, but 70.7 cm. The absolute error is a positive .7 cm. It is the deviation of the actual measurement from the true value. Let X_∞ represent the true value and X_1, our first measurement. The absolute error is $X_1 - X_\infty = 70.7 - 70 = .7$. The relative error is the ratio of the absolute error to the true value, or .7/70, which is 1 per cent. Let us assume that a second measurement is 68.6. The absolute error is now -1.4 and the relative error is 2 per cent, in this case a 2 per cent underestimation. Absolute errors have much to do with the number of decimal places and are important in addition and subtraction. Relative errors have to do with the number of significant figures and they play a role in multiplication and division and in powers and roots.

The number of significant figures in any numerical result is the number of digits that are known to be correct. For example, if we are told that the mean value of a measurement is 37.2 mm. we may assume that it is correct to the nearest tenth of a millimeter and the result has three significant figures. The correct value lies between 37.15 and 37.25. If it were expressed as .0372 meter, we would still say that it is correct to only three significant figures. But if the result were given as 37.20, the zero is not now just a 'filler'; it means that there are four significant figures. A measurement given as 78,000,000 is correct to only two significant figures. The true value lies between 77,500,000 and 78,500,000. But, if written as 78,000,000. with the decimal point after it, it is correct to eight significant places. In any statistical study, the number of significant figures should be decided upon in advance and kept in mind. In the answers only the correct digits should be retained; otherwise it may appear that statistical 'juggling' has brought forth refined answers from originally crude measurements.

A few rules will now be enumerated:

1. In addition (or subtraction), "one doubtful figure in any column will render that whole column doubtful; hence all figures to the right of that column should be discarded in the answer" (8, p. 3). If all the figures in the last column have a possible error of a half unit, for example, if they are 'rounded' figures, that column should be discarded in the answer.

2. In subtraction watch for reduction in the number of significant figures. The difference between two numbers, each given to five significant figures, may result in only two significant figures. For example, the difference $4.2819 - 4.2784 = .0035$.

3. A product or quotient of two numbers should not be written with more significant figures than appear in the number with the fewest significant figures. The relative error of a product or quotient may be as large as the sum of the relative errors of the separate items.

4. The relative error in the nth power of a number is n times as great as the relative error of the number itself. The relative error of the nth root of a number is only $1/n$ as large as the error in the number.

5. The relative error of an arithmetic or geometric mean of a set of numbers will be comparable with the relative errors in the numbers themselves—greater than the smallest and less than the largest.

6. In the use of logarithms of numbers, if the number with the least number of significant figures has n correct digits, then an n-place logarithmic table (or at the most an $n + 1$ place table) should be used.

7. In the rounding of numbers by dropping insignificant figures, the rule is that, if the first rejected figure is 5 or more, the figure preceding should be increased by one; otherwise it should be left unchanged. If the rejected figure is exactly 5, then the preceding figure may be raised when it is odd and left unchanged when it is even. For example, 2.71828 may be rounded to 2.7183 or to 2.718 or to 2.72; 5.2496 would become 5.250, the final zero being significant. The number 7.375 would become 7.38, but 7.385 would be rounded to 7.38.

Aids in Computation.—In addition to the best calculating machines that are available, the student may find the following tables of great service:

"Barlow's Tables," Spon & Chamberlain, New York, 1919.
  This booklet gives the squares, cubes, square roots and cube roots, and reciprocals of all integer numbers up to 10,000.

CRELLE, A. L., "Rechentafeln," G. Reimer, Berlin, 1907.
  This gives the products of numbers up to 1000 times 1000.

DUNLAP, J. W., and A. K. KURTZ, "Handbook of Statistical Nomographs, Tables and Formulas," World Book Company, Yonkers, 1932.
  Many charts for the graphic solution of different statistical computations and various tables for the same purpose. The most complete classified list of statistical formulas in existence.

HOLZINGER, K. J., "Statistical Tables for Students in Education and Psychology." University of Chicago Press, Chicago, 1925.
  Some of the more useful tables also found in the preceding reference.

PEARSON, KARL, "Tables for Statisticians and Biometricians," 3d ed., Cambridge University Press, London, 1930.
  Very complete tables, most of which will be used only by the advanced student of statistics.

REFERENCES

1. BORING, E. G., "A History of Experimental Psychology," D. Appleton-Century Company, Inc., New York, 1929.
2. BROWN, J. F., A methodological consideration of the problem of psychometrics, *Erkenntnis*, 1934, **4**, 46–61.
3. BROWN, WM., and G. H. THOMSON, "The Essentials of Mental Measurement," Cambridge University Press, London, 1925.
4. FECHNER, G. T., "Elemente der Psychophysik," reprint, Breitkopf und Härtel, Leipzig, 1889.
5. FISHER, A., "The Mathematical Theory of Probabilities," The Macmillan Company, New York, 1926.
6. GALTON, F., "Memories of My Life," Methuen & Company, Ltd., London, 1908.
7. HOLZINGER, K. J., "Statistical Methods for Students in Education," Ginn and Company, Boston, 1928.

8. HUNTINGTON, E. V., Mathematical memoranda, in Rietz, "Handbook of Mathematical Statistics," Houghton Mifflin Company, Boston, 1924.

9. MÜLLER, G. E., "Zur Grundlegung der Psychophysik," T. Grieben, Berlin, 1878.

10. TITCHENER, E. B., "Experimental Psychology," Vol. II, Pts. I and II, The Macmillan Company, New York, 1905.

11. TODHUNTER, I., "A History of the Mathematical Theory of Probability," Macmillan & Company, Ltd., London, 1865.

12. WALKER, H. M., "Studies in the History of Statistical Method," Williams & Wilkins Company, Baltimore, 1929.

PART I
PSYCHOPHYSICAL METHODS

CHAPTER II

THE METHOD OF AVERAGE ERROR

(METHOD OF REPRODUCTION)

INTRODUCTION

The method of average error is one of the oldest and most fundamental of the psychophysical methods. It demonstrates the way in which measurements are made in all the sciences. We can never measure the *true* value of anything. All we can do is to take a large number of measurements of a thing. The measurements will differ from one another by small amounts. By finding an *average* of these measurements, we can obtain a value that represents them all. The average, however, is not necessarily the *true* value that we are seeking to know; it is merely the *best* value obtained from all our measurements, and it only approximates the true value.

Measurements Are Errors.—Every measurement that we make is, in a sense, an error, for it deviates from the true value that we want to find, and it deviates even from the average. Only in very rare cases does any one measurement actually coincide with the average. And whether or not the average itself even coincides with the true value, we can never know.

All the above remarks are true whether we are measuring the length of a table, the weight of a diamond, the temperature of water, or the mental ability of a college freshman. Whereas the other sciences frequently confine their interest to the averages or best values alone, psychology is interested in the errors as such. For all 'errors of observation,' as they are called by the other sciences, are dependent upon the human observer who makes them. All measurements are made by a living, reacting organism. The psychologist wants to know the reasons for these errors of observation which he makes.

Making Measurements Involves Perception and Motor Adjustment.—Observation is fundamentally a matter of perception. In most physical measurements the observation is taken by noting

23

the position of a pointer on a scale, as in the case of thermometers, spectroscopes, and balances. Experience has shown that the visual sense makes finer discriminations of this sort than any other sense is able to make. It falls within the province of psychology to make accurate tests of human capacities to discriminate small differences, visual or otherwise. Psychologists also want to know what influences within the organism, including attention, mental sets, and the like, control the formation of judgments made during observation.

Other psychological factors that enter into the process of measuring are to be found in the motor manipulation of the instruments of measurement. For example, to take a crude illustration, if the instrument is a meter stick and if we are attempting to measure the length of a room, we will rarely or never place the meter stick in just the same positions on successive trials. In instruments of greater precision than that of a meter stick, motor adjustments play a much smaller role; screws and levers replace fingers and arms. But insofar as motor adjustments do enter into the process of measuring, to that extent psychology is interested.

Thus, the 'errors of observation' that are avoided and condemned by the other sciences become meat for psychology. We not only wish to know the causes of errors of measurement but we also wish to know the extent to which one individual observer differs from another, how the various senses compare as instruments of precision, and how within the same sense the various attributes can be discriminated.

The Fundamental Statistics.—As with the other sciences the statistical procedures connected with the method of average error consist in finding (1) some kind of an average or measure of **central tendency,** whether it be the **arithmetic mean,** the **median,** or the **mode,** and (2) some measure of **dispersion** or **variability** of the measurements around the average, whether it be the **standard deviation, average deviation, probable error,** or some other. These values are fundamental to all measurement, psychological or physical or biological. All the psychometric methods of later chapters will rest upon these fundamental values.

In using the method of average error in its stricter psychological sense, the typical task presented to the subject is to adjust one stimulus so as to make it appear equal to another stimulus of a similar kind. The stimuli may be two lights, two weights, or two sounds, one of the two being a standard fixed quantity S and the other being a continuously variable V. The experimenter E sets V now entirely too great and now entirely too small. The observer O adjusts it until he is satisfied that for him it equals S.

EARLY HISTORY

According to Titchener (13, II, p. 160) the method is a "free gift to psychophysics from the exact sciences of physics and astronomy." K. A. Steinheil published a paper in 1837 in which he described a method of equating variable lighted surfaces to the brightness of certain stars. A similar method of measuring the brightness of stars was employed by P. A. E. Laugier.

Fechner introduced the method into psychophysics, describing his use of it in his "Elemente" with visual and tactual measurements. In his revision of the "Elemente" in 1882 he gave the details of his procedure, which are worth quoting.

A certain distance, *e.g.*, between compass points or parallel threads, is presented. This I call the normal distance. I am to make another distance, the error distance, as nearly equal to this as it can be made by eye. First of all, starting from an error distance that is too large or too small, I adjust it roughly, in an irresponsible sort of way, to apparent equality with the normal. Then I consider whether or not it really corresponds to sensible equality, and I shift the boundary of the error distance, thread or compass point, to and fro—until I seem, with a definitive adjustment, to have touched equality as closely as I may (4, p. 105).

This is essentially as the procedure stands today, although certain alterations have been suggested. G. E. Müller, for example, would have O adjust the variable stimulus back and forth in the region of equality, attempting to find the total range of settings that can be taken as equal. Having found this range, O then tries to find the midpoint of that range. Others have found such a task very difficult to follow out. Still others have not permitted O to shift the variable setting back and forth in order to satisfy himself that the two are equal. Moving V toward the point of equality from one direction, O may not change direction, but must take pains to stop just when he has reached the point of equality. This procedure has been used by Tschelpanow, by Hamilton, and by Kellogg (9). This alteration would probably make a decided change in O's attitude, and also in the results, for various reasons.

EXPERIMENT I. THE MÜLLER-LYER ILLUSION

Problem.—To find the extent of the Müller-Lyer illusion.
Material.—A Müller-Lyer illusion board (see Fig. 1).

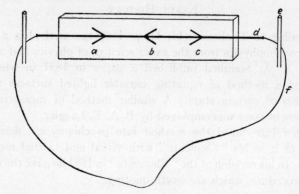

Fig. 1.—A simple arrangement of the Müller-Lyer illusion. The long black line, *d*, slides in a slot in the board which furnishes the background. Either *a* or *c* of the three acute angles may be attached to the central line and so made to move with it. The observer manipulates the apparatus by pulling on the string *f* which slides on the two vertical metal rods *e*.

Procedure:

1. Set up the illusion board at a distance of about 6 ft. from *O*. Do not let this distance change throughout the experiments.

2. *E* is to prepare the instrument for each trial and to read and record the result, and *O* is to set the instrument by pulling upon the strings, so that the two segments of the horizontal base appear to him to be equal.

3. *O* should attempt to establish some criteria by which he judges equality or inequality. He should report these criteria to *E*, and should also report any changes in criteria as the experiment progresses.

4. The instrument is set by *E* as follows:

    a. In 100 observations the constant half of the base line is to be placed at *O*'s right and the variable at his left. In the other 100 observations the board is turned over so that *S* is at the left and *V* at the right. These two sets of trials will be called *R* and *L* series, respectively, depending upon whether *V* is right or left.

    b. In half (50) of the *R* and the *L* series, *V* is to be set noticeably greater than *S*, and in the other 50 trials of each set *V* is noticeably less than *S*. In the former case, *O* has to move the adjustable end of the line inward and in the latter case he moves it outward. These two types of series will be called *I* and *O*, respectively, according as the movement is inward or outward.

    c. *E* should vary the settings still further. In adjusting the apparatus for an *I* trial, for example, he should sometimes make *V* very much greater, sometimes just slightly greater, and sometimes just moderately greater. He must not let *O* begin with the same setting each time. *O* should not see the process of setting.

5. The order of trials should be fixed beforehand and followed strictly. A good arrangement is as follows: Divide the 200 trials into groups of 25. The eight groups should be: *RO, LI, LO, RI, LI, RO, RI, LO.* Within each group of 25 trials, the great, medium, and small differences may be distributed in chance order, or by some prearranged plan that is unknown to *O.* A prearranged plan is always better than one left to chance.

6. *E* records in a properly prepared table the scale readings of *O*'s adjustments to the point of equality.

7. In adjusting the figure, *O* should proceed slowly. He may let his eyes wander over the figure at will. If he should suddenly find that he has gone beyond the point of phenomenal equality, he may readjust back and forth by small amounts until he is satisfied. If he remains in a state of indecision too long, it is best to end the trial and to repeat it later.

8. Rests should be taken after each group of 25, or oftener, depending upon *O*'s inclinations, in order to avoid strain and fatigue.

9. Find the scale reading when the two halves of the illusion are set at physical equality. Neither *E* nor *O* should know what this is before all the trials are completed.

Treatment of Results.—A typical set of results from an experiment, conducted in every way like the one outlined above, is given in Table 1 together with the method of treatment. The standard stimulus, the side of the Müller-Lyer illusion with the feathers, was 140 mm. in length, and the variable was the side with the arrowheads. Table 1 gives the actual measurements obtained from *O*'s settings.

The Constant Errors.—There are several things that we wish to know about the data in Table 1. The final objective, of course, is to measure the extent of the illusion. What length of line with arrowheads equals a line of 140 mm. with feathers? This we can find from the average of the 200 measurements. It is the largest **constant error** or **systematic error** in the whole set of measurements. Constant errors are produced by a uniform condition or set of conditions and they tend in the same direction, either toward overestimation or toward underestimation. As we expected from the beginning of these observations, the constant error is one of underestimation.

But there are other constant errors not quite so apparent in the data. One is a **space error** and the other is an **error of movement.** That is the reason for making measurements under *R* and *L* and under *O* and *I* conditions and for keeping those measurements separate for individual treatment. We do not know beforehand

TABLE 1.—THE 200 MEASUREMENTS OF THE VARIABLE STIMULUS IN THE MÜLLER-LYER ILLUSION

Right				Left			
Out		In		Out		In	
156	157	159	155	151	154	151	154
158	158	160	158	150	152	153	152
155	156	159	159	157	151	156	151
159	158	156	160	152	150	161	153
157	160	156	155	154	150	161	153
156	156	158	160	151	147	163	157
158	155	159	159	165	157	160	156
160	159	153	160	155	157	166	156
158	160	158	156	152	152	152	151
160	159	155	156	150	152	153	161
159	158	160	153	157	154	156	152
158	159	153	157	154	155	152	150
160	157	156	156	150	154	162	161
165	160	156	156	154	150	163	162
159	156	157	157	154	151	162	160
159	156	158	158	157	151	160	163
155	165	153	156	165	154	159	163
157	157	155	152	154	153	154	162
156	158	160	159	147	165	157	160
160	159	156	157	152	154	151	162
159	156	157	157	155	155	150	161
156	159	157	158	151	157	160	160
157	154	152	160	153	164	162	160
156	160	157	153	155	157	161	166
164	155	151	151	154	154	160	159

whether the two halves of *O*'s visual field possess equal spatial values. He may have a constant tendency to overestimate one-half of a horizontal extent as compared with the other. If *O* does have any such predisposition, the measurement of the illusion with only one arrangement, either *R* or *L*, would give an erroneous result. In measuring an illusion we want a value that holds good generally for a particular *O* and not merely under a too restricted set of conditions. In the same way, we want to take account of *O*'s error of movement. The outward adjustments might give one average result and the inward adjustments another.

By obtaining an equal number of L and R observations and also an equal number of O and I adjustments, the constant errors of space and of movement should naturally cancel one another in the computation of the grand average of the 200 measurements. But by *fractionating* the data into several sets, we can measure the extent of these two additional constant errors in addition to finding the extent of the main constant error. From an inspection of Table 1 it is almost impossible to guess in which direction the errors of space and of movement lie—whether overestimation is on the side of R or L, or whether it is on the side of O or I.

The Variable Errors.—The **variable errors** are also of interest, especially the manner in which they scatter around the average. They are called variable because, unlike the constant errors, their causes are unknown or uncontrolled and because they have no uniform trend or direction. They are both positive and negative with respect to the average, and in the long run they tend to cancel one another, an equal number falling on either side of the average. The size of the variable errors can be represented by a single value, which is known as the **standard error** of the distribution, or by the **probable error**.

From the data in Table 1, we shall want to find the arithmetic mean and either the standard deviation or the probable error of the distribution for the following combinations of measurements:

1. R (both O and I).
2. L (both O and I).
3. O (both R and L).
4. I (both R and L).
5. All 200 measurements combined.

Frequency Distributions

The 200 measurements as they appear in Table 1 are of little significance. By inspection one can observe that the great majority of them fall between 150 and 160 mm., with very few above or below that range. If a calculating machine is available, little labor is required to calculate an average and some measure of variability. Even when machine calculation is possible, however, we often wish to gain a better picture of the distribution as a whole. Let us consider first the 100 measurements listed under the condition "Right."

Tallying the Frequencies.—The first step is to find the number of times each measurement occurred. This is best done by a tallying process. Merely counting each number every time it appears in the table is an inaccurate, inefficient procedure. In column 1 of Table 2 we have listed the single measurements, from 151 through 165. It would seem at first thought that each of these numbers stands for a single point. This is not true. A measurement of 155 mm. cannot mean exactly 155 mm. for the reason that the measurements were taken merely to the nearest millimeter, fractions of millimeters being neglected. In Table 1 and in Table 2, 155 mm. means an observation that was anywhere from 154.5 to 155.5. In other words, every number in column 1 stands for a range of values or an interval of one whole millimeter and not just a point. For the sake of reminding ourselves that this is true, in column 2 are written the upper and lower limits of the intervals. The numbers in column 1 stand for the midpoints of those intervals.

TABLE 2.—FREQUENCY DISTRIBUTION FOR THE R-MEASUREMENTS

(1) Measurement (X)	(2) Interval (i)	(3) Tallied frequencies	(4) Numerical frequencies (f)	(5) fX
165	164.5–165.5	//	2	330
164	163.5–164.5	/	1	164
163	162.5–163.5		0	000
162	161.5–162.5		0	000
161	160.5–161.5		0	000
160	159.5–160.5	//// //// ////	15	2400
159	158.5–159.5	//// //// //// /	16	2544
158	157.5–158.5	//// //// ////	14	2212
157	156.5–157.5	//// //// ////	14	2198
156	155.5–156.5	//// //// //// ////	20	3120
155	154.5–155.5	//// ///	8	1240
154	153.5–154.5	/	1	154
153	152.5–153.5	////	5	765
152	151.5–152.5	//	2	304
151	150.5–151.5	//	2	302

$$N = 100 \quad \Sigma fX = 15733$$

$$M = \frac{\Sigma fX}{N} = \frac{15733}{100} = 157.33$$

Grouping the Frequencies.—Table 2 gives us at once a much more significant picture of the scattering of measurements for the 100 observations made under condition R. We now see that with very few exceptions they fall between 154 and 161 and that 158 is about the center of the cluster within that range. We could proceed from this point to find a mean and a measure of variability. But the labor of computing these values can be shortened still more by grouping the data into **class intervals** (or **step intervals**). In Table 2 each class represents a range of 1 mm. There is no reason why we could not make that range (which is designated by the symbol i, for interval) greater than 1 mm. and thereby reduce the number of classes.

The number of classes is determined by several considerations. If the range of all the measurements is narrow, as in Table 2, the number of classes will be small even if the size of the interval is only 2 mm. If the total range is very great, more classes are possible, but for the sake of convenience the size of the class interval is made larger and the number of classes is decreased. Grouping data into classes always introduces a slight error into the computations, and the smaller the number of classes, the greater the error. This is known as the **error of grouping.** In selecting the size of the class interval, therefore, one has to steer between the desire for convenience and the desire for accuracy.

The total range for the R data in Table 1 is from 151 through 165, or a total of 15 points. If the interval is 2 mm., there will be 8 classes. Writers on statistics usually recommend not less than 10 and not more than 25 classes, although it is probably safe to say that in practice from 10 to 15 classes is the usual number. Less than 10 classes are not infrequently used. For the sake of illustrating the grouping process, the writer uses only 8 classes in the problem in Table 3. Ordinarily, in such a case one would let $i = 1$ mm. and there would be 15 classes as in Table 2.

We could set up a new frequency distribution by revamping Table 2, combining the classes by two's. Generally that is not the way it is done. One begins with a set of measurements like those in Table 1. Having decided upon the size of the interval, the next task is to establish the limits of each interval. Since we have decided to let $i = 2$ mm., and since we are accustomed to count by two's, we might naturally begin the intervals at 150, 152, 154, and so on up to 164. But it must be remembered that a measurement of 150 actually includes all those from 149.5 to 150.5. Therefore, we must begin each class interval .5 lower than the limits just suggested. They will have to be 149.5, 151.5, 153.5, and so on up to 163.5. These are to be the lower limits. What shall the upper limits be? Naturally the upper limit of each class should reach the lower limit of the class next higher.

But it is customary not to write the limits in just that way. Instead of 149.5 to 151.5, we write 149.5 to 151.4, or 149.5 to 151.49. That is, the upper limit approaches very closely but does not quite equal the lower limit of the next higher class. There are good reasons for this. Suppose that the original measurements had been made to the nearest tenth of a millimeter and that the class intervals were still to be 2 mm. A measurement of 151.5 would be difficult to place if we let that value stand for the limits of two adjacent classes. In the present problem that difficulty will not arise, but we shall name the limits of the intervals in the customary manner.

There are exceptions to the rules just given. There are cases in which a measurement does not represent the *midpoint* of a small range, but rather the *lower limit* of an interval. For example, mental-test scores are usually not treated as midpoints. A score of 60 is taken to mean not less than 60 and the inference is that it stands for an interval from 60 to 60.99 rather than from 59.5 to 61.49. An individual who makes a score of 60 points, we assume, has just lacked making 61, or has made in reality something between 60 and 61. The same applies to the use of age measurements. Ordinarily a six-year-old child is one anywhere between 6.00 and 6.99 years of age. Some investigators prefer to speak of a six-year-old child as being anywhere from 5.50 through 6.49 years. This puts the measurements in the same category as those in Table 2. In the first two cases cited in this paragraph, class intervals must begin with whole numbers. In the third case they must begin at the half-unit position. The student should be quite clear what variety of measurements he has to deal with before deciding the question of limits to his class intervals.

Another thing to be decided is what single value shall be used to represent each class interval. In Table 2 this was a very easy matter. When i is greater than 1, there is sometimes difficulty in deciding this question, although a little clear thinking will enable one to meet any particular case. In general we make the assumption that the measurements in any class are evenly distributed throughout the interval and that the midpoint of the interval is its best representative value. It can be seen from the shape of the distribution in Table 3 that the measurements are probably not distributed evenly or even symmetrically over an interval. Below the average they probably bunch more toward the upper limits of the intervals and above the average they cluster more toward the lower limits. To assume an even distribution throughout the intervals has a tendency to widen the scatter and to increase the measure of variability. This is the error of grouping referred to before. A correction for this error is given later in this chapter. The average is probably not affected by the process of grouping. In Table 3, column 2, the midpoints are given for the various intervals. In this simple example of grouping, the midpoint is easy to find. When i is greater than 2, it is probably wise to make a diagram such as the following, until one is reasonably practiced in estimating midpoints.

Midpoint = 52.0

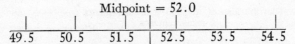

TABLE 3.—FREQUENCY DISTRIBUTION OF THE R-MEASUREMENTS GROUPED IN CLASS INTERVALS

(1) Interval	(2) Mid-point	(3) Tallied frequencies	(4) Numerical frequencies
163.5–165.4	164.5	///	3⎫
161.5–163.4	162.5		0⎪ 48
159.5–161.4	160.5	//// //// ////	15⎬
157.5–159.4	158.5	//// //// //// //// //// ////	30⎭
155.5–157.5	156.5	//// //// //// //// //// //// ////	34
153.5–155.4	154.5	//// ////	9⎫
151.5–153.4	152.5	//// //	7⎬ 18
149.5–151.4	150.5	//	2⎭

$N = 100$

GRAPHIC REPRESENTATION OF DISTRIBUTIONS

It is often desirable to show what the distribution of frequencies looks like when plotted in the form of a **histogram** or in the form of a **frequency polygon**. Figures 2*A* and 2*B* show two pairs of overlapping frequency polygons obtained from the data in Table 1. Figure 3 shows both a histogram and a frequency polygon for all 200 measurements combined. In either case, along the **abscissa** or X-axis, we lay off the values of the class intervals, using some convenient distance as the unit. The end values or lower limits of the class

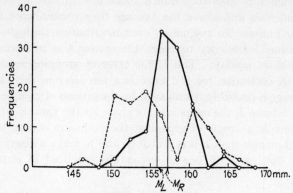

FIG. 2A.—Distributions of the 100 R-measurements (———) and the 100 L-measurements (– – – – –).

intervals, or some convenient integers, are written along the line representing the abscissa. Along the **ordinate** or Y-axis, we lay off units of frequency. The distance allowed to each degree of frequency is again a matter of convenience.

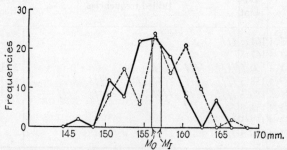

FIG. 2B.—Distributions of the 100 O-measurements (———) and the 100 I-measurements (– – – – –).

The histogram is sometimes called a **column diagram.** It is a series of rectangles, each with the base equal to the class interval and its height equal to the number of cases in that class. Thus each single case is represented by a small area, and every column of such units has an area proportional to the number of cases in that interval. The sum of the areas of all the columns represents N, the total number of cases.

In plotting the frequency polygon we locate a series of points. The midpoint of each class interval is taken as the X value, or abscissa value of each class of measurements, and the frequency is the Y value or ordinate value. It will be noticed that in Fig. 3 the dotted line of the frequency polygon passes through the points in the middle of the top of each column and that the points are connected by straight lines. The polygon is probably a more correct representation of a distribution for two reasons. It does not assume, as does the histogram, that the cases within any class

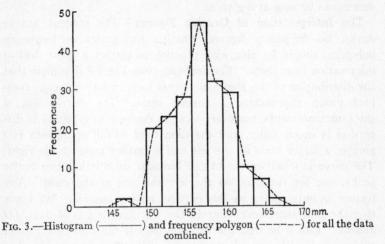

FIG. 3.—Histogram (————) and frequency polygon (------) for all the data combined.

are evenly distributed throughout that class interval. It suggests that the cases in any interval, above or below the mean, are really bunched more on the side of the interval nearest to the mean. Finally—and this may be a result of what has just been said—the polygon approaches more closely in shape the smooth normal distribution curve that is seen in Fig. 4. It is inferior to the histogram in only one respect. Both are drawn so that the total number of measurements is in proportion to the total area included within the boundaries of the figure. But because of the somewhat irregular upper boundaries of the class intervals in the usual polygon, the area under the boundary does not truly represent the proportion of cases falling within that interval. As the polygon approaches the smooth distribution curve, however, this error is overcome and the area in any class interval then gives a correct idea of the proportion of the cases in that class.   In practice, this is no handicap to the use of the frequency polygon.

In all the frequency polygons the means have been represented in the form of vertical lines erected perpendicular to the X-axis at the values of the means.   These values are stated exactly in Table 5, on page 53.   It can be seen that the mean is in every case approximately the 'center of gravity' of the distribution.   Approximately half of the area of the polygon should be found on either side of the vertical line at the mean.   When two distributions are shown overlapping, as in Figs. $2A$ and $2B$, the relative positions of the two means can be seen at a glance.

The Interpretation of Graphic Figures.—The student having drawn his frequency figures, whether histograms or frequency polygons, should be able with practice to extract a great deal of information from them.   For example, from Fig. $2A$ it is plain that the distribution of the R-measurements forms a homogeneous compact group approaching a normal shape.   The distribution of the L-measurements, however, does not conform to type.   The dispersion is much wider, and the data tend to fall apart into two groups, a larger mass at the left and a smaller mass at the right. The curve is what we would call **bimodal** since it has two major peaks, one for the mass at the left and one at the right.   Any feature as outstanding as this requires an explanation.   We know that the L-measurements contain two fractions or sets of data, LO and LI.   Can it be that the two sets tend to fall into two distinct groups and with two distinct averages?   This is possible, but without examining the two distributions, LO and LI, separately, we have no right to say that this is the cause of the bimodal polygon in Fig. $2A$.   When the writer compared these two distributions, he found that, on the whole, the LO cases formed the greater bulk of the mass at the left and the LI cases for the most part were responsible for the smaller peak at the right, but there was much overlapping of the two distributions.   If the number of L-measurements had been doubled, the total distribution might have filled up most of the gaps in the frequency polygon in Fig. $2A$, but it is doubtful whether this would eliminate the bimodal distribution.   The difference between the means of the LI- and LO-measurements was found to be about 4 mm., which is likely to be significant, so that the two peaks of the combined distribution would probably stand apart no matter how many more experiments were made under the same conditions. The reason for this conclusion will be clearer after the discussion of the **significance of differences** later in this chapter.

Figure 2*B* shows two almost identical distributions for the *O*- and *I*-measurements. The former measurements give a rather smooth unimodal polygon. The latter give a more irregular boundary, but it is probably a unimodal distribution, needing only additional measurements to make it smooth. The dispersions of the two are apparently about equal, but the mean of the *I*-measurements is slightly greater than that for the *O*-measurements, as can be seen by the vertical lines that have been erected at those two values on the *X*-axis. The difference between the means is also suggested by the relative positions of the two contours, the dotted lines being in advance of the solid ones nearly all the way along the whole range of measurements.

Skewness.—While, as was said before, the line that is erected at the mean of a distribution normally divides the whole frequency surface into two equal parts, this is not always the case. It is the case when the polygon is relatively smooth and symmetrical. Sometimes it is interesting to compare the two halves of the same distribution, the right and the left. It may happen that the two halves are not at all the same shape; the one may have a much wider scatter of values on the *X*-axis than the other. When this is true we speak of the distribution as a whole as being *skewed*. The meaning of **skewness** and how to measure its degree will be discussed more fully in the following chapter. Whenever the student finds a distribution that is skewed, he should look for a reason. In Fig. 2*A* the polygon for the *L*-measurements comes nearest to being skewed of any of the distributions we have discussed. The bunching of cases near the mean on the left and the prolongation of the distribution on the right we call a *positive* skewness. This is only slightly true of the distribution just mentioned in Fig. 2*A*. A *negatively* skewed curve is of course just the opposite; the bunching is at the right of the mean.

The Best-fitting Normal Distribution Curve.—By a process that will be described in the following chapter, we can find the theoretical normal distribution curve which comes nearest to any obtained frequency distribution. We see such a normal curve overlapping the original polygon for the whole 200 measurements in Fig. 4.

The smooth curve represented there is the kind of distribution we should expect to obtain if we had made thousands of measurements instead of only 200. The best-fitting curve is shown here with its arithmetic mean and standard deviation so that the student may have a better conception of the computations about to follow. We

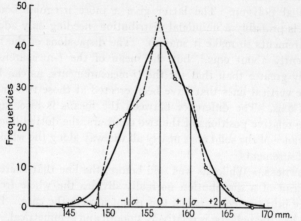

FIG. 4.—The best-fitting normal frequency distribution curve (————) and the frequency polygon (– – – – –) of the observed data.

shall now turn to the computation of certain well-known measures of central tendency and of dispersion.

MEASURES OF CENTRAL TENDENCY

The Mode.—For a quickly and easily computed measure of central tendency, the mode will serve. The **mode** is the measurement that has the greatest frequency. In an extremely large number of measurements we should expect more of them to coincide with the true value, or the unit nearest to it, than with any other value. In a relatively small number of trials, however, some other single value may be obtained a greater number of times than the best one. In Table 1, for example, in the 100 ungrouped R-measurements, the greatest number of times any one value appears is 20, for the stimulus value of 156 mm. We are going to find that the arithmetic mean is 157.36, which would lead us to expect more measurements of 157 than of any other amount. The mode that is found from ungrouped data is thus often misleading. By using grouped data we obtain a mode that is usually nearer the truth. In Table 3 the greatest frequency comes in the interval 155.5 to 157.4. Assuming that the 34 cases are evenly distributed, or even that they are symmetrically distributed throughout this interval, we may take the midpoint of the interval as the modal value. The mode from this procedure is 156.5, which is nearer the mean than the first one we obtained.

Even with grouped data it is difficult at times to decide upon the location of the mode because there may be more than one very large frequency. These large frequencies may be side by side or they may be separated by intervals of lower frequency, as we find in the frequency polygons in Figs. 2A and 2B.[1] In Table 3, for example, two intervals lead all the rest in the number of frequencies. It might seem most reasonable to take the mode as lying midway between the two since their frequencies are so nearly the same. This would make the mode 157.5, which is still nearer the mean than before. Indeed, at times more than two classes must be taken into consideration. The student must use discretion in deciding how many intervals to use in locating the mode. To take the L-distribution in Fig. 2A as an illustration, the maximal frequency is 19 in the interval 153.5 to 155.4. This would make the mode 154.5, which is probably as well as a single mode can be established for this distribution. It was remarked before that this distribution is distinctly bimodal. If we were to locate the two modes, one for the mass at the left and one at the right, the latter is easily established at 160.5. The mode at the left is probably not 154.5, as was suggested by the total distribution, but 152.5, the midpoint between the two maximal points of about equal size. The modes for the two distributions in Fig. 2B would be placed at the same point, namely, 156.5, although for the O-distribution the mode might be located more accurately at 155.5, or midway between the two outstanding frequencies.

It is evident from the amount of guesswork involved in attempting to locate the four modes just mentioned that no mode is a very reliable kind of average. However, when the number of cases is very large, the mode may be surprisingly close to the mean, as in the total distribution in Fig. 3. The mode would be placed exactly at 156.5. The mean is 156.64, so the discrepancy is exceedingly small and the mode has given a very accurate average with a

---

[1] Kelley (8, p. 60) has suggested a *sliding average method* of finding the mode in such cases as this.

minimum of labor. A mode, nevertheless, is regarded as a preliminary value and some other measure of central tendency, either
median or mean, is computed to replace it when time is available.

The Median.—The **median** is the value of the midmost measure.
It divides the total number of measurements into two equal parts.
In the case of the 100 R-measurements in Table 1, for example, it
is the stimulus value above which there are 50 and below which there
are 50 frequencies. If one had the 100 measurements placed in
order of their size, from the smallest to the largest, one could count
up to the 50th and 51st, and the value midway between them, if
there is a gap at all between them, is the median. If N is an uneven
number, then there is a single midmost value which is the median.
The median given in terms of a formula applying to ungrouped data
is

$$Mdn = \frac{N+1}{2} \text{ measure in order of size} \tag{1}$$

As usually happens, however, either when N is even or when it is
odd, there are a number of measures found at the value which
is midmost. In Table 1 the 50th and 51st R-measurements come
along with 12 others at the value of 157. No one would be prepared
to call 157 the exact median, for there are 40 frequencies below that
value and 48 above it. We can determine the midmost value of the
100 measurements more accurately than that. We assume that the
12 measurements of 157 mm. are evenly distributed over the range
from 156.5 to 157.5. The median is above 10 of these 12 measurements and below 2 of them, in the interval between 156.5 and 157.5;
$^{10}\!/_{12}$ of that distance is .83. The lower limit, 156.5 plus .83, is
157.33, which may be taken as an exact estimate of the median for
the ungrouped data. Since the student will usually deal with
grouped data, we shall illustrate how the median is found by using
the distribution as grouped in Table 3, column 4.

Starting at the lower limit of the distribution and summing the
frequencies, we find that the 50th case lies in the interval 155.5 to
157.4. Eighteen of the cases lie below the lower limit of that
interval. This means that the remaining 32 cases, which we need
in order to reach the 50th measurement, fall above the point 155.5 in
the interval 155.5 to 157.4. There are 34 cases in this interval.
The 50th case lies $^{32}\!/_{34}$ of the way between 155.5 and 157.5; $^{32}\!/_{34}$ of
2 is equal to 1.88. The 50th case lies 1.88 mm. above 155.5, or at

157.38, which is the median. This is practically identical with the arithmetic mean to be found later, the latter being 157.36.

As a check upon the calculation of the median, it is often wise to compute it by starting from the uppermost value in the range and working downward. Summing the frequencies, we find 48 above the point 157.5 (see Table 3, column 4). We need 2 more of the 34 frequencies in the next lower interval. The median is $\frac{2}{34}$ of 2 mm. below 157.5, the upper limit of the class that contains it; 2/34 of 2 is .12, and $157.5 - .12 = 157.38$, which checks with the median just found from the other end of the range.

Formulas can be given for these processes. First for calculating the median from below up,

$$Mdn = l + \left[\frac{\frac{N}{2} - F_l}{f_p}\right]i \qquad (2a)$$

and secondly from above down,

$$Mdn = u - \left[\frac{\frac{N}{2} - F_g}{f_p}\right]i \qquad (2b)$$

where l = the lower limit of the class containing the *Mdn.*

u = the upper limit of the class containing the *Mdn.*

F_l = the sum of the frequencies below the class containing the *Mdn.*

F_g = the sum of the frequencies above the class containing the *Mdn.*

f_p = the frequency of the class in which the *Mdn* lies.

The median has several points in its favor as a measure of central tendency. It is almost as quickly and easily determined as the mode, and yet it is more reliable. It makes use of all the measurements. It will coincide with the arithmetic mean when the distribution is symmetrical about its midpoint. When N is relatively small, the median is sometimes preferred to the mean. This is especially true when one or more measurements are located far off at one end of the range. In the process of finding the mean, all the measurements are given their chance to influence the value of the central tendency, and the farther from the mean they are, the more weight they have. One or two extreme values among 15 or 20, let us say, would therefore have a disproportionate 'weight' in placing the mean. In finding a median, every value above or below the central tendency has just as much influence as any other, no matter how far from the median it is. It is merely a matter of counting cases and not weighting them according to their distance from the center of gravity as is done in finding the mean. In later chapters the student will find examples in which the median is the best value for a distribution. Other methods of computing the median will also appear, some of which are more accurate than the one just described.

The Arithmetic Mean.—The most generally used measure of central tendency, and the most reliable one when the distribution is normal, is the **arithmetic mean.** It is found, as every student already knows, by dividing the sum of the measurements X by the number of them,

$$M = \frac{\Sigma X}{N} \tag{3}$$

When data are grouped as in Table 2, the formula becomes

$$M = \frac{\Sigma f X}{N} \tag{4}$$

There are several advantages to be found in using data grouped in class intervals to compute the mean. In the first place we have fewer values to work with. In our illustrative problem there are only 8 frequencies in place of the original 100 measurements. In the second place, by adopting as our working unit the class interval, we can deal with small numerical values in place of the large ones with which we started. Since there are only 8 intervals, our new scale of measurement has only 8 units. We could, if we chose, make the zero point of the new scale at the midpoint of the interval 147.5 to 149.5, the first interval below the one that has any measurements in it, and the intervals higher would then fall in line with the values 1, 2, 3, and so on up to 8. But we can keep our numbers still smaller by placing the zero point at about the middle of our new scale, for example, in the interval whose midpoint is 156.5. We call this value, 156.5, the **guessed average** M', since the actual mean is not far from the middle of the whole range and since the actual mean is usually taken as the zero point in any distribution. The other class intervals will then have values as given in column 4 of Table 4. These values are deviations from the guessed average in terms of i as the unit. They are designated by the symbol x'. A true deviation from the mean M is called x. In other words, $x = X - M$, and $x' = X' - M'$. The first of these two equations is in terms of the actual mean and the original unit of measurement. The second is in terms of the guessed average and the class interval is the unit.

The next step is to multiply every deviation by its corresponding frequency to give the values of column 5. If the guessed average coincided exactly with the mean of the distribution, the sum of the (fx')'s would be zero. The algebraic sum of the column is a positive 43, which means that M' is lower than M. We find a correction c', which is equal to $\Sigma fx'/N$, or .43. The symbol c' indicates that we are dealing with a guessed average and with a class interval as the unit. The actual correction in the mean, c, is equal to $(c')i$. In this problem, i is 2, so c becomes $+.86$. The guessed mean must be corrected to the extent of $+.86$, which gives 157.36 as the actual mean. In terms of a formula, the mean is

$$M = M' + c = M' + i\left(\frac{\Sigma fx'}{N}\right) \qquad (5)$$

TABLE 4.—COMPUTATION OF THE MEAN OF THE R-MEASUREMENTS AND THEIR VARIABILITY, USING A GROUPED DISTRIBUTION

(1) Class interval	(2) Midpoint (X)	(3) Frequencies (f)	(4) Deviations (x')	(5) fx'	(6) fx'²
163.5–165.4	164.5	3	+4	+12	48
161.5–163.4	162.5	0	+3	0	0
159.5–161.4	160.5	15	+2	+30	60
157.5–159.4	158.5	30	+1	+30	30
				+72	
155.5–157.4	156.5	34	0		0
153.5–155.4	154.5	9	−1	− 9	9
151.5–153.4	152.5	7	−2	−14	28
149.5–151.4	150.5	2	−3	− 6	18
				−29	

$$N = 100 \qquad\qquad \Sigma fx' = 43 \quad \Sigma fx'^2 = 193$$

$$c' = \frac{\Sigma f x'}{N} = .43 \qquad c = (c')i = .86 \qquad M = M' + c = 157.36$$

$$\sigma' = \sqrt{\frac{\Sigma f x'^2}{N} - c'^2} = \sqrt{\frac{193}{100} - .1849} = \sqrt{1.7451} = 1.32$$

$$\sigma = (\sigma')i = 2.64 \qquad PE = .6745\sigma = 1.78$$

$$\sigma_M = \frac{\sigma}{\sqrt{N}} = .264 \qquad PE_M = .178$$

Measures of Dispersion or Variability

The Standard Deviation.—The standard deviation (σ) is sometimes called the *root mean square* deviation. It is, in fact, the square root of the mean of the deviations squared. The simplest formula for σ is[1]

$$\sigma = \sqrt{\frac{\Sigma f x^2}{N}} \qquad (6)$$

in which x is a deviation from the obtained means and equals $(X - M)$. This formula applies, then, only when the exact deviations are used, the mean being known. When the deviations are taken from a guessed average and are measured in terms of a class interval, as in the present solution, the formula is

$$\sigma = i\sqrt{\frac{\Sigma f x'^2}{N} - c'^2} = i\sqrt{\frac{\Sigma f x'^2}{N} - \left(\frac{\Sigma f x'}{N}\right)^2} \qquad (7)$$

In the example in Table 4, $\Sigma f x'^2$ is equal to 193; c'^2 equals .1849. The standard deviation in terms of the class interval σ' is 1.32. In terms of millimeters σ is 2.64.

The meaning of the standard deviation may be made clearer by referring to the normal distribution curve. Figure 4 shows the distribution of the entire 200 measurements. The actual distribution is shown in the form of a polygon in dotted lines and the best-fitting theoretical normal curve is drawn in solid lines. The whole range has been divided into σ-units, or units of 3.87 mm. For practical purposes every normal distribution curve includes about six σ-units, *i.e.*, the range is from -3σ to $+3\sigma$, and measurements rarely fall outside these limits. The range from -1σ to $+1\sigma$ includes 68.26 per cent, or about two-thirds of all the cases.

---

[1] When σ is given without a subscript, it always refers to the standard deviation of a distribution of single measurements. There are sigmas for many other statistical constants but they will always appear with appropriate subscripts.

The Probable Error.—It is sometimes more convenient to use the probable error *PE* of the distribution rather than the standard deviation. This is because the range from $-1PE$ to $+1PE$ contains 50 per cent of the measurements if the distribution is normal. Twenty-five per cent of the measurements lie above $1PE$ and 25 per cent lie below $-1PE$. The *PE* is found directly from σ by the formula

$$PE = .6745\sigma \tag{8}$$

For the distribution in Fig. 4 the *PE* is 2.61. Fifty per cent of the measurements should therefore fall between 154.53 and 159.75. Since the total range usually falls within $\pm 4.5PE$ from the mean, there should be no cases below 145.62 or above 169.11, and there actually are none, the lowest being 147 and the highest 167.

It is well to remember that the mean, the standard deviation, and the probable error belong to the smooth theoretical curve rather than to the actually obtained distribution. In using those values, we assume that, had we taken thousands of measurements of exactly the same type, the distribution would approach the smooth form of the solid line in Fig. 4. There is always the possibility that this would not be so. For practical purposes, however, we can usually assume that the three values are somewhere near the truth.

The Computation of the Standard Deviation without Grouping.— For the computation of σ without grouping the data, when a calculating machine is available, the formula is more conveniently put in the form

$$\sigma = \sqrt{\frac{\Sigma X^2}{N} - M^2} \tag{9}$$

in which X represents as usual the single measurements and M is the mean of the X's. It is still more convenient to use the formula

$$\sigma = \frac{1}{N}\sqrt{N\Sigma X^2 - (\Sigma X)^2} \tag{10}$$

In either case, the sums of the X's and the sums of the squares of the X's can be computed at the same time if the dials of the calculator are not cleared in the process.

Sheppard's Correction for the Effects of Grouping.—The effect of grouping into class intervals, as was said before, tends to increase the dispersion. Sheppard's correction for this is accomplished by the formula

$$_c\sigma = \sqrt{\sigma^2 - \frac{i^2}{12}} \qquad (11a)$$

or in terms of σ',

$$_c\sigma = i\sqrt{\sigma'^2 - \frac{1}{12}} \qquad (11b)$$

It should be added that this correction may be used only when the distribution curves have 'high contact,' *i.e.*, when the tails do not cut the X-axis but are asymptotic to it. In practice this correction is rarely employed, though when accuracy is at stake it should be. Since σ is used to estimate the accuracy of the mean, and since a larger σ indicates less accuracy, the failure to use Sheppard's correction errs on the side of safety. That is, the accuracy of the mean will be underestimated and little harm is done if the correction is omitted. When N is relatively small, less than 100 for example, σ is not so very reliably determined, being subject to 'errors of sampling.' The small amount of correction that the Sheppard formula provides therefore adds little accuracy to a constant in which there may already be greater errors. Sheppard's correction is of maximum value when N is relatively large and when the grouping of measurements is in a few broad class intervals. It can be seen from formulas (11a) and (11b) that, the larger i is, the greater the reduction in σ. When i is only 2, as in the present problem, the correction is very slight. For the total distribution of 200 observations, the uncorrected σ is 3.87 and the corrected σ is 3.83.

The Average Deviation.—A measure of variability that is simple in meaning and easy to compute is the **average deviation** AD. It is also known as the **mean variation** MV or as the **mean deviation** MD. It is simply the arithmetic mean of all the deviations disregarding algebraic signs. The deviations may be from the mode, median, or mean. The formula, when dealing with raw ungrouped data and with deviations from the mean, is

$$AD = \frac{\Sigma|x|}{N} \qquad (12)$$

in which $\Sigma|x|$ is the absolute sum of all the deviations $(X - M)$ whether negative or positive in sign. When X is greater than M, we use the positive differences $(X - M)$. When X is less than M, we use the positive differences $(M - X)$. In machine calculations it is convenient to take advantage of the fact that the sum of the deviations above the mean is equal to the sum of the deviations below the mean. We can cut the work in two, therefore, by dealing only with the deviations on one side of the mean and doubling their sum to give $\Sigma|x|$. The formula is then as follows:

$$AD = \frac{2(\Sigma X_g - N_g M)}{N} = \frac{2(N_l M - \Sigma X_l)}{N} \quad (13)$$

where ΣX_g and ΣX_l are the sums of the measurements greater than and less than the mean, respectively, and where N_g and N_l are the numbers of measurements greater than and less than the mean, respectively.

When dealing with data that are grouped in class intervals with a guessed average, the formula is

$$AD = \left[\frac{\Sigma|fx'| + c'(F_l - F_g)}{N} \right] i \quad (14)$$

in which $\Sigma|fx'|$ is the absolute sum of the (fx')'s, disregarding signs (see column 5 of Table 4); F_l is the sum of the frequencies for those steps whose midpoints are lower than the mean; F_g is the sum of the frequencies for those steps whose midpoints are greater than the mean; and i is the size of the step interval.

In the problem of Table 4, for example, the AD is

$$\frac{101 + .43(52 - 48)}{100} \times 2 = \frac{101 + 1.72}{100} \times 2 = \frac{102.72}{100} \times 2 = 2.05.$$

The average deviation is a quickly found substitute for the standard deviation or the probable error. It may even be used to estimate the value of σ or of the PE. The method for doing so will be discussed presently. The AD is to be preferred to the other two measures of variability when the distribution is decidedly not normal. For example, the distribution of the L-measurements that appears in Fig. $2A$ is almost bimodal and decidedly flat as compared with the normal curve. In this case the AD might be a better measure of variability when comparing this distribution with others. The AD's for the various distributions are given in Table 5.

The Quartile Deviation.—Another measure of variability found even more readily than the AD is the **quartile deviation** Q or the **semi-interquartile range.** It is based upon the same principle as the median and has sometimes been called the **median deviation.** Q is, in fact, the median of the deviations. It is one-half of the range of measurements containing the middle 50 per cent of the frequencies. In size it is almost identical with the PE. It will be recalled that the middle 50 per cent of the cases fall within $\pm 1PE$. The only difference is that the PE refers to the theoretical curve and the range from $-1PE$ to $+1PE$ may not contain exactly half of the cases, whereas Q refers to the actual distribution and by actual count half of the cases fall between $-1Q$ and $+1Q$. The point on the scale that is $1Q$ below the median is usually called Q_1 and the point at $+1Q$ is called Q_3. The median marks the point Q_2. These three points divide the total frequency into four equal parts called **quartiles.** The range from Q_1 to Q_3 is the interquartile range. We can find two values for Q, either $Q_3 - Q_2$ or $Q_2 - Q_1$. When the distribution is perfectly symmetrical about the median, of course, the two would be identical in size. Rarely are they exactly the same. We therefore take the range from Q_1 to Q_3 and divide it by two, finding the semi-interquartile range as the best estimate of Q. The formula is

$$Q = \frac{Q_3 - Q_1}{2} \tag{15}$$

Using the distribution in Table 4 again, let us find Q_3, Q_1, and Q. Q_3 and Q_1 are found in the same way as the median except that, instead of counting cases up to the 50 per cent point, we count cases to the 25 and 75 per cent positions. To find Q_1 first, the 25th case lies in the interval 155.5 to 157.4, in which there are 34 cases. Q_1 lies $\frac{7}{34}$ of 2 units above the point 155.5, or at 155.91 mm. For this computation we can adapt formula $(2a)$ if we use $N/4$ in the numerator instead of $N/2$. Q_3 is best calculated from the other end of the distribution, using formula $(2b)$ revised as $(2a)$ was revised. Q_3 then equals $159.5 - \frac{7}{30}$ of 2, or 159.03. The interquartile range is $159.03 - 155.91$, or 3.12. Q is 1.56, by formula (15). Compared with the PE of the same distribution (1.78), Q is noticeably smaller. Recalling that the PE refers to the theoretical best-fitting normal curve and that Q applies to the actual distribution, the inference is that our actual distribution is more compactly bunched near the middle than is the normal curve.

Estimating One Measure of Variability from Another.—When the distribution is normal, or practically so, definite relationships exist between these various measures of variability so that, knowing one, we can estimate all the rest. The following list will permit all forms of estimation:

$$Q = PE = .84535AD = .6745\sigma.$$
$$AD = 1.1829Q = 1.1829PE = .7979\sigma.$$
$$\sigma = 1.4826Q = 1.4826PE = 1.2533AD.$$

The Coefficient of Variation.—We frequently want to compare two distributions as to variability as well as to central tendency. Any of the measures of variability will do for this purpose if we are dealing with the same scale of measurement. The σ or the PE of a distribution is always given in terms of the unit of the original scale of measurement. In the case of our illustrative problem, the unit is a millimeter. It is obvious that we cannot compare two PE's if one is in terms of millimeters and the other is in terms of years or in terms of the number of words spelled correctly. Even when two measures of variability are given in terms of the same unit, a direct comparison is sometimes misleading.

For example, let us take two forms of reaction-time measurement, both made in terms of 1 sec. as the unit. A certain subject has a standard deviation of .022 sec. in simple reaction time to a visual stimulus and a standard deviation of .033 sec. in choice reaction to a visual stimulus. On the surface it would seem that this subject is 50 per cent more variable in the choice reaction than in the simple reaction. On second thought, the normal subject has a longer reaction time in the choice reaction than in the simple reaction. Let us assume that this subject's average times are .300 and .200 sec., respectively. The subject therefore has more room to vary up and down the scale about the mean of .300 than about the mean of .200. Not that any of the reactions approach the zero point, but there is probably a certain minimal time below which it is physically impossible for the subject to go. This limit is nearer to the mean of the simple reactions than it is to mean of the choice reactions. In this case it is regarded as more appropriate to compare *relative variabilities* rather than *absolute variabilities*. The measures of variability already discussed measure absolute variability. The relative variability takes into consideration the size of the means. Using σ

as the measure of variability, the **coefficient of variation** V is given by the formula

$$V = \frac{100\sigma}{M} \tag{16}$$

This formula answers the question, "What percentage of the mean is the standard deviation?" For the reaction-time problem, V is 11 per cent for the simple reaction time; V is 11 per cent for the choice reaction also. The relative variabilities are equal. Other coefficients of variability may be computed by using instead of σ the PE, the AD, or Q. It goes without saying that one can compare V's only when they are derived from the same measure of variability.

Certain cautions should be observed in applying V. It is probably unsafe to use V unless the scale of measurement has an absolute zero point. This eliminates most mental tests. Passing no questions in a test does not usually mean exactly zero ability in that test. Most tests are made up of items varying in difficulty from very easy to very difficult. An additional item passed at the easy end of the scale is not equivalent to one passed at the difficult end of the scale. In other words, a mental-test scale rarely has equal units throughout. This is another requisite for applying V to a scale of measurement. As usual it requires intelligence to apply this statistical tool and to interpret the result. The student must always keep in mind the kind of measuring stick he is using.

The Reliability of Statistical Constants

Since measures of central tendency and of variability are themselves derived from limited and fallible data, they must be subject to a certain amount of error. Can we tell in any way the likelihood that our averages and our measures of variability are close to the truth? We can never measure all the single cases of the phenomenon that we wish to quantify. We must always be content with samples of the whole universe from which our few measurements are drawn. We attempt as best we may to collect 'random' samples —samples that, so far as we know, are not biased; samples that are truly representative of the universe; samples in which any known constant errors have been balanced against one another. Even a mean is a variable quantity. To prove this, all one has to do is to repeat one's measurements a second time, and a third, and so on. Each time the mean will be slightly different.

Suppose in our illustrative problem of the illusion we had taken not 1 but 100 sets of measurements—that we had obtained 100 distributions similar to that of Table 4, and 100 means. These means would themselves form a normal distribution. In fact the distribution of means is more likely to approach the normal form than is any set of the same number of single measurements. The distribution of the means has in turn its standard deviation and its average. One would reasonably expect that the dispersion of the means would be much narrower than the dispersion of a like number of single measurements. This is true. The σ of this distribution is very much smaller than that for the single measurements.

Fortunately, by means of simple mathematical formulas we are able to find the σ and the PE of the mean without taking a single additional measurement. It is reasonable to suppose that the more single measurements we make of a thing, the more certain we should be that our mean is correct. In other words, the PE of the mean PE_M is inversely proportional to N, the number of measurements. Statisticians have shown that the PE_M is not exactly proportional to $1/N$, but rather is proportional to $1/\sqrt{N}$. The same holds true for σ_M. The two formulas are[1]

$$\sigma_M = \frac{\sigma}{\sqrt{N}} \tag{17}$$

and

$$PE_M = \frac{PE}{\sqrt{N}} = \frac{.6745\sigma}{\sqrt{N}} \tag{18}$$

Reliability for Small Numbers of Observations.—When N is less than 30, formula (17) does not hold. The reliability drops more rapidly as N decreases among the smaller numbers as the following formulas imply:

$$\sigma_M = \frac{\sigma}{\sqrt{N-1}} \qquad \text{(when } 20 \leqq N < 30) \tag{17a}$$

$$\sigma_M = \frac{\sigma}{\sqrt{N-2}} \qquad \text{(when } 10 \leqq N < 20) \tag{17b}$$

$$\sigma_M = \frac{\sigma}{\sqrt{N-3}} \qquad \text{(when } N < 10) \tag{17c}$$

---

[1] The concept of **quotidian variability** has been recently introduced by Woodrow (16). This refers to the variability of an individual O from day to day as compared with his more limited variability under more homogeneous conditions during a single day's measurements.

In reality, formula (17a) is the correct one for σ_M, regardless of how large N is. When N is greater than 30, it matters very little whether we use N or $(N - 1)$ in the formula. The same considerations apply to the PE_M.

The σ and *PE* of the Median.—We can signify the reliability of a median in a similar manner by finding its σ or its PE. The formulas are

$$\sigma_{Mdn} = 1.2533\frac{\sigma}{\sqrt{N}} \tag{19}$$

and

$$PE_{Mdn} = .84535\frac{\sigma}{\sqrt{N}} \tag{20}$$

In terms of the class interval and the frequency of the class interval containing the median,

$$\sigma_{Mdn} = \frac{i\sqrt{N}}{2f_p} \tag{21}$$

where i = the size of the class interval.

f_p = the frequency of the interval including the median.
According to Shen (12), formulas (19) and (20) presuppose a normal distribution. As these formulas imply, when compared with formulas (17) and (18), the median is about 25 per cent more variable than the mean and hence it is less reliable as a measure of central tendency under the usual circumstances. But when the distribution is leptokurtic (see page 106), the median is more reliable than the mean. The ratio of σ_{Mdn} to σ_M is given by the formula

$$\frac{\sigma_{Mdn}}{\sigma_M} = \frac{iN}{2f_p\sigma} \tag{21a}$$

in which the symbols have the same meaning as in formula (21). When this ratio is greater than 1.00, the mean is the more reliable; when it is less than 1.00, the median is the more reliable.

The Reliability of Measures of Variability.—We can find the reliability of almost any statistical constant expressed in terms of its standard error or its probable error. This is true also of the σ, *PE*, *AD*, and *Q*. The following formulas apply:

$$\sigma_\sigma = \frac{\sigma}{\sqrt{2N}} \tag{22}$$

$$\sigma_{PE} = \frac{PE}{\sqrt{2N}} \tag{23}$$

$$PE_\sigma = .4769\frac{\sigma}{\sqrt{N}} \tag{24}$$

$$\sigma_{AD} = .6028\frac{\sigma}{\sqrt{N}} \tag{25}$$

$$\sigma_Q = .7867\frac{Q}{\sqrt{N}} \tag{26}$$

TABLE 5.—A SUMMARY OF THE AVERAGES AND MEASURES OF DISPERSION AND OF RELIABILITY FOR THE FOUR PARTIAL SETS AND FOR ALL THE DATA COMBINED

Set	Mode	Median	Mean	σ	PE	AD	Q	σ_M	PE_M
R.....	157.5	157.38	157.36	2.64	1.78	2.05	1.56	.264	.178
L......	154.5	154.97	155.92	4.68	3.16	3.89	4.04	.468	.316
O.....	155.5	156.02	156.06	3.84	2.59	2.87	2.31	.384	.259
I......	156.5	157.25	157.22	3.70	2.50	2.98	3.05	.370	.250
All....	156.5	156.65	156.64	3.87	2.61	3.02	2.76	.274	.185

COMBINING SETS OF DATA

In the computations represented in Table 5 we have not hesitated to pool sets of observations obtained under various arrangements into larger distributions. In doing so, we assume that the errors of space and of movement balance each other and become, for practical purposes, like variable errors. There are times when such pooling is not desirable from the standpoint of accuracy and truth. When two distributions are pooled, for example, the two may have distinctly different means or two different dispersions, or both.

The Geometric Mean.—Kirschmann recommends (10, p. 402) that, when two means, such as M_R and M_L, are distinctly different, but when the two sigmas are about the same, then the mean of the combined distribution shall be the **geometric mean** rather than the arithmetic mean. A geometric mean of two numbers is given by the formula

$$M_G = \sqrt{a_1 \times a_2} \tag{27}$$

The geometric mean of two numbers is the square root of their product. As applied to the R- and L-distributions,

$$M_G = \sqrt{157.36 \times 155.92} = \sqrt{24,535.5712} = 156.64.$$

This coincides exactly with the arithmetic mean, owing to the fact that the two means are so near together. Usually the geometric mean is smaller in value than the arithmetic mean; it is never greater.

To generalize the formula for N cases,

$$M_G = \sqrt[N]{a_1 a_2 a_3 \ldots a_N} \qquad (28)$$

The solution is best reached in such a case by the use of logarithms. The formula then becomes

$$M_G = \text{antilog}\left[\frac{\Sigma(\log a)}{N}\right] \qquad (29)$$

The solution of the problem for the mean of the R and L data combined is as follows:

$$
\begin{aligned}
\log 157.36 &= 2.19689 \\
\log 155.92 &= 2.19290 \\
\Sigma(\log a) &= \overline{4.38979} \\
\frac{\Sigma(\log a)}{N} &= 2.19490
\end{aligned}
$$

antilog 2.19490 = 156.64.

The reason Kirschmann uses the geometric mean in this place instead of the arithmetic mean is that it is thought that our perception of visual distances follows Fechner's law. We must accordingly average logarithms of stimulus values, and that is just what the computation of the geometric mean involves. The writer is somewhat skeptical, however, as to whether Fechner's law applies strictly to length of lines, or to many kinds of material that the student may use in this kind of problem. Not knowing just what psychophysical law does apply, it is probably safest to use the arithmetic mean of the two partial means that make up the total distribution. When the difference is small, the arithmetic mean and the geometric mean are almost identical. When the difference is not small, unless it is relatively certain that Fechner's law applies, the arithmetic mean is probably the better of the two.

Weighting the Observations According to Reliability.—In the above discussion it was assumed that the two means that were averaged were equally reliable. It is an accepted rule in statistical method that the reliability of a mean is proportional to $1/\sigma_M^2$ (15, p. 156). In finding the average of two means, therefore, the reliabilities should be considered if they differ appreciably. It is obvious that, the more reliable a measurement is, the greater should be its weight in determining a mean. The general formula for finding the mean of weighted observations is

$$_wM = \frac{\Sigma WX}{\Sigma W} \tag{30}$$

When averaging the two means, M_R and M_L, or any two similar means, we construct the following equation:[1]

$$_wM_t = \frac{M_R\left(\dfrac{1}{\sigma_R^2}\right) + M_L\left(\dfrac{1}{\sigma_L^2}\right)}{\dfrac{1}{\sigma_R^2} + \dfrac{1}{\sigma_L^2}}$$

which can be simplified to the form

$$_wM_t = \frac{M_R\sigma_L^2 + M_L\sigma_R^2}{\sigma_R^2 + \sigma_L^2}.$$

In general terms, the mean of two means weighted for reliability is

$$_wM_t = \frac{M_1\sigma_{M_2}^2 + M_2\sigma_{M_1}^2}{\sigma_{M_1}^2 + \sigma_{M_2}^2} \tag{31}$$

There is only one case in Table 5 to which formula (31) applies and that is for the R- and L-measurements in which the two σ's are distinctly different. Accordingly we have

$$\frac{(157.36)(.219399) + (155.92)(.069802)}{.219399 + .069802} = 157.01.$$

This mean of the total distribution is greater than the one found before (156.64), owing to the fact that the mean of the R-measurements is weighted about three times as heavily as the mean for the L-measurements. The exceptionally high σ for the latter is due to a tendency toward a bimodal distribution. When the L-measurements are considered alone, there is undoubtedly a greater

[1] The subscripts of σ (R and L) stand for M_R and M_L here.

error of movement than when they are taken together with the
R-measurements. The difference between the two M_t's is small
enough to cause little concern. Since the distribution of the 200
measurements is so obviously normal and unimodal, we may accept
the mean given in Table 5 (156.64) as essentially correct. The fact
that, when all the measurements are pooled, a normal distribution
is obtained illustrates how the two constant errors of space and
movement become variable errors and balance each other so as to
restore the condition of normality in the total distribution.

Finding a Standard Deviation from Combined Sets of Data.—
We have seen how a mean of all the data combined may be
obtained from the means of the fractionated data under the various
conditions just enumerated. It is also possible to find the σ of
the combined sets without compiling a new frequency distribution.
It is sometimes very convenient to do this when data are obtained
in sets and when the σ of each set has already been computed. The
following formula will take care of the general case:

$$\sigma_t^2 = \frac{1}{N_t}[N_1(\sigma_1^2 + d_1^2) + N_2(\sigma_2^2 + d_2^2) + \cdots + N_n(\sigma_n^2 + d_n^2)]$$

$$(32)$$

where N_t = the total number of cases in the combined sets.
σ_1, σ_2, and σ_n = the standard errors of the sets.
N_1, N_2, and N_n = the numbers of observations in the various sets.
d_1, d_2, and d_n = the deviations of the means of the sets from the
                      mean of the combined data.

When $N_1 = N_2 = N_n$, the formula[1] reduces to

$$\sigma_t^2 = \frac{1}{n}[(\sigma_1^2 + d_1^2) + (\sigma_2^2 + d_2^2) + \cdots + (\sigma_n^2 + d_n^2)] \quad (33)$$

in which n is the number of sets. It must be noted that the above
equations give σ_t^2 and that σ_t is the square root of the entire expression
at the right of the equality sign in either case.

As an illustration of how the formula is applied, we may use the
combination of the R- and L-data, with the means and sigmas from
Table 5. Since $N_R = N_L$, we may resort to formula (33).

[1] These formulas were kindly suggested to me by Professor Harry Helson.
Similar but less convenient formulas have been suggested by Kirschmann (10,
p. 409) and by others.

$$\sigma_t^2 = \frac{1}{2}[(2.64)^2 + (.72)^2 + (4.68)^2 + (.72)^2]$$
$$= \frac{1}{2}(6.9696 + .5184 + 21.9024 + .5184)$$
$$= 14.9544.$$
$$\sigma_t = 3.87$$

which coincides with the sigma previously found from the total distribution and given in Table 5.

THE COMPUTATION OF CONSTANT ERRORS

The Error of the Illusion.—To return to our problem of the Müller-Lyer illusion, we still have the task of determining the extent of the constant errors. We can draw the information we need from Table 5. The main constant error, the error of the illusion, is 156.64 mm. − 140.00 mm., or 16.64 mm. A line 140 mm. long with feathers is phenomenally equal to one of 156.64 mm. with arrowheads. The ratio of the two lines is 1:1.119, or the one is 11.9 per cent longer than the other. If the feathers and arrowheads have equal and opposite effects upon the central lines, the effect of each type of ending is half the total error, or 8.32 mm. That is, the feathers lengthened the 140 mm. line by 8.32 mm. and the arrowheads shortened a 156.64 mm. line by the same amount. Theoretically, either line would appear equivalent to an isolated horizontal line of 148.32 mm. if the above assumption is correct.

The Space Error.—The space error is easily found from the first two rows of Table 5. The difference between the two means is 1.44, the mean of the measurements at the right being 1.44 mm. greater than the mean of the measurements at the left. The space error is only half of this difference, however, or .72. In other words, the line on the right is underestimated, on the average, to the extent of .72, whereas the line at the left is overestimated to the same extent. The overestimation and underestimation are made in reference to the mean of all the measurements, 156.64 mm. The space error s, in terms of a general formula, is

$$s = \frac{M_R - M_L}{2} \tag{34}$$

The Error of Movement.—In a similar manner the error of movement m is

$$m = \frac{M_O - M_I}{2} \tag{35}$$

When this formula is applied to the means in Table 5, m is —.58, or is on the side of the inward movements. In other words, when the movement is outward, there is an average overestimation of .58 with respect to the grand average. When the movement is inward, the opposite is true.

The Reliability of Differences

Constant Errors Are Differences.—The constant errors of space and of movement need not always be computed as a matter of routine but they are often of interest for their own sakes. Their causes can frequently be ascertained and O can make the necessary compensations for them in subsequent observations should it be desirable for him to correct them. They are often so small as to merit little or no attention. At other times they may be so pronounced and so consistent as to demand an explanation, and an explanation may lead to a discovery of a new fact or principle. When are they sufficiently large to warrant study, and when are they so small as to be of no consequence, either theoretical or practical? Statistical methods yield us a very convenient test of reliability of such constant differences. The procedure about to be described has a variety of applications wherever differences between averages are treated. No really scientific investigator draws conclusions based upon differences that have not been tested for their significance unless the differences are so great that mere inspection shows them to be beyond question. Most differences with which psychology deals are so small and the overlapping between distributions is so great that only an accepted test of significance will suffice to show whether or not any obtained difference is a real one.

Differences are Normally Distributed.—Differences, like averages, if repeatedly measured, have their normal distribution. We can tell from the distribution of the differences what the chances are that the difference which we obtained would always be greater than zero. For example, we found the difference between M_R and M_L to be 1.44 mm. Is this difference merely due to chance? It is rather small, and perhaps, if we were to repeat the experiment with two new sets of measurements, the difference might be in the opposite direction, with M_L greater than M_R. Fortunately, a statistical device enables us to decide this question without finding a large number of differences.

Let the normal distribution curve in Fig. 5 represent the theoretical distribution of differences that we would get if we actually repeated the sets of measurements a large number of times. The mean of this distribution of the differences is placed at the value of the difference that we actually obtained, namely 1.44 mm. The zero point of the scale lies at the extreme left of the distribution. The shaded portion represents the total proportion of the differences that would be positive, *i.e.*, greater than zero. The unshaded portion lying to the left of the zero point gives the proportion of the negative differences that would probably occur. The problem is to find the proportion of the total area under the curve that is shaded. This gives us the probability that our obtained difference is in the correct direction.

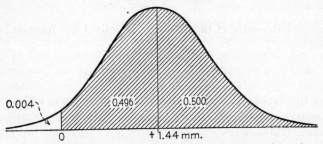

F IG. 5.—Normal distribution of differences, showing the proportions of negative (unshaded) and positive (shaded) differences.

The Standard Error and Probable Error of a Difference.— We need first to know the sigma of the distribution of differences. The sigma of a difference $\sigma_{\text{diff.}}$ is obtainable from the sigmas of the two means M_1 and M_2. The formula is

$$\sigma_{\text{diff.}} = \sqrt{\sigma_{M_1}^2 + \sigma_{M_2}^2 - 2r\sigma_{M_1}\sigma_{M_2}} \tag{36}$$

where σ_{M_1} = the standard error of the first mean.

σ_{M_2} = the standard error of the second mean.

r = the coefficient of correlation between corresponding pairs of observations in the two distributions.

Such a correlation as was just mentioned might occur, for example, in the use of mental tests. A test is given to a group of subjects before and after they have lost 48 hours of sleep; if we want to know whether there is a significant change in the average test score due to loss of sleep, there would be a positive correlation between single pairs of measurements taken before and after. The subjects would tend to keep their same relative positions in the group in spite of the loss of sleep. The coefficient of correlation must therefore be used in formula (36) in finding the standard error of the difference. It can be seen that, if r is positive, it will increase the expression $2r\sigma_{M_1}\sigma_{M_2}$; this, in being deducted from the total expression under the radical, lowers the $\sigma_{\text{diff.}}$. The greater r is, the smaller the $\sigma_{\text{diff.}}$ becomes.

In the present experiment, however, the observations R and L were not paired off in any conceivable manner, so there can be no correlation involved. If r equals zero, as in this example, the formula for σ becomes

$$\sigma_{\text{diff.}} = \sqrt{\sigma_{M_1}^2 + \sigma_{M_2}^2} \tag{37}$$

If the probable error of the difference is desired, the formula is very similar:

$$PE_{\text{diff.}} = \sqrt{PE_{M_1}^2 + PE_{M_2}^2} \tag{38}$$

For the data in Table 5 there are two differences in which we are particularly interested. These, together with their σ's and PE's, appear in Table 6.

TABLE 6.—DIFFERENCES, STANDARD ERRORS AND PROBABLE ERRORS OF DIFFER-ENCES, CRITICAL RATIOS, AND PROBABILITIES OF POSITIVE DIFFERENCES

Difference		$\sigma_{\text{diff.}}$	$PE_{\text{diff.}}$	CR_σ	CR_{PE}	Probability
M_R–M_L	1.44	.538	.363	2.68	3.98	.996
M_O–M_I	1.16	.534	.360	2.17	3.22	.985

The Critical Ratio and Its Use.—Table 6 needs further explanation. The symbol CR_σ stands for the **critical ratio** (also called the **experimental coefficient**) in terms of sigma. It is obtained by the formula

$$CR_\sigma = \frac{\text{diff.}}{\sigma_{\text{diff.}}} \tag{39}$$

In other words, it is the ratio of the difference to its standard error. It enables us to say just how far below the average difference (see Fig. 5) a difference of zero falls, *in terms of sigma as the unit*. When we know this, from Table B (Appendix) we can find the proportion of the shaded surface of Fig. 5 that lies between a difference of zero and the mean. Thus, for the difference $M_R - M_L$, the zero point falls 2.68σ below the mean difference, which is 1.44. All the negative differences that we would ever expect to find under the same conditions fall farther than 2.68σ below the mean. From Table B we find that the area between the mean and 2.68σ from the mean is equal to .496 of the entire area under the curve. The shaded portion that lies *above* the mean is of course exactly one-half or .500 of the total area. The total shaded area, representing all the positive differences, is therefore equal to the sum of these two proportions, or .996. This is the probability of a positive difference. There are 996 chances in 1000 for the difference $M_R - M_L$ to be positive and only four chances for it to be negative. Certainly the odds are strongly in favor of a positive difference. It can be seen from Table 6 that we can reach the same conclusion by using the $PE_{diff.}$ instead of $\sigma_{diff.}$. It is usually less work to use the latter. If the PE is used, Table C must be consulted to find the probability rather than Table B.

Very often a writer does not carry the test of significance beyond the critical ratio. If the CR_σ is at least 3.00 (or if the CR_{PE} is at least 4.50), we may say that the difference is certain beyond reasonable doubt. If the CR_σ is between 2.00 and 3.00 (or the CR_{PE} is between 3.00 and 4.50), we may say that the difference is fairly certain. The CR can always be increased by reducing the size of the $\sigma_{diff.}$, and the latter in turn can be made smaller by increasing the number of observations from which the average is drawn, provided that this does not in turn increase the sigma of the distribution. These relationships often determine the number of observations that one should make in attempting to detect the real size and the assurance of any difference.

Significance of Differences When N Is Small.—The standard error of a difference between two means, as was seen, is derived from the standard errors of the two means. When N is relatively small, the standard errors of the means are underestimated; consequently the standard error of the difference is too small and the critical ratio is too large. The significance of the difference is not so great as the above simple tests would indicate. This error of small samplings is counteracted to some extent by the use of altered formulas for the standard error of the mean as in formulas (17a), (17b), and (17c).

Fisher (5) gives a more accurate notion of the significance of small samples. In his method, formula (17a) (with $\sqrt{N-1}$ in the denominator) is employed no matter what the size of N. But the method requires larger critical ratios for small values of N than for large ones. The probability of a positive difference, which was derived from the critical ratio as in Table 6, holds strictly only when N is infinite. In Table K of the Appendix, the last column gives the necessary data for Fisher's test of significance. For each number of 'degrees of freedom' (see page 308) at the left of the table, the corresponding values of t are given in the last column. Fisher's t corresponds to our critical ratio. For every 'degree of freedom' (which in problems like the present one equals $N-1$) two values of t are given. The one in ordinary print which is given first is that critical ratio which Fisher regards as "significant." The probability is .05 that so great a difference[1] could arise in a 'chance' situation. The second one is regarded as "very significant" and it corresponds with a probability of .01, or 1 chance in 100, that so great a difference could arise by chance. Notice that a critical ratio of 2.576 is very significant when $(N-1)$ equals a very large number, but a ratio of 2.626 is required for the same degree of significance when $(N-1)$ equals 100 and a ratio of 2.845 when $(N-1)$ is 20. In the problem with which we deal in Table 6, N equals 100 and the number of degrees of freedom is 99. The latter does not appear in Table K. When $N-1$ is either 90 or 100, a CR_σ must approximate 2.63 to be "very significant." Only one of the two CR_σ's in Table 6 is that large. A CR_σ of approximately 1.98 is "significant," and the other CR_σ of 2.17 fully meets that requirement. The full benefit of Fisher's test of significance is felt when N is less than 30. But even with larger samplings it is a quick and meaningful test to apply.

Significance of Differences in General.—Not only differences between means may be treated in the manner described above; differences between other constants, such as percentages, proportions, coefficients of correlation, and the like, may also be tested for reliability. Under some circumstances the process of computing the standard error of a difference must be modified. One modification, when pairs of measurements are correlated, has already been mentioned. There are other cases, such as in the use of selected, nonrandom, comparison groups (3). Unless the student is sure of his ground in making any variations, it is safest to calculate the

---

[1] That is, a difference as *large* as the obtained one in *either* direction.

actual differences individually and find their mean and the standard error of the mean of the differences. The ratio of this mean to its standard error can be accepted as a valid critical ratio.

EVALUATION OF THE METHOD OF AVERAGE ERROR

As compared with the other psychophysical methods, the method of average error has the distinct practical advantage of economizing the time of both *E* and *O*. Every trial gives a measurement, whereas in other methods several trials and several judgments are required to obtain what is equivalent to a single measurement. The method is therefore especially useful wherever a number of measurements must be made in a limited time (6, p. 18).

The method has also been hailed as the "most natural" of methods since the discrimination is made in connection with action on the part of *O*. Titchener replies that judgments in all the psychophysical methods involve action, at least of the verbal type, on the part of *O* (13, II, p. 147). But it may be said that the muscular activity of *O* in the method of average error involves an active adjustment of the stimulus, whereas in the other methods *O* must take the stimuli as they come to him; he is permitted to do nothing with them by way of changing their quantity or size. Titchener admits that being able to control the stimulus does induce a favorable attitude in *O* (13, II, p. 147) and that it is sometimes baffling in the other methods not to be able to do anything with the stimuli. The active participation of *O*, aside from being able to control the stimulus, may have its beneficial influence. This difference may be noted, for example, in the difference in *O*'s attitude in passive and in active estimations of weights.

Criticisms of the Method. *Perceptual versus Motor Errors.*— Müller has criticized the method on the score of the muscular participation of which we have just spoken. The average measurements, he says, are partly dependent upon the "uncertainty of the hand" (11, p. 80). Under the "uncertainty of the hand" we may include several things. The most obvious, perhaps, is the occasional inability of *O* to stop the moving apparatus exactly at the point of phenomenal equality, no matter how hard he tries. This difficulty can be overcome by providing *O* with arrangements consisting of levers, worm gears, or screw adjustments with which to manipulate the setting of the stimulus. Another thing that might be included is the feeling of muscular effort. This may act as a distracting influence, on the one hand, vying with visual comparison and therefore making visual comparisons less accurate; on the other hand it may act as an irrelevant criterion, if O comes to depend upon it for his judgments of equality or inequality.

Fullerton and Cattell took seriously the distinction between "errors of perception" on the one hand and "errors of movement" on the other. After O had made an adjustment of a stimulus, they would ask him to state whether the standard and variable stimuli then appeared to be equal. Anyone who has been a subject in one of these experiments will agree that, often, the moment he ceases his adjustments, he may notice that the two stimuli are not exactly equal. Fullerton and Cattell (6) obtained a great many such judgments, and from the number of right and wrong judgments they were able to compare the margin of error as obtained by O's original settings and the margin of error of his visual observations made following the settings. The former errors were greater on the average than the latter, presumably from the contamination of the judgments with the "uncertainty of the hand" (6, pp. 111 ff.). Titchener, however, minimizes the importance of these muscular contaminations and states that, if the apparatus is easily and accurately adjustable, one need not be concerned about them (13, II, p. 147).

The Constant Time Error.—There is one inherent characteristic of the method on which all agree and which puts certain limitations upon its usefulness. This is the constant time error. A model must necessarily be observed *before* a reproduction can be made. This limits its value to situations in which both standard and variable stimuli are simultaneously present. In lifting weights, for example, when it is known that the second of two weights is overestimated, the weight that O would make equivalent to a preceding standard would tend to be too light. The result could be corrected if we knew the average amount of the time error for each particular O in judging lifted weights. But this we rarely know.

The same time error enters into the study of time intervals. When O reproduces given standard time intervals, he is subject to a constant tendency either to overestimate or to underestimate the second of two intervals. Whether we are working with weights or with time intervals, we should really know O's constant tendencies with regard to time errors. This we can determine by some other method, in which case we might as well have used the other method from the start.

Other Uncontrolled Errors.—Another time factor that may interfere with the validity of the results is the time taken by O to make a setting. This is usually uncontrolled. O is permitted within limits to take his own time. He is not permitted to make his settings so swiftly that they are carelessly done, nor is he permitted to dally too long and so impede the progress of the experiment. Within these limits, will variations in speed of adjustment influence the results? If O were permitted to make only one movement, in or out, we should readily expect such an influence to be at work. But since O may readjust the stimulus a number of times before ceasing his movements, the speed of his movements probably has little effect. Each O will probably adapt himself to a tempo that is suitable to him and to the experimental situation, and E may impose upon him any reasonable limits that he feels are adequate. An exact timing of O's adjustments would be out of the question for it would defeat some of the good points of the method. Fullerton and Cattell believed that a change in the time of the movement did have its effect upon the judgment, but Titchener maintained that such errors as they have pointed out can be attributed to such factors as "timidity, warming up, and anxiety" (13, II, p. 150). These factors can be noticed and reported by O and can be brought under control to some extent.

Type of Problem to Which the Method Is Adapted

In general it can be said that the method applies only in those cases in which O can manipulate the variable stimulus, and then only if the variable stimulus is *continuously* variable. The method has probably found its most useful application in the study of visual extent (*Augenmass*), as in the classical Galton bar experiment and in the measurement of geometric illusions, as was illustrated in this chapter. It has been used in the study of visual intensities, in matching colored papers to equivalent grays, and in measuring the chromas of colors. It can likewise be used in the study of tonal attributes, pitch, intensity, volume, or brightness. It has been adapted to the study of bodily movements, O being asked to reproduce a certain pull on a dynamometer or a certain extent or time of movement of the arm. It can be adapted to certain problems in memory, for example, memory for size and shape of objects after different time intervals. Although it is a convenient method for the investigation of the sense of time, it should rarely be used for such a purpose. When O tries to reproduce a standard time interval, his own reaction time enters into his response. This would be only a minor source of error when the standard time intervals are relatively large, but it invalidates the results when the time intervals are small.

The Measurement of Difference Limens.—Fechner suggested that the method of average error could be used to measure the *DL* (see page 112), and he has been followed in this belief by many others, including Volkmann, Wundt, Münsterberg, Sanford, Higier, Merkel, Fullerton, Cattell, James, Jastrow, and Kirschmann. Not all of them maintain that the *PE* of the distribution of measurements is a quantity equivalent to the *DL* that is found by other methods, but all do agree that the *PE* is at least roughly proportional to the *DL* and that it measures inversely the sensitivity of *O*.[1] Kirschmann, for example, says (10, p. 401), "One has no right to identify the average error with the *DL*, although one can regard it as proportional to the *DL*." He also states that Weber's law can be verified by the use of any of the measures of dispersion, and that the law will be satisfied if

$$\frac{PE}{M} = K \tag{40}$$

$$\frac{\sigma}{M} = K' \tag{41}$$

$$\frac{AD}{M} = K'' \tag{42}$$

The notion has also a great number of objectors. G. E. Müller was quick to point out that the *DL* measures a magnitude, whereas the *PE*, or any similar quantity, measures precision (11, p. 80). Titchener cites experimental evidence to show that the two are usually proportional, although under some special conditions they may be far from proportional (13, II, 183 *f.*) Brown and Thomson have more recently expressed the opinion, "Although there is a certain amount of proportionality between the values, this propor-

---

[1] Urban (14) has maintained that the average deviation of the dispersion is the most appropriate constant to use in this case. He gives proof that under certain conditions the *AD* is equivalent to one-half the 'interval of uncertainty' of his constant process (see pages 188 *ff.*) and so is a comparable index of sensitivity.

tionality is not complete. Under certain conditions the two values vary in opposite directions" (1, p. 57). The authors are undoubtedly thinking, however, of the distribution of the 'equal' judgments as obtained in the method of constant stimulus differences, which any experienced investigator knows are contaminated with judgments of 'doubtful' and so are not at all comparable with the judgments of equivalence as obtained in the method of average error. In the latter method O seeks to produce and to judge only equal stimuli. In the method of constant stimulus differences, O is set to observe differences whenever he can find them. It is not surprising, then, that the PE of the distribution of 'equal' judgments may at times vary in the opposite direction to the DL in the method of constant stimuli.

Kellogg has recently attacked the question experimentally (9). With light intensities and sound intensities he used both the method of average error and the method of constant stimulus differences. In 106 cases out of 120 the σ obtained by the former method was smaller than the corresponding σ obtained by the latter method. This means that the two methods give numerically different measurements of differential sensitivity. Both methods might still verify Weber's law, however, if both increase in proportion to the magnitude of the standard stimulus. But the correlation between the two sets of σ's, obtained by the two different methods, was .81 for the light stimuli and only .35 for the sound stimuli (9, p. 59). The discrepancies between the two are so large that one or both must be invalid for the testing of Weber's law. Since the σ's for the method of average error were on the whole more variable from day to day in the same observer, Kellogg concluded that it is an inferior method for testing Weber's law. But it might be mentioned that Kellogg did not follow the letter, and perhaps the spirit, of the method of average error since he permitted O to make only one movement of the stimulus in bringing it to the point of equality, not allowing any further adjustments. His method of computing the σ's in the method of constant stimulus differences is also open to question since it involves certain guesses about the ends of the distributions of judgments. In view of these facts, all we can say is that the PE found in the method of average error is roughly proportional to the DL as found by other methods and that further experimental work is needed to determine the nature of the relationship between the two.

Problems

1. The following data were obtained from 100 observations made with the Galton bar. The standard was a line 120 mm. long which O was to reproduce at either the right R or left L and by moving the terminus of the variable stimulus either inward I or outward O.

LO	LI	RO	RI
123	122	116	119
121	120	118	120
117	122	115	119
112	114	119	116
117	114	117	116
120	113	116	118
122	117	118	119
114	120	120	113
117	117	118	118
119	120	120	115
113	116	119	120
119	123	118	113
116	120	120	116
123	114	125	116
118	120	119	117
114	112	119	118
114	116	115	113
121	118	117	115
118	120	114	120
117	117	120	116
119	117	119	117
112	114	116	117
119	112	117	112
117	117	116	117
114	114	124	111

Treat these data according to the procedures described in this chapter, applying just as many of the devices as are appropriate. Give reasons for your choices of procedure, wherever you have chosen one of two or more alternatives, and interpret your results.

2. The following is a frequency-distribution table of the Army Alpha scores of 200 students entering an engineering college. Apply to these data as many of the procedures described in the present chapter as seem appropriate.

Class Interval	Frequencies
190–199.9	3
180–189.9	5
170–179.9	9
160–169.9	12
150–159.9	23
140–149.9	35
130–139.9	31
120–129.9	20
110–119.9	23
100–109.9	12
90– 99.9	13
80– 89.9	9
70– 79.9	3
60– 69.9	0
50– 59.9	2

3. Find the geometric mean of the following two sets of values and compare with the arithmetic mean in each case:

   a. 24.7 and 5.9.

   b. .82, .57, .91, and .78.

4. The following data[1] were derived from a study of the effect of a strong contraction of the arm muscles upon the height of the patellar reflex. The average height of 30 knee jerks (given in degrees of arc) was obtained for each of 50 subjects under two conditions, a normally relaxed condition which obtains

Normal	Tensed	Normal	Tensed	Normal	Tensed	Normal	Tensed
35	31	37	36	24	29	33	29
32	16	27	34	13	18	29	22
14	19	27	33	26	30	28	36
27	24	22	30	20	30	4	8
19	22	24	34	4	14	19	21
8	23	6	19	1	18	11	16
29	26	14	19	18	18	23	26
23	24	17	23	29	30	23	21
34	36	19	19	24	20	22	30
37	35	16	23	18	26	31	35
26	30	30	26	26	34	18	28
19	29	33	39	21	28	31	26
24	26	7	15				

[1] From R. C. Hall, "*The Patellar Reflex Studied in Relation to Certain Traits of Personality*," master's thesis on file in the University of Nebraska Library, 1935.

during the ordinary sitting posture and the strong muscular contraction occurring a fraction of a second before the reflex. The chief problem of interest is to find the average difference between the two sets of measurements and to determine whether that difference is statistically significant.

a. Find the difference between the means, the standard error of the difference, the critical ratio, and the probability of a positive difference, assuming that the measurements are uncorrelated.

b. Find the significance of the difference, assuming a correlation of .72 between the two sets of measurements.

c. Compute the 50 actual differences, their mean, and its standard error. Compare this standard error with the two already found.

REFERENCES

1. BROWN, WM., and G. H. THOMSON, "The Essentials of Mental Measurement," Cambridge University Press, London, 1925.
2. DUNLAP, J. W., and A. K. KURTZ, "Handbook of Statistical Nomographs, Tables, and Formulas," World Book Company, Yonkers, 1932.
3. EZEKIEL, M., "Student's" method for measuring the significance of a difference between matched groups, *J. Educ. Psychol.*, 1932, **23**, 446–450.
4. FECHNER, G. T., "Revision der Hauptpunkte der Psychophysik," Breitkopf und Härtel, Leipzig, 1882.
5. FISHER, R. A., "Statistical Methods for Research Workers," 4th ed., Oliver & Boyd, Edinburgh, 1932.
6. FULLERTON, G. S., and J. McK. CATTELL, On the perception of small differences, *Pub. Univ. Penn., Phil. Series*, no. 2, 1892.
7. GARRETT, H. E., "Statistics in Psychology and Education," Longmans, Green & Company, New York, 1926.
8. KELLEY, T. L., "Statistical Method," The Macmillan Company, New York, 1924.
9. KELLOGG, W. N., An experimental comparison of psychophysical methods, *Archiv. Psychol.*, 1929, no. 106.
10. KIRSCHMANN, A., Grundzüge der psychologischen Maszmethoden, in Abderhalden's "Handbuch der biologischen Arbeitsmethoden," Abt. VI, Teil A, Urban und Schwarzenberg, Berlin, 1927.
11. MÜLLER, G. E., "Zur Grundlegung der Psychophysik," T. Griefen, Berlin, 1878.
12. SHEN, E., Note on the sampling error of the median, *J. Educ. Psychol.*, 1935, **26**, 154–156.
13. TITCHENER, E. B., "Experimental Psychology," Vol. II, Pts. I and II, The Macmillan Company, New York, 1905.
14. URBAN, F. M., Die Methode des durchschnittlichen Fehlers, *Arch. ges. Psychol.*, 1930, **74**, 141–162.
15. WELD, L. D., "Theory of Errors and Least Squares," The Macmillan Company, New York, 1926.
16. WOODROW, H., Quotidian variability, *Psychol. Rev.*, 1932, **39**, 245–256.
17. YULE, G. U., "Introduction to the Theory of Statistics," 5th ed., Charles Griffin & Company, Ltd., London, 1919.

CHAPTER III

PROPERTIES OF THE NORMAL DISTRIBUTION CURVE

The normal distribution curve has served so many uses throughout the whole range of mental measurements that it is important for the student to learn something about its nature. Not every student of psychology can become an embryo mathematician, but every one can develop, to some degree at least, a sense of what is fit and what is unfit procedure in the use of some of the tools of mathematics. He should be able to appreciate something of the essential characteristics of the normal curve in order that he may know when and how to use it, and when not to use it and why. In general we may use the normal distribution curve with any given set of data for one of two reasons. Either we can see by inspection that the frequencies distribute themselves very close to the normal form and we can by means of mathematical devices test the closeness of fit, or we can in addition show logical reasons why such measurements as we have made should be distributed normally.

The normal distribution curve is often referred to as the **normal probability curve,** and probabilities are linked up with the so-called 'laws of chance.' It can be shown that in a sense the repeated measurements of the same thing are determined by the laws of chance. It is this fact that enables us to find a logical connection between the distribution of measurements and the normal distribution curve. It will be worth while, therefore, to look into the theory of probabilities, at least in an elementary way, and to see what connection there is between probabilities and measurements.

ELEMENTARY THEORY OF PROBABILITY

The Meaning of Probability.—Everyone knows that when a coin is tossed into the air the chances of its landing with head or tail up are fifty-fifty; this means that, granting a perfectly balanced coin and an unbiased throw, the chances are exactly even for getting a head or a tail. In 100 throws one would rightly expect 50 heads and

50 tails. Stated in more mathematical terms, we say that the probability of getting heads is 1/2, or .50, and the probability of getting tails is also 1/2, or .50. The probability of getting a head *or* a tail is the sum of the two probabilities, 1/2 + 1/2, or 1.00. A probability of 1.00 is of course absolute certainty; we are absolutely certain to get either a head or a tail. A mathematician's coin never stands on edge!

In throwing a single die the probability of getting a one spot is 1/6, or .167. Likewise, the probability of getting a two spot, or any other specified number of spots not greater than six, is .167. The probability of getting a one *or* a two is 2/6 or .333. The probability of getting a one *or* a two *or* a three is 3/6 or .50, and so on, with the total probability again being 1.00 for getting *some* number from one to six. The total probability is always equal to 1.00.

As another example, let us suppose tnat an urn contains 50 white balls and 50 black balls thoroughly mixed. You reach in and draw out one ball. The probability that the ball you draw will be white is .50, and likewise the probability that it will be black is .50. Let us suppose that another urn has 80 balls in it, 8 of which are white, 24 black, and 48 red. The probability of drawing a white ball is 8/80 or .10, of drawing a black ball 24/80 or .30, and of drawing a red ball 48/80 or .60. The sum of these three probabilities is again 1.00. The probability of getting a white or a black or a red ball is certainty.

Definition of Probability.—Suppose, now, we are interested only in one of the three above possibilities, for example, in getting a white ball. We can ask, what is the probability of *not* getting a white ball? If the probability of getting a white ball is .10, the probability of not getting one is 1.00 − .10, or .90. We shall designate the former probability by the letter p and the latter by q. We may say, then, that p is the probability of the occurrence of an event and q is the probability of its not occurring. It has already been emphasized that $p + q$ always equals 1.00. We are now ready for a formal definition of probability which may be given as follows:

If an event can happen in a certain number of distinguishable ways, and if some of the ways be regarded as favorable, then the ratio of the number of favorable ways to the total number of ways is called the probability of the event occurring favorably, PROVIDED *the total number of ways of occurrence be regarded as equally likely.*

If the student is ever puzzled in deciding what the probability of a given event is, he should always remember that it is the number of ways in which the event can happen favorably, divided by the total number of ways in which it can occur at all. In tossing a coin, heads can come in only one way, but the total number of ways the coin can lie is two. The probability of heads is .50. In throwing a die, the number of ways a five spot can turn up is only one; the total number of possible ways the die can lie is six. The probability of any one way is .167. In the first urn problem the number of ways of drawing a white ball in one draw is 50; the total number of ways is 100. The probability of a white ball is 50/100 or .50. The second urn problem can be fitted to the definition in just the same way.

Notice that the end of the definition states "provided the total number of ways of occurrence be regarded as equally likely." If a coin is not symmetrical, if a die is 'loaded,' if the balls in an urn are of different size or weight or are not thoroughly mixed, the ways of occurrence are not equally likely. The mathematician demands 'ideal' conditions. Nature may sometimes give us some lopsided coins, loaded dice, and nonrandom distributions of balls in urns. If a coin is tossed N times and heads come up M times, we would expect the fraction M/N to equal exactly $\frac{1}{2}$. As a matter of fact this result is very rarely obtained. M/N is very close to $\frac{1}{2}$; but only if N is extremely large, for example, in the thousands, will M/N be so nearly equal to $\frac{1}{2}$ that the difference is infinitesimal. We speak of the fraction M/N as the *empirical* probability of an event. It is obtained from the actual counting of events rather than from a priori notions of the nature of the events. In applying their definition of probability to natural events, when $p = \frac{1}{2}$, mathematicians would state the matter somewhat as follows:

$$\lim_{N \to \infty} \frac{M}{N} = \frac{1}{2}$$

which reads: The limit of the ratio M/N, as N becomes extremely large, is equal to $\frac{1}{2}$. It is well for the student to remember this when dealing with empirical probabilities.

The Probability of a Repeated Event.—Let us take as an example, again, the urn with 50 white and 50 black balls. What is the probability that in two successive drawings you would get two white balls? We shall assume that, after the first ball was drawn, it was put back and the balls were stirred up again so as to restore the original probability. The probability of drawing a white ball the first time is 1/2, and the probability of drawing one the second time is also 1/2. Recall the definition of probability—the number of favored ways (WW) divided by the total number of ways. There are two ways in which the drawing can happen in the first trial, *i.e.*, W or B. For each one of these ways there are two ways in which the second drawing can occur. The total number of ways is four, specifically, WW, WB, BW, and BB. The probability we are looking for is 1/4 or .25. What is the probability of drawing three white balls in three successive draws? There is only one favored way, namely WWW. The total number of ways is eight, and so p is 1/8 or .125. The probability of four white balls in four successive drawings is 1/16 or .0625. It should be clear by now that, in order to find the probability of a repeated or combined event, we multiply the probabilities of the single events. The probability of two successive white balls is ½ × ½ or ¼; that of three successive white balls is ½ × ½ × ½, or ⅛, and so on.

The same reasoning holds for the repeated tossing of a coin. The probability of three heads in three successive throws is 1/8. Now for a new type of question. In tossing two coins simultaneously, what is the probability of getting one head and one tail? Here there are *two* favorable ways. We could have HT or TH. The total number of ways is four, the other two, unfavored ways, being HH and TT. The probability is 1/2. In tossing three coins the probability of getting two heads and one tail is 3/8. In tossing four coins the probability of getting two heads and two tails is 6/16. In all these cases it will be noted that the denominator of the fraction, the total number of ways, is 2^n, where n is the number of coins. It will be noted also that the numerator depends upon the number of combinations of two that can be found with three or four coins. Three coins or objects taken two at a time give three combinations. Four coins taken two at a time give six combinations. One could write out all the single possibilities, for example, the three coins could give HHT, HTH, or THH. The four coins could give HHTT, HTHT, HTTH, THHT, THTH, or TTHH. But there is a general formula by which the number of combinations of n objects taken r at a time can be readily calculated. It is

$$_nC_r = \frac{n!}{r!(n-r)!} \tag{43}$$

The formula reads: The number of combinations of n objects taken r at a time equals n **factorial** divided by r factorial times $(n-r)$ factorial. The expression n factorial is expanded as follows: $n(n-1)(n-2)(n-3) \cdots (n-n+1)$, and the other factorials are expanded likewise. Solving the last example given on page 74, four coins taken two at a time,

$$_nC_r = \frac{4 \cdot 3 \cdot 2 \cdot 1}{(2 \cdot 1)(2 \cdot 1)} = 6.$$

Assume now that we have 10 coins that are tossed together. What are the probabilities of getting the various numbers of heads and tails? The total number of ways in which 10 coins could fall is $(2)^{10}$ or 1024. The value 1024 will be the denominator of every fraction expressing a probability. The numerators are to be found by using formula (43). Table 7 gives the results and Fig. 6 expresses the distribution of probabilities graphically.

TABLE 7.—THE PROBABILITIES OF GETTING EACH NUMBER OF HEADS AND TAILS IN TOSSING 10 COINS

Heads	Tails	Favored ways	Probabilities (p)		q $(q = 1 - p)$
			Fractions	Decimals	
0	10	1	1/1024	.00098	.99902
1	9	10	10/1024	.00977	.99023
2	8	45	45/1024	.04395	.95605
3	7	120	120/1024	.11719	.88281
4	6	210	210/1024	.20498	.79502
5	5	252	252/1024	.24609	.75391
6	4	210	210/1024	.20498	.79502
7	3	120	120/1024	.11719	.88281
8	2	45	45/1024	.04395	.95605
9	1	10	10/1024	.00977	.99023
10	0	1	1/1024	.00098	.99902
	Σ	1024	1024/1024	.99983	

The Binomial Expansion.—It is often pointed out that the probabilities of the various numbers of heads in tossing a group of coins are given by the terms of the **binomial expansion.** Every student remembers that $(p + q)^2$ is equal to $p^2 + 2pq + q^2$. The coefficients of the three terms of this expansion are 1, 2, and 1, respectively. If we substitute for p and q the probabilities of our problem, we have $(\frac{1}{2} + \frac{1}{2})^2$, which gives $\frac{1}{4} + \frac{1}{2} + \frac{1}{4}$, when expanded. These are the three probabilities of getting 0 heads,

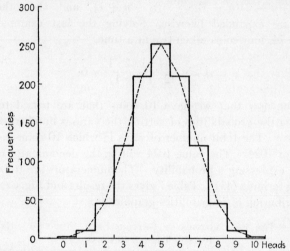

FIG. 6.—Theoretical frequencies of the various numbers of heads in 1024 throws of ten coins.

1 head, and 2 heads, respectively, when tossing two coins. With three coins the expansion is of $(\frac{1}{2} + \frac{1}{2})^3$, which equals

$$\frac{1}{8} + \frac{3}{8} + \frac{3}{8} + \frac{1}{8},$$

giving the probabilities of 0 heads, 1 head, 2 heads, and 3 heads, respectively. The general formula is

$$(p + q)^n = p^n + \frac{n}{1}p^{n-1}q + \frac{n(n - 1)}{1 \times 2}p^{n-2}q^2 +$$
$$\frac{n(n - 1)(n - 2)}{1 \times 2 \times 3}p^{n-3}q^3 + \frac{n(n - 1)(n - 2)(n - 3)}{1 \times 2 \times 3 \times 4}p^{n-4}q^4 + \cdots + q^n.$$

Students who are familiar with the terms of the binomial expansion may prefer to use them in working out the probabilities in tossing coins.

Normal Expectancy.—Table 7 gives the theoretical probabilities of getting the various combinations of heads and tails with 10 coins.

If 10 coins are actually tossed a large number of times, we can predict the expected number of cases of each number of heads. For example, in 1024 throws we would expect 120 of them to result in three heads and 210 of them to result in four heads, and so on. These are the normal expectancies. The general formula for predicting a normal expectancy E is

$$E = Np \tag{44}$$

in which N is the total number of trials and p is the theoretical probability that a case will fall in a certain category.

Let us designate by the symbol B the number of cases actually falling in a certain category, for example, the category three heads and seven tails in our coin-tossing problem. Let us suppose that B actually equalled not 120 but 125. The standard error of B is

$$\sigma_B = \sqrt{Npq} \tag{45}$$

in which p is the *empirical* probability of the event, and it is derived from the ratio B/N and $q = 1 - p$. If B is 125 and N is 1024, $p = .122$ and $q = .878$.

$$\sigma_{125} = \sqrt{1024(.122 \times .878)} = \sqrt{109.6868} = 10.47.$$

Thus, if in tossing 10 coins 1024 times we get three heads 125 times, we could easily assume that the theoretical expectancy was 120. Or, if we were to repeat the experiment, it would not be at all unreasonable to expect 120 since this deviates by only 5 from the obtained frequency and 5 cases is scarcely one-half the standard error. Were we to reverse the question and ask, "When the theoretical expectancy is 120, how reasonable is an obtained frequency of 125?", we then let $B = 120$, $p = .117$, and $q = .883$. The σ_B then becomes 10.29. Again, a difference of 5 cases is only a half sigma removed from B and so a frequency of 125 might easily arise by chance.

The Standard Error of a Proportion.—It is perhaps more customary to deal with the proportion of the cases falling in a certain category, namely, p, than with the frequency or number of cases B. The standard error of a proportion is given by the formula

$$\sigma_p = \sqrt{\frac{pq}{N}} \tag{46}$$

in which p, q, and N have the same meanings as before.[1] In the problem just solved, in which $p = .122$, $q = .878$, and $N = 1024$,

$$\sigma_p = \sqrt{\frac{(.122)(.878)}{1024}} = \sqrt{.00010461} = .010.$$

We may say of such an obtained p, when $N = 1024$, that there are practically no chances that with repeated trials p would exceed .152 or fall below .092, since these limits include the range of plus and minus 3σ. The probable error is, of course, given by the usual formula $.6745\sigma$.

The σ and the PE of a proportion are two of the most useful and fundamental constants in statistics. Repeatedly our measurements are made to fall into categories, sometimes in as few as two, and sometimes in very many, as when they are grouped in class intervals. Suppose we find by experiment that 17 out of 20 subjects were facilitated in a mental task by the influence of caffeine whereas 3 were apparently inhibited. What is the probability that caffeine generally facilitates mental work and what is the likelihood that results lying in the same direction would be found again? In this problem $p = {}^{17}\!/_{20}$ or .85 and $q = .15$, N being 20. The σ of this proportion is .066. What is the likelihood that p would always be greater than .50, at which the chances are even for facilitation and inhibition? A p of .50 is .35 below .85, or 5.3 times σ_p. It therefore seems highly improbable that under the same conditions p would be less than .50. Edgerton (4) has given some very convenient tables for solving either σ_p or PE_p. When

$$p = q = .50,$$

the formula is simplified to

$$\sigma_p = \frac{.5}{\sqrt{N}} \qquad (47)$$

It might seem more pertinent to ask, in the case of the last problem, how likely it is that we would find 85 per cent of 20 cases tending in the same direction if actually there were no consistent effects of caffeine. If this is the actual situation, the theoretical

---

[1] Formulas (45) and (46) apply strictly only to theoretical probabilities. They apply with slight errors to empirical probabilities, however, except when p approaches .00 or 1.00 very closely.

probability is .5 and formula (47) applies. Then σ_p is equal to .112. The obtained deviation is +.35 from a chance probability of .50 and this deviation is 3.14 times σ_p. The probability that such a deviation will occur by pure chance is indeed very small; in fact, there are only about 8 chances in 1000 (from Table B, Appendix) for such a deviation by chance. Since N is small, Fisher's test is very appropriate here. When $(N - 1)$ is 19 and when t in Table K is 2.86, there is less than 1 chance in 100 that so large a deviation could occur in a random situation. In this problem t is 3.14, and hence the obtained p is highly significant.

MATHEMATICAL FUNCTIONS

The Meaning of a Mathematical Function.—Like most of the sciences, psychology is perpetually seeking to find laws that state in a simple way the manner in which one variable depends upon another. For example, how does memory ability of the individual depend upon age? In the law of forgetting, how does the percentage retained depend upon the time elapsed since the impression was formed? In the well-known Weber law, how does the just noticeable increment of a stimulus depend upon the magnitude of that stimulus? As we vary the exposure time of a color stimulus, how will the duration of the negative after-image vary? In the psychophysical law of Fechner, how rapidly does the sensation increase in intensity as we increase the stimulus intensity? How does the ability in any mental test vary with increasing age of those tested? In all these examples one variable depends upon another. As one variable increases or decreases, there is a corresponding change in the other. One of the variables we call the **independent variable** and the other the **dependent variable.** In the last example, age is the independent variable. Choose any age you wish, and if the mathematical relationship between age and the score in a mental test is known, you can predict the most probable score. The score, in other words, *depends* upon the age that you arbitrarily choose. We could, of course, turn the variables around and predict the age of an individual from his test score. In this case we have made the test score the independent variable and the age the dependent variable.

Ordinarily we assign the symbol Y to the dependent variable and the symbol X to the independent variable. For example, we say that the circumference of a circle is a function of its diameter. If we call the circumference Y and the diameter X, we can set up the equation: $Y = 3.1416X$. No matter what value we assign to X, we can find a corresponding value for Y by using this equation. And if we were to locate for every pair of values of X and Y a point on coordinate paper, the series of points would lie in a straight line. We would say that the function is *linear* in form.

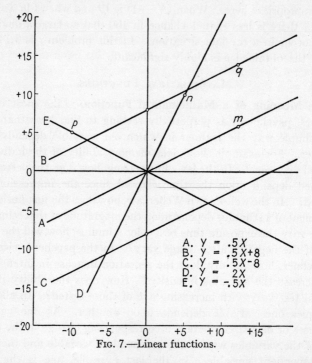

A. $Y = .5X$
B. $Y = .5X+8$
C. $Y = .5X-8$
D. $Y = 2X$
E. $Y = -.5X$

Fig. 7.—Linear functions.

Linear Functions.—It is important for the student to grasp the meaning of functions, whether they appear in the form of an equation or whether they appear plotted in graphic form. With a little practice and close observation one can learn to picture to oneself a graphic representation of a function when the equation is given, or to guess the type of equation when the graph alone is given. In Fig. 7 a number of linear equations are plotted. Line A, for example, represents the equation $Y = .5X$. From the equation it can readily be seen that, when X equals zero, Y also equals zero. The line therefore passes through the **origin**. When X equals 1, Y equals .5; when X equals 2, Y equals 1; and so on. For every gain of one unit in the X-variable there is a gain of only a half unit in the Y-variable. The coefficient of X, namely, .5, determines the *slope* of the curve. This coefficient always tells us how rapidly Y is increasing as compared with X. In this equation Y is gaining only half as fast as X.

The slope of a line can be found, roughly, from the coordinate system in which it is plotted, by using the following procedure: Select any point far out along the line, such as the point m in Fig. 7, line A. Note both the X value and the Y value of that point. The slope of the line is equal to the Y value of this point divided by its X value, or $\frac{6}{12}$, which is .5. To come back to the equation for this line, $Y = .5X$; if we divide both sides of the equation by X, the result is $Y/X = .5$. So it can be seen that any Y value divided by its corresponding X value gives the slope of the line.

Now notice line D with its equation $Y = 2X$. In this function Y is increasing two times as rapidly as X. The slope of the line is 2, which can be verified by taking a point such as point n where $Y/X = \frac{10}{5} = 2$. The steeper the line, the greater the slope. The slope of lines that lie entirely within the first **quadrant,** *i.e.,* the quarter of the diagram in which both Y and X are positive, may vary all the way from zero when the line is perfectly horizontal or parallel to the X-axis to infinity when the line is perpendicular to the X-axis.

Now notice line E with its equation $Y = -.5X$. Here the slope of the line is negative. When X gains, Y loses, and vice versa. But in either case Y changes only one-half as rapidly as X. The student can find the slope by making use of point p in the usual way, but remembering that the X value of this point is negative and the Y value positive.

It is an axiom of mathematics that two points determine the position of a line. It can be seen that, if we knew only that our function is linear and that it passes through the two points $(0, 0)$ and $(12, 6)$, we have the complete function plotted by drawing a straight line through those two points. Let us suppose, to take a simple example, that we knew that the scores in a certain mental test increased with age in the form of a straight line. We know also that the average six year old makes a score of 3 and that the average fourteen year old makes a score of 7. Knowing only these three facts, the nature of the function and the two necessary points for drawing the line, we are ready to predict the most probable score for any age between six and fourteen. This is one of the great conveniences of a mathematical function. It enables us to interpolate or to predict a host of additional values from the measurement of only a few.

The student should note that the statement about prediction applied only to the ages between six and fourteen. To predict beyond those limits is always a risky procedure unless one knows beforehand that the same mathematical function applies beyond those values. It should also be noticed that the *most probable* scores can be predicted. This qualification is necessary because, in psychology especially, no two variables are so perfectly measured or so perfectly isolated that we can expect exact predictions. There is always a margin of error in our predictions owing to the imperfect correlation of the two variables concerned.

To return to Fig. 7, let us notice line *B*. The equation is

$$Y = .5X + 8.$$

The slope of this line is .5 and it is obviously parallel to line *A* which has the same slope. The only reason that it is so much higher in the field than line *A* is that there is +8 in the formula. This additional **constant** is known as the *Y*-intercept. It will be noticed that line *B* intercepts the *Y*-axis at the value $Y = 8$. We may now state the general formula for a straight line: $Y = a + bX$, in which *b* is always the slope of the line and *a* is the *Y*-intercept. It will be seen that the equation for line *C* in Fig. 7 follows that rule. Whenever a line passes through the origin, *a* equals zero; thus it is simply omitted entirely, as in the formula $Y = .5X$.

A slight change will now have to be made in the rule given above for reading the slope of a line from a diagram. Point *q* on line *B* in Fig. 7 has an *X* value of 12 and a *Y* value of 14, and yet the slope is not $14/12$. The slope is no longer Y/X, but $(Y - a)/X$. For the proof of this, consider the general formula, $Y = a + bX$. Transposing, we have $bX = Y - a$. Dividing by *X*,

$$b = \frac{Y - a}{X},$$

which gives us the general formula for finding the slope of a line. The constant *a* can always be read directly from the figure by finding where the line crosses the *Y*-axis.

Nonlinear Functions.—Only one type of nonlinear function will be used here to illustrate what happens when we use powers of X in the equation. In Fig. 8 note the result when we use the simple equation $Y = X^2$. We get, not a straight line, but a **parabola** with two curved branches. The two branches are perfectly symmetrical about the Y-axis, the one being a mirror reflection of the other. The reason is simple. It does not matter whether X is

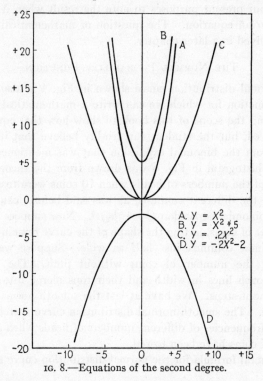

A. $y = X^2$
B. $y = X^2 + 5$
C. $y = .2X^2$
D. $y = -.2X^2 - 2$

IG. 8.—Equations of the second degree.

positive or negative; X^2 is always positive. If X is either plus or minus 2, Y is 4; if X is plus or minus 3, Y is 9, and so on. Curve B with the formula $Y = X^2 + 5$ is a duplicate of curve A, except that all points are raised by the constant amount 5. As in the linear equations, the constant here is the Y-intercept. The slope of these curves can be altered by changing the coefficient of X^2. In equations A and B, the coefficient of X^2 was really 1, although this needed no mention. When the coefficient is .2, as in curve C, the slope of the two branches is considerably reduced. By making the coefficient of X^2 smaller and smaller, we could make a whole family of parabolas, each one flatter than the one before.

Curve D shows what happens when the coefficient of X^2 is made negative and when the Y-intercept is also negative. The slope is of the same degree of flatness as for curve C, but the branches extend in the downward direction, just the reverse of curve C. We could go on complicating the equation in other ways, but it is sufficient for our present purposes to note the result when X^2 is introduced into an equation. The question of mathematical functions will be revived in a later chapter.

THE NORMAL PROBABILITY FUNCTION

The normal distribution curve shown in Fig. 4 is also a mathematical function for which we can write a mathematical equation. It is beyond the scope of this book to show how that equation has been derived, but the student can readily believe that it has been derived from the binomial expansion that was mentioned on page 75. The histogram in Fig. 6 was drawn from the theoretical distribution of the numbers of heads when 10 coins were tossed. The heights of the different columns, as was said before, can be found from the binomial expansion $(\frac{1}{2} + \frac{1}{2})^{10}$. Now suppose we double the number of coins, letting the shape of the curve remain the same, with the new columns just half as wide. Suppose we keep on increasing the number of coins without limit. The rectangles then approach lines in width and their tops merge into a smooth curve without steps. We have at last the smooth normal distribution curve. The smooth normal distribution curve therefore represents the frequencies of different numbers of heads when an infinite number of coins have been tossed.

The general formula for the normal distribution curve is given as follows:

$$Y = \frac{N}{\sigma\sqrt{2\pi}}e^{\frac{-x^2}{2\sigma^2}} \tag{48}$$

where N = the number of measurements.

π = pi, or 3.1416.

σ = sigma, the standard deviation of the distribution.

e = the base of the Napierian system of logarithms and has the fixed value of 2.718.

x = a deviation $(X - M)$.

Formula (48) looks rather formidable. Let us see what it means. The first terms, N, σ, and the square root of 2π, are constant for any given distribution. They have nothing important to do with the general shape of the curve. The symbol e is also a constant value, namely, 2.718. The independent variable x appears in the **exponent** of the number 2.718. Y changes according to that exponent, and the value of the exponent changes according to the value of x. Let us assign a few values to x and then see what happens to Y. If x is equal to zero, the whole exponent becomes zero. We know that any number to the power zero is equal to 1, no matter what that number may be. Thus e to the power zero equals 1. We know from this fact that the expression $e^{\frac{-x^2}{2\sigma^2}}$ will never be greater than 1 and that, when x departs from zero, either plus or minus, this expression becomes smaller. The curve will be symmetrical about the Y-axis because of the x^2 in the equation. Whether x is $+.3$ or $-.3$, for example, x^2 is a positive .09. The effect is not unlike that obtained in Fig. 8 for the equation

$$Y = -.2X^2 - 2.$$

In both this and the normal equation, as x increases Y decreases, Y being at a maximum when x equals zero.

When x is zero, $Y = N/\sigma\sqrt{2\pi}$. Because of this fact we often use the expression

$$y_0 = \frac{N}{\sigma\sqrt{2\pi}} \tag{49}$$

y_0 being called "the Y-variable when x is zero." It is an important part of the equation as will be seen later. It is very readily determined if we know N and σ. After substituting in this equation the value for π and extracting the square root of 2π, we have

$$y_0 = \frac{N}{2.5066\sigma} \tag{50}$$

It will be noticed that instead of capital X we have used the small x in these formulas. This is because capital X stands for the raw measurements in terms of the scale of our 'yardstick,' whatever it may be. In the problem in the preceding chapter, the unit of measurement was the millimeter and the raw measurements were in the region of 150 to 160 mm. The *origin* of our scale of measurement was 0 mm. In applying the formula for the normal curve to any set of data, we must make two changes. We must change our unit of measurement, and we must shift the origin. The origin is shifted to the mean of the distribution. In the case of the 200 measurements in the last chapter, the origin becomes 156.64. This value would then be known as zero. All the other measurements would have to be translated into **deviations,** $x = (X - M)$. A measurement of 156 would become $-.64$. A measurement of 160 mm. would become $+3.36$.

The other change, the change in the unit, consists in making the sigma of the distribution the new unit of measurement. Any measurement that is made in terms of sigma as the unit is called a **standard measure,** or sometimes it is called a **deviate.** In the distribution referred to above, sigma was 3.87 mm. To translate the two deviations found above ($-.64$ and $+3.36$) into standard measures, we divide them by 3.87. They become $-.165\sigma$ and $+.867\sigma$, respectively. The general formula for translating a raw measurement into a standard measure is

$$z = \frac{X - M}{\sigma} = \frac{x}{\sigma} \tag{51}$$

Note the use of σ in the denominator of the exponent in formula (48) and also in formulas (49) and (50).

The Law of Error.—It has been said before that every measurement is in a sense an error since in all probability it deviates from the mean and from the true value of the thing we are attempting to measure. Since measurements tend to distribute themselves in the form of the normal curve, we sometimes speak of this distribution as the **law of errors.** *The farther away from the mean an error lies, the less likely it is to occur.* This is a rough way of stating the law of errors. But we can state the law more exactly than that for we know how rapidly the frequency or the probability of the error decreases as its size increases. This probability is proportional to the Y value in the mathematical formula for the normal distribution curve [formula (48)]. In other words, the law of error stated *quantitatively* is the formula for the normal probability curve. The probability of an error is a function of its size. Small errors are the rule and large ones the exception. And yet in extremely rare cases we may expect to find very large errors. It will be noticed that the two 'tails' of the normal curve in Fig. 4 become **asymptotic** to the X-axis, *i.e.*, they approach it as their limit, but never actually touch it. It is theoretically possible to obtain an error of infinite size but this would occur infinitely seldom. On the other hand, one can never tell whether or not the very next error will be an infinitely large one. The probabilities are that the next error will be small. In fact, it is more probable that the next measurement will coincide with the mean than that it should be any other one value.

Theory of Errors.—But is there any logical reason why errors of measurement should obey the normal law? The normal curve is derivable from the tossed-coin experiment and from the laws of chance. Is there anything in ordinary measurements that resembles the tossing of coins? What is there in measurement that corresponds to the coins with their heads and tails?

Let us assume that in making any single measurement a number of single, independent factors are at work. Each factor is as important as any other one, just as each coin in the coin-tossing experiment is as important as any other. Each factor, also like a coin, has two ways of acting, two ways of affecting the measurement, both equally likely to occur. If the factor acts in one way, it tends to increase the magnitude of the measurement by a given amount, by one unit of effect. If the factor acts in the opposite way, it tends to decrease the size of the measurement.

In any set of measurements there are probably a great number of these hypothetical factors. But let us take a simple illustration in which there are six such factors. Let us suppose that this applies to the judgments made in the Müller-Lyer illusion in which the mean was approximately 157 mm. Assume that each hypothetical factor has the power to displace the measurement by 1 mm., adding to the result when it comes 'heads up' and detracting from it when it comes 'tails up.' When all six of them by chance come 'heads up,' the measurement is 157 plus 6, or 163. When all six of them come 'tails up' the measurement is 151. When there are three heads and three tails, the measurement is at the mean, or exactly 157. Table 8 will give the probable frequencies Np of the different measurements.

In the actual measurements, of course, many more than six factors are undoubtedly at work and each one need not influence the measurement by exactly 1 mm. It does not require much search to guess what some of these factors might be. Some are to be found in the apparatus and some in the observer. The apparatus is not constructed perfectly and it may slide under the pull of the observer more easily at one time than at another or at one spot rather than at another. The slightly uneven textures of the paint in the line and in the background may lend themselves as cues which the observer at times depends upon. In the observer the factors are partly perceptual and partly motor. The adjustment of the eye muscles, the point of fixation, the shifting of attention, the fluctuation of attention, the changing self-instruction, all vary from time to time. The use of different arm and finger muscles, the shifting of bodily posture, the shifting of muscular tensions, and the change in the mode of pulling on the strings are but a few of the motor factors that enter into the complex set of determiners of the measurements.

TABLE 8.—THE PROBABLE FREQUENCIES OF MEASUREMENTS OF DIFFERENT SIZE ASSUMING SIX HYPOTHETICAL FACTORS

Number of heads	Number of tails	Size of measurement	Probable frequency
0	6	151	1
1	5	153	6
2	4	155	15
3	3	157	20
4	2	159	15
5	1	161	6
6	0	163	1
			Total 64

FITTING DATA TO THE NORMAL CURVE

Smoothing a Frequency Distribution.—It is undoubtedly clear to the student that, the smaller the number of measurements in any distribution, the more irregular is the contour of the frequency polygon. It is sometimes desirable to attempt to predict what the smoother distribution curve would look like if perhaps 1000 measurements had been made. There are two rather simple but not very exact devices that can be used for smoothing a distribution. Both are based upon the principle of the *moving average*. A moving average is found for each three neighboring frequencies. The new frequency y'_k, will be the mean of the original frequency y_k and the two frequencies on either side of it, y_j and y_l. This process may be carried out either graphically or arithmetically. The graphic process will be illustrated first.

Graphic Smoothing.—In Fig. 9 the original frequencies in the distribution of the 200 measurements of the Müller-Lyer illusion problem are plotted as small circlets. The dotted lines are drawn so as to connect alternate points, *i.e.*, points y_j and y_l in each group of three successive points. At the ends of the polygon two frequencies of zero are used. The next step is to draw a vertical line from point y_k to an intersection with the construction line

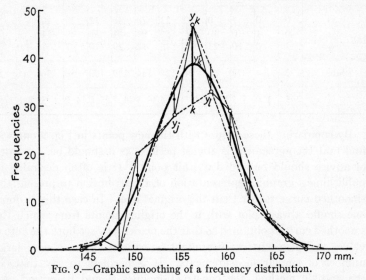

FIG. 9.—Graphic smoothing of a frequency distribution.

that connects points y_j and y_l at the point k. The new point y_k' is now located at the midpoint of the vertical line ky_k. All the other points are revised in a similar manner. If it is apparent that the new points approach a fairly normal form without any inversions,[1] then the smoothing may be considered complete and a continuous smooth line may be drawn through the new points. If the new points do not give something approaching the normal curve, or if there are inversions, the same smoothing process may be repeated in exactly the same manner, using the new points instead of the original ones. It is obvious that, when a polygon requires more

[1] An inversion means a sudden reversal of direction of the trend of the curve, giving a 'zigzag' contour.

than one smoothing, there is small likelihood that the final smoothed curve will predict very accurately what the true distribution of a large number of cases really is.

Arithmetical Smoothing Process.—The arithmetical process, which corresponds to the graphic one just described, weights the point y_k twice as much as the two neighboring points. The method as carried out with the very same distribution is as follows:

TABLE 9.—THE ARITHMETICAL SMOOTHING OF A FREQUENCY POLYGON

X	145	147	149	151	153	155	157	159	161	163	165	167	169
y_j	0	0	2	0	20	23	28	46	32	29	10	7	2
$2y_k$	0	4	0	40	46	56	94	64	58	20	14	4	0
y_l	2	0	20	23	28	46	32	29	10	7	2	0	0
Sum	2	4	22	63	94	125	154	139	100	56	26	11	2
y_k'	.5	1.0	5.5	15.8	23.5	31.3	38.5	34.7	25.0	14.0	6.5	2.8	.5

By comparing these values with the new points in Fig. 9 one will find that the agreement is almost perfect, as it should be. A word of advice should be added at this point. It is often desirable in publishing a graphic representation of a distribution to present the smoothed curve rather than the original one. In case this is done, one should always plot with it the original points from which the smoothed curve is obtained so that the reader may see both the actual values and also what values might be expected from a very large number of similar measurements. It is needless to say that, in the graphic method, the construction lines should be erased and only the smoothed curve and the original points left for display.

Finding the Best-fitting Normal Curve.—If the reader will recall the mathematical formula for the normal distribution curve [formula (48)], he will see that if we know three things we can find directly from the formula any corresponding values of Y and X. We need only to know N, σ, and the mean. The other symbols in the equation are already known. We must know the mean because the x in the formula is a deviation from the mean. As in the case of the simpler mathematical functions discussed on pages 79 *ff.*, we can arbitrarily assign different values to x, calculate the corresponding values of Y, and then draw a curve through the points so located. Fortunately, we do not have to go through the labor of computing the values for $e^{\frac{-x^2}{2\sigma^2}}$, since they have been given in tables already worked out by statisticians. We assume that $N = 1$ and also that $\sigma = 1$. The formula for the normal curve then becomes

$$Z = \frac{1}{\sqrt{2\pi}} e^{\frac{-z^2}{2}} \qquad (52)$$

where $\quad Z = \dfrac{Y\sigma}{N}.$

$\qquad\quad Y = \dfrac{NZ}{\sigma}.$

$\qquad\quad z = \dfrac{x}{\sigma}.$

Table 10 shows how the process of fitting data to the best normal curve is accomplished. Column 1 gives the original X values, the midpoints of the intervals being used. Column 2 gives the deviations of those X values from the mean. Column 3 lists the standard measures, or the deviations in terms of sigma as the unit. Column 4 is obtained from column 3 by using Table B in the Appendix. It contains the values of Z as obtained from formula (52). To find the values of Y', as in column 5, the Z values must be multiplied by N/σ', σ' being the standard deviation in terms of the class interval.

TABLE 10.—THE PROCESS OF FINDING THE BEST-FITTING NORMAL DISTRIBUTION CURVE FOR THE MÜLLER-LYER DATA

(1)	(2)	(3)	(4)	(5)	(6)	(7)	(8)	(9)
X	$X - M$ (x)	$\dfrac{x}{\sigma}$	Z	Y' $\left(\dfrac{NZ}{\sigma'}\right)$	Y	$Y - Y'$	$(Y - Y')^2$	$\dfrac{(Y - Y')^2}{Y'}$
146.5	−10.14	−2.620	.0129	1.3	2	.7	.49	.377
148.5	− 8.14	−2.103	.0439	4.5	0	−4.5	20.25	4.500
150.5	− 6.14	−1.587	.1132	11.7	20	8.3	68.89	5.888
152.5	− 4.14	−1.070	.2251	23.3	23	− .3	.09	.004
154.5	− 2.14	− .553	.3423	35.4	28	−7.4	54.76	1.547
156.5	− .14	− .036	.3987	41.2	47	5.8	33.64	.816
158.5	1.86	.481	.3553	36.7	32	−4.7	22.09	.602
160.5	3.86	.997	.2424	25.1	29	3.9	15.21	.606
162.5	5.86	1.514	.1267	13.1	10	−3.1	9.61	.734
164.5	7.86	2.031	.0507	5.2	7	1.8	3.24	.623
166.5	9.86	2.548	.0155	1.6	2	.4	.16	.010

$$\Sigma = 199.1 \quad 200$$

$$\chi^2 = 15.707$$
$$n = 11$$
$$P = \ .159$$

Goodness of Fit.—The sum of the theoretical frequencies is 199.1, which is very close to the total of the observed frequencies, namely, 200. The sum of the Y' values would naturally not quite reach N, since in the theoretical curve there are some frequencies beyond the range of the X values listed above. Column Y gives the observed frequencies which may be compared with the theoretical ones. The discrepancies between the two will be found in column 7. Only three of the discrepancies are negligibly small. Two of them are much too large. The throwing together of data that contain significant constant errors, such as these data, is likely to have some such effect. Just how serious are these discrepancies? Does the distribution approach normality sufficiently well to be called normal? There is a convenient method given by Pearson for determining how well data fit the best-fitting normal curve.

Pearson's test of **goodness of fit** is illustrated in Table 10 in the last three columns. First we find the discrepancies. Then we square them. Finally we divide every squared discrepancy by its corresponding Y' or theoretical frequency. The sum of these values (in column 9) is called χ^2 (**chi square**). From this value and from the number of *cells* or classes we can find in one of Elderton's Tables (reproduced in modified form as Table D) a value P which tells about the goodness of fit. P is interpreted to mean the probability that, in a random sampling of measurements such as we have obtained, we should find as bad a fit or a worse fit than we did. Thus, if P is equal to .90, then there are 90 chances in 100 that we might obtain as poor a fit as we have or worse. There would be only 10 chances in 100 that the fit would be better.

In finding Pearson's P-coefficient, we need to know χ^2 and n, the number of cells. For the data in Table 10 those values are 15.707 and 11, respectively. From Elderton's Table (Table D) we find that P is .159. Interpreted, this means that, if the distribution of measurements such as we have is normal, then there are only 159 chances in 1000 that another random sample of 200 measurements would deviate as much, or more, from normality as the set that was obtained. This would seem to be a rather small probability. It would seem that there is only about one chance in nine of as bad a fit or a worse fit. Yet statisticians have agreed to be rather liberal and they would probably call this a 'fair' or 'medium' fit. Culler (3, p. 186) has summarized the opinions of a number of statisticians on the interpretation of the Pearson P-coefficient. Culler's interpretations are:

P	Description
1.00–.75	Superlative
.74–.50	Excellent
.49–.25	Good
.24–.10	Medium or fair
.09–.05	Poor
Below .05	Unacceptable

A word of warning should be offered in the general use of the Pearson P-coefficient. Under some circumstances it may lead to obviously absurd results. For example, if the data fall into many class intervals with very long tails extending at either end of the distribution, it may often happen that along these tails there are relatively large discrepancies which, when divided by the extremely small Y'''s, yield unduly high χ^2's. If this is obviously the case, the best plan is to combine the last few class intervals at the ends or to leave them out of consideration entirely. Fisher (6, p. 86) recommends that no class in which Y' is less than 5 be used alone. If this rule is followed, there are three classes in Table 10 which should be combined with others. At the lower end of the distribution we combine two, giving a joint Y' of 5.8 and a combined Y of 2. The discrepancy is 3.8; squared and divided by Y', it is 2.490. At the upper end, likewise, two classes should be combined. Y' is 6.8; Y is 9; the discrepancy is 2.2; squared and divided by Y', it is .712. Substituting these two new relative discrepancies for the four old ones and summing column 9 again, χ^2 becomes 13.389; n is now 9 instead of 11; and P, from Elderton's Table, is now .153 or approximately what it was before. There are times, however, when grouping frequencies at the tails will change P appreciably, and one can feel that this procedure gives more valid results.[1]

THE AREA UNDER THE NORMAL CURVE

Proportion of the Area Above or Below a Given Deviate.— We have already seen the relationship between frequencies and probabilities. They have been regarded as interchangeable in the discussions of the ordinates of the normal distribution curve. Especially is this true when we think of a distribution in histogram

[1] A rough test of the normality of a distribution is suggested by J. W. Dickey, Normalcy as a statistic, *J. Educ. Psychol.*, 1934, **25**, 437–446.

form. It was said that the number of measurements is represented by the area within each rectangle or column of the histogram. The total area under the smoothed normal curve then represents the sum of an infinite number of such rectangles, and the amount of area is proportional to N, the total number of measurements. In terms of probability the total area has the value of 1.00 or complete certainty. It may be remembered that in fitting data to the normal curve in Table 10 we assumed that N was equal to 1.00. It is convenient now to make the same assumption since all our tables for finding areas when X values are given are based upon this same assumption.

Table B gives the proportions of the area that lie between the mean and a given deviate z. It will be recalled that z stands for a standard score, *i.e.*, a deviation $(X - M)$ divided by σ. We are now ready for some problems. What is the probability that a measurement will fall below a point 1σ above the mean? This is equivalent to asking what proportion of the measurements lie below $+1\sigma$. In Table B we look in the z column for the value 1.00. The value in the p column which is opposite this z value is .3413. In other words, 34.13 per cent of the total area lies between the mean and $+1\sigma$. In addition to this, *all* the area *below* the mean must be added to the .3413. Exactly one-half or .5000 of the area lies below the mean. Therefore, .8413 of the total area lies below $+1\sigma$. The probability of a measurement falling below $+1\sigma$ is .8413 (see Fig. 10*A*).

We might ask next what proportion of the cases comes *above* $+1\sigma$. Since .8413 of the cases fall below, all the remaining proportion of the cases is above that point. The remaining proportion is found by the difference 1.000 − .8413, or .1587. Or it may be found by considering only the upper half of the distribution. Knowing that .3413 lie between the mean and $+1\sigma$, and that the remaining cases are included in the .5000 above the mean, we find the difference between these two values, which is again .1587. Figure 10*A* shows graphically the areas of which we have been speaking.

As a further problem we may ask what proportion of the cases lies below the point $-.5\sigma$. This is the shaded area at the left in Fig. 10*B*. Referring to Table B we find .5 in the z column and corresponding to it an area of .1915. This much of the total area lies between the mean and $-.5\sigma$. But we want to know about the area *below* $-.5\sigma$. We deduct .1915 from .5000 and find that it is

.3085, in other words, 30.85 per cent. The total area *above* −.5σ is, of course, .6915. This can be found in one of two ways, either .1915 + .5000, or 1.0000 − .3085.

In the same distribution (Fig. 10*B*), what is the probability that a case will be higher than +1.5σ? Between the mean and that point are .4332 of the cases. There is a probability of .0668

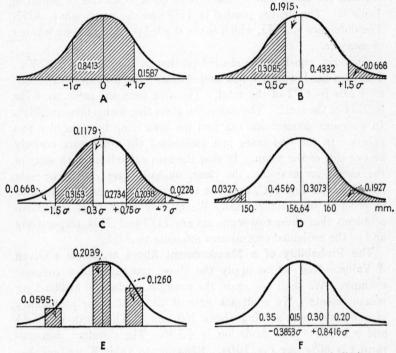

Fig. 10.—Areas under the normal distribution curve within certain limits.

that a measurement will exceed 1.5σ. It will be noted in Table B that between the mean and 3.0σ there are .4987 of the cases. Between +3σ and −3σ there are twice as many, namely, .9973, or practically all the cases. Only 3 cases in 1000 (or 27 in 10,000) would be beyond those limits. That is why we say that for practical purposes all our measurements will fall within the limits of +3σ and −3σ.

The Proportion of the Area Lying between Two Given Deviates.— Suppose we put the problem as follows: What proportion of the cases lies between -1.5σ and $-.3\sigma$? The shaded area at the left in Fig. 10*C* shows this region graphically. The shaded area is obviously a part of, or is included within, the area between the mean and the point -1.5σ. The shaded part includes all this except that region between the mean and $-.3\sigma$. We need to deduct the latter portion, the area between the mean and $-.3\sigma$, from the whole portion between the mean and -1.5σ. Both these areas can be found in Table B. The smaller portion is .1179 and the larger one is .4332. The difference is .3153, which is the shaded portion that we wanted to measure.

Similarly, consider the shaded portion to the right in Fig. 10*C*. This area lies between $+.75\sigma$ and $+2.0\sigma$. The area from the mean to $+2.0\sigma$ is .4772 of the total. The area from the mean to $+75\sigma$ is .2734 of the total. The difference gives the shaded area, or .2038. In a similar manner one can find the area lying between any two points. In the two cases just mentioned the areas were entirely on one side of the mean. In case the area extends on both sides of the mean, for example, the clear, unshaded area between $-.3\sigma$ and $+.75\sigma$ in Fig. 10*C*, then the two parts are found and summed in order to obtain the total. We already know from the above problems that these two segments are .1179 and .2734, respectively and so the unshaded central area amounts to .3913.

The Probability of a Measurement Above or Below a Given *X* Value.—Now let us apply the above procedure to a concrete example. We shall use again the example of the 200 Müller-Lyer measurements. We shall ask first of all, what is the probability of a measurement's being above 160 mm.? The mean is 156.64 and σ is 3.87. The deviation is $+3.36$. The standard measurement z is $.868\sigma$ (see Fig. 10*D*). Referring to Table B, we find that the corresponding area is .3073. This proportion of the measurements lies between the mean and 160. The proportion of the measurements *above* 160 is then $.5000 - .3073$, or .1927; 19.27 per cent of the cases theoretically come above 160; 19.27 per cent of 200 is 38.5 cases. By actual count in Table 1 there are 36 if we assume that one-half the 23 cases *at* 160 are really above that point.

In the same distribution, what proportion of the cases falls below 150 mm.? The deviation of 150 from the mean is -6.64. The standard measurement is 1.716. Between the mean and 150 we shall find .4569 of the area. *Below* 150, then, there are .0431, or 4.31 per cent of the cases; 4.31 per cent of 200 is 8.6 cases. As a matter of fact, there are 6 cases falling below 150 if we include one-half the cases at 150 mm.

The Probability of a Measurement between Two X Values.— We can also find what proportion of the cases lies between 150 and 160 mm. This is the unshaded area in Fig. 10D. That part above the mean we already know, namely, .3073; also that part below the mean, namely, .4569. The total unshaded area is .7642; 76.42 per cent of 200 gives 152.8 cases. As a matter of fact, 158 measurements were within the range from 150 to 160.

Let us take a narrower range of measurements, for example, from 155.5 to 157.5. These are the limits of one of the class intervals that were used. Figure 10E shows this region graphically. A rectangle or column has been drawn intentionally within this interval since this is the way in which a histogram is constructed. We can now find what the area of that rectangle of the histogram should be in the theoretical normal distribution.

The measurement 155.5 has a standard value of $-.295\sigma$. The point 157.5 has a standard value of $+.222$. The corresponding areas from the mean to those points are .1160 and .0879, respectively. The total area in the rectangle is therefore the sum of these two, or .2039; 20.39 per cent of 200 is 40.78 cases, or approximately 41. The number of measurements actually falling in that interval was 47. Now it will be noticed in Table 10, column 5, that the theoretical frequency in the interval 155.5 to 157.5 is 41.2. In other words, by finding the theoretical areas of the columns of the histogram, we have a second method of determining the theoretical frequencies and hence of fitting data to the best-fitting normal curve.

To take two more examples, what are the theoretical frequencies, or areas, between 159.5 and 161.5 and between 149.5 and 151.5? The student should work these out for himself; he will find them to be 25.2 and 11.9, respectively. The actual frequencies for those intervals were 29 and 20, respectively. The theoretical frequencies as found by the method in Table 10 were 25.1 and 11.7, respectively. We could go on, of course, and find the theoretical frequencies for all the other intervals, using this new method of curve fitting. The method has nothing to recommend it over the one already explained in Table 10, however, and for this reason will not be illustrated in full here. It is more important for the student to see the relationship between ordinates and the areas of the rectangles of the histogram.

The Limits on the *X*-axis for a Specified Proportion.—We can reverse our questions and ask for the *X* values above which, below which, or between which, a certain area lies. For example, above what point would the highest 20 per cent of the measurements be found? Now we have to work in a reverse direction. But let us see what the question means graphically. Figure 10*F* shows the area farthest to the right where the highest 20 per cent of the cases come. The lowest *X* value for this region divides the right half of the total distribution into two segments. The segment next to the mean includes 30 per cent of the cases. This is the proportion that we look up in Table E. We find that the point which includes 30 per cent of the cases from the mean is .8416. This is the abscissa value and it is a standard measurement, *i.e.*, in terms of σ as the unit. In answer to the problem just raised we can say that the highest 20 per cent of the cases come above $+.8416\sigma$.

As a second example, let us ask below what point the lowest 35 per cent of the cases would fall. The proportion .35 is .15 distant from the mean. The diagram shows this 15 per cent. From Table E the sigma value is $-.3853$.

As a third example, between what points will we find the middle 50 per cent of the cases? The curve being symmetrical about the mean, this would include 25 per cent on either side of the mean. From Table E we find, as the alert student should already expect, a sigma value of .6745. This is the distance of $1PE$ from the mean. The student may now better appreciate why we say that the probable error is $.6745\sigma$.

To apply the last three problems to our concrete problem of 200 measurements, we merely translate the standard measurements already obtained into the units of our original scale, namely, milli-meters. One σ equals 3.87 mm. Therefore we must multiply each standard measurement that we have obtained above by 3.87. The highest 20 per cent of the cases lie above $.8416\sigma$, or above 3.26 mm. above the mean. The mean being 156.64, the point we are looking for is 159.9. The lowest 35 per cent fall below $-.3853\sigma$ or -1.49 mm. from the mean. The point on the original scale, below which, theoretically, are 35 per cent of the cases, is 155.15. The two points within which are the middle 50 per cent of the cases are $.6745\sigma$ in either direction from the mean. In terms of milli-meters, this distance is 2.61. The middle half of the measurements should fall between 154.03 and 159.25.

Applications of the Areas under the Normal Curve.—There are many useful applications of the procedures that we have just been examining, involving the areas under different parts of the normal distribution curve. Some of these will not be discussed here but will be left for later chapters when they come more directly into use. One or two applications are appropriately mentioned here.

One of these the student has already used without realizing its full significance. This application involved the determination of the significance of a difference that was discussed in the preceding chapter. The student will now understand more fully the meaning of the procedure that was described on pages 58 *ff.* and illustrated in Fig. 5. Figure 5, as was said at that place, illustrates the distribution of all the differences we would expect to obtain from repeated sets of observations. The actual difference is assumed to be the mean of the distribution. A difference of zero falls somewhere below the mean. The shaded area represents that proportion of all the differences greater than zero, and hence all the positive differences. The unshaded area represents the proportion of differences that will probably be negative. The deviation of a difference of zero from the mean is extremely easy to find since $(X - M)$ is equivalent to the obtained difference itself. The diff./$\sigma_{\text{diff.}}$, which was called the critical ratio in the preceding chapter, will now be recognized as a standard measurement or $(X - M)/\sigma$. The remaining steps are now so familiar that it is unnecessary to review them here.

The Cumulative Normal Distribution Curve

The Meaning of Cumulative Distribution.—One of the more general applications must be mentioned at this point. This is the **cumulative distribution,** or the **ogive** curve as it was called by Galton. This distribution is not of the original frequencies but it is based upon the sums of the frequencies. Starting with the lowest class interval, the cumulative frequency of any interval is the sum of all the frequencies in the classes below plus the frequency in that interval. In Table 11 will be found the original frequencies f of our illustrative problem and in the following column are the cumulative frequencies cf. In the table we also find the theoretical frequencies f' as obtained in Table 10, and also the cumulative theoretical frequencies cf'. Both sets of cumulative frequencies, actual and theoretical, are plotted against the stimulus values in Fig. 11. The solid line represents the ogive based upon the actual frequencies,

and the dotted line represents the best-fitting theoretical ogive.
The theoretical curve is drawn in simply for the sake of comparison.
The succeeding remarks will apply to the actual distribution unless
it is otherwise specified.

It should be noticed that the points are now plotted, not at the
midpoints of the intervals, but at the upper limits of the intervals.
At the point 157.5 on the X-axis, for example, we place the ordinate
at 120 because 120 of the cases were lower than 157.5. Similarly,
at 161.5 the ordinate is 181 because 181 cases were lower than that
X value. All 200 cases were lower than 167.5, or the upper limit of
the highest class interval.

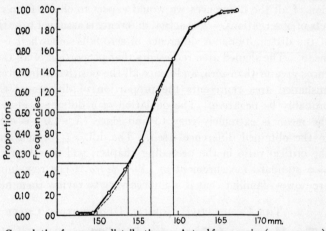

Fig. 11.—Cumulative frequency distributions. Actual frequencies (————),
theoretical frequencies (– – – – –).

The Mathematics of the Cumulative Normal Curve.—In this
connection it should be recalled that ordinates of the noncumulative
normal curve may be regarded as areas approaching columns or
rectangles in form. The ordinate values on the ogive curve therefore
represent the sums of the areas of all the rectangles *below* the different
X values. The ogive curve is mathematically known as the **integral**
of the normal distribution curve. Its general mathematical formula
is written:

$$p = \int_{-\infty}^{x} \frac{1}{\sigma\sqrt{2\pi}} e^{\frac{-x^2}{2\sigma^2}} dx \qquad (53)$$

where x = a deviation from the mean, as usual.

p = the proportion of the area below any assigned value of x.

The integral sign is an elongated letter S which stands for *sum*. The limits on the abscissa that bound the area are given at the top and bottom of the integral sign. The expression dx is merely a sign of differentiation and need not concern the nonmathematical student. The formula may be interpreted as follows: The proportion p of the area under the curve between the limits of minus infinity to a given x value is equal to the sum of all the ordinates between those two limits. The ordinates, from the original formula for the normal curve, [see formula (48)], are equal to the expression follow-

TABLE 11.—ACTUAL AND THEORETICAL NORMAL FREQUENCIES, CUMULATIVE FREQUENCIES, AND PERCENTILE RATINGS

Interval	f	cf	f'	cf'	p	p'	Upper limits (x)
145.5–147.4	2	2	1.3	1.3	.010	.0065	147.5
147.5–149.4	0	2	4.5	5.8	.010	.0290	149.5
149.5–151.4	20	22	11.7	17.5	.110	.0875	151.5
151.5–153.4	23	45	23.3	40.8	.225	.2040	153.5
153.5–155.4	28	73	35.4	76.2	.365	.3810	155.5
155.5–157.4	47	120	41.2	117.4	.600	.5870	157.5
157.5–159.4	32	152	36.7	154.1	.760	.7705	159.5
159.5–161.4	29	181	25.1	179.2	.905	.8960	161.5
161.5–163.4	10	191	13.1	192.3	.955	.9615	163.5
163.5–165.4	7	198	5.2	197.5	.990	.9875	165.5
165.5–167.4	2	200	1.6	199.1	1.000	.9955	167.5

ing the integral sign. The values of p corresponding to a given x can be obtained directly from tables of the normal probability integral, or they can be obtained less directly from Table B after the fashion of the problems just illustrated, particularly the problems illustrated in Figs. 10A and B.

Some Uses of the Ogive Curve.—The ogive curve is useful in various ways, some of which will be mentioned here. In the first place it serves as a graphic method of finding the median of the distribution. The median, it will be remembered, is the value on the X-scale that divides the measurements into two equal groups.

Graphically, it is the point where the ogive curve cuts across the halfway mark on the Y-axis; it is the X value where p equals exactly .50. P equals .50 in this problem when the cumulative frequency is 100. If a line is drawn at the level of $p = .50$ until it cuts the ogive, and if a perpendicular is then dropped from the intersection thus made to the X-axis, the median may be read off immediately. In Fig. 11 the median appears to be 156.7. This checks very closely with the median that was found by interpolation in the preceding chapter, namely, 156.65.

In addition to the median we can find graphically the measure of dispersion Q, the **quartile deviation.** From Fig. 11 we can see that Q_3 is 159.3 and Q_1 is 153.9. Q is found to be 2.7. The Q of the distribution was previously found to be 2.76. The fineness of the graphic method depends upon the exactness of the drawing and the amount of magnification used.

Percentile Ranks.—The ogive curve is especially useful in the field of mental tests in finding the percentile ranks of test scores. A **percentile rank**[1] means the rank of a given score among 100, assuming 100 individuals had been tested and ranked. An individual with a percentile rank of 75 is better than 75 in 100 and poorer than 25. In Fig. 11 we can find for illustrative purposes what 'score' in terms of millimeters the 75th 'individual' would make. The 75th percentile corresponds to an X value of 159.3. The 63d percentile corresponds to a measurement of 158.0. And so we could go on, finding the measurement that corresponds to any given rank. We can reverse the process and find what percentile rank should be assigned to any 'score.' A measurement of 155, for example, would have a percentile rank of 32. A measurement of 165 would have a rank of 97.5.

Graphic Solution for Percentile Ranks.—In the set of data used here the matter of finding corresponding percentile ranks and 'scores' is an easy one since the 200 cases divide themselves very conveniently into 100 divisions. When N is not a multiple of 100, or even of 10, the problem is less convenient but not difficult. Once the ogive is drawn, the topmost point represents the 100 per cent level. No matter what the graphic unit is on the ordinate, one can proceed to divide the total distance from zero up to the 100 per

[1] The more accurate term is **centile.** Custom has dictated the use of the term 'percentile.'

cent level into 10 equal units and draw horizontal lines at those levels. This divides the total range into **deciles,** which are often fine enough divisions for practical purposes. When percentile ratings are required, smaller subdivisions can be drawn or interpolations can be made. If the plotted ogive from the observed frequencies is clearly irregular because of an insufficient number of measurements, it is proper to draw by inspection the best-fitting ogive and to derive the percentile values from the smoothed curve. Better yet, the best-fitting ogive may be obtained, like the dotted one in Fig. 11, from the theoretical frequencies of the normal distribution.

Arithmetical Solution of Percentile Ranks.—The corresponding percentile ratings for every class interval can be found arithmetically by means of a process that is illustrated in Table 11. Having the cumulative frequencies, we next find the *rate*, which is equal to $1/N$. In our illustrative problem the rate is .005. Each cumulative frequency is multiplied by the rate to find the percentile rank. It must be remembered that these percentile ranks belong to the topmost values of the class intervals; these are shown at the right-hand side of Table 11. The percentile ranks p and p' were computed for both the actual and the theoretical distributions. Any intermediate ranks can be found by interpolation. Where the greatest accuracy is desired, the size of the class interval should be made small and the number of classes large.

Thurstone (13) suggests a convenient process of finding percentile ranks with a calculating machine. Percentiles are found for the midpoints of the intervals as well as for the upper limits. Step one consists in finding $1/2N$, or half the rate that is usually employed. Step two is the multiplication of the frequency of the lowest class interval by $1/2N$. This gives the percentile rating for the midpoint of the lowest class interval. This should be recorded (see Table 12), but the amount is left to accumulate in the calculator. As step three, the same frequency is multiplied once more by $1/2N$ to give the percentile rating of the upper limit of the lowest class interval. This is recorded as in the next to the last column of Table 12. Without clearing the machine, the frequency of the next interval is entered into the machine, is multiplied once and then twice, and is allowed to accumulate, and so on with all the remaining frequencies. As a check, the last entry in the p_u column should be exactly 1.00.

TABLE 12.—MACHINE COMPUTATION OF PERCENTILE RATINGS FROM ORIGINAL
FREQUENCIES

Midpoint	f	$f/2N$	p_m	p_u	Upper limit
146.5	2	.0050	.0050	.0100	147.5
148.5	0	.0000	.0100	.0100	149.5
150.5	20	.0500	.0600	.1100	151.5
152.5	23	.0575	.1675	.2250	153.5
154.5	28	.0700	.2950	.3650	155.5
156.5	47	.1175	.4825	.6000	157.5
158.5	32	.0800	.6800	.7600	159.5
160.5	29	.0725	.8325	.9050	161.5
162.5	10	.0250	.9300	.9550	163.5
164.5	7	.0175	.9725	.9900	165.5
166.5	2	.0050	.9950	1.0000	167.5

FREQUENCY DISTRIBUTIONS THAT ARE NOT NORMAL

It would be a serious error to leave the student with the impression that all distribution curves that are met in psychological work are normal and that other types of curves do not in reality exist. Pearson and others have pointed out at least 15 different types of distribution curves of which the Gaussian curve is only one. Advanced statistical workers frequently make tests of their distributions in order to see to which type they probably belong. The treatment of these various types is entirely beyond the scope of this book. The student of advanced statistics will find these types treated by Elderton (5), Jones (10), and Kelley (11). The average student will find a knowledge of the normal curve and of certain deviations from normality sufficient for his practical needs. Some of the more common departures from normality have already been referred to and they will be discussed briefly here.

Skewness and How to Measure It.—In the skewed curve there is only one mode but this peak of greatest frequency is shifted to either the right or left of the middle of the range. If shifted to the left, the skewness is said to be positive; if to the right, the skewness is negative. There are several methods of measuring the degree of skewness. One simple method which is adequate when the skewness is moderate is given by the formula

$$Sk = \frac{3(M - Mdn)}{\sigma} \qquad (54)$$

As an illustration, let us take the distribution for the L-measurements represented in Fig. 2A.

$$Sk = \frac{3(155.92 - 154.97)}{4.684} = \frac{2.85}{4.684} = .609.$$

This would be considered a moderate degree of skewness.

From the make-up of formula (54), it can be seen that, if the mean is greater than the median, the bunching is toward the lower end of the scale and, $(M - Mdn)$ being positive, the skewness is positive. When the bunching is at the higher end of the scale, with the median greater than the mean, $(M - Mdn)$ is negative and the skewness is negative. When M equals Mdn, as in the perfectly symmetrical curve, the skewness is zero.

There are a number of possible causes for skewed distributions. One cause is a selective factor, or set of factors, which causes the measurements to deviate from a random sampling. If in testing the intelligence of fourteen-year-old boys we used only those below the ninth grade, we would probably find a distribution that is positively skewed because the brighter fourteen-year-old boys in the high-school grades had been eliminated. Another frequent cause in mental testing is the use of a test that is too difficult or too easy for the group to which it is applied. If the test is too difficult, the skewness is likely to be positive; if the test is too easy, it may be negative. Another cause may be the measuring instrument. If units of amount near the lower end of the scale are in reality smaller than those at the upper end, there will be an apparent bunching of cases at the lower end and therefore a positive skewing effect. If we eliminate all these factors causing artificial skewing, and other such factors as well, the skewness may express the actual facts. The distribution may in reality be one lacking in symmetry. Should this be distinctly so, the application of the statistics of the normal curve is questionable and one of Pearson's other types should be used.

Kurtosis.—Of all the items of information which we customarily desire to know about a distribution, **kurtosis** comes sixth in the list according to Kelley (11, p. 44). The other items come in the order:

1. What is it a distribution of? This involves such questions as the nature of the variable or scale; the unit of measurement and

whether it is constant; whether there is an absolute zero point and where it is located.

2. The number of cases or the population.

3. Some measure of central tendency.

4. Some measure of dispersion or variability.

5. A measure of symmetry or lack of symmetry, *i.e.*, skewness.

6. The kurtosis, or degree of bunching at the center.

7. Tendency toward bimodality.

Of the preceding list the first five items have already been discussed at length. Only a few words will be said concerning the last two. A relatively sharp-pointed distribution is called **leptokurtic** and a broad, flat distribution approaching a rectangular form is called **platykurtic**. The normal curve, neither sharp nor flat, is **mesokurtic**. The mathematical importance of kurtosis lies in its use as a criterion of the type of distribution involved. Pearson's curves differ from one another according to the degree of kurtosis. Since we shall not deal with these various types here, it is sufficient for us merely to become acquainted with the terms.

A rough indication as to whether a curve is leptokurtic or platykurtic can be had by comparing the values of PE and Q. Recall that the former is the measure of dispersion of the best-fitting normal curve and that Q measures the dispersion of the actual measurements. If Q is distinctly greater than the PE, the curve tends to be platykurtic; if Q is less than the PE, it is leptokurtic; if Q is equal to PE, it is mesokurtic. Judged from these standards, the curves represented in Figs. 2 and 3 deviate from the normal in nearly every case. Reference to Table 5 shows that the R-distribution and the O-distribution are probably slightly leptokurtic; the L-distribution and the I-distribution are platykurtic, while the total distribution approaches very nearly the normal, mesokurtic condition.

Departures from Unimodality.—Some distributions depart very strikingly from the usual unimodal curve. There are some distributions, called 'U-shaped,' which seem the very antithesis of the normal curve. Such distributions have been known to result from measurements of suggestibility (9, p. 68). Other curves, called 'J-shaped,' have a maximal frequency at one extreme of the range. Such curves have been obtained in measuring what Allport calls 'institutional behavior' (1). Under time restrictions for the parking of automobiles in a large city, for example, the numbers of cars left in a parking place for varying intervals of time form a J-shaped curve, with the shortest time interval having the greatest number of cases. The same type of distribution occurs with regard to the stopping of motor cars at stop signals.

In all these unusual distributions one must be sure that the measuring scale is not to blame, in part at least, for a real distorting effect. In the measurements just cited it is not always possible to set up a good linear measuring scale. Even though the units employed may be physical ones, such as hours or minutes, we must be sure that they are *psychologically* equal before we decide about the nature of the resulting distribution curves. However, the many examples just cited should warn the student against a universal application of the normal Gaussian frequency distribution and its statistical constants. It is true that the great majority of the distributions he will meet will approach the normal type. But they should be demonstrably near enough to the normal type, as shown by means of the inspected histogram or polygram, by the fitted and tested best-fitting normal curve, or by some good logical grounds, before the data are treated accordingly.

Problems

1. What is the probability that a coin will turn up four heads in succession?
Ans. 1/16.

2. What is the probability of getting two heads in five throws of a coin?
Ans. 5/16.

3. With two dice, what is the probability of throwing two three's? A two and a three? *Ans.* 1/36; 1/18.

4. In throwing three dice, what is the probability of getting a sum of nine spots? *Ans.* .116.

5. Toss six pennies a total of 128 times, recording each time the number of heads. Find the frequency with which the number of heads, from zero to six, landed upward. Plot a histogram giving the actual frequencies. Calculate the expected frequencies and plot them in the form of a frequency polygon overlapping the histogram. Present all your calculations.

6. In throwing a die 1000 times, what is the most probable number of one spots? *Ans.* 167.

7. In 5000 tosses of a coin, there were 2625 heads. Is that a reasonable number to expect? Explain.

8. In 7200 throws of a die, what is the most reasonable number of one spots to expect? Is 1100 a reasonable number to expect? Explain.

9. A box contains 1000 balls, some white and some black. In making 25 draws (replacing the one drawn each time and shaking them up), there were 15 white and 10 black balls. What is the most probable proportion of white

balls in the box? How much error may be expected in this estimate? Would 700 white balls be an unreasonable number of white balls to expect in examining the whole 1000? Explain.

10. Answer the following questions concerning the distribution found in Problem 2 on page 69:

    a. What proportion of the cases in the theoretical distribution from which these cases came would lie above a score of 150? Below 100? Between 80 and 135? Between 100 and 150?

    b. Above what score would the highest 10 per cent lie? Below what score the lowest 30 per cent? Between what scores the middle 40 per cent?

11. Using the same distribution as in the preceding problem,

    a. Draw a smoothed distribution curve, using both the graphic and the calculated frequency methods.

    b. Find the theoretical frequencies for the best-fitting normal curve and apply Pearson's test for goodness of fit.

12. For the same distribution, estimate the amount of skewness. Draw a conclusion concerning skewness and also concerning kurtosis, if possible.

13. Translate the scores of the same distribution into a set of percentile ranks, applying the various devices described in this chapter.

14. On the basis of the preceding problem, find the percentile ranks of individuals making scores of: 72, 99, 125, 151, 178, and 192.

REFERENCES

1. ALLPORT, F. H., in P. S. Achilles, "Psychology at Work," Whittlesey House, McGraw-Hill Book Company, Inc., New York, 1932.

2. BORING, E. G., The logic of the normal law of error in mental measurement, *Amer. J. Psychol.*, 1920, **31**, 1–33.

3. CULLER, E., Studies in psychometric theory, *J. Exper. Psychol.*, 1926, **9**, 169–194.

4. EDGERTON, H. A., and D. G. PATERSON, Table of standard errors and probable errors of percentages for varying numbers of cases, *J. Appl. Psychol.*, 1926, **10**, 378–391.

5. ELDERTON, W. P., "Frequency Curves and Correlation," 2d ed., C. & E. Layton, London, 1927.

6. FISHER, R. A., "Statistical Methods for Research Workers," 4th ed., Oliver & Boyd, Edinburgh, 1932.

7. GARRETT, H. E., "Statistics in Psychology and Education," Longmans, Green & Company, New York, 1926.

8. HOLZINGER, K. J., "Statistical Methods for Students in Education," Ginn and Company, Boston, 1928.

9. HULL, C. L., "Hypnosis and Suggestibility," D. Appleton-Century Company, Inc., New York, 1933.

10. JONES, D. C., "A First Course in Statistics," George Bell & Sons, Ltd., London, 1927.

11. KELLEY, T. L., "Statistical Method," The Macmillan Company, New York, 1924.

12. THURSTONE, L. L., "The Fundamentals of Statistics," The Macmillan Company, New York, 1927.

13. ———, Note on the calculation of percentile ranks, *J. Educ. Psychol.*, 1927, **18**, 617–620.

14. YULE, G. U., "Introduction to the Theory of Statistics," 5th ed., Charles Griffin & Company, Ltd., London, 1919.

CHAPTER IV

THE METHOD OF MINIMAL CHANGES

(METHOD OF LIMITS)

SENSORY THRESHOLDS AND WEBER'S LAW

The method of minimal changes arose in connection with the determination of sensory thresholds, and to this day that is its primary function. Therefore, before proceeding to an examination of the method, it is important that the meaning of sensory thresholds and Weber's law be made clear. Figure 12 will help in this.

The Two Psychophysical Continua.—The vertical line at the left represents some particular **physical continuum,** *i.e.*, any series of physical phenomena that differ only in magnitude. For example, the energy of a sound wave, or any one physical change that corresponds to a variation in loudness would be such a continuum. Another example would be the weight of an object as measured in grams or in pounds. Still another example would be the length of a horizontal straight line measured in centimeters. Such physical series, whether they are measured in terms of space, time, or energy, have a range in value from zero to infinity.

Our sensory responses form a corresponding series parallel to the physical series. We may call this series a **psychological continuum.** By 'continuum' in either case is meant a closely graded series, one step merging imperceptibly into the next and the whole forming a straight line signifying changes in a single direction. A series of grays, extending from extreme white to extreme black, satisfies such a definition of a psychological continuum.

The Stimulus Limen.—The psychological continuum in any case is not so extensive in range as its corresponding physical continuum. This is illustrated in Fig. 12. At the extreme lower end of the physical scale there are stimuli that make no impression at all upon the nervous system, and there is no sensory response to them. Stimuli a little stronger than these may arouse sensory responses, but only rarely and under the most favorable conditions. Stimuli

110

still stronger than these produce responses more than rarely; after a certain higher stimulus value is reached a response may always be expected under normal conditions. There is no *single* stimulus value at any point on the scale below which a response never occurs and above which a response always occurs. There is a rather indefinite, twilight region, a region of uncertainty, in which part of

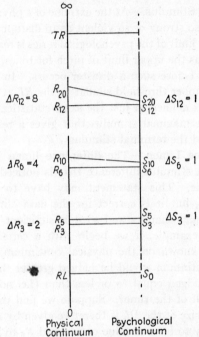

FIG. 12.—The two psychophysical continua. (The physical continuum has been broken into segments in this illustration in order to show better the true relationship between *R* and *S*. It is really continuous, as the name implies.)

the time a response occurs and part of the time it does not. It is generally agreed that we should adopt that stimulus value which gives a response exactly half the time, in other words, the stimulus that has a probability of .50 of producing a response, as the **stimulus limen** *RL*.[1] Above the *RL*, stimuli give a response more than half

---

[1] The letter *R* comes from the German word *Reiz*, which is the equivalent of the English word 'stimulus.' In psychophysics *R* never stands for "response." A response, following the psychophysical tradition, is designated by *S*, which originally stood for 'sensation.'

the time; below it they elicit a response less than half the time, as indicated by the dotted portion of the line in Fig. 12. Corresponding to the *RL*, the diagram in Fig. 12 shows a sensory value of S_0. This is the hypothetical zero point for the psychological continuum. We cannot say that S_0 is a zero amount of sensation, but it may be treated as such and it forms a point of reference for the psychological scale.

The Terminal Stimulus.—At the extreme of a physical continuum, stimuli may be so strong or so violent as to disrupt the sense organ before the upper limit of the psychological series is reached. But in a few cases, such as the upper limit of pitch for tones, the sense organ fails to respond before such a disaster occurs. In the latter cases we can find an upper threshold similar to the *RL* at the lower limit. This threshold is defined in just the same statistical manner as the lower one. The maximal stimulus that gives a response just half the time is called the **terminal stimulus** *TR*.

The Difference Limen.—The **difference limen** *DL* is similarly defined. It is a stimulus difference that is noticed exactly 50 per cent of the time. This statement may have to be altered and elaborated later, but it is correct for the data obtained from the method of minimal changes and so it is sufficient for our present purposes. For example, if we begin with a certain stimulus R_3, having a value known on the physical continuum, what stimulus on the same continuum would be judged greater than R_3 just half the time, and judged equal to or less than (*i.e.* not greater than) R_3 the other half of the time? Suppose we find that R_5 is such a stimulus. The size of the *DL* is therefore given by $R_5 - R_3$. If R_5 happens actually to have a value of five and R_3 to have a value of three on the physical scale, the *DL* is equal to two physical units. It is simply the increment (or decrement) that is observed half the time. It will be noticed in Fig. 12 that we have labeled the *DL*, about which we have just been talking, DL_3; this means it is the *DL* when R_3 has been taken as the starting point or the standard R_S. The notation ΔR is also used. Delta, as usual, stands for a small increment, and the expression ΔR is merely a more general name for any such small increment. The *DL* is one such small increment which has already been defined.

Corresponding to R_3 and R_5, we find on the psychological continuum the notations S_3 and S_5. These are two sensory responses, S_3 being the one most commonly aroused by R_3, and S_5 being the one most commonly aroused by R_5. We cannot say that S_3 and S_5 have the same values as their stimuli R_3 and R_5, respectively, nor even that they are proportional to their stimuli in value. S_3 and S_5 are to be evaluated on the psychological scale. Unfortunately we cannot give each one a psychological value with reference to the zero point, S_0. We can only say how far apart S_3 and S_5 are. We can say in this case that S_3 and S_5 are just one unit apart. In other words, a sensory difference that is noticed correctly half the time under standard conditions may be taken as a unit of measurement on the psychological scale.

Weber's Law.—Now if we take another standard stimulus R_6 and obtain DL_6, we shall find, if Weber's law holds, that R_{10} is judged greater just 50 per cent of the time. DL_6 is therefore four physical units. The corresponding sensory difference, however, is again just one unit. In the diagram this is denoted by the expression $\Delta S_6 = 1$. Again, with a standard of 12 units R_{12}, the DL is 8 units. In other words, for *equal* increments on the psychological scale we have proportional increments on the physical scale. The DL is in direct proportion to the standard stimulus. The ratio of the DL to R_s (the standard stimulus) is $2:3$. In the form of an equation, Weber's law may be stated as follows:

$$\Delta R = KR \tag{55}$$

where ΔR is any defined increment in a stimulus R, and K is the ratio of the increment to R. K is a constant for a given observer and a given continuum under a given set of conditions. Dividing through both sides of equation (55) by R, we obtain the usual form of Weber's law,

$$\frac{\Delta R}{R} = K \tag{55a}$$

and this may have a familiar ring when put into words: The just noticeable increment to any stimulus bears a constant ratio to that stimulus.[1]

[1] It is of interest to know that Weber's law, or, in more general terms, the relativity of human judgments, was appreciated long before Weber. Fullerton and Cattell point out (7, p. 21) that it was inherent in the Mosaic system of tithes, as Bernoulli had already suggested (1730). Bouguer, the same authors relate, had demonstrated the law with intensities of lights in 1760 and this was verified by Lambert in 1764.

The Weber Ratio.—The constant K is sometimes called the **Weber ratio,** and this ratio has been determined by experiment for a number of different kinds of stimuli. Weber found that for weights lifted by hand the ratio was about 1/30 to 1/40 and for length of lines it was about 1/100. The *DL* for brightness of lights has been found to be from 1/60 to 1/200, depending upon the observer. For hearing, K has varied in the neighborhood of 1/5 to 1/8. For pressures on the skin it has varied from 1/10 to 1/30, depending somewhat upon the part of the body to which the stimuli were applied. Observers other than Weber have found the ratio to range from 1/20 to 1/100 for lifted weights, depending upon the individual. Since the Weber ratio may remain relatively constant for the same individual and for one kind of stimuli, it can be used as a measure of individual differences in sensitivity. An individual who can detect a difference of 1/100, or 1 per cent, in lifted weights is much more sensitive than one who can detect a difference of only 1/20, or 5 per cent. The sensitivity is inversely proportional to K, and therefore it may be measured by $1/K$. But this would be a valid measure only if Weber's law is known to hold for the particular sense material in question.

Exceptions to Weber's Law.—There are certain limitations to the law which must be mentioned and certain doubts as to whether Weber's law is the universal psychophysical law. It may, after all, be merely a special case of a more general law. The discussion of this question will be postponed until the latter part of this chapter. It is sufficient here to say that the Weber ratio does not hold at the extreme ends of a physical continuum; in fact, it holds for only a relatively short span among the medium stimulus values. Even within this middle range the Weber ratio may undergo progressive changes from the lower stimulus values to the higher.

The problem of the relationship between ΔR and R is just as real, however, whether Weber's law holds or whether it does not. It is of interest and importance to us to know whether it does hold for any particular series of stimuli, and if it does hold, what the value of the Weber ratio K is. If it does not hold, what is the functional relationship between ΔR and R? Undoubtedly ΔR is a function of R. Weber's law assumes that the function is a linear one. The student will see from an examination of formula (55) that the law is in the form of a linear equation. If for any kind of stimuli a linear equation will not hold, then it is our business to find what other kind of equation does satisfy the relationship of ΔR to R. It is in the attempt to solve such problems that the method of minimal changes was developed.

HISTORY OF THE METHOD

The Method of Just Noticeable Differences.—The method of minimal changes grew out of the so-called method of **just noticeable differences.** It is difficult to say who first suggested the method of just noticeable differences and writers on psychophysics disagree. Wundt attributes the method to Weber who was using it in 1829 to measure just noticeable differences in passive pressure and in lifted weights. Fechner remarks that Delezenne had used the method as early as 1826. According to Lipps, Lambert and Bouguer had used a similar method in 1760. Titchener (16, II, p. 100) sees no reason why we should not give credit to Sauveur who worked with such a method as early as 1700. There is no assurance that any of these investigators had borrowed the method from earlier sources; it may have been original with each one of them. We are more certain of the facts that Fechner improved the method, that G. E. Müller gave it a better theoretical foundation, and that Wundt elaborated the procedures in great detail and gave to the method of minimal changes its final essential form.

The original method of just noticeable differences presupposed that the human observer can recognize a just noticeable difference (j.n.d.) when he sees one. Weber, for example, would set the variable stimulus R_V equal to the standard stimulus R_S and then increase R_V (or decrease it) step by step, in very small amounts, until the observer reported that he perceived a j.n.d.

Fechner recommended a change in the method which has been permanently adopted. He recommended the approach to the j.n.d. not only from the position of equality as Weber had done but also from positions of extreme inequality. R_V is either decidedly greater than (or less than) R_S, and then R_V is made to approach R_S by small steps until O reports that the difference is no longer noticeable. This gave rise to the notion of the **just not noticeable difference** (j.n.n.d.). It may be that Lichtenfels had preceded Fechner in distinguishing between the j.n.d. and the j.n.n.d., for in 1851 he had reported its use in finding the two-point tactual threshold. He found the one-point limen as well as the two-point limen.

But, as would be expected, the j.n.d. and the j.n.n.d. gave two distinct measurements of the difference limen, the latter usually being somewhat smaller than the former. Is one a better measure of differential sensitivity than the other? It was not a long jump to the conclusion that neither was by itself a true measure of the limen, but that the true limen lay between the two. This conclusion was best brought out by Müller who asserted that the difference limen is not an observable psychological quantity as Weber and others had thought. It is rather an ideal, calculated, statistical value to be reached by averaging the j.n.d. and the j.n.n.d. (14, pp. 63 *f.*). This conception of the limen, not only of the *DL* but also of limens in general, has become the prevailing one since Müller's time.

Wundt's Method of Minimal Changes.—In 1880 Wundt introduced what he called the method *Minimaländerungen* (21, pp. 326 *ff.*). The striking thing about the method for him was the serial order in which the stimuli were presented. The *O* knows much about the arrangement of the stimuli. He knows at the beginning of the series whether it is one of increasing differences or of decreasing differences. Wundt seemed to regard this as one of the virtues of the method. *O*'s judgments of successive stimuli are determined by all his previous judgments in the series. He is able to keep in mind the particular kind of change that is to occur. His attention can be relaxed at first but it increases to a maximum as the limen is approached. This eliminates the necessity for a maximal degree of attention for every stimulation and guarantees a favorable attitude for observation at the critical moment. The method of Wundt has been called the method *with complete knowledge*. *E* knows where the point of physical equality is and *O* knows when the series starts with equality and when it starts with a difference in a given direction.

Constant Errors of Habituation and Expectation.—Others see serious constant errors in Wundt's procedure. One is the **error of habituation**. This tendency, if *O* is not on his guard, will induce him to continue to give the same judgment too long in any one series. He may suddenly become aware of the fact that the difference has changed to equality, or vice versa, *after* the phenomenal change should normally have occurred. The result would be that the point of j.n.n.d. would be much nearer the point of equality than the point of j.n.d. Of course, since the *DL* is obtained from the mean of these two points, the error of habituation would be canceled out, assuming that this error is equally strong in both the *ascending* and the *descending* series. By ascending series is meant those which start from equality and increase the difference, and by descending series is meant those which start with obvious differences and approach equality.

Wundt's procedure may introduce still another constant error, the **error of expectation.** This factor induces O to be too ready for a change in any series; the heightened attention and the strong expectation, as in all cases of suggestion, may force an early change, or he may report a change before any has phenomenally occurred because he thinks a change ought already to have occurred. This expectation factor, if stronger than the habituation factor, makes the j.n.d. measurement nearer the point of equality than is the j.n.n.d. The former DL, based on the j.n.d., would therefore be smaller in size than the latter. But again the use of both ascending and descending series tends to cancel out this constant error of anticipation. Wundt recognized these errors and maintained that it is better to work with full cognizance of them and to cancel them out as best one can by varying the order of the stimuli than to work with haphazard order of presentation, in which the same constant errors may be present but not so well controlled.

The Stimulus Error.—Other serious errors in the procedure with complete knowledge may be pointed out. One of these is the so-called **stimulus error** which has been made much of by Titchener, Boring (1), and others. Since O knows when the two stimuli at the beginning of a series are physically equal, he may take his two corresponding phenomenal experiences as also being equal, whereas, if he did not know that the two stimuli are equal, the two experiences might be phenomenally unequal. This may have its influence upon the judgments of the entire series. Again, in the descending series, starting with two stimuli that are physically unequal, he may keep in mind this fact of physical inequality, for example, the fact that R_V is greater than R_S; this phenomenal relationship he maintains until he guesses that it is about time for R_V to equal R_S. Now we know from other methods, when the relationship between R_V and R_S is changed haphazardly and in a manner entirely unknown to O, that, when R_V is physically greater than R_S, O's judgment may be the reverse, that R_V is less than R_S in a small proportion of the times. There has been a great deal written about the stimulus error, much of it beside the point and too much of it bound up with this or that fundamental point of view in psychology. Whenever the term is used in this book it will merely mean that certain items of knowledge about the stimulating conditions serve as *irrelevant criteria* in the formation of O's judgments. Further discussions of 'stimulus errors' will be found from time to time.

The Method with Part Knowledge.—A modified procedure, suggested by both Titchener (16, I, pp. 55 *ff.*) and Kirschmann (11, p. 414), overcomes to some extent the stimulus error. It has been called the method *with part knowledge.* Instead of setting R_V equal to R_S, every series is begun with the two stimuli noticeably different. If R_V is set at the beginning so as to appear decidedly greater than R_S, E does not end the series when O reports 'equal,' but keeps on until O makes the second change in his judgments, namely, the report of 'less.' The *part knowledge* consists in the fact that O knows in which direction the change in the stimulus difference is tending. This undoubtedly keeps his judgments in line, so that his only report at the first part of a descending series is that R_V is greater than R_S, until he notes a lack of difference. His report tends not to revert back from $R_V = R_S$ to the previous judgment, but to continue until he can say R_V is less than R_S, at which point the series ends.[1] The extent of the part knowledge can be further reduced by altering the starting points of the series so as to produce long, short, and medium series.

We are now ready to illustrate how the method is applied, first in the determination of an RL and secondly in the measurement of a DL. In the second experiment we shall also be interested in whether or not Weber's law holds for the data obtained.

EXPERIMENT II.   THE *RL* FOR PITCH OF SOUNDS

Problem.—To measure the stimulus limen for pitch of tones.

Materials.—Appunn's lamella (16, I, p. 1); scraps of felt or cotton.

Preliminary Arrangements:

1. Clamp the vise firmly to the edge of a table. Felt or cotton may be placed under the vise and under the legs of the table, if necessary, to prevent any rattling noises.

2. O should be seated with eyes closed and with one ear directly in front of the source of the sound, as close to it as the vibrating instrument will permit. The

---

[1] According to Titchener (16, II, p. 21) it was Kraepelin who in 1891 called the procedure the *method of limits.* This name arose from the fact that the series always ends when O reaches a limit at the point of change in his judgments. The name is commonly used at the present time although it would seem to the writer that it is not so suggestive as *minimal changes.*

distance of O's ear from the instrument should be kept constant throughout, and O should raise and lower his head to keep his ear on a level with the small disk at the end of the vibrating strip. A better arrangement would be to clamp the lamella to a table whose height is adjustable.

3. E starts the lamella vibrating by seizing the upper edge of the disk with his thumb and forefinger, pulling it away from O's ear, and releasing it. It should be released from the same distance each time by a quick, clean withdrawal of the hand. A clumsy release will set up overtones or noises in the instrument. If overtones persist in spite of E's adept manipulations, they may be damped by wrapping a bit of felt or cotton about the strip just below the disk.

4. Just before actuating the lamella, E should give O a warning "Ready, now" signal, at least $1\frac{1}{2}$ seconds before releasing the bar.

5. O must have preliminary practice in the hearing of very low tones, so that he will be able to judge when he hears a tone and when he does not. Let him contrast the sounds which are emitted by frequencies of 24 d.v. (double vibrations) and 6 d.v. until he notes what the difference is. Then let him contrast sounds produced by frequencies nearer together until he is sure of his standard for judging 'tone' or 'noise.'

Procedure:

1. In half the series of observations E starts with a frequency that clearly gives a tone and decreases the frequency by 1 d.v. at a time until O reports a change, in this case, 'no tone' or 'noise.' This is called a descending series. In the other series, the ascending ones, E begins with a frequency which is always judged as a noise and increases the frequency by 1 d.v. steps until O reports a tone.

2. Since O knows the direction of the series, he must give his closest attention to the stimuli to be on his guard against two subjective errors. He must not anticipate a change and report it too soon, nor must he expect an indefinite continuation of the same sound and delay his report of a change too long.

3. Order of series: In order to control the errors of expectation and habituation, E should vary the length of the series, making some series long (L), some medium (M), and some short (S). Knowing the approximate point of O's RL from preliminary tests, E can fix the starting point of both ascending and descending series beforehand. L series should include about 10 to 12 judgments; M series, 6 to 9 judgments; and S series, 4 to 6 judgments. In an experiment of 20 series, 10 ascending and 10 descending, a good assortment is 6 S series, 8 M series, and 6 L series. A chance order, but better still an order fixed by some prearranged plan, may be used for the order of the S, M, and L series. The ascending and descending series should be alternated as follows:

dadad   adada   adada   dadad

The student will notice that this is the old familiar counterbalanced order, and it is introduced as usual to take care of practice and fatigue effects. Rests may be taken between each group of five series or oftener if O requires them. If O becomes too confused during any series, the whole series should be given over again after a rest or after further series have been completed.

4. Arrange a table with 20 columns for the 20 series, like Table 13 page 120. Record O's judgments in the proper places in the table, writing a plus sign when

TABLE 13.—RECORD SHEET FOR THE METHOD OF MINIMAL CHANGES

Stimulus Values	d	a	d	a	d	a	d	a	d	a	a	d	a	d	a	d	a	d	a	d
22																				
21	+											+								
20	+											+								
19	+						+		+			+				+				+
18	+		+				+		+			+				+		+		+
17	+		+				+		+			+		+		+		+		+
16	+		+		+		+		+			+		+		+		+		+
15	+		+		+		+		+			+		+		+		+		+
14	+		+		+		+		+		+	+		+		+		+		+
13	+		+	+	+		+		+		−	+	+	+		+	+	+	+	+
12	+	+	+	−	+	+	+	+	−		−	+	−	+		−	−	+	−	−
11	−	−	+	−	+	−	+	−		+	−	−	−	−	+		−	−	−	
10		−	−	−	−	−	−	−		−	−		−		−		−		−	
9		−		−		−		−		−	−		−		−		−		−	
8		−		−		−				−					−				−	
7		−		−		−				−					−					
6		−								−					−					
5		−								−					−					
Limens	11.5	11.5	10.5	12.5	10.5	11.5	10.5	11.5	12.5	10.5	13.5	11.5	12.5	11.5	10.5	12.5	12.5	11.5	12.5	12.5

Double Vibrations per Second

he reports a tone and a minus sign when he reports a noise. End each series the moment *O* changes his judgment from "Tone" to "No tone," or vice versa. Impress upon him the importance of close attention.

COMPUTATION OF THE *RL*

The Average *RL*.—We shall assume for the sake of an easy, reasonable method of computation that each series gives one measurement of the *RL*. The limen, we shall suppose, is a shifting point, a point that is fairly well restricted to one stimulus value during any one series owing to the uniform set of conditions existing throughout that series. From series to series these conditions will differ somewhat, and the limen will vary accordingly over a narrow range of values according to the law of error. The limen in each series is taken as the midpoint between the last two stimulus values. On the one side of this midpoint all the judgments were plus and on the other side they were minus. The most probable and the best value for the *RL* of this observer is the mean of these 20 limens. The mean is 11.7 d.v. The sigma of the distribution is .87 and the sigma of the mean is .20. The chances are 68 in 100 that all other means similarly derived would be within .20 of a d.v. of the obtained *RL*, 11.7.

Computation of the Constant Errors.—If we want to know something about the relative effects of the factors of habituation and expectation, we must treat the data for the ascending and descending series separately. The means and sigmas for these are given in Table 14. The difference of .4 d.v. is only .93 times its standard deviation, which indicates that the two factors were nearly equally balanced. Since the mean of the ascending series is higher than the mean of the descending series, *O* was slightly more under the influence of the factor of habituation than he was under the influence of anticipation, but the difference is insignificant.

Practice and Fatigue Effects.—It might be of interest in some problems also to know whether there were any progressive changes in the limen during the whole course of the experiment. We can fractionate the data into two parts, the one including the first 10 series and the other the last 10 series. The difference is .8 d.v. in favor of the last 10 series and this difference is 2.05 times its standard error. This is almost significant enough to suggest a lowering of the limen as if by a practice effect during the course of the experiment.

TABLE 14.—THE MEANS, STANDARD DEVIATIONS, AND DIFFERENCES BETWEEN THE *RL*'S FOR TONES UNDER DIFFERENT CONDITIONS

	All data	Ascending series	Descending series	First 10 series	Last 10 series
Mean	11.7	11.9	11.5	12.1	11.3
σ	.87	.92	.77	.80	.75
σ_M	.20	.33	.27	.28	.26
diff.	.....	.4		.8	
$\sigma_{diff.}$	.....	.43		.39	
CR_σ	.....	.93		2.05	

EXPERIMENT III. THE *DL* FOR GRAYS

Problem.—To measure the *DL* for brightness and to test Weber's law as applied to the brightness series.

Materials.—Two disks, one black and one white, 20 cm. in diameter, for the color rotator. Two similar disks 15 cm. in diameter. Gray background to match approximately the brightness of the rotating disks. Protractor.

Procedure:

1. The color rotator is set up in good illumination, either artificial or natural, which can be kept constant throughout the observations, in front of the gray screen. *O* is seated about 4 ft. distant.

2. *E* prepares a standard stimulus of the larger disks, composed of 180 deg. each of black and white. The small disk is the variable stimulus during the first set of trials.

3. The ascending series begin with R_V being set decidedly darker than R_S, and the descending series begin with R_V decidedly lighter. R_V is to be changed by small steps until *O* reports 'equal' and then finally 'lighter' (or 'darker' as the case may be). *O always judges in terms of R_V.*

4. The size of the steps is determined by two important considerations. The steps should not be so small that the series is very long, for *O* cannot keep his attitude constant over so long a period, and fatigue also sets in. The steps should not be so large as to yield very short series, for this means crude measurements. A few preliminary series should be made and the best size of step should be based on the number of 'equal' judgments made in a single series. A good range of equal judgments is from three to seven in a series. Fernberger (6) has found that, on the whole, larger steps and short series give more satisfactory results than smaller steps and long series. He lays down the rule that no series should exceed 10 steps.

5. The order of the series, ascending and descending, should be counterbalanced as usual. Short, medium, and long series should be introduced.

6. The constant space error should be taken care of by placing R_V in the outer region (on the large disk) half the time. A convenient procedure is to arrange the series in four groups of six each as in Table 15, giving them in the order: 6 *VO* (variable outside), 12 *VI*, and 6 *VO*.

7. In another set of observations the standard disk should be made up of 90 deg. of white and 270 deg. of black. If convenient, other standards may be used for further sets of observations.

8. A convenient way of keeping records is seen in Table 15. A plus sign means $R_V > R_S$; an equality sign means $R_V = R_S$; and a minus sign means $R_V < R_S$.

Results:

TABLE 15.—JUDGMENTS OF DIFFERENCES IN BRIGHTNESS BY THE METHOD OF MINIMAL CHANGES. STANDARD STIMULUS: 180 DEG. WHITE AND 180 DEG. BLACK

R	VO						VI						VI						VO						Code
	d	a	d	a	d	a	a	d	a	d	a	d	d	a	d	a	d	a	a	d	a	d	a	d	
220	+												+							+					
216	+												+							+					
212	+									+			+							+					
208	+		+							+			+							+					
204	+		+					+		+	+		+							+		+			
200	+	+	+					+		+	+		+							+		±		+	9
196	+	±	+					+	+	+	+		+	+						±		=		+	8
192	+	+	=	+				+	+	+	+		+	+	+	+	=	+	=			=		+	7
188	+	=	=		=			+		+	+	=	+	+	=	+	=	=	=	=		=		+	6
184	=	=	−	+	=	+	+	=		=	=	=		=	=	=	=	=	=	=	=	+	=		5
180	=	−		=	=	=	=	=	+	=	=	−	=	+	=	=	=	+	=	=	−	=	=	−	4
176	−	−		=	=	=	=	=	=	=		=	=	=		=	−	=	=	=	−	−	−	=	3
172	−		=	−	−	=		=	−	=			−	−		=		=	−	−	−		−		2
168	−	=		−	−			−					−						−	−		−			1
164	−	=		−	−			−					−						−	−		−			0
160	−		−	−				−					−						−	−		−			
156	−		−				−							−					−			−			
152	−		−				−							−					−						
148			−					−														−			
144			−					−																	
L_u	6	7	8	5	7	5	5	6	4	6	6	7	6	4	6	7	6	4	7	8	7	9	5	6	
L_l	4	5	6	1	3	3	2	4	2	3	2	5	3	3	4	2	4	2	3	4	5	4	3	5	

COMPUTATION OF THE *DL*

The Upper and Lower Limens.—Every series yields two measurements of the *DL*. It measures the stimulus that is one *DL* lighter than the standard, this stimulus being denoted by the symbol L_u, standing for **upper limen,** and it measures the stimulus that is one DL darker than the standard, this being denoted in Table 16 by L_l, or the **lower limen.** In Wundt's terminology these same points were symbolized by r_o (*Oberegrenzreiz*) and r_u (*Unteregrenzreiz*). Following the principle laid down in Experiment II, we locate the limens midway at the change of judgments. L_u is located midway between the plus and equal signs, and L_l midway between the equal and minus signs. Heavy lines are drawn at these points in Table 15 so as to facilitate the location of these values. In the last column of Table 15, a "Code" is given for the sake of shortening the numbers in computation. The midpoints of the steps are given small integral values. At the bottom of each column the code values for L_u and L_l are given. We can now proceed to find the means and standard deviations, using the code values. We can make the change back to degrees as the units, by remembering the fact that 4 deg. is the unit of the coding scheme, and the zero point of the coding scheme is at 162 deg. The coding system is equivalent to choosing a step interval i of 4 deg. and a guessed average M' of 162 deg.

The Constant Errors.—If we wish to know the extent of the constant errors of space, habituation, and expectation, we must of course fractionate the data in two ways, first into two groups VO and VI, and then into two other groups a and d. It is usually important to do this even if one is not particularly concerned about the size of the constant errors. If those errors are too great or if the different means for the fractionated data differ very much in reliability, the data may have to be treated in two separate groups throughout. The same precautions must be taken here in the combining of sets of data that were observed in Chapter II.

In Table 16 are found the means of the data classified according to the groupings just discussed. It will be seen that the reliabilities

TABLE 16.—MEANS AND STANDARD DEVIATIONS OF THE LIMENS

	V outside		V inside		Ascending		Descending		All combined	
	L_u	L_l	L_u	L_l	L_u	L_l	L_u	L_l	L_u	L_l
Mean	188.7	177.3	184.3	174.0	184.0	173.0	189.0	178.3	186.5	175.7
σ	5.0	5.1	4.2	4.0	4.8	4.7	4.0	3.4	5.1	4.9
σ_M	1.6	1.6	1.3	1.3	1.5	1.5	1.3	1.1	1.1	1.0

of the various means, as measured by their sigmas, are approximately the same, so no weighting is necessary in combining them.

The Difference Limens.—What, now, are the difference limens that we set out to find, and what is the Weber ratio $\Delta R/R$? The upper *DL* may be taken as 186.5 − 180, or 6.5 deg., and the lower *DL* as 180 − 175.7, or 4.3 deg. But unfortunately the brightness values of the stimuli are not accurately measured in terms of degrees of white. The measurement would have been accurate if we had used a black paper that reflected no light whatsoever. There is no such black paper. The photometric value of our disk is always equal to the total amount of illumination reflected to the eye by the white *plus* that reflected by the black. We can estimate the total illumination of any disk if we know the relative reflecting power of black as compared with white. If we knew, for example, that the white paper reflected 50 times as much light per degree of surface as the black, then, letting 1 deg. of black be our unit of illumination and letting each degree of white be 50 units, we could compute the stimulus value for any proportion of black and white. For example, 180 deg. of white and 180 deg. of black would give a total illumination of $(180 \times 50) + (180 \times 1)$, or 9180 units.

It would be best, where very accurate limens are wanted, to calibrate the particular black and white papers by means of a photometer. Kirschmann's photometer (2) is often used for this purpose. The calibration is a lengthy process in itself, however, and, for the sake of demonstrating the method of minimal changes and a test of Weber's law, we may dispense with that process. It is probably safe to assume that the typical white and black used in the psychological laboratory have a brightness ratio of 25:1 [Kirschmann (11, p. 404) gives a ratio of 23.32:1]. The illumination of any proportion can be estimated accurately enough for the student's purposes by means of the general formula:

$$I = B + 25W$$

where B = the degrees of black.

W = the degrees of white on the color disk in question.

Absolute *DL*'s and Relative *DL*'s.—Table 17 gives the liminal stimuli and the *DL*'s in terms of photometric units. It also presents the mean *DL* (DL_m) and the three Weber ratios, K_u, K_l, and K_m. These constants have been derived from the following formulas:

$$DL_u = L_u - R_S \qquad (56a)$$

$$DL_l = R_S - L_l \qquad (56b)$$

$$DL_m = \frac{L_u - L_l}{2} \qquad (56c)$$

$$K_u = \frac{DL_u}{R_S} \qquad (57a)$$

$$K_l = \frac{DL_l}{L_l} \qquad (57b)$$

$$K_m = \frac{DL_m}{R_S} \qquad (57c)$$

TABLE 17.—LIMINAL STIMULI, DIFFERENCE LIMENS, AND WEBER RATIOS FOR TWO STANDARD STIMULI, GIVEN IN PHOTOMETRIC UNITS

R_S, degrees of white	R_S, photo-metric units	L_u	L_l	DL_u	DL_l	DL_m	K_u	K_l	K_m
180°	4680	4836	4576	156	104	130	.033	.022	.028
90°	2520	2609	2460	89	60	74.5	.035	.024	.030

As is usually to be expected where Weber's law holds, the two absolute DL's for a given R_S are unequal; DL_u is slightly greater than DL_l. The former is the just observable increment to R_S, whereas the latter is the just observable increment to L_l. But if Weber's law holds exactly, the *relative* DL's should be equal, *i.e.*, K_u should be equal to K_l. For both cases in Table 17—the thresholds for a standard of 90 deg. white and 270 deg. black were obtained in the same manner as those for the standard that we have been using heretofore—K_u is noticeably greater than K_l. Unless the DL's are obtained from a very large number of series, perhaps 100, one cannot expect to use K_u and L_l alone as tests for Weber's law. With no more than 24 series of observations, one ordinarily uses the mean DL and K_m as the test value for Weber's law and compares them with other such test values. For example, with the standard of 90 deg. white, K_m is almost identical with the K_m that was found with the standard of 180 deg. One would not be content to say from these two tests alone, even though they agree so well as to the value of the relative DL's, that Weber's law is satisfied. Many other standards must be used covering much of the range of stimuli before such a generalization can be made. The procedure thus far merely illustrates the way in which Weber's law is tested.

Quotient Limens.—For the sake of completeness, it should be said that two other test values are sometimes used, though very infrequently. They have been called the **quotient limens,** designated by the letter C. There are also three of these values, C_u, C_l, and C_m. The following formulas are used:

$$C_u = \frac{L_u}{R_s} \tag{58a}$$

$$C_l = \frac{R_s}{L_l} \tag{58b}$$

$$C_m = \frac{R_s + DL_m}{R_s} \tag{58c}$$

Needless to say, C must be a constant if Weber's law holds.

An Irregular Case.—The experiment just described will illustrate the method of minimal changes under rather ideal conditions. The student will find that, when it is applied in general to different kinds of stimuli and under different conditions, and especially whenever it is not possible to take care of all constant errors successfully, disturbing results may be obtained. The student will often be forced to exercise his common sense and to apply his limited statistical experience to meet the situation. One of the more common irregularities is to find that both L_u and L_l are greater than (or less than) the standard stimulus. For example, a student who was working with grays and with a standard composed of 180 deg. of white and 180 deg. of black, found that L_u was 193.50 and L_l was 183.25. This is an extreme case, perhaps, but not an unusual one by any means. How shall we deal with it?

The Point of Subjective Equality.—The photometric values for the standard and for the two limens, respectively, were 4680, 5004, and 4758. According to the usual process, DL_u would be 324 units and DL_l would have the absurd value of -78 units. Finding the mean DL helps us somewhat. DL_m is 123 units. But now the question arises, how shall we find the relative DL? Ordinarily, we would find the quotient $123\!/\!4680$. But the value of the physical standard is no longer a reasonable one to use. L_l is the stimulus that is reputedly just observably less than the standard. It is not reasonable to say that a brightness valued at 4758 is just observably darker than a brightness valued at 4680, when physically the latter is actually darker. In other words, L_l is just observably different from a subjective standard which is itself physically lighter than R_s. There is a stimulus value between 4758 and 5004 for the variable stimulus that is phenomenally equal to the standard stimulus with its value of 4680. This variable that is psychologically equivalent to the standard stimulus is called the **point of subjective equality** (*PSE*). How shall it be measured?

Wundt has suggested that this so-called 'estimation value' (*Schätzungswert*) or the 'equivalent value' (*Äquivalentswert*) of Kirschmann can be found by means of one of the following formulas:

$$PSE = L_u - DL_m \qquad (59a)$$
$$PSE = L_l + DL_m \qquad (59b)$$
$$PSE = R_s + \frac{DL_u - DL_l}{2} \qquad (59c)$$

It is, in other words, the midpoint between the two limens, or the arithmetic mean of those two limens. These formulas rest on the assumption that the upper and lower *DL*'s are equal. If Weber's law is known to hold, this assumption is obviously unjustified. The *PSE* in that case would not be the arithmetic mean but the *geometric* mean of the two. The *PSE* would then be equal to $\sqrt{L_u \times L_l}$. But if we do not know that Weber's law applies, and above all if our major problem is to test Weber's law, it is probably best to follow Wundt in the calculation of the *PSE*.

In the specific problem we have been discussing, the *PSE* is taken as 4881, the *arithmetic* mean of the two limens, and that is the value of the new standard with which DL_m is to be compared. K_m is then $123/_{4881}$, or .025.

The Constant Error of Estimation.—Having found the *PSE*, we can compare it with R_s and determine what the direction and the extent of the phenomenal shift in the standard have been. The difference,

$$EE = PSE - R_s \qquad (60)$$

Wundt called the **error of estimation** (*Schätzungsdifferenz*). If this error is positive, it means that on the whole, the variable stimulus was underestimated; if it is negative, R_V was overestimated.

It might be of interest or significance at times to seek the cause or causes of such a constant error. If the error is not large, however, and if in the computation of the relative *DL* it has been allowed for by using the *PSE* in place of R_s, as outlined on page 128, the student need not be concerned further about it.

USES AND CRITICISMS OF THE METHOD

The Measurement of Thresholds.—As was said at the beginning of this chapter, the method of minimal changes has been used primarily for the measurement of thresholds. It is generally applicable wherever the stimulus series is variable in equal small steps. It has been used to find intensity thresholds for sounds, odors, tastes, colors, temperature, pain, lights, and tactual sensations, to name only a few types of stimulus limens. The procedures may have to be modified to some extent to meet certain peculiarities of some sense departments. For example, descending series cannot be used with success in measuring taste and smell thresholds owing to the rapid adaptation in the latter case and to the persistence of the stimuli in both. Helson found, in a study of the lowest illumination necessary for perceiving visual form, that the descending series had to be given up since a knowledge of the form made it difficult for *O* to decide just when the form had vanished (10).

There is hardly a qualitative or quantitative psychological variable that yields a *DL* measurement to which the limiting procedure will not apply. In addition to the *DL*'s for the simpler sensory attributes, one can find with this method *DL*'s for more complex perceptual variables such as length of lines, areas of rectangles and the like, time intervals, and thresholds for visual movement, although Stratton found (15) that the method had to be rejected in his study of movement.

One should, of course, mention in this connection the measurement of two-point limens, tactual and visual, and difference limens of localization of auditory impressions. The mapping of such things as color zones and blind spots probably comes under the limiting principle and might be included in the list of applications. There is a derivative of the method which is used in finding equivalent stimuli—the so-called **method of equivalents,** which will be discussed shortly. This involves finding the point of subjective equality rather than limens. The extent of the Müller-Lyer illusion could have been measured by this method. *E* might have changed the setting of the variable side by small amounts until O reported 'equal' instead of letting O himself adjust it.

Some Criticisms.—Some criticisms of the method have already been mentioned and steps taken to meet them have been explained. The errors of habituation and expectation and of practice and fatigue are minimized by the order and arrangement of the series. The stimulus error is partially, although not fully, eliminated. One should, perhaps, say stimulus *errors*, for there are many aspects of the stimuli and O's knowledge about them which help to form his judgments. In addition to those already discussed, there is the size of the step between stimuli. Undoubtedly, at least in the measurement of a DL, the size of the step influences O's judgments. If O has had any previous experience with the method, he comes to expect a certain length of series, or at least to expect a certain approximate spread of the equality judgments. E usually chooses the size of the step with this in mind. Having a preconceived notion that Weber's law holds, E will use smaller steps in the lower part of the scale and larger steps in the upper part of the scale. It is conceivable that, with a highly experienced O and E, unless measures are taken to prevent it, Weber's law or any other law could be demonstrated to hold merely by a systematic choice of steps. It may therefore be a good plan in some cases to vary the size of the step in different series of the same set of observations. For example, if in the experiment for determining the DL for brightness the customary steps were 168, 171, 174, 177, 180, 183, 186 deg., etc., the step might be made larger or smaller in some of the series, or it might begin at other points, as 170, 173, 176, 179, 182, 185, etc. To be systematic, the same alteration should be made in all four arrangements, a and d series, and VO and VI arrangements.

Limiting DL Not Identical with Other DL's.—It is rather doubtful whether the DL as found by the method of limits is ever directly equivalent to a DL that is obtained with other methods, the method of constant stimuli, for example. Although the concept of a DL is the same for both methods, the procedures for obtaining it are different.

Even with the revised procedures, with their advantages over the old method of just noticeable differences, the limiting method would seem to have the lurking reservation that the DL is a relatively fixed, if not observable, quantity or sense distance. It is assumed to be a distance that can be approached from either side by small steps and limited repeatedly until its true location can be approximated. Each series of observations has its own *DL* or is a single measurement of the *DL*, and the final *DL* is a mean of a number of these measurements. In that sense and to that extent, the *DL* is a statistical affair, as Müller has pointed out. But the whole method, with its emphasis upon reaching a limiting point and ending a series the moment that limit is reached, seems to presuppose the implicit assumption that the liminal stimulus is one above which we *always* obtain one kind of judgment and below which we *always* obtain another. It is the thin dividing point between 'difference' and 'equality.'

Now we know that, if *O* were permitted to continue the series beyond the limit, he would not infrequently reverse his judgment. This would introduce additional light upon the transition from a *region* of 'difference' to a region of 'equality,' or vice versa, and it would place less unwarranted weight upon the single terminal judgments of a series. *O* is trained not to reverse his judgment later in the series after he has once made the decisive change. This places an undue importance upon those terminal judgments and seems to the writer to be but one step removed in theory from the just noticeable difference of Weber.

It may be said in defense of the method that, even if the limiting *DL* is not identical with other *DL*'s, it may still be a valid test of Weber's law. It is a psychological increment, obtained under certain specified conditions, and it should be comparable with *DL*'s found by other methods in the sense that it is proportional to them. There are many different ways of measuring small sense distances which we may include under the general rubric of ΔR. One of these, for example, is the standard deviation or the probable error of the distribution as found in the method of average error. Another could be a stimulus difference that is correctly observed in any specified proportion of the times, for example, 75, 80, or 90 per cent. We can find the *DL* by the method of constant stimulus differences, but even with this method there are at least four fundamentally different ways of calculating it, all of which are acceptable, though no two of the *DL*'s are identical. They are roughly proportional to each other, and, so long as one keeps in mind the process by which they were obtained, they are all useful. It is possible to show the mathematical relationships between some of them, and in time we may be able to estmate any one *DL* from any other.

VARIATIONS OF THE METHOD

Continuous Variation of the Stimulus.—Under some circumstances, instead of altering R_v by small steps, it is convenient to produce in it a continuous change. This type of series may be regarded, theoretically, as one in which the size of the steps is infinitely small. It is a great time saver whenever it can be used. It can be employed, for example, in measuring visual thresholds, as with the Nagel adaptometer or with an optical bench, or in measuring auditory thresholds, as with the Stern variators. It is typically the kind of variation that one uses in mapping the blind spot or the color zones. It is similar to the method of reproduction or the procedure in the method of average error, except that E varies the stimulus instead of O and the change in R_v is never reversed in the same series or observation.

Haphazard Presentation of Stimuli.—In 1891 Kraepelin introduced a procedure that substituted a haphazard order of presentation for the serial order of presentation of the stimuli. His main motive was to eliminate the errors of habituation and of expectation. The procedure has been called the method *without knowledge*. No single judgment is imbedded in a series of judgments, and O knows almost nothing about the conditions surrounding each stimulation. The DL as obtained from this method completely satisfies Müller's statistical definition.

Several objections can be offered against the haphazard presentation of stimuli in the method of minimal changes. From a theoretical standpoint it would seem that the method of minimal changes has been entirely deserted, for the changes from one R_v to the next in a series are large as well as small in a hit-and-miss order. The notion of approaching a limit from either side also seems to be entirely abandoned except in the computation of the threshold. It will be seen later that the procedure of obtaining data is practically the same as in the method of constant stimuli, the only differences being that more stimuli are used for fewer trials each and that the computation of the limen varies. In both respects the haphazard order of presentation in the method of minimal changes seems inferior to the constant method.

From a practical standpoint, the procedure in computing a limen is rather uncertain. In the same set of observations for a 'series' of stimuli that has been presented in haphazard order, the three

categories of judgment, 'greater,' 'equal,' and 'less,' do not come
in three compact, homogeneous groups as they do when the serial
order is used. The three classes of judgment are often somewhat
mixed. For example, in a series of 12 stimuli, reading across the
table, beginning with a difference $R_V < R_S$ and proceeding through
equality to a difference $R_V < R_S$, the 12 judgments might be:
lleleeggeggg. Where, now, in this series can one locate the points
of j.n.d. and the points of j.n.n.d.? Just where in the series is the
most probable lower *DL* and just where is the most probable higher
DL?

Titchener recommends (16, II, p. 132) that we find from each series
four values as follows:

    a. the smallest R_V that is greater than R_S,

    b. the greatest R_V not greater than R_S,

    c. the smallest R_V not less than R_S,

    d. the greatest R_V less than R_S.

The upper and lower *DL*'s are then found as follows:

$$DL_u = \frac{a+b}{2} - R_S \tag{61a}$$

and

$$DL_l = R_S - \frac{c+d}{2} \tag{61b}$$

It will be seen that Titchener's method adheres closely to the principle of limits. The process just described locates the thresholds by
a kind of interpolation process.

Kirschmann (11) recommends a procedure that departs from the
limiting method and approaches in principle the constant process.
The L_u is the stimulus value that is judged greater than R_S exactly
half the time; L_l is judged less than R_S half the time. If no single
stimulus is so judged, one must interpolate in order to find a stimulus
that would probably give 50 per cent of the judgments 'equal'
and the remaining 50 per cent 'greater' or 'less,' as the case may be.
The *PSE* must be found, and it may be either the *mode* or the
median of the *equality* judgments. When only a relatively few
series are obtained, this procedure is, of course, very inaccurate.
One would do better to reduce the number of variable stimuli to
about five or seven and use the method of constant stimulus
differences.

The Method of Equivalents

In a broad sense, the method of average error as described in Chapter II is a method of equivalents. The main problem involved is for O to adjust one stimulus until it appears equivalent to a standard. It is possible to accomplish the same end by letting E do the adjusting and by asking O merely to judge when the point of equality has been reached. The adjustment may be made by E in small steps, in serial changes, or by a continuous variation of the stimulus. It is nearly always more expeditious for O to do the adjusting rather than E, and by continuous rather than stepwise changes. But circumstances may require the less expeditious methods. For example, suppose we want to find out what distance between two points applied to the forehead is equivalent to a longitudinal distance of 5 cm. on the forearm. O cannot manipulate the variable stimulus nor can it be changed continuously. The method of minimal changes is easily adapted to such a problem. The series are begun on either side of the point of subjective equality and are extended through the range of equality judgments to the first change beyond. The computation of the *PSE* is the final result, and this may be obtained in one of three ways:

1. Following the limiting theory, one would find the upper and lower limits of the range of equality judgments. The *PSE* would then be taken either as the arithmetic mean or as the geometric mean of these two limits, depending upon whether Weber's law is known or properly assumed to be true.

2. One might determine the median of the 'equal' judgments for each series, and then find the mean of these values. This would give a value for the *PSE* which is identical with the arithmetic mean of the two limits.

3. One might also find the mean of all the equality judgments after the manner of finding an average error. Since O is set to find equality in this method just as he is in the method of reproduction, an 'average error' and its standard deviation would seem to be logical values to compute.

Brief History of the Method of Equivalents.—The method was first used in 1831 by Weber (16, II, p. 191), who found that a passive pressure of 4 oz. on the forehead is equivalent to a pressure of 1 oz. on the lips. Wundt (1858) used it to equate visual and tactual distances. Fechner gave the method its name and computed the results according to the method of average error. Camerer (1884) applied to the method the principle of the method of limits, and Fechner adopted Camerer's procedure.

Historical applications of the method are interesting to note. J. N. Czermak (1857) found that the second hand of a watch appears to move faster in direct than in indirect vision. He suggested that a similar phenomenon occurs on different areas of the skin, a fact that was confirmed by Vierordt (1868). Jastrow (1886) compared distances estimated by the fixated eye to distances perceived by the span of the thumb and forefinger and by free arm movement. Henri (1898) worked on the apparent difference between two compass points at different places across the face. Wundt (1902) equated brightness for direct and indirect vision. Others have used the method to equate vertical and horizontal distances and distances traversed by different limbs or segments of limbs, and to equate time intervals, filled and unfilled. On the whole, the method has a wealth of applications and it will serve wherever the method of reproduction cannot be used conveniently.

WEBER'S LAW

We return now to Weber's law. One frequently finds the expression "Weber-Fechner" law, but many writers object to such a joint nomenclature, maintaining that the two laws are essentially different. Fechner's law has been derived mathematically from Weber's law; but notice that the mathematical statements of the two laws contain different variables. In Weber's law, $\Delta R = KR$, whereas in Fechner's law, $S = C \log R$. The former does not contain S as one of the variables, whereas the latter does. ΔR measures a small increment on the physical continuum—an increment that is correctly judged in a specified proportion of the cases. Fechner assumed that, corresponding to ΔR, there is always a ΔS which can be regarded as a mental unit. If that assumption is incorrect, we may not properly speak of a Weber-Fechner law. Other reasons will be brought out in later pages for distinguishing between the two laws. We shall confine our present remarks to Weber's law; the student will find a treatment of Fechner's law in the chapter to follow.

The Range of Applicability of Weber's Law.—Following Weber's first discovery of the law in 1834, many investigators have sought to find whether or not it applies to a great many types of experiences.

Fechner demonstrated that the law held for vision in 1858, and since that time it has been shown to apply to almost all sense departments, at least approximately in the middle ranges of intensities, and even to the strength of feelings. But other investigators have shown very wide departures from the law. Helmholtz found that the law failed to apply to visual intensities. Aubert, likewise, found the Weber ratio varied from $\frac{1}{3}$ at low intensities to $\frac{1}{164}$ at high intensities. König and Brodhun later found that the ratio decreased sharply at first, then remained fairly constant, and finally increased slightly, with increasing R. The latter result was more recently verified by Hecht. Hecht concluded with respect to vision, "The evidence shows unequivocally that, as the intensity rises, the ratio $\Delta I/I$ first decreases and then increases" (9). The letter I here stands for intensity of the stimulus. Recent work in the field of audition shows a shifting Weber ratio for different intensities and for different frequencies.

Substitutes for Weber's Law. 1. *Fullerton's and Cattell's Square Root Law.*—Weber's law has so often been found wanting when accurate and extensive measurements are made that various proposals have been made to meet the situation. Among these proposals we have the **square root law** of Fullerton and Cattell. To state the law in their own language, "The error of observation tends to increase as the square root of the magnitude, the increase being subject to variation, whose amount and cause must be determined for each special case" (7, p. 25). Stated in mathematical terms,

$$\Delta R = K\sqrt{R} \tag{62}$$

The student should note especially the expression "*error of observation*" in the above definition. This follows from the belief of the authors that ΔR is a measure of the average error of observation. Consider the diagram in Fig. 13*A*. The line *XL*, when observed repeatedly by the same *O*, has a shifting length. Sometimes it appears longer and sometimes shorter. If we could plot a distribution curve of all the lengths that the line takes and their frequencies, we would have a normal distribution as shown, with the most frequently appearing length at the mean. The probable error of this distribution may be taken to measure the 'error of observation' of line *XL*. If this theoretical distribution seems unreal to the student, let him recall the distribution of lengths of line obtained in Chapter II. We can approach such a distribution of observations in practice by asking *O* to reproduce a large number of times on paper a standard line that is set up before him. Such a distribution obtained in practice would not be identical with the theoretical distribution of observed lengths for the reason that both the observed standard line and *O*'s reproductions fluctuate about their mean at the same time; also the errors are partly a product of *O*'s motor variability. But aside from these contaminating factors, it is reasonable to assume a fluctuation of observed values about a mean, just as Fullerton and Cattell have postulated.

Suppose, now, that we observe a line *XT* which is twice the length of line *XL*. The new segment *LT*, being equal to the old one *XL*, should have the same error of observation. If Weber's law is

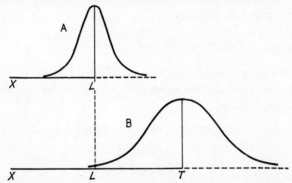

Fig. 13.—Errors of observation and their distributions at different magnitudes of the stimulus.

correct, we must assume that the errors of observation in the two halves summate and that the average error for the whole line *XT* is twice that for either half. But this would be true only if the errors in *XL* and *LT* were so perfectly correlated that at any one moment of observation they lay in the same direction, *i.e.*, in the direction of enlarging or diminishing the two segments together. Fullerton and Cattell deny such a correlation between simultaneous errors and maintain that by chance (without any correlation at all) the errors in the two segments lie in opposite directions as often as in the same direction. From this assumption they derive their square root law.

2. *Woodworth's Generalized Law of Errors.*—In order to understand this more fully, it is necessary to follow Woodworth's reasoning and to introduce a new statistical idea (20). Woodworth reopened

the question of Weber's versus the Fullerton-Cattell law, because most investigators, including Fullerton and Cattell themselves, had found that most psychophysical data fitted neither law but fell somewhere between the two, now approaching Weber's law more closely and now the square root law. ΔR usually increases less rapidly than R but more rapidly than $\sqrt{R}$.

Woodworth believed that the trouble lay in the fact that the simultaneous errors of observation, in segments of a line, for example, were neither perfectly correlated, as Weber's law would demand, nor entirely uncorrelated, as the square root law would demand. There is a statistical formula by which we can predict the variability of sums of measurements from the variabilities of the quantities summated. The probable error of a distribution of sums of two quantities, for example, is given as

$$PE_\Sigma = \sqrt{PE_1^2 + PE_2^2 + 2rPE_1PE_2} \tag{63}$$

To take our simple case of doubling the length of a line, let us assume that $PE_1 = PE_2$ and then substitute the latter for the former in formula (63). Then

$$\begin{aligned} PE_\Sigma &= \sqrt{2PE_1^2 + 2rPE_1^2} \\ &= \sqrt{2PE_1^2(1 + r)} \\ &= PE_1\sqrt{2(1 + r)}. \end{aligned}$$

Dividing both sides of the equation by PE_1,

$$\frac{PE_\Sigma}{PE_1} = \sqrt{2(1 + r)} \tag{64}$$

Assume that $r = 1$; then the ratio PE_Σ/PE_1 becomes 2. That is, the error of observation of the double length (PE_Σ) is two times as great as the error of observation of one-half the line $(PE_1 = PE_2)$. Weber's law is satisfied. Assume that $r = 0$; the ratio becomes $\sqrt{2}$ and the Fullerton-Cattell law is satisfied. Assume that r is some value between 0 and 1, and some law between Weber's and the Fullerton-Cattell law holds. This should enable us to satisfy any set of data. The value of r could be obtained from the data by the use of formula (64) after solving it for r.

3. *The Generalized nth Power Law.*—The writer has elsewhere cast serious doubt upon the validity of Woodworth's law (8). It

is logically doubtful, also, whether errors in segments of lines, or in intensities of stimuli, have any separate and real existence or meaning. In order to take care of the well-established fact that most data fall between Weber's law and the Fullerton-Cattell law, a new **nth power law** was proposed and tested. It suggests that ΔR is not proportional to R or to the square root of R, but to some power of R. The formula for this law is

$$\Delta R = KR^n \tag{65}$$

where K and n must be found in order to suit the particular set of data.

Both Weber's and the Fullerton-Cattell laws are special cases of this more general law. In the former, the power n equals 1; in the latter, n equals $.5$. Since most data have been found to follow a law lying somewhere between Weber's law and the Fullerton-Cattell law, n will usually be some value between $.5$ and 1. There is no theoretical reason, however, why n should not at times fall outside those limits; in fact, the writer has found n equal to $.489$ for some data on sound intensities. It is too early in the course of this volume to explain how the values for K and n may be obtained from a set of data. That is a problem which belongs under the topic of curve fitting, to be treated in a later chapter. It is sufficient here to say that the power law is so general and so flexible that it will fit almost any set of data obtained, except perhaps at the very extreme ends of the physical scale where the continuity in the relationship between ΔR and R breaks down and possibly no mathematical law holds. The power law also has its advantages in the measurement of the sensitivity of any particular O. Recall that, under the assumption of Weber's law, the Weber ratio, or K, which equals $\Delta R/R$, was taken as an inverse measure of sensitivity. But since K was not found constant for different intensities of stimuli, it could not be so employed. K in the power law, which we can designate as K_n, will be constant over wide ranges of intensity. It equals $\Delta R/R^n$ and can be used as a constant index of sensitivity once the exponent n is known.[1]

4. *Other Substitutes for Weber's Law.*—Even the power law, or any general mathematical function, may fail to satisfy certain cases. The dependence of ΔR upon R may be of an entirely different nature

[1] Further treatment of the nth power law will be found in the following chapter. Some attempt to rationalize the law will be made in Chapter X.

than any law that has been mentioned here.   For the history of the search for a universal psychophysical law that would be an improvement over Weber's law, the reader is referred to Klemm's "History of Psychology" (12).   Two recent suggestions might be mentioned here.   Macdonald and Allen find, in working with sounds and with tactual sensations, a law which, when translated into the symbols and the form that we have used in this chapter, reads as follows (13):

$$\Delta R = \frac{K}{\log R}.$$

Another suggestion comes from Cobb as a warning against the phenomenon of contrast in the measurement of thresholds, in vision especially.   When the two stimuli R_S and R_V are side by side, as they usually are in vision, the one influences the other.   Both are in turn influenced by their background.   In order to take account of these mutual effects, Weber's law requires a modification, which Cobb (4) supplies.   Still other special cases involving the influences of context, figure ground, and other perceptual factors are met in psychophysical work.   An unraveling of all these factors and their effects will greatly extend the frontiers of our knowledge of the perceptive processes.

Problems

1. The following data were obtained according to the methods described in Experiment II in the determination of the stimulus limen for pitch:

First 10 series		Second 10 series	
Ascending	Descending	Ascending	Descending
16.5	18.5	15.5	15.5
19.5	19.5	15.5	19.5
17.5	18.5	14.5	14.5
14.5	16.5	12.5	15.5
16.5	15.5	15.5	17.5

Compute the limens and their significance and the constant errors as prescribed on page 121.

2. The following data were obtained according to the methods described in Experiment III in the determination of a difference limen for brightness, with a standard stimulus composed of 180 deg. white and 180 deg. black.

Upper limen				Lower limen				Point of subjective equality			
VO		*VI*		*VO*		*VI*		*VO*		*VI*	
a	*d*	*a*	*d*	*a*	*d*	*a*	*d*	*a*	*d*	*a*	*d*
183	181	181	181	177	179	177	179	180	180	179	180
181	187	181	181	173	183	177	179	177	185	179	180
187	189	181	183	181	187	179	179	184	188	180	181
179	183	181	183	173	179	177	177	179	180	176	181
183	187	177	183	177	179	175	179	176	181	180	183
179	181	181	183	175	177	179	179	180	181	177	179

Compute the various limens, the points of subjective equality, and their significance in accordance with the procedures given on pages 123 *ff*.

REFERENCES

1. BORING, E. G., The stimulus-error, *Amer. J. Psychol.*, 1921, **32,** 449–471.
2. ——, Delboeuf disks and the Kirschmann photometer, *Amer. J. Psychol.*, 1917, **28,** 279 *f*.
3. BROWN, WM., and G. H. THOMSON, "The Essentials of Mental Measurement," Cambridge University Press, London, 1925.
4. COBB, P. W., Weber's law and the Fechnerian muddle, *Psychol. Rev.*, 1932, **39,** 533–551.
5. FECHNER, G. T., "Elemente der Psychophysik," Breitkopf und Härtel, Leipzig, 1860.
6. FERNBERGER, S. W., On the relation of the methods of just perceptible differences and constant stimuli, *Psychol. Monog.*, 1913, **14,** no. 61.
7. FULLERTON, G. S., and J. McK. CATTELL, On the perception of small differences, *Pub. Univ. Penn., Phil. Series*, no. 2, 1892.
8. GUILFORD, J. P., A generalized psychophysical law, *Psychol. Rev.*, 1932, **39,** 73–85.
9. HECHT, S., The nature of the photoreceptor process, in Murchison, "Foundations of Experimental Psychology," Clark University Press, Worcester, 1929.
10. HELSON, H., and E. V. FEHRER, The rôle of form in perception, *Amer. J. Psychol.*, 1932, **44,** 79–102.
11. KIRSCHMANN, A., Grundzüge der psychophysischen Maszmethoden, in Abderhalden, "Handbuch der biologischen Arbeitsmethoden," Abt. VI, Teil A, Urban und Schwarzenberg, Berlin, 1927.
12. KLEMM, O., "A History of Psychology," trans., Charles Scribner's Sons, New York, 1914.
13. MACDONALD, P. A., and D. M. ROBERTSON, The psychophysical law, *Phil. Mag.*, 1930, **10,** 1063–1073.
14. MÜLLER, G. E., "Zur Grundlegung der Psychophysik," T. Griefen, Berlin, 1878.

15. STRATTON, G. M., The method of serial groups, *Psychol. Rev.*, 1902, **9,** 444–447.
16. TITCHENER, E. B., "Experimental Psychology," Vol. II, Pts. I and II, The Macmillan Company, New York, 1905.
17. URBAN, F. M., "The Application of Statistical Methods to Problems of Psychophysics," Philadelphia, 1908.
18. ――――, On the method of just perceptible differences, *Psychol. Rev.*, 1907, **14,** 244–253.
19. ――――, Die psychophysischen Maszmethoden als Grundlagen empirischer Messungen, *Arch. ges. Psychol.*, 1909, **15,** 261–355; **16,** 168–227.
20. WOODWORTH, R. S., Professor Cattell's psychophysical contributions, *Arch. Psychol.*, 1914, no. 30, 60–74.
21. WUNDT, WM., "Grundzüge der physiologischen Psychologie," 4 aufl., W. Englemann, Leipzig, 1890.

CHAPTER V

EQUAL-APPEARING INTERVALS

THE METHOD OF EQUAL SENSE DISTANCES (MEAN GRADATIONS) AND WEBER'S LAW

Whereas the method of minimal changes had to do mainly with liminal differences, the methods discussed in this chapter are concerned with the equating of supraliminal differences. In its original form, the method of equal sense distances required the observer to bisect a given distance on a particular psychological continuum. Given two sound intensities, R_1 and R_3, the latter being of greater intensity than the former, O had the problem of finding a stimulus R_2 such that the interval $R_1 - R_2$ equalled $R_2 - R_3$. The method was of great interest for several reasons. The possibility of measuring supraliminal distances greatly extended the bounds of mental measurement. Quantitative psychology need no longer content itself with measuring thresholds alone. Very quickly the method was applied to the testing of Weber's law. This law had originally applied to liminal differences. Would it also apply to greater differences?

The method also furnished a device for testing the use of the j.n.d. or the DL as a psychological unit. If a DL as measured in one part of a continuum is really equivalent to a DL found in another part of the same continuum, then two equal sense distances should contain the same number of units. Not that intense sensations are merely heaps or summations of smaller sensations; this notion has long since disappeared from the minds of thinking psychologists. A unitary change in sensation is regarded as analogous to a change in degree of temperature on an ordinary thermometer. In the latter case a change from 10 to 20 deg. may be regarded as equivalent to a change from 20 to 30 deg. Will the analogy between sensory DL's and degrees of temperature hold?

Equal Sense Distances and Weber's Law.—If Weber's law holds for any series of stimuli which compose a physical continuum and

143

which give rise to a corresponding psychological continuum, the stimulus R_2, which bisects an interval $R_3 - R_1$, should be the geometric mean of R_3 and R_1. In mathematical form, if Weber's law is satisfied,

$$R_2 = \sqrt{R_1 R_3} \qquad (66)$$

The proof for this is as follows: Let the interval $R_2 - R_1$ be regarded as a small but supraliminal increment to R_1, and likewise let the interval $R_3 - R_2$ be regarded as an equal small increment to R_2. In other words,

$$R_2 - R_1 = \Delta R_1.$$
$$R_3 - R_2 = \Delta R_2.$$

Weber's law is satisfied when

$$\frac{\Delta R_1}{R_1} = \frac{\Delta R_2}{R_2} = K$$

or when

$$\frac{R_2 - R_1}{R_1} = \frac{R_3 - R_2}{R_2} = K \qquad (67)$$

Multiplying (67) through by $R_1 R_2$,

$$R_2(R_2 - R_1) = R_1(R_3 - R_2).$$
$$R_2^2 - R_1 R_2 = R_1 R_3 - R_1 R_2.$$
$$R_2^2 = R_1 R_3,$$

and so

$$R_2 = \sqrt{R_1 R_3}.$$

History of the Method of Equal Sense Distances.—It is said (15, II, p. 210) that the first recorded attempt to bisect a sensory interval was made by the physicist Plateau during the 1850's, an account of which was published in 1872. Plateau asked eight artists to paint a gray paper that would lie exactly halfway between a black and a white paper. The eight observers were able to agree very well upon the bisecting gray, but the mean value did not satisfy Weber's (or Fechner's) law. Assuming that the white paper had a photometric value of one unit and the black a value of zero, the gray has a value of $\frac{1}{8}$. While the gray and white stimuli had the physical ratio of $1:8$, the corresponding psychological ratio was $1:2$.

From this Plateau concluded that the brightness increased as the cube root of the stimulus. He did not allow for the fact that black paper has a photometric value greater than zero, which would bring the results more nearly into line with Weber's law. The important thing, however, is Plateau's demonstration that sensory intervals can be bisected with reliable results. He had planned to continue the experiment, bisecting each half, then each fourth, and so on, but the plan was never completed. He did inspire Delboeuf to make a systematic study which was carried out in the sixties and published in 1873. Delboeuf devised his well-known rotating disks which give three steps of gray (2). One of the stimuli was varied by small amounts in series, just as in the method of minimal changes, until O reported the two intervals equal. Lehmann later (1886), in order to eliminate some of the contrast effects, placed each gray upon a separate color rotator. These studies, with others, demonstrated that the bisecting stimulus was usually near the geometric mean, thus satisfying Weber's law.

But it was not long until other investigators using other types of stimuli, visual, auditory and tactual, found decisive divergencies from Weber's law. Merkel, in particular, usually found that R_2 was more often nearer the arithmetic mean than the geometric mean. This meant that judgments of sense distances were absolute and not relative to the part of the scale from which they were taken. By 1902 Wundt was ready to accept a new law, Merkel's law, along with Weber's, or at least as its chief exception. Plausible explanations have been found for Merkel's findings. Angell had already found by 1891 that E could lead O to an R_2 that was nearer the geometric mean, or to one nearer the arithmetic mean, by controlling the starting points of the series of observations. Others, especially Titchener, have pointed out the importance of that universal disturber, the stimulus error, in the method of equal sense distances. "The besetting difficulty of the method," says Titchener, "is, without question, the R-error" (15, II, p. 203). O is very likely to take a common-sense attitude and judge, not in terms of distances or intervals between sensations, but in terms of what he knows about the stimuli. He adopts the self-instruction to find a *stimulus* that shall be midway between the two terminal stimuli. Since he does this indirectly via his knowledge of the nature of the stimuli rather than directly by the comparison of sense intervals, R_2 naturally approaches the physical (arithmetic) mean.

The *n*th Power Law Applied to Supraliminal Differences.—
The writer does not believe that Weber's law will necessarily be
satisfied even when only direct and relevant criteria are used.   In
fact, from the dissatisfaction found with Weber's law in the preceding
chapter, we should expect it rarely to be satisfied.   The truth of
the matter seems to be that R_2 will vary between the geometric mean
and the arithmetic mean for different types of stimuli and for different observers.   Even liminal differences, we have found, do not
completely obey Weber's law.   Liminal differences are proportional,
sometimes to R, sometimes to $\sqrt{R}$, but more often to something
between R and $\sqrt{R}$.   Because of this the writer has proposed that
any small increment ΔR is proportional to R^n, where n varies, usually
between 0 and 1 (6).   Let us suppose that this also holds for a ΔR
as large as we find by the method of equal sense distances.   To repeat
the type of reasoning given above in equation (67),

$$\frac{R_2 - R_1}{R_1^n} = \frac{R_3 - R_2}{R_2^n} = K_n \qquad (68)$$

$$R_2^n(R_2 - R_1) = R_1^n(R_3 - R_2)$$

and

$$R_2^n = R_1^n\left[\frac{R_3 - R_2}{R_2 - R_1}\right].$$

Taking the *n*th root of both sides of the equation,

$$R_2 = R_1\left[\frac{R_3 - R_2}{R_2 - R_1}\right]^{\frac{1}{n}} \qquad (69)$$

We know R_1, R_2, and R_3 from the experimental data.   It is necessary to find the value of n.   We can solve equation (69) for n by
taking logarithms of both sides:

$$\log R_2 = \log R_1 + \frac{1}{n}\log\left[\frac{R_3 - R_2}{R_2 - R_1}\right].$$

Transposing,

$$\frac{1}{n}\log\left[\frac{R_3 - R_2}{R_2 - R_1}\right] = \log R_2 - \log R_1.$$

$$\frac{1}{n} = \frac{\log R_2 - \log R_1}{\log\left[\dfrac{R_3 - R_2}{R_2 - R_1}\right]}.$$

And so, from the reciprocals,

$$n = \frac{\log \left[\dfrac{R_3 - R_2}{R_2 - R_1} \right]}{\log R_2 - \log R_1} \qquad (70)$$

EXPERIMENT IV. THE BISECTION OF A SOUND INTERVAL

Problem.—To divide a certain interval of sound intensities into two subjectively equal parts, and to test Weber's law.

Materials.—Sound pendulum; silent metronome or pendulum.

Description of the Sound Pendulum.—As pictured in Fig. 14, Volkmann's sound pendulum consists of a suspended rod which terminates in a hard-rubber ball that strikes against a block of hardwood at the end of its fall. The intensity of sound is measurable in terms of a graduated scale with 1 deg. of arc as the unit.

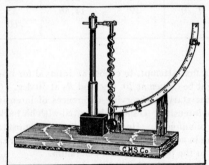

Fig. 14.—Volkmann's sound pendulum. (*Through the courtesy of C. H. Stoelting Company.*)

Three adjustable 'releases' can be fixed at different positions on the scale. *E* should acquire considerable skill in starting the pendulum from the three releases in succession before beginning the experiment with *O*. With practice *E* can learn to operate the releases with only a 1-sec. time interval as timed by a silent pendulum. Care should be taken to eliminate all but the sharp, clear sound of the ball striking the block. As the ball rebounds from the block, *E* should be prepared to catch it with one hand while he manipulates the releases with the other.

The intensity of the sound made by the pendulum is not exactly proportional to the angle through which it swings. It is rather in proportion to the vertical height of the fall of the ball as it swings through that angle. The intensity *I* is given by the formula,

$$I = \sin^2 \frac{\theta}{2},$$

in which θ (theta) is the angle at which the pendulum starts its fall. In order to facilitate the translation of degrees of arc into intensity values, the following table may be used (15, II, p. 196).

TABLE 18.—SOUND INTENSITIES FOR THE VARIOUS DEGREES OF ARC FOR THE
VOLKMANN SOUND PENDULUM

Angle	I	Angle	I	Angle	I
10°	1.00	30°	8.82	40°	15.40
12	1.44	31	9.40	42	16.90
14	1.95	32	10.00	44	18.47
16	2.55	33	10.62	46	20.10
18	3.22	34	11.25	48	21.78
20	3.97	35	11.90	50	23.42
22	4.79	36	12.57	52	25.30
24	5.69	37	13.25	54	27.13
26	6.66	38	13.95	56	29.01
28	7.70	39	14.66	58	30.94
				60	32.92

Procedure:

1. It is best, in a first attempt, to choose an interval for bisecting that is not too great. R_1 might be chosen at 20 deg. and R_3 at 50 deg. O should be given some practice at the start in observing differences of intensity and especially intervals or steps of intensity. O should be seated with his back to the apparatus with eyes closed or blindfolded. He should under no circumstances be permitted to see the pendulum in action while he observes intervals, nor should he be given any clues by E as to the positions of the pendulum.

2. The arrangement of series should be as in the method of minimal changes. The middle stimulus R_V is to be varied over a range of values in ascending and descending series. O is always to judge whether the second interval is greater than, equal to, or less than, the first, no matter how the series is given. The same rules concerning size of minimal change, length of series, and order of series should be approximately the same as in the usual method of limits. In a descending series R_V is decreased, and in an ascending series R_V is increased in intensity. A new variation in the arrangement of series enters into this experiment. There is perhaps a time error and so there should be a frequent reversal in the time order of the three stimuli. Half the series should begin with R_3 and half with R_1. A complete cycle of series with counterbalanced orders can be obtained in eight series arranged as shown in the table at the top of page 149.

3. The total number of series is most conveniently set at some multiple of eight; 24 or 32 series are usually practical numbers.

4. It is very desirable that E should determine in preliminary trials approximately where O's point of subjective equality (*PSE*) lies, and should arrange the starting points of the series with an equal balance on either side of this point.

5. Prepare a table similar to Table 19 for recording O's responses. While O is always to judge in terms of the *second* interval which he hears, one may keep the records as in Table 19, reversing the plus and minus judgments for the series in which R_1 is given first.

Series	Time order	Direction
1	R_3 to R_1	d
2	R_3 to R_1	a
3	R_1 to R_3	a
4	R_1 to R_3	d
5	R_1 to R_3	a
6	R_1 to R_3	d
7	R_3 to R_1	d
8	R_3 to R_1	a

6. O should be warned about any possible use of secondary criteria. Frequently O visualizes the pendulum, associating a given sound intensity with a certain visual position of the bob, and then chooses a middle visual position as the criterion of subjective equality. This is more likely to happen if O has had an opportunity to see and hear the swinging pendulum at the same time. Sometimes O forms a kind of absolute standard of an R_V that is midway and watches for the ideal standard to come in each series. The human organism is too resourceful in finding criteria for judgments in psychophysics. O should estab-

TABLE 19.—DATA SHEET FOR JUDGMENTS OF THE BISECTING SOUND STIMULUS

R_V	R_V	R_3 d	R_3 a	R_1 a	R_1 d	R_1 a	R_1 d	R_3 d	R_3 a	R_3 d	R_3 a	R_1 d	R_1 a	R_1 d	R_1 a	R_3 d	R_3 a	R_3 a	R_3 d	R_1 d	R_1 a	R_1 d	R_1 a	R_3 a	R_3 d
40	15.4	+						+												+					
39	14.7	+						+												+					+
38	14.0	+		+				+												+					+
37	13.3	+		+				+										+		+					+
36	12.6	+		+		+	+	+								+		+		+					+
35	11.9	+		+		+	+	+								+		+	+	+	+	+	+		+
34	11.3	=		+		=	+	+				+		+		+		+	+	=	+	=	+	+	=
33	10.6	=		+	+	=	+	+	+	+		+	=	+		=	+	+	=	+	=	=	=	=	=
32	10.0	=		+		=	=	=	+	+	+	=		+		=	=	=	=	=	+	−		=	−
31	9.4	=		=	=	=	=	=	=	+	=	+	+	+		+	+	=	=	=	−	+	−	−	
30	8.8	−	+	=		−	−	=	=	+	−	+	=	+		+	−	=	−	=	−		=	−
29	8.3	=	=			−		=		=		=		=		=	−	−		=				=	
28	7.7	=		−		−		=		=		=		=		−				−				=	
27	7.2	−				−		=		=		=								−					
26	6.7	−		−		−				−		−								−					
25	6.2	−		−						−		−													
24	5.7	−								−															
23	5.2	−				−				−															

lish his criteria early in the experiment and should adhere to them throughout the observations. He should be required to state his criteria at frequent intervals during the experiment, and *E* should *write down at once* any such reports from *O*.

Computation of the Bisecting Stimulus.—Consider a typical table (Table 19) of data obtained from the same apparatus and procedure with the limiting stimuli at 10 and 60 deg. This table is similar in appearance to Table 15 of the preceding chapter, but in the present case we are interested primarily in the point of subjective equality *PSE*. We therefore need consider only the median of the equality judgments for each series. These medians are shown graphically in the table by means of the heavy horizontal lines. The *PSE* that we are looking for is the central tendency of these values. In finding the mean *PSE* and its *PE*, it matters very little for practical purposes whether we use degrees of arc or units on the scale of physical intensities. Both values are given for all stimuli in the first two columns of Table 19. Using the former, the mean *PSE* is 30.9 deg., the *PE* of the distribution is 1.05 deg., and the *PE* of the mean is .22 deg. Translating the mean into intensity units from Table 18, we find it to be 9.34 units. If we obtain the mean *PSE* from measurements on the intensity scale, it is 9.36, with a *PE* of .59 and a PE_M of .13 unit of intensity. The relatively small *PE*'s indicate that for this *O* and this set of conditions the point that divides the intensity interval into two equal distances is quite reliably determined.

The next question to be answered is whether the obtained value for R_2 lies nearer the arithmetic mean or the geometric mean. The former is 16.96 and the latter is 5.74. R_2 lies between the two and somewhat nearer to the geometric mean. But Weber's law is by no means satisfied.

Will the *n*th power law apply to these results? Solving equation (70) in order to find *n*, we have

$$n = \frac{\log\left[\dfrac{23.56}{8.36}\right]}{\log 9.36 - \log 1}$$

$$= \frac{\log 2.8182}{.9713} = \frac{.4499}{.9713} = .46.$$

But this result alone is not sufficient to test the power law. We do not know whether the same power, *n* = .46, will apply if other sense distances are bisected on the same scale of auditory intensities. Only by finding the mid-stimulus for a number of intervals selected from different parts of the scale could the power law be adequately tested.

Variations of the Method.—Certain variations of the method of minimal changes also apply here. One can use the method 'without knowledge' in which, once the range has been roughly determined for stimuli that give equality judgments, the stimuli within that range are given in haphazard order. Such results are subject to the same kind of treatment as was suggested on page 133, determining that stimulus value for R_2 which is judged 'greater' and 'less' equally often. Such data may also be treated by any one of the constant processes to be described in the next chapter. If the middle stimulus is subject to continuous variation, the method of average error may be applied.

The study of supraliminal distances need not be confined to the bisection of intervals. One can reverse the process and require O to double a certain stimulus value; thus we have the so-called method of *doubled stimulus*. Similar to this is the process of duplicating a given stimulus distance. In this procedure, instead of placing R_V between two fixed terminals, it may be given at one of the extremes of the total interval being studied. R_1 or R_3 varies instead of R_2. This procedure, in some of its applications, becomes a close neighbor of the method of equivalents already mentioned. A method of *several gradations* (*Mehrfachen Abstufungen*) is also suggested, in which two or more stimuli are interpolated at equal intervals between two terminals. A slight variation of this is the successive halving of an interval, with the purpose of finally arriving at liminal differences. None of these proposed variations have been given a serious trial, but it would seem that a study of the relationship and consistency of liminal to supraliminal differences would require their use.

Other Applications of the Method.—Aside from the problems already referred to, involving visual, auditory, and tactual intensities, the method has not been very widely applied. Fullerton and Cattell (5) applied it to the measurement of the extent and the force of arm movements with not completely satisfactory results. A great many, including Lorenz, Münsterberg, and Pratt (11), have applied it to the bisection of tonal intervals. It was at first thought that all musical intervals involved the same relative tonal distance or pitch difference, no matter from what part of the musical scale they were taken. In general this has not been found true; the results depend very much upon musical training and the attitude of O and upon the size of the interval bisected. On the whole the equation of psychological distances, as in the method of equal-appearing intervals, has had a much wider scope of usefulness in theoretical and in practical problems. To that method we now turn our attention.

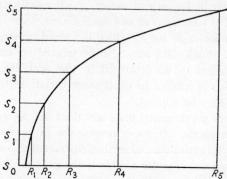

FIG. 15.—Graphic representation of Fechner's logarithmic law.

EQUAL-APPEARING INTERVALS AND FECHNER'S LAW

Fechner's law, as the student already knows, is given the following mathematical form:

$$S = C \log R \tag{71}$$

in which R is measured in terms of the absolute threshold as the unit. A sensory magnitude is proportional to the logarithm of the stimulus that arouses it. In graphic form the functional relationship is to be seen in Fig. 15. This shows more clearly than any statement how, for equal increases in sensory intensity, the increases in stimulus intensity must be ever enlarging. In connection with the more familiar Weber law, it is plain to be seen that $R_2/R_1 = R_3/R_2 = R_4/R_3 = R_5/R_4$. Or, if we regard every interval of stimulus increase as a ΔR, then it can be seen that ΔR_1 (which is the difference $R_2 - R_1$) is to R_1 as ΔR_2 is to R_2, and so on, or, in general, $\Delta R/R = K$, which is our old familiar statement of Weber's law.

The Derivation of Fechner's Law from Weber's Law.—Starting with Weber's equation, $\Delta R/R = K$, in which ΔR is a relatively small stimulus increment for example, a j.n.d., Fechner assumed that all corresponding small increments in S are psychologically equal. Let ΔR decrease in size and ΔS decreases correspondingly with it. Let these decreasing values be called δR and δS, respectively, and assume with Fechner that

$$\delta S = c\frac{\delta R}{R} = K$$

where c is the constant of proportionality between δS and $\delta R/R$. This equation is known as Fechner's *fundamental formula* (*Fundamentalformel*). Since all the S increments are equal, δS may be used as the unit of the sensory scale and any S value is the sum of all the δS's from zero up to that particular S value. To summate all the δS's means to integrate the above equation. The result of the integration is

$$S = c \log_e R + C$$

where C = the constant of integration.

e = the base of the natural logarithms.

In order to find the value of C in terms of R values, we may make the following substitutions: Let R_0 be the value of R when $S = 0$, R_0 being the absolute threshold. Substituting these values ($S = 0$ and $R = R_0$) in the above equation,

$$0 = c \log_e R_0 + C$$

from which, by transposing,

$$C = -c \log_e R_0.$$

The complete formula then becomes

$$\begin{aligned} S &= c \log_e R - c \log_e R_0 \\ &= c (\log_e R - \log_e R_0) \\ &= c \log_e \frac{R}{R_0}. \end{aligned}$$

This means that R should be measured in terms of the absolute threshold value as the unit. And in order to use the common logarithms in place of the natural system, we need to change the coefficient c to some other symbol, for example, C.

Then
$$S = C \log \frac{R}{R_0}.$$

This is the final form of Fechner's *measurement formula* (*Massformel*). Since we do not always know the value of R_0, and since the expression $C \log R_0$ is a constant that can be calculated from experimental data, perhaps the more useful form of the law is

$$S = C \log R + a,$$

in which
$$a = C \log R_0{}^*.$$

EXPERIMENT V.   SANFORD'S LIFTED-WEIGHT EXPERIMENT

Problem.—To test Fechner's law for lifted weights by the method of equal-appearing intervals.

Materials.—A set of Sanford's weights described by Titchener as follows (15, I, p. 33): "Set of weighted envelopes, of 5 to 100 gr. The envelopes are heavy 'pay' envelopes, of manila paper, about 6.5 by 11 cm. They are stiffened by a piece of cardboard, . . . cut to twice the size of the envelopes and then folded. To weight the envelopes, pieces of heavy paper or of card are pasted, or strips of thin sheet lead are sewed, to the inner surfaces of the stiffening card. Scraps of loose paper may be dropped into the fold, to make the weight exact. The weight of the envelope in gr. is written on the inside of the envelope flap, and the flap itself tucked in; the envelopes are not to be sealed. The series consists of 108 envelopes: (*a*) extra standard of 5 gr.; (*b*) extra standard of 100 gr.; (*c*) 26 envelopes, 5 to 10 gr., differing by 0.2 gr. increments; (*d*) 30 envelopes, 10.5 to 25 gr., with 0.5 gr. increments; (*e*) 25 envelopes, 26 to 50 gr., with 1 gr. difference; and (*f*) 25 envelopes, 52 to 100 gr., with 2 gr. differences."

The uneven distribution of weights over the range from 5 to 100 gr. requires comment. We are justified in assuming that some 'law of diminishing returns' such as Fechner's does hold. If the weights were evenly spaced physically, *O* would find more weights piling up in the lower groups. His tendency to even up the number of weights in the different piles would tend to overthrow or to obscure the real psychophysical law. On the other hand, any distribution we may choose may prejudice his sorting in the direction of any law we might assume. This difficulty has never, to the knowledge of the writer, been overcome.

---

* We cannot be concerned here with the question of the validity of Fechner's assumptions or with the various interpretations that have been placed upon the law. Our task is rather to consider the experimental and statistical methods that are used in applying empirical tests of the law. For historical and theoretical treatments of Fechner's law, see Boring (3, pp. 274–285), Klemm (10, Chap. 9), and Titchener (15, II, pp. 61–91).

Procedure:

1. *O* sits at a low table. The two extra standard weights are placed some distance apart, the remaining weights being shuffled in a heap on the table.

2. *O* lifts each weight grasping the flap end with the thumb and forefinger of his right hand. He may compare each weight with either or both of the standards if he so wishes, or one weight with another. His main task is to make five groups of weights such that the differences between neighboring piles shall seem equal to him. He may lift each weight as many times as he desires and shift any weight from one pile to another until he is satisfied with the result.

3. Each pile is weighed on a balance, the number of weights of each pile noted, and the average weight computed.[1]

4. The sorting of the weights should be repeated once or twice more in the same manner, and a grand average should be computed for each of the five steps.

TABLE 20.—AVERAGE WEIGHTS IN GRAMS FOR THE FIVE STEPS OR SENSORY INTERVALS, FROM LOWEST TO HIGHEST INTENSITY

	Sensory values				
Trial	1	2	3	4	5
1	6.68	10.67	19.97	40.38	77.73
2	6.37	10.85	23.50	47.41	82.53
3	6.50	11.13	22.15	44.10	78.29
Means	6.52	10.88	21.87	43.96	79.52
Ratios	......	1.67	2.01	2.01	1.81
log *R*	.8139	1.0366	1.3399	1.6431	1.9004

The Test of Fechner's Law.—Some typical results are tabulated in Table 20. The ratio of each stimulus to the one just preceding is

[1] This is the procedure of the traditional Sanford experiment, to find the average weight or *R* value for a corresponding psychological scale value. This is not the best statistical procedure. To do this means to find the regression of *R* upon *S*. It is equivalent to asking the question, "For any given *S* value what is the most probable *R* value?" What we really want is the reverse; for any given *R* value what is the most probable *S* value? This involves finding the mean or median *S* value for every weight we use. The two regression curves will be of the same type, in this case logarithmic, but the value of *C* in Fechner's formula will be different, unless there is a perfect correlation between *R* and *S*. The reasons for this will be made clear in Chapters X and XI. For the sake of testing Fechner's logarithmic law we may proceed in the traditional manner, which in this case is simpler since there are only five means to compute, for the five *S* values, whereas there would be a much greater number to compute if we were to find one for each of the separate *R* values.

not exactly constant, as the law requires, but it is fairly so. A graphic representation of the relationship of S to R is given in Fig. 16. It is clear that the functional relationship between S and R is of the logarithmic form as in the theoretical case shown in Fig.

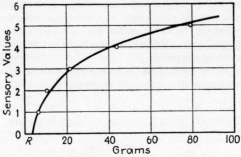

FIG. 16.—Graphic relationship between the sensory steps and the stimulus values in Sanford's lifted-weight experiment.

15. A still better graphic test, however, is to compute the log R values, as has been done in the last line of Table 20, and plot the five S values against the corresponding log R values, as in Fig. 17. The points thus plotted should fall in a line without any noticeable

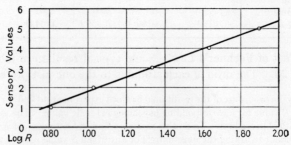

FIG. 17.—Linear relationship between the S values and the log R values for Sanford's lifted-weight experiment.

curvature if Fechner's law is satisfied. In Fig. 17 the points fit the straight line very closely. This result is rarely obtained with the Sanford weights. Cowdrick (4) reports that with most Os the results more nearly fulfill the Fullerton-Cattell law than Fechner's, but with practice the results tend more in the direction of Fechner's law.

EXPERIMENT VI. THE PERCEPTION OF THE DENSITY OF PATTERNS OF SPOTS

Problem.—To determine by the method of equal-appearing intervals whether Fechner's law applies to the perception of numbers of dots.

Materials.—Five sets of 23 cards each, every card containing dots or letters or other identical spots scattered uniformly over an area 2½ in. square. The numbers of spots should vary in number from 15 to 74 as follows: 15, 16, 17, 19, 20, 22, 24, 26, 28, 30, 32, 35, 37, 40, 43, 46, 49, 53, 56, 60, 64, 69, and 74. The number of spots should be written on the back of each card. Extra standards of 15 and 74 spots should be supplied. It will be noticed that the physical intervals increase as the number of spots increases, forming a geometric series as in the case of the Sanford weights. If Fechner's law is not satisfied with this condition in its favor, we can be quite sure that it does not apply to these stimuli.

Procedure:

1. *E* shuffles the five sets together and hands them to *O* who is to sort them into nine piles so that the difference in apparent density or number of spots is the same from one pile to the next. In general, an uneven number of piles is preferable. This enables *O*, if he desires, to use the middle pile as well as the two terminal piles as anchorage points for the whole scale. This relates the task to some extent to that of bisecting an interval. Not that there is anything more accurate about bisecting intervals than in arranging equal steps, but, if *O* has the opportunity to use the bisecting method in addition to the equating of small intervals, a greater internal consistency for the scale as a whole may be attained. If the bisecting principle is to be carried out to the fullest extent, the number of steps should be 5, 9, or 17. This allows for successive subdivisions or bisections. The number of steps will of course depend upon other factors, including the range of *R* values to be judged, the fineness of the scale desired, and the discriminating powers of *O*. In this particular problem, the bisecting principle may be employed to the extent that the standards with 15 and 74 dots are placed at the extremes, and *O* may begin by selecting a bisecting stimulus.

2. It is to be taken for granted that *O* will not count the dots, and he should not try to estimate the exact number on any card. He is to judge rather by the total impression and to report to *E* what his chief criteria are.

3. *O* repeats the sorting process 10 times in the same manner, so that every card with a given *R* value will have been judged a total of 50 times.

4. *E* keeps a record of the placements for every *R* value so that in the end he will have a tabulation of the frequencies with which every *R* value is placed in every pile. The piles are assigned values such as appear in the first row of Table 21, 0–1, 1–2, 2–3, etc. The assignment of an interval to each pile, in place of a discrete number as might have been expected, gives a truer picture of the psychological scale and permits easier treatment of the data. While *O* has been forced to place the stimuli in discrete piles, to him each pile actually represents a short range of psychological values; hardly any two placed in the same pile seem to him exactly equal. The values of one pile merge over into those of the next; for example, witness *O*'s repeated indecision as to the placement of specimens in one of two neighboring piles. In each cell of the table appears the obtained

frequency and also the cumulative frequency. Examples of obtained data are given in Table 21.[1]

TABLE 21.—FREQUENCIES AND CUMULATIVE FREQUENCIES FOR EVERY R VALUE AS JUDGED AT EVERY STEP IN THE PSYCHOLOGICAL SCALE

R	0–1	1–2	2–3	3–4	4–5	5–6	6–7	7–8	8–9	9–10	10–11	Mdn	Q
71	9	10	11	6	4							2.10	.95
	9	19	30	36	40								
89	3	9	14	5	3	3	2	1				2.57	1.01
	3	12	26	31	34	37	39	40					
117			3	6	10	10	8	2	1			5.10	1.01
			3	9	19	29	37	39	40				
135					7	13	8	5	3	2	2	6.00	1.08
					7	20	28	33	36	38	40		
198							2	2	5	7	24	10.17	.72
							2	4	9	16	40		

EQUAL-APPEARING INTERVALS AS A SCALING DEVICE

Computation of Scale Values.—The procedure here is somewhat different from that used with the Sanford weights. In the latter case we found the mean R value for the weights placed in each pile. Here we find the mean (or median) of the S values for every corresponding R value. Here we must recognize fully the fact that we want to know the regression of S upon R, S being the dependent variable and R the independent variable. For any given R value, which is fixed and known by the nature of our experiment, we ask to know the best estimate of the corresponding S value. The most probable S value is, as usual, a mean or a median. A further reason for finding the central tendency of the S values is that, in the usual application of the method of equal-appearing intervals, the R values are unknown and unobtainable, as with specimens of handwriting, advertisements, and the like. In these cases it is merely desired to find the psychological-scale values of the materials. Here, obviously, it is the central tendencies of the S values that must be calculated.

[1] The data of Table 21 were obtained from stimuli having from 68 to 198 dots; O was instructed to arrange them in 11 apparently equidistant piles.

For these central tendencies the median is a better estimate than the mean. In normal distributions, of course, the mean and the median are identical. But, as may be seen in Table 21, the distributions for those stimuli near the ends of the scale are skewed and must be so by the very nature of the method. There is a piling up of judgments in the end groups. This is the so-called *end effect*, one of the most serious difficulties of the method. In the middle of the range of stimuli the mean would be just as adequate as the median, but at the ends of the range the median undoubtedly gives a much truer estimate of the *S* value, so medians are used throughout.

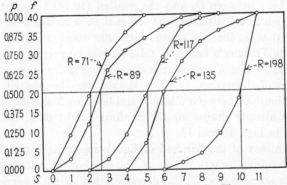

FIG. 18.—Graphic solution of the scale values in the Thurstone card-sorting experiment, using the data in Table 21.

The medians may be obtained in one of several ways.[1] One may find them by the interpolation method illustrated in Chapter II, or one may use a graphic solution, drawing an ogive for every distribution from the cumulative frequencies, as was done in Fig. 18. In this figure may be seen the five ogives for the data in Table 21. The median is read off immediately by observing where the curve crosses the frequency of 20. The various methods yield essentially the same results.

Dispersions of the Judgments.—It can be seen either from Table 21 or from Fig. 18 that some of the distributions have wider dispersions than others. Such differences are not very great in the judgments of material as homogeneous in nature as weights or

[1] In addition to the methods of finding a median mentioned here, any of the additional methods described in the following chapter will be applicable.

numbers of dots. With material like handwriting samples or drawings, such differences are sometimes striking and significant. These dispersions can be measured as usual by means of σ, PE, or Q. Since interpolated medians are used here, Q is the measure of dispersion employed. The various medians and the Q's will be seen in Table 21. It is not so easy to measure the dispersions for those stimuli lying near the ends of the scale. If R equals 198, Q is only .72, which is smaller than all other Q's, owing to the fact that the upper branch of the ogive rises so abruptly to its limit. If we consider only the lower branch in this case—and we may properly regard it as the genuine lower half of a truncated ogive—we find that Q_1 is 9.14. Between Q_1 and the median (10.17) is an interval of 1.03, which as an estimate of Q brings it more in line with what we should expect in the case of this particular distribution.

Testing Fechner's Law.—A table should be prepared giving the R values, the log R values, the corresponding S values, and their measures of dispersion. Curves should then be plotted showing the relationships between S and R and between S and log R, similar to those already drawn for the Sanford weight data, *i.e.*, similar to those in Figs. 16 and 17.

Applications of the Method of Equal-appearing Intervals.—The most promising practical use of the method of equal-appearing intervals seems to be in the determination of psychological scale values for samples of materials like handwriting or drawings, when there are far too many stimuli to be handled by other more reliable methods such as paired comparisons or order of merit. As early as 1910, Thorndike (12) had asked 40 judges to sort 1000 samples of penmanship into 11 equally spaced piles, preliminary to the development of a permanent rating scale that should have a small number of samples spaced at equal psychological units as to quality. Incidentally, he found that the results from paired comparisons did not agree exactly with those from judgments of equal intervals. Two of his suggestions for scaling such samples are worth remembering. Samples covering the entire range of quality should be used, extending beyond the terminal values; otherwise the stimuli in those terminal piles cannot be accurately determined. He also advises us to begin with a very large number of samples, culling to eliminate those that fall between points on the scale. This tends to keep the steps discrete and the resulting gaps aid in a clearer comparison of intervals.

Hollingworth (9) asked 10 *O*s to classify 39 jokes into 10 categories as to degree of humor. He found the procedure quicker, less monotonous, and less fatiguing than the ranking method. Hillegas (8) used the method along with others in preparing his scale for rating English compositions. In this, as well as in other cases, however, the scale values obtained by this method are not generally trusted and other methods are brought in for the final evaluations. This mistrust has been vindicated in a careful study by Hevner (7). As compared with the ranking method and paired comparisons, this procedure is less dependable. As checked against the other two methods, the intervals judged equal are in reality not all equal. The intervals in the upper range of *S* values are actually greater than those in the lower range of values. Just why the better specimens of handwriting were not sufficiently separated from one another is not known. Unless there are checks that can be made upon the results of this method, it should never be used alone. Its chief usefulness so far seems to be in the preliminary stages of the scaling process when very large numbers of stimuli must be sorted.

The Development of Scales for Social Attitudes.—One recently proposed application is the scaling of propositions that are designed to reflect social attitudes. Thurstone suggests (13) that scales of opinions can be set up to indicate the strength of sentiment of an individual or of a group of individuals on almost any social question, for example, attitudes for or against militarism, for or against the established church, and for or against prohibition. The scaling procedure is somewhat as follows: Suppose that the question upon which we wish to measure attitudes is that of compulsory military drill in universities. First, several groups of people are asked to write out their opinions on this question. Next, from 100 to 150 statements are selected from all the collected material, with an attempt to cover the whole range of opinion, pro and con, with neutral statements between. Several requirements are laid down for the statements. They must be short and to the point. They must be in a form that can be accepted or rejected. Acceptance or rejection must mean something about the attitude to be measured. No 'double-barreled' statements are used. Each statement is then printed on a card. Two or three hundred *O*s are asked to arrange the statements in equal-appearing steps, keeping the two extreme piles and the middle or neutral pile in mind as 'standards.' *O*s of widely varying attitudes on the subject should be used. The computation of scale values for the statements is carried out in just the same way as for the cards with different numbers of dots in Experiment VI.

In the end, what is wanted is a set of statements, 25, for example, which shall be unambiguous and valid and which shall be distributed rather evenly over the whole range of opinion. As a test of ambiguity Thurstone (13) recommends the use of the standard error of the distribution for each statement. Some will be found to have wider dispersions over the scale than others. The validity or relevance of an item must be obtained in other ways. The simplest test is to select for each statement another which has approximately the same scale value. Such pairs of statements, if they really express opinions about the attitude in question and little or nothing else, should receive about the same number of endorsements from the same group of subjects to whom the scale is applied. If they receive quite different numbers of endorsements, then one or the other is likely to be irrelevant. The assumption is that all relevant opinions lie on the linear scale that extends between the two extremes of the scale. An irrelevant statement lies off at one side of this line. A more satisfactory test of relevancy is to apply the principle of the 'method of similar reactions' which Thurstone describes. A still more competent and rigorous test of the relevancy and of the purity of an item is to apply factor analysis, which is discussed in Chapter XIV.

The application of the scale of some 25 opinions is simple. The *O*s are asked to mark with a plus sign every statement they wish to endorse. The score for each person is the average scale value, or, perhaps better still, a median scale value, of all the items he endorses. A measure of dispersion may be computed for the individual; this, according to Thurstone, measures his 'tolerance' on the issue. The scores may then be treated like any mental-test scores. Frequency distributions of groups can be formed. The mean and standard error of the distribution of a group can be computed and this group can be compared with another on the same basis, or the same group can be measured before and after a movie or a debate that might be expected to change attitudes. The dispersion of a group may indicate something about its 'heterogeneity' on the issue in question. Bimodal distributions may indicate cleavages in opinion on the subject. Indeed, there seem to be many ways of using data obtained from such scales, and their great significance in the treatment of psychosocial problems has already been demonstrated.[1]

Criticisms of the Methods Involving Judged Intervals.—But the reader must be reminded again of the still doubtful status of equated psychological intervals. There is the finding of Hevner (7) that intervals among the stronger stimuli are underestimated as compared with those among the weaker stimuli. Much earlier, Ament (1) had found that, in a bisected interval, the higher of the two segments contained fewer j.n.d.'s than the lower. Whether the judgment of supraliminal differences can ever be brought into line with judgments of liminal differences is hard to say. Whether irrelevant criteria are more strongly operative in judgments of supraliminal than liminal differences we do not know, though there are indications that this is true. There is another possible factor that may enter into judgments where more than two stimuli are simultaneously involved. That factor may be called the 'gestalt effect.' The appearance of the series as a whole may determine the placement of the parts. Progress in solving these problems would seem to await a closer scrutiny of the processes of judgments themselves, whether the judgments are in the form of comparison of pairs of stimuli or in the form of the arrangement of equal supraliminal steps.

Problems

1. The data given at the top of page 164 were obtained from an experiment on the bisection of an interval of sound intensity following the procedure of Experiment IV. The terminal stimuli were 20 deg. and 50 deg. for R_1 and R_3, respectively.

Treat these data according to the procedures given on pages 150 *f*.

2. The data given at the bottom of page 164 were obtained from a card-sorting experiment which followed the instructions of Experiment VI.

Compute the median scale values of the 23 stimuli and test the data for Fechner's logarithmic law as shown at the top of page 165.

[1] Remmers and others have recently introduced variations in the scaling of social attitudes which mean great economy (H. H. Remmers, Studies in higher education, *Bull. Purdue Univ.*, 1934, 35, no. 4). They have shown that the same scale of opinions is adequate for the same *class* of social objects, for example, school subjects, racial groups, occupations, and vocations. They have also shown that the opinions may be presented to the subject being tested in the order of scale value rather than in haphazard order. This means a great saving in time required to find a median scale position for an individual.

Ascending series		Descending series	
R_1 first	R_3 first	R_1 first	R_3 first
35.0	34.0	34.5	36.0
38.5	36.5	37.5	34.5
38.5	36.0	37.0	37.0
38.0	37.5	36.5	36.0
38.0	35.0	36.5	37.0
39.0	37.5	38.0	38.0

Stimulus values	Scale values								
	1	2	3	4	5	6	7	8	9
15	14	18	7	1					
16	16	19	3	2					
17	7	18	11	4					
19	8	18	9	3	2				
20	3	12	14	3	6	2			
22	1	11	14	12	2				
24	..	3	12	14	9	2			
26	..	2	9	18	9	2			
28	..	..	2	20	17	1			
30	..	..	..	26	11	3			
32	..	..	2	10	16	9	3		
35	..	..	..	8	17	14	1		
37	..	..	..	8	18	10	4		
40	..	..	..	2	14	14	10		
43	..	..	..	..	12	19	9		
46	..	..	..	2	6	18	14		
49	..	..	..	..	2	14	23	1	
53	..	..	..	..	..	10	25	5	
56	..	..	..	..	..	12	22	6	
60	..	..	..	..	..	5	22	11	2
64	..	..	..	..	..	..	14	20	6
69	..	..	..	..	..	..	7	17	16
74	..	..	..	..	..	..	6	20	14

a. Plot the scale values against the stimulus values. Does the trend of the points seem to follow the logarithmic curve as illustrated in Fig. 15?

b. Find the logarithms of the stimulus values and plot the scale values against log R. Is Fechner's law fulfilled?

c. Find the logarithms of the scale values and plot log S against log R. Is the trend more linear in this case or in the former? State your conclusion.

REFERENCES

1. AMENT, W., Ueber das Verhältnis der ebenmerklichen zu den übermerklichen Unterschieden bei Licht- und Schallintensitäten, *Phil. Stud.*, 1900, **16,** 135–139.
2. BORING, E. G., Delboeuf disks and the Kirschmann photometer, *Amer. J. Psychol.*, 1917, **28,** 279 *f.*
3. ———, "A History of Experimental Psychology," D. Appleton-Century Company, Inc., New York, 1929.
4. COWDRICK, M., The Weber-Fechner law and Sanford's weight experiment, *Amer. J. Psychol.*, 1917, **28,** 585–588.
5. FULLERTON, G. S., and J. McK. CATTELL, On the perception of small differences, *Pub. Univ. Penn., Phil. Series*, 1892, no. 2.
6. GUILFORD, J. P., A generalized psychophysical law, *Psychol. Rev.*, 1932, **39,** 73–85.
7. HEVNER, K., An empirical study of three psychophysical methods, *J. Gen. Psychol.*, 1930, **4,** 191–212.
8. HILLEGAS, M. B., A scale for the measurement of quality in English composition, *Teach. Coll. Rec.*, 1912, **13,** no. 4.
9. HOLLINGWORTH, H. L., Judgments of the comic, *Psychol. Rev.*, 1911, **18,** 132–156.
10. KLEMM, O., "A History of Psychology," trans., Charles Scribner's Sons, New York, 1914.
11. PRATT, C. C., Bisection of tonal intervals larger than the octave, *J. Exper. Psychol.*, 1928, **11,** 17–26.
12. THORNDIKE, E. L., Handwriting, *Teach. Coll. Rec.*, 1910, **11,** no. 2.
13. THURSTONE, L. L., Attitudes can be measured, *Amer. J. Sociol.*, 1928, **33,** 529–554.
14. ———, Fechner's law and the method of equal appearing intervals, *J. Exper. Psychol.*, 1929, **12,** 214–224.
15. TITCHENER, E. B., "Experimental Psychology," Vol. II, Pts. I and II, The Macmillan Company, New York, 1905.
16. URBAN, F. M., Ueber die Methode der gleichen Abstufungen, *Arch. ges. Psychol.*, 1931, **80,** 291–312.
17. ———, The Weber-Fechner law and mental measurement, *J. Exper. Psychol.*, 1933, **18,** 221–238.

CHAPTER VI

THE CONSTANT METHODS

The constant methods are generally regarded as the most accurate and the most widely applicable of all the psychophysical methods. They are employed with convenience in the measurement of stimulus limens, differential limens, equal sense distances, and equivalent stimuli, and in the determination of many other psychological constants outside the sphere of psychophysics as well as within its limits. Briefly, the method is conducted as follows:

After preliminary trials E selects a limited number of stimuli, usually four to seven, which are presented to O a very large number of times, usually from 50 to 200 times each, in a prearranged order unknown to O. In finding an RL, each stimulus is presented alone and O judges either the presence or absence of the desired experience, for example, 'two' when studying the two-point threshold. In finding a DL, each stimulus is presented simultaneously with, or in temporal sequence with, a single standard and O is to report whether the one stimulus is apparently 'greater' or 'less' than the other; if he is uncertain, he reports 'doubtful.' The former procedure is known as the **method of constant stimuli** and the latter as the **method of constant stimulus differences**. In either case the limens are computed from the proportions of judgments of different kinds for every stimulus. The history of the constant methods is much involved with controversy and with statistical procedures new to the student and will be better understood after the present-day practices have been explained. Let us first consider two typical experiments.

EXPERIMENT VII. THE TWO-POINT TACTUAL THRESHOLD

Problem.—To measure the longitudinal two-point limen on the forearm by the method of constant stimuli.

Materials.—Aesthesiometer; millimeter scale.

Procedure:

1. E selects an appropriate region on the volar surface of O's forearm.

2. By using the method of minimal changes, E determines the approximate two-point limen and also the range of stimuli that are judged neither 'two' nor

166

'one' 100 per cent of the time.   Ten series, five ascending and five descending, should be sufficient.   Five separations of the compass points are chosen at equidistant intervals such that the greatest will probably give about 90 per cent judgments of 'two' and the smallest about 10 per cent.

3. *E* then arranges a succession of stimuli to be used, observing the following considerations: Each series of five is ordinarily given before going on to the next, although this need not be strictly followed.   Each of the stimuli should follow every other one equally often.   A scheme of rotation, too elaborate for *O* to grasp, can be worked out.   When a complete rotation is completed, it may be followed in reverse order or repeated as many times as necessary, until every stimulus has been applied 100 times.

4. *E* gives a preparatory signal, "Ready, now," and in 1 to 2 sec. lowers the aesthesiometer points evenly and perpendicularly upon *O*'s arm, leaving them in contact with the arm not longer than 2 sec.   *O* is to judge promptly.   If in doubt, *O* may say, "Doubtful," in which case the judgment may be recorded, but that trial is repeated later, obtaining a judgment of 'one' or 'two' to replace the doubtful judgment.

5. Frequent rest periods are essential; otherwise *O* develops lasting after-images which, when assimilated into the sensory pattern, give impressions of two when only one should have been felt.   At the beginning of every new working period, *O* should be given a 'warming-up' session during which he reestablishes his criteria of 'twoness.'

6. The inclusion of a separation of zero (one-point stimulations, sometimes known as *Vexierversuche*) is a matter concerning which there are differences of opinion.   Some recommend that no single-point stimulations be given because *O* resorts to guessing and to dependence upon irrelevant criteria (he commits the stimulus error).   They argue that, if *O* knows that two points are always applied, he is compelled to establish criteria of 'twoness.'   He might be trained at the start to discriminate such tactual patterns as the 'dumbbell,' 'double-paddle,' line, long-oval, and short-oval forms which Friedline (17) and others have pointed out.   On the other hand some recommend the inclusion of a few random *Vexierversuche* in order to reassure *O* of his criteria and to keep him on his guard against unwarranted judgments of 'two.'   Helson[1] has urged the inclusion of zero separation as one of the regular stimuli, which involves a spacing of other stimuli in the series so that zero separation will lie at one of the stimulus steps. It is found that the regular inclusion of one point in the series has a stabilizing effect upon *O* and the proportion of 'two' judgments fits into the picture consistently with the judgments of the other stimuli.   This is not in line with earlier results (26) which indicate a *paradoxical error*, an undue proportion of 'two's' for zero separation.   The student may choose one of the alternatives proposed here and he should interpret his results accordingly.

Treatment of Results:

1. Find the proportion of 'two's' for every stimulus value.   To illustrate, the following results were obtained by a typical student.

---

[1] In a personal communication to the writer.   An article on the subject will appear soon in the *American Journal of Psychology*.

TABLE 22.—DATA FOR THE TWO-POINT LIMEN

Stimulus separation (R), mm........	8	9	10	11	12
Proportion of two's (p).............	.01	.05	.29	.66	.93

2. The next step is the crucial one, the computation of a limen. There are six acceptable ways of doing this, ways which will now be described in detail.

THE COMPUTATION OF AN ABSOLUTE LIMEN

1. The Linear Interpolation Method.—The two-point limen, as strictly defined in psychophysics, is that separation of two points which yields 50 per cent judgments of 'two' and 50 per cent judgments of 'one.' It can readily be seen from the data just given that such a stimulus lies between 10 and 11 mm. The simplest solution is a linear interpolation between the proportions of .29 and .66 to find the limen L which would have given a proportion of exactly .50. We may assume that the two points for $p = .29$ and $p = .66$ are joined by a straight line, as in Fig. 21 they appear to be. The interpolation of a median is, of course, no new task for the student. The limen, at $p = .50$, lies .21/.37 of the way in the stimulus interval between 10 and 11 mm., or $10 + .57 = 10.57$ mm. A general formula to fit this particular problem may be given:

$$\frac{L - R_l}{.50 - p_l} = \frac{R_h - R_l}{p_h - p_l}$$

where R_h = the stimulus immediately higher than the limen.

　　　R_l = the stimulus immediately lower than the limen.

　　　p_h = the proportion of 'two's' for the stimulus immediately higher than the limen.

　　　p_l = the proportion of 'two's' for the stimulus immediately lower than the limen.

Solving for L, we have

$$L = R_l + \frac{(R_h - R_l)(.50 - p_l)}{(p_h - p_l)} \tag{72}$$

Objections to the Linear Interpolation Method.—*a.* The linear interpolation method is objectionable because it does not use all the data. In the example above, only two of the five proportions are employed. This is obviously a wasteful procedure. To overcome this objection, some investigators recommend that in the experimental procedure we use only two stimuli, which are carefully chosen so as to lie on either side of the limen. In many cases this curtailment of the method is justifiable, as has been shown by Linder (29).

b. The assumption that the curve is a straight line between two points is open to question. However, in the immediate neighborhood of the limen most psychometric curves of this type are so nearly linear that an insignificant error is made by interpolation.

c. No measure of reliability or of dispersion can be found. We usually want a *PE* for our limen. Further interpolation enables us to estimate this, however, if more than two stimuli have been used. The functional relationship between the proportions and the stimulus values approaches a normal ogive, or the familiar cumulative frequency curve. The interpolated limen is really a median of that distribution. We can obtain Q, the semi-interquartile range, by finding where the ogive crosses the 25 per cent point and the 75 per cent point. Interpolating, we find Q_1 to be 9.83 and Q_3 to be 11.33. The interquartile range, $Q_3 - Q_1$, is 1.50, and Q is therefore .75 mm. It should be pointed out that objection *b* applies even more properly to these interpolations, since the normal ogive is nonlinear in the neighborhood of $p = .25$ or .75 (see Fig. 21).

The estimation of the quartile values, Q_1 and Q_3, also makes possible a more accurate determination of the limen. We may then find the mean of the three interpolated values, the R values at 25, 50, and 75 per cent, namely, 9.83, 10.57, and 11.33. This mean is 10.58. In this average, four of the observed proportions of Table 22 have been used. This helps to remove objection *a*, that not all the data were used in finding the limen. One more thing these results can tell us, and that is whether or not the distribution is symmetrical or skewed. In a symmetrical curve $(Q_3 - L)$ ought to equal $(L - Q_1)$. For these data the two quartile distances are both .75. The curve is apparently perfectly symmetrical.

2. Finding the Arithmetic Mean.—This procedure must be accredited to Spearman (37). The assumptions are made that the limen itself is a varying point on the physical scale and that every application of a stimulus locates that point roughly, above or below that R value. For example, with the R value at 11 mm., if O reports 'two,' the limen is below 11 mm.; with the R value at 12, if O reports 'one,' the limen is above 12 mm. To return to our illustrative problem of Table 22, at an R value of 8 mm., O reported

'two,' only once in 100 times.   This means that 99 of the limens
are above 8 mm. and 1 of them is below that point.   With an *R*
value of 9 mm., there were 5 reports of 'two.'   Interpreted in the
same manner, 95 of the limens are above 9 mm. and 5 are below.
Now if 1 of the limens is below 8 mm. and 5 are below 9 mm., 4 of
them must lie between 8 and 9 mm.   In the same manner, 24 of
them lie between 9 and 10 mm., 37 between 10 and 11 mm., 27 between
11 and 12 mm., and 7 above 12 mm.   The ogive distribution with
which we started has thus been transformed into a noncumulative
distribution of the normal form.

The greatest difficulty in this procedure, an error that is sometimes
fatal to its use, is the 'tail assumptions' that have to be made.
We find that one of the limens falls below 8 mm.; but just how far
below?   Since there is only 1 case in 100, we are fairly safe in
assuming that this case falls between 7 and 8 mm.   But there are
seven of the cases above 12 mm.   Shall we assume that all these
cases lie between 12 and 13 mm.?   This is very unlikely, but we are
compelled by Spearman's method to do so unless we resort to common sense.[1]   In the latter case, since we already know that the
distribution is symmetrical about the median and that the intervals
8 to 8.9 and 12 to 12.9 are approximately equidistant from the
median as found by linear interpolation (10.57), they should contain
about the same numerical frequencies.   Some of the seven cases
undoubtedly lie above 13, and had 13 mm. been employed in the
stimulus series some of the seven cases would have been divided
with the interval 13 to 13.9.   As a guess, we might divide the seven
unevenly, giving five to the interval 12 to 12.9 and two to the
interval 13 to 13.9.   The distribution would then read as in Table 23.

The results compare very favorably indeed with those from the
interpolation method.   This would not always be the case.   We
fortunately chose tail assumptions that were near the truth.   Had

---

[1] According to Thomson (41, p. 75) the simplest tail assumption, that the class
interval just beyond the terminal stimulus value at either end of the series
contains all the remaining frequencies, may be made when certain conditions
are satisfied.   First, the proportion of .50 must lie in the region of the middle
stimulus.   With five stimuli that have been judged 100 times each, the smallest
p should be not less than .06 and the greatest *p* not larger than .94.   With seven
stimuli when *n* is 100, the range should be from .04 to .96.   When *n* is greater
than 100, the terminal *p*'s should be nearer 0 and 1.00.   Thomson describes
other ways of estimating tail frequencies (41) when the simplest tail assumption
cannot be made, but these are too detailed to be included here.

we assumed that all seven of the highest limens fell between 12 and 12.9 mm., the *PE* would have been .69 instead of .72, whereas from the interpolation method it is estimated at .75. Probably it is never wise to depend too much upon the sigma of the distribution obtained with this procedure unless the proportions cover the range from 0 to 1.00, or very nearly so. The measure of scatter

TABLE 23.—SOLUTION OF THE TWO-POINT LIMEN BY SPEARMAN'S METHOD OF THE ARITHMETIC MEAN

R-value	f	x'	fx'	fx'^2
7– 7.9	1	−3	− 3	9
8– 8.9	4	−2	− 8	16
9– 9.9	24	−1	−24	24
10–10.9	37	0	0	0
11–11.9	27	1	27	27
12–12.9	5	2	10	20
13–13.9	2	3	6	18

$$\Sigma = 100 \qquad\qquad 8 \qquad 114$$
$$\text{Mean} = 10.58 \quad \sigma = 1.07 \quad PE = .72 \quad PE_M = .072$$

will otherwise always be too small, unless the proper tail assumptions can be made. It is useless, if not misleading, to apply Sheppard's correction (see page 45), since this would make still smaller a sigma that is probably already too small. If only a mean of the limens is wanted, the error of the tails is not nearly so important. But even if only a limen is wanted and if there is much uncertainty about the tails, an interpolated median is probably a better value to determine, since a median is relatively unaffected by the extreme measurements in a distribution.

3. The Median of the Best-fitting Ogive Curve.—In still another process, we assume that the best measure of the limen is the median of a theoretical normal ogive which comes nearest to the points of our observed distribution. The procedure has been devised by G. E. Müller and by Urban; it has sometimes been called the 'Müller-Urban method,' sometimes the 'Urban process,' or again the *constant process*.[1] The assumption is that, if the experiments

---

[1] Brown and Thomson (9) make the pertinent suggestion that we let the term 'constant method' apply only to the procedure of securing the data and that we let 'constant process' apply to one of the methods (Urban's) of computing a limen.

had been repeated indefinitely under ideal conditions, the proportions when plotted against the *R* values would have given a perfectly smooth ogive.

By a process of curve fitting we can predict that ideal curve from our data and use its median as the limen we seek.   The reader may recall from Chapter III the process of fitting data to the normal

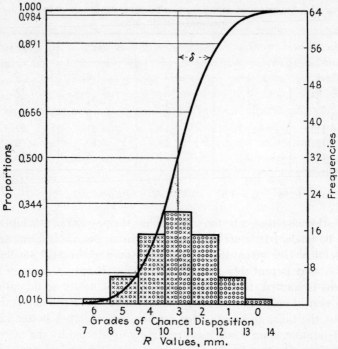

Fig. 19.—Boring's chart of the psychometric function for the two-point limen.

curve and the fact that a computed mean and a sigma for any set of data describe the theoretical best-fitting normal curve. Other curves than the normal ogive might be chosen to which to fit the data. We know that the proportions *p* increase as *R* increases, and that, roughly, the increase is slow at first (with positive acceleration), becoming more rapid as the median is approached and then slower as $p = 1.00$ is approached (negative acceleration). It is quite natural, however, to regard our observed proportions as probabilities and to treat them as such. The reasoning of the coin-tossing experiment that was discussed in Chapter III can be very easily applied to the present method. Let us follow Boring's (3) argument in this.

Theory of Probability Applied to the Limen.—Let us assume that the stimulated organs, including the brain with its momentary states of equilibrium, are variously disposed toward a given impression. These dispositions are dependent upon a great many different factors ('coins'), each one of which can be favorable or unfavorable for a judgment of a given category ('two'). These dispositions, being independent, are favorable and unfavorable in chance combinations. For a weaker, or smaller, stimulus more of them must be favorable than for a stronger, or larger, stimulus. To simplify matters, let us assume six such factors operative in the two-point limen experiment. All six factors must be favorable simultaneously in order that a separation of 8 mm., let us say, can arouse a report of 'two.' At least five must be favorable for a report of 'two' at a separation of 9 mm.; at least four at 10 mm., and so on, as Fig. 19 shows. Assuming 64 trials with each stimulus, the theoretical probability of a 'two' at 8 mm. is $\frac{1}{64}$; at 9 mm., $\frac{1}{64}$ plus $\frac{6}{64}$, and so on. In terms of proportions, these probabilities are .016, .109, .344, .656, .891, and .984, respectively (see Fig. 19).

A New Formula for the Cumulative Normal Curve.—While the mathematical formula for the cumulative curve can be derived from that for the normal distribution curve (see page 84), in connection with the constant process, an important change is made. The formula becomes

$$p = \int_{-\infty}^{\delta} \frac{h}{\sqrt{\pi}} e^{-h^2\delta^2} dR \qquad (73)$$

where p = the proportion of judgments of a certain category.

δ = the deviation of a stimulus from the limen, or $(R - L)$.

h = the 'measure of precision' of the curve.

The other symbols have the same meaning as before. Compare this formula with formula (53) on page 100. The new symbol δ replaces the former x. δ is the distance of any stimulus from the limen, or it is equal to $(R - L)$, just as x represented the distance of a measurement from the mean or was equal to $(X - M)$. The only really new component of formula (73) is the symbol h, which takes the place of the more familiar σ. h measures the precision or steepness of a distribution whereas σ measures its spread or scatter. The two are inversely related by the formula

$$h^2 = \frac{1}{2\sigma^2} \tag{74}$$

The larger the value of h, the more steeply does the ogive curve rise. In other words, h is related to the slope of the cumulative curve. The relationships of h and δ to the ogive curve are given graphically in Fig. 20. Three ogives having the same median but different slopes are shown.

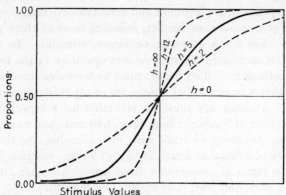

FIG. 20.—The phi-gamma function for varying values of h.

The Phi-gamma Function and the Phi-gamma Hypothesis.— In finding the best-fitting cumulative curve for any set of data, it is convenient to use tables of the normal probability integral. Whereas in fitting data to the noncumulative normal curve we had to express our abscissa values in terms of σ or $(X - M)/\sigma$, here we have to express them in terms of h. Since h and σ are inversely related, it is only natural that we shall want the data expressed in terms of $h\delta$, which means $h(R - L)$. This expression has been called gamma (γ). Gamma, then, is the distance of any stimulus from the limen, given in terms of h. The formula for the cumulative curve given in terms of γ is

$$p = \int_{-\infty}^{\gamma} \frac{1}{\sqrt{\pi}} e^{-\gamma^2} d\gamma \tag{75}$$

This has been called the *phi-gamma* or *$\phi(\gamma)$ function*, or the *phi function of gamma*. The assumption that psychophysical data as obtained in the constant methods fit the phi-gamma function is the so-called **phi-gamma hypothesis**.

Applying the Method of Least Squares.—In fitting data to the normal curve we can construct the whole curve merely from knowing the mean and the standard deviation. In the present problem, we know neither the mean nor sigma, neither the limen nor its precision, neither L nor h. All we have is a series of R values and their corresponding proportions. We proceed by using the proportions as a means of finding the γ's in the prepared tables, which give for every value of p the corresponding value of γ. Knowing that $\gamma = h\delta$, and knowing each δ from the fact that $\delta = (R - L)$, we can find as many solutions for h as there are stimuli. Not all these values of h will agree with one another. The best value of h will be some kind of an average. We proceed by the *method of least squares* (see page 297) to find that value of h which will give the best-fitting curve. The best-fitting curve according to the method of least squares is that one of such a median and slope that *the sum of the squares of the deviations from the experimentally observed points will be a minimum.*

Weighting the Observations.—While, as was just said, we can find a value for h from every pair of values, not every observed value of p is given an equal weight in deciding the best value of h. Some proportions are given more advantage than others in fixing that important constant. Müller argued that the proportions near .50 should be weighted more than the proportions deviating in either direction from .50. Each p is used to find a corresponding theoretical γ from the probability tables. There are undoubtedly some errors in the observed proportions, some being too large and others being too small. These errors will be reflected in the corresponding gammas that we find in the table. But an error in p near .50, where p is changing at its maximum rate, as compared with the change in R (or γ), is not nearly so serious as at the extremes where a slight error in p is reflected in a large error in γ. Müller's weights therefore were intended to equalize the effect of the various proportions upon the determinations of the various corresponding gammas. Müller's weights have a maximum value of 1.000 for $p = .50$ and a minimum of 0.004 at $p = .01$ or .99 (43, I, p. 101).

Urban has pointed out that a further weighting of the observed values should be made. It is a principle of the method of least squares, and common sense will agree that, in finding an average value from a number of observations, the more reliable observations should have greater importance than the less reliable ones. The reliability of an observation is inversely proportional to the square of its standard error. The sigma of any observed proportion, σ_p, is equal to $\sqrt{pq/N}$, in which $q = 1 - p$ and N is the total number of cases. Leaving out of account N, which is constant for any set of data in the method of constant stimuli, σ_p is proportional to $\sqrt{pq}$. The reliability of p, being inversely proportional to the square of σ_p, is therefore given by $1/pq$, and this is essentially the Urban weight. Urban's weights vary from 4.00 at $p = .50$ to 101 at $p = .01$ (or $p = .99$) (9, p. 67; 10, p. 80). In practice a combined Müller-Urban weight is employed, the combined weight being a product of the two. These weights have been conveniently worked out for us by Urban and they can be seen in the W column of Table G (see the Appendix). It will be noted that they still have a maximum of 1.00 at $p = .50$ and a minimum at $p = .01$ (or .99).

The Least Square Solution for L and h.—The method of solving for L and h by Urban's constant process has been reduced to a routine so that little comprehension of the least square technique is required to carry it out. We shall follow the routine proposed by Boring (2). Using the data from the two-point limen experiment already employed above, a convenient table (Table 24) is prepared. Column 1 of the table contains the R values. Column 2 which is labeled 'x' contains temporary R values that have the convenience of being very small numerically. This device is not new to the student. It involves the selection of a guessed average near the center of the range of R values and of a new unit, the class interval. The convenience of using a class interval is a very good reason for having chosen the stimuli at equidistant intervals. Column 3 contains the proportions. Column 4, labeled 'W,' contains the weights that are to be found in Urban's table (Table G).

It will be noticed that Urban's table gives no proportions below .50. Since the weights above and below $p = .50$ are perfectly symmetrical, this is unnecessary. For any p less than .50, find $1.00 - p$ and look for that value in the table. For $p = .29$, for example, the corresponding $1.00 - p$ is .71, and the W for this is .8939.[1]

---

[1] Culler has argued (10, p. 80) that there are some slight inaccuracies in the Müller weights since they are merely approximations and that we lose little in accuracy by dropping the last two decimal places. When as many as 100 judgments have been obtained for every stimulus, however, and when machine calculation is possible, the four decimal places may well be used.

TABLE 24.—COMPUTATION OF THE TWO-POINT LIMEN BY URBAN'S CONSTANT PROCESS

(1)	(2)	(3)	(4)	(5)	(6)	(7)	(8)	(9)	(10)
R	x	p	W	γW	xW	x^2W	$x\gamma W$	γ	Rich's check
8	-2	.01	.1127	$-.1854$	$-.2254$	.4508	.3708	$-$	.5235
9	-1	.05	.3519	$-.4093$	$-.3519$	.3519	.4093	$-$	.3519
10	0	.29	.8939	$-.3498$	.0000	.0000	.0000	$-$	.5441
11	$+1$	.66	.9398	.2741	.9398	.9398	.2741	$+$	3.3676
12	$+2$	.93	.4351	.4540	.8702	1.7403	.9080	$+$	4.4076
		Σ	2.7334	$-.2164$	1.2327	3.4828	1.9622		9.1947

$$h' = \frac{\overset{\Sigma W}{(2.7334)}\overset{\Sigma(x\gamma W)}{(1.9622)} - \overset{\Sigma(\gamma W)}{(-.2164)}\overset{\Sigma(xW)}{(1.2327)}}{\underset{\Sigma W}{(2.7334)}\underset{\Sigma(x^2W)}{(3.4828)} - \underset{\Sigma(xW)}{(1.2327)}\underset{\Sigma(xW)}{(1.2327)}}$$

$$= \frac{5.36348 + .26676}{9.51989 - 1.51955} = \frac{5.63024}{8.00034} = \underset{h'}{.7038}$$

$$L' = \frac{\overset{\Sigma(xW)}{(1.2327)}\overset{h'}{(.7038)} - \overset{\Sigma(\gamma W)}{(-.2164)}}{\underset{\Sigma W}{(2.7334)}\underset{h'}{(.7038)}} = \frac{.86757 + .2164}{1.92377}$$

$$= \frac{1.08397}{1.92377} = \underset{L'}{.563}$$

$$h = \frac{h'}{i} = \frac{.704}{1} = \underset{h}{.704}$$

$$L = R_0 + iL' = 10 + (1)(.56) = \overset{L}{10.56}$$

$$PE = \underset{h}{\frac{.4769}{(.704)}} = .68 \qquad PE_L = \underset{h\ \sqrt{n}}{\frac{.5978}{(.704)(10)}} = .085$$

CHECK: $(3.4828)(.7038) - (1.2327)(.8037)(.563) = 1.9628$
$\qquad \underset{\Sigma(x^2W)}{} \underset{h'}{} \qquad \underset{\Sigma(xW)}{} \underset{h'}{} \underset{L'}{} \qquad \underset{\Sigma(x\gamma W)}{}$

Column 5 contains the products of γW, also to be found in Urban's table. The xW's in column 6 can also be found there, likewise the x^2W's of column 7 and $x\gamma W$'s of column 8. Column 9, headed with γ, merely contains the signs, $+$ or $-$, of gamma. Gamma is given with a minus sign whenever p is less than .50 and with a positive sign when p is greater than .50.   This is because

$$\gamma = h\delta = h(R - L).$$

Whenever p is less than .50, R is less than L and δ is a negative quantity; h being positive, γ must necessarily be negative.   After all values are obtained from Urban's table, the signs of all the values in the data sheet should be checked.   The algebraic signs of the W's are always positive.   The resulting signs in the other columns will therefore depend entirely upon the signs of x and γ.

The next steps are to find the sums of columns 4 through 8 and to record them at the bottom of the table.   It is always desirable to check the work done so far.   Errors may have been made in using Urban's tables.   Signs may have been reversed by mistake. We are aided in the checking process by a convenient table prepared by Rich (35).   For every combination of p and x that we are likely to meet in practice Rich has computed the sum of the five values in each row of our table: $W + \gamma W + xW + x^2W + x\gamma W$.   Entering Rich's table (Table H) with each combination of p and x, we find the corresponding sums and write them in column 10 of our work table.   If there are no errors in our work, the sum of this column should equal the sum of the last row of the table.

We now have, in the five sums, the values from which to compute h and L.   We need only apply formulas already given us.

$$h' = \frac{\Sigma W \times \Sigma(x\gamma W) - \Sigma(\gamma W) \times \Sigma(xW)}{\Sigma W \times \Sigma(x^2W) - \Sigma(xW) \times \Sigma(xW)} \tag{76}$$

The expression h' is used instead of h since we are still using the working unit of the table, the class interval.   To find h,

$$h = \frac{h'}{i} \tag{77}$$

The limen is readily found, as follows:

$$L' = \frac{\Sigma(xW) \times h' - \Sigma(\gamma W)}{\Sigma W \times h'} \tag{78}$$

and

$$L = R_0 + L'(i) \tag{79}$$

R_0 being the R value for $x = 0$.

The Probable Error of the Limen.—Since h and σ are related by the formula $h^2 = 1/2\sigma^2$, it is now possible to find the standard error of the distribution. It will be of interest to compare this value, and also the PE, with those measures of dispersion already computed by the interpolation method and by Spearman's method. The above equation reduces to

$$\sigma = \frac{1}{h\sqrt{2}} \qquad (80)$$

and

$$PE = \frac{.6745}{h\sqrt{2}} = \frac{.4769}{h} \qquad (81)$$

This method gives a PE equal to .68 as compared with one of .75 for the linear interpolation method and one of .72 for Spearman's method. Assuming that the constant process gives the best estimation of this value, we can conclude that Spearman's method gave a better estimate of the PE in this case than did the interpolation method. Had we made a less reasonable tail assumption, that the seven highest limens lay between 12 and 12.9, a PE of .69 would have been obtained.

What is the probable error of the constant process limen? A number of suggestions have been made for computing this value but objections have been raised to most of them. We shall adopt a PE_L suggested by Culler (10, p. 85). According to Culler the PE_L is the probable error of a median. The PE_{Mdn} is generally given by formula (20):

$$PE_{Mdn} = \frac{.84535\sigma}{\sqrt{N}}.$$

Substituting h for σ, we have

$$PE_L = \frac{.84535}{h\sqrt{2n}} = \frac{.5978}{h\sqrt{n}} \qquad (82a)$$

in which n is the number of times each R was applied.[1]

---

[1] According to Culler (12) this formula is a close estimate of the probable error of the limen only when the number of stimuli is less than five. With more than five stimuli, the PE_L is underestimated; it can be estimated more accurately

The PE_L in our illustrative problem is .085. This is acceptably small, but it is slightly larger than the PE_M found by Spearman's method, namely .072. This is mainly because a mean is typically more reliable than a median of the same distribution. It is to be remembered that Culler's PE_L is based upon the h of the best-fitting theoretical curve and is valid only when the fit is acceptable.

Plotting the Best-fitting Curve.—It is often of interest and of significance to find the theoretical proportions of the best-fitting curve and to show graphically or otherwise how well the curve actually fits the data. The procedure here is very similar to that already used in fitting the normal noncumulative curve. The essential difference is the use of h and δ in place of σ and x. The work should be systematically arranged as in Table 25. The sources of the values in columns 2 and 3 are obvious. The values for p' are found from Hoisington's table (Table I). An additional p' for $R = 13$ was found for the sake of extending the theoretical curve. One can find as many additional points as are needed in order to draw a more complete ogive.

Pearson's method of testing the goodness of fit is much the same as that employed with the normal curve (page 92). One difference will be noted in column 9 where the squares of the discrepancies are divided by $p'q'$, whereas in the case of the noncumulative curve we divide the squares of the discrepancies by Y'. To facilitate the calculation of the values in column 9 we use the reciprocals of $p'q'$ which are given in Table J. These are recorded in column 8. The values in column 9 are the products of the corresponding quantities in columns 7 and 8. In the computation of chi square, k is equal to the number of times each stimulus is applied. By the use of Table D, when χ^2 is .77 and n is 5, we find that P equals approximately .98. There are only 2 chances in 100 of a better fit.

It is unfortunate that proportions near 0 or 1.00 carry as much weight $(1/p'q')$ as they do. This fact sometimes leads to absurd

---

by altering the formula as follows:

$$PE_{Mdn} = \frac{.84535}{h\sqrt{2\Sigma nWp}} \tag{82b}$$

where W = the Urban weight.

   n = the number of judgments of a certain category given to a particular stimulus.

   p = the corresponding proportion.

results. For example, consider two *O*s who have completed the same experiment with the same set of stimuli. The less sensitive *O* will have a wider dispersion of judgments, with the result that he gives few proportions above .75 or below .25. The more sensitive *O* has a higher *h*, a steeper curve with proportions approaching 0 on the one hand and 1.00 on the other. The more sensitive *O*'s discrepancies between *p* and *p'* may be numerically smaller than

TABLE 25.—TEST OF GOODNESS OF FIT TO THE PHI-GAMMA FUNCTION

(1)	(2)	(3)	(4)	(5)	(6)	(7)	(8)	(9)
R	δ' $(R-L)$	γ' $(h\delta')$	p'	p	$(p-p')$	$(p-p')^2$	$\dfrac{1}{p'q'}$	$\dfrac{(p-p')^2}{p'q'}$
8	-2.56	-1.802	.005	.01	$+.005$	.000025	201.0	.0050
9	-1.56	-1.098	.060	.05	$-.010$	.000100	17.7	.0018
10	$-.56$	$-.394$	.289	.29	$+.001$	.000001	4.9	.0000
11	.44	.310	.670	.66	$-.010$	.000100	4.5	.0004
12	1.44	1.013	.924	.93	$+.006$	.000036	14.3	.0005
13	2.44	1.718	.992					

$$\Sigma = .0077$$

$$x^2 = k\Sigma\left[\frac{(p-p')^2}{p'q'}\right] = (100)(.0077) = .77 \qquad P = .98$$

those for the less sensitive *O*, and yet, because of the greater weights for very large and very small proportions, Pearson's *P* is much higher for the poor *O* than it is for the good *O*. The Pearson *P* for two *O*s, indeed for the same *O* at different times, should never be compared unless the ranges of proportions are approximately the same. Because of this and other limitations of the Pearson *P*, it is often more significant to plot the two curves for *p* and *p'* together and to inspect the discrepancies in graphic form. This has been done in Fig. 21.

4. **The Normal Interpolation Process.**—The normal interpolation process is a recent suggestion of Newhall (32). It is undoubtedly an improvement over the usual linear process. The essence of the method is to translate the proportions into deviations from the mean in terms of the standard deviation of the distribution. These values, which are in reality standard measures $(R - L)/\sigma$, are assumed to have a linear relationship with *R*. Objection (*b*) against the linear interpolation method is practically removed.

The first step in this process is to enter Table E with each one of the proportions—or rather the deviation of *p* from .50—and to find the corresponding values of x/σ, which we shall call S. For proportions less than .50 these will of course have a negative sign.

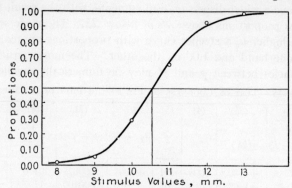

FIG. 21.—The best-fitting phi-gamma function for the two-point limen data.

For the five proportions of our illustrative problem the sigma values are given in Table 26.

TABLE 26.—COMPUTATION BY THE NORMAL INTERPOLATION PROCESS

R	8	9	10	11	12
p	.01	.05	.29	.66	.93
S	−2.326	−1.645	−.553	.413	1.476

The next step is to find that R value which corresponds to $S = 0$. This lies between R_{10} and R_{11} and is to be found by the general formula

$$L = R_l + \frac{-S_l}{(S_u - S_l)}(R_u - R_l) \tag{83}$$

where R_l = the R value next lower than L.

R_u = the R value next higher than L.

S_l and S_u = the corresponding S values.

For this particular problem,

$$L = 10 + \frac{.553}{.966}(11 - 10) = 10.57.$$

The value of σ can also be found by interpolation. Find the R value that corresponds to $S = +1\sigma$ and also the one that corresponds to -1σ. The former, as interpolated between R_{11} and R_{12}, is 11.55;

the latter is 9.59. The distance of either from *L* is exactly .98, which may be taken as *σ*. The *PE* is .66. These are smaller values than have been estimated for *σ* and *PE* by any of the other processes. They are open to an objection which applies to the other interpolation method, namely, that each value is obtained from only two points in the total distribution. An examination of Fig. 22 will show how serious this limitation may be. In this figure the *S* values have been plotted against the corresponding *R* values as obtained from

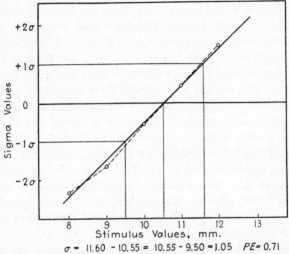

$$\sigma = 11.60 - 10.55 = 10.55 - 9.50 = 1.05 \quad PE = 0.71$$

Fig. 22.—The normal graphic solution of the two-point limen from constant data.

Table 26. Although the points so plotted do form a linear relationship, and although a straight line can be drawn through the points by inspection, certain points deviate from that best-fitting line and may throw the interpolated values to one side of the best or most probable positions.

5. The Normal Graphic Solution.—Newhall's process might very well be carried a step further in order to avoid the criticism just offered. The limen and the sigma distances from the limen may be solved in such a way as to let all the points determine every one of the three values, *L*, +1*σ*, and −1*σ*. Since the plotted points in Fig. 22 theoretically and actually approach a straight line, we can draw a best-fitting line through those points by inspection. A very good device for this is to stretch a black thread across the line of plotted points and to adjust it so that its height and its slope come as near as possible to all the points. The points nearest the limen should be given more consideration than those at the extremes of the range, in accordance with the principles of the Müller-Urban weights. Once the line is carefully drawn, one can read off the three desired values and compute L (still considered as a median); from the value for σ, PE can be calculated. By inspection L and σ are 10.5 and 1.05, respectively, and the PE is accordingly .71. Here our constants depend not merely upon two neighboring points, but upon the distribution as a whole, as they do in the Urban process.

6. Kelley's Least Square Process.—The discussion naturally brings us to a sixth procedure, that of Kelley. This process differs from Urban's only in the fact that the data are fitted to the best-fitting normal ogive by using σ instead of h (23, p. 326). The method (and Urban's as well) is made clearer by a study of Fig. 22. The procedure is carried out in much the same manner as that proposed earlier for Urban's process. Using the observed proportions, one finds the corresponding S values (which correspond to Urban's γ's) from Table E; the S values are weighted with the Müller-Urban weights or their equivalent. Finally, the best-fitting line is found by the method of least squares. Kelley's procedure is applicable whenever Urban's process is applicable, but it has the disadvantage that no complete tables such as Urban's and Rich's have ever been prepared for its use.

Summary of the Results.—Table 27 summarizes in one place the limens and their measures of reliability as obtained by the various processes that have been described. It will be noted that all methods give almost exactly the same estimation of the limen and very similar measures of dispersion. This is because the distribution of the data is so very close to normal. The probable errors of the

TABLE 27.—SUMMARY OF THE TWO-POINT LIMENS AND THEIR PROBABLE ERRORS

Method	L	h	PE	PE_M	PE_{Mdn}
Linear interpolation	10.58	....	.75	....	.09*
Arithmetic mean	10.58	....	.72	.072	....
Constant process	10.565	.704	.68	....	.085
Normal interpolation	10.57	....	.66	....	.08*
Normal graphic	10.55	....	.68	....	.08*

* These values are to be regarded only as rough estimates.

limens, however, vary from .072 to .09, which gives some notion of the relative reliabilities of the different limens, although only the Spearman limen differs significantly from the others in reliability.

Choice of the Processes in Practice.—There are six different procedures for treating data from the constant method. Which one shall be used? A few suggestions can be made, but the research worker will always have to exercise his own good judgment.

1. The linear interpolation method is most appropriately used when:
   a. Only two stimuli near the limen have been employed.
   b. The distribution is so lacking in normality that it does not fit an ogive curve.
   c. Only a threshold measurement is wanted and its PE is immaterial or need only be approximated.
   d. Four stimuli have been used and the 25 per cent and 75 per cent points can be interpolated as well as the 50 per cent point.
   It should not be used when:
   a. Five or more stimuli have been employed.
   b. An accurate L and PE_L are wanted.
   c. Stimuli do not give proportions on both sides of .50.
   d. There are inversions of the first order in the data, at least in the vicinity of the limen.
2. Spearman's process for the mean threshold may be used:
   a. When proportions extending very near to 0 and 1.00 are obtained.
   b. When, in narrower ranges, reasonable tail assumptions can be made.
   c. When the number of stimuli is relatively large; never with less than five stimuli.
   d. Assuming (a) to be true, when a very accurate limen is wanted. The PE of a mean is usually smaller than the PE of a median.
   e. When there are no inversions of the first order in the data. Such inversions would lead to negative frequencies.
3. Urban's constant process may be used:
   a. When four or more stimuli are employed.
   b. When Spearman's shorter method cannot be used.
   c. When the data give a reasonable promise of fitting a theoretical ogive. This will be true in about 90 per cent of the cases with the usual Os; the more practiced the O, the better the data will fit the curve, according to Culler (11, p. 289).
   d. When the most accurate measure of dispersion, either h or σ, is wanted.
   e. Only when enough observations have been made to justify the time and energy demanded; relatively few collections of data qualify.
   f. Only when distributions are relatively symmetrical about the limen.
4. Newhall's normal interpolation will apply:
   a. Whenever the linear interpolation method applies, and with greater accuracy.

    b. In some cases where linear interpolation does not apply:
        (1) When both of two stimuli are on one side of the limen, an extrapolation may be performed.
        (2) When five or more stimuli have been employed and when the writer's variation of the method (graphic solution), as shown in Fig. 22, is introduced.
  5. The normal graphic method may be used:
    a. When there is insufficient time to compute either an Urban limen or a limen by Kelley's process.
    b. When greater accuracy is required than that provided by the two interpolation methods.
    c. Only when a straight line can be easily adjusted to the plotted points, *i.e.*, when the fit of the points to a line is very close.
  6. Kelley's process has the same virtues and limitations as Urban's; they need not be repeated here.

If the amount of time spent in computation of a limen is to determine our choice, the methods ordinarily come in the following order, the one requiring the least time being placed first: linear interpolation, normal interpolation, normal graphic, arithmetic mean, Urban's phi-process, and, lastly, Kelley's normal process. The distinction between the last two is based upon the fact that we have Urban's and Rich's tables to assist us in the former and not in the latter. From the point of view of accuracy the methods may be placed in the following order, the most accurate being mentioned first: Urban's and Kelley's processes; arithmetic mean or normal graphic, depending upon the 'tails' and the goodness of fit; normal interpolation; and, last of all, the linear interpolation method. From the standpoint of reliability of the limen, as measured by its *PE*, Spearman's mean is undoubtedly best, since the *PE* of a mean is usually smaller than the *PE* of a median.

EXPERIMENT VIII. THE *DL* FOR LIFTED WEIGHTS

Problem.—To find the differential limen for lifted weights by the method of constant stimulus differences.

Materials.—Set of seven weights, 185, 190, 195, 200, 205, 210, and 215 gr., 200 gr. being the standard; rotating table with a soft felt surface; metronome.

Procedure:

1. The seven weights are placed at equal intervals around the edge of the rotating table, which can be turned quickly and noiselessly from one position to another. The table and the weights are shielded from *O*'s vision, or *O* is blindfolded.

2. *O* sits with his lifting arm on an arm rest so that his hand hangs freely in a position to grasp with a simple wrist movement any weight that is brought within reach.

3. The metronome is set to beat seconds with the bell sounding every fourth second. *O* is given preliminary practice in lifting the weights as timed by the metronome. *O* lifts one weight at the sound of the bell, sets it down at the second stroke, removes his hand, and waits for the bell again, at which moment he lifts the second weight for 1 sec. A pause of 8 sec. is given between pairs, during which time *O* makes his judgment. He is to make a judgment of 'greater,' 'less,' or 'doubtful,' but he is to avoid saying 'doubtful' unless it is necessary.

4. In order to cancel out the constant time error, in half the observations the standard is given first and in half it is given second, the variable being given first. *E* should keep his records accordingly. *O* is *always* to judge the second of a pair in terms of the first and is never to know whether standard or variable comes first.

5. *E* should plan a prearranged order for the pairs of stimuli, so that every variable follows every other one an equal number of times. This is to counterbalance any intraserial effects. Each pair of weights should be judged 100 times, 700 judgments in all.

6. *E* should frequently ask *O* for descriptions of the criteria used in judging the weights. All investigators who have given the question of *O*'s attitude much consideration agree that the 'stimulus attitude' is superior to all others. This is a form of the oft-dreaded stimulus error but results show that it is the most natural and the most dependable of all the attitudes that can be assumed. Dependence upon specific sensory criteria may be acquired with practice, but this is difficult for the naive observer. Even practiced *O*s fail to stick to any one sensory criterion such as pressure in the fingertips, strain in the forearm, or sensory masses in the wrist. It is better, then, for *O* simply to make the direct judgment: "This weight is heavier (or is lighter) than the one just preceding."

Results.—These are compiled showing for every variable stimulus the proportions of judgments '*g*,' '*d*,' or '*l*,' as in Table 28.

TABLE 28.—DATA FROM LIFTED WEIGHTS

R	'greater'	'doubtful'	'less'
185	.05	.04	.91
190	.12	.18	.70
195	.15	.25	.60
200	.30	.42	.28
205	.55	.35	.10
210	.70	.18	.12
215	.85	.09	.06

COMPUTATION OF THE *DL*

It is to be regretted that there is still no general agreement as to the best method of computing a *DL* from data obtained with the method of constant stimulus differences. It should be recalled that the *DL* is statistically defined as that stimulus difference which can be observed correctly 50 per cent of the time. As in the method of minimal changes, we can find a DL for an incremento the standard, which we shall call DL_g, and also a DL for a decretment from the standard, to be called DL_l. The former we can find from the judgments 'greater' and the latter from the judgments 'less.' There are several methods for doing this, including the methods already described for finding an absolute limen with constant stimuli.

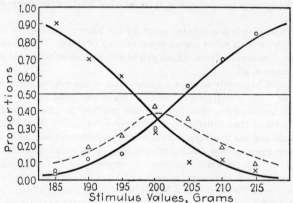

Fig. 23.—Distributions of the judgments from the lifted-weight data.

Figure 23 shows graphically the three distributions represented in Table 28. It is clear that the judgments 'greater' give an ogive with a positive slope and that the judgments 'less' give a similar curve with a negative slope. The judgments 'doubtful' give something approaching a normal distribution, as might be expected, but this condition is seldom very clearly realized. The various constants that may be computed will be found in Table 32: the upper limen L_g and lower limen L_l and their PE's; the upper and lower DL's, DL_g and DL_l and their PE's; the mean DL and its PE; the point of subjective equality PSE; and the new constant IU, or the **interval of uncertainty**. The last is the distance $L_g - L_l$, or $2DL$, and it is sometimes used as an inverse measure of sensitivity. The other constants have approximately the same meanings as in the method of minimal changes.

1. Linear Interpolation.—The student needs no additional instruction in how to use the linear interpolation method here, except as to the computation of the PSE. The assumption is made that this value is the median of the distribution of 'doubtful' judgments. For this reason it is a very capricious value and it rarely coincides with the *PSE* as determined in other ways. Since the *IU* is equal to 2*DL*, it is very easily calculated by this process. The same objections and limitations voiced previously for this method also apply here.

2. Arithmetic Mean.—This is carried out just as before and with the same precautions about tail assumptions. Under some circumstances the *PE*'s of the distributions are not at all accurate. The *PSE*, to be consistent, is the arithmetic mean of the 'doubtful' judgments.

3. Urban's Constant Process.—This is the most commonly used procedure with lifted-weight experiments and others in which a very large number of judgments have been made. Since the student sometimes experiences difficulties in fitting data to the *descending* ogive which we have for the judgments 'less,' an illustrative problem is worked out here using the data found in Table 29. The only thing that is really new in this case is a different arrangement of the algebraic signs. Notice that, when x is negative, γ is usually positive. The value for h', and so for h, will be negative, and it should be so treated throughout, *with one exception—i.e.*, in determining the *PSE*.

The Meaning and Use of Xi.—Urban has defined the point of subjective equality as that stimulus value at which the probability of a judgment 'greater' is equal to that of a judgment 'less.' In Fig. 23 this point is at the crossing of the two ogives. This particular *PSE* has been given the name of *xi* (or ξ) to distinguish it from all others. It is probably the most accurate of the *PSE*'s that we might find. A *PSE* that is based upon the 'doubtful' judgments is always open to question, since we do not know just what the 'doubtful' judgments mean. Even when the category 'equal' is substituted for 'doubtful,' standards of equality are continually shifting and many, if not the majority, of equality judgments are really doubtful. It is often important to find the value of xi for it reveals the presence of constant errors. The time error is usually canceled out by the reversal of the order of the pairs of stimuli, but, if the two time orders are kept separate and two sets of limens computed, its extent can be determined. Xi is found by the formula

$$\xi = \frac{h_g L_g + h_l L_l}{h_g + h_l} \tag{84}$$

When h_g approximately equals h_l, the formula reduces to

$$\xi = \frac{L_g + L_l}{2} \tag{85}$$

TABLE 29.—THE CONSTANT PROCESS FOR THE JUDGMENTS 'LESS' FROM THE LIFTED-WEIGHT EXPERIMENTS

R	x	p	W	γW	xW	x^2W	$x\gamma W$	γ	Rich's check
185	−3	.91	.5059	+.4796	−1.5177	4.5531	−1.4388	+	2.5821
190	−2	.70	.9043	+.3353	−1.8085	3.6170	−.6706	+	2.3775
195	−1	.60	.9768	+.1750	−.9768	.9768	−.1750	+	.9768
200	0	.28	.8830	−.3639	.0000	.0000	.0000	−	.5191
205	+1	.10	.5376	−.4871	+.5376	.5376	−.4871	−	.6386
210	+2	.12	.5953	−.4946	+1.1907	2.3813	−.9892	−	2.6835
215	+3	.06	.3954	−.4346	+1.1861	3.5582	−1.3039	−	3.4012
		Σ	4.7983	−.7903	−1.3886	15.6240	−5.0646		13.1788

$$h' = \frac{\overset{\Sigma W}{(4.7983)}\overset{\Sigma(x\gamma W)}{(-5.0646)} - \overset{\Sigma(\gamma W)}{(-.7903)}\overset{\Sigma(xW)}{(-1.3886)}}{\underset{\Sigma W}{(4.7983)}\underset{\Sigma(x^2W)}{(15.6240)} - \underset{\Sigma(xW)}{(-1.3886)}\underset{\Sigma(xW)}{(-1.3886)}}$$

$$= \frac{-24.30147 - 1.09741}{74.96864 - 1.92821} = \frac{-25.39888}{73.04043} = \underset{h'}{-.34774}$$

$$L' = \frac{\overset{\Sigma(xW)}{(-1.3886)}\overset{h'}{(-.34774)} - \overset{\Sigma(\gamma W)}{(-.7903)}}{\underset{\Sigma W}{(4.7983)}\underset{h'}{(-.34774)}} = \frac{.48287 + .7903}{-1.66856}$$

$$= \frac{1.27317}{-1.66856} = \underset{L'}{-.7630}$$

$$h = \frac{-.34774}{5} = \underset{i}{-.0696}$$

$$L = R_0 + iL' = 200 + (5)(-.7630) = \overset{L}{\mathbf{196.18}}$$

$$PE = \frac{.4769}{.0696} = \mathbf{6.86} \qquad PE_L = \frac{.5977}{(.0696)(10)} = \mathbf{.86}$$

CHECK: $\underset{\Sigma(x^2W)}{(15.6240)} \; \underset{h'}{(-.34774)} - \underset{\Sigma(xW)}{(-1.3886)(-.34774)} \underset{h'}{(-.76304)} = \underset{L'}{}$

$$-5.06464$$
$$\Sigma(x\gamma W)$$

TABLE 29.—THE CONSTANT PROCESS FOR THE JUDGMENTS 'LESS' FROM THE LIFTED-WEIGHT EXPERIMENTS.—(*Continued*)

R	δ' $(R-L)$	γ' $(h\delta')$	p'	p	$p-p'$	$(p-p')^2$	$\dfrac{1}{p'q'}$	$\dfrac{(p-p')^2}{p'q'}$
185	-11.18	$+.778$	.864	.91	$+.046$	.002116	8.5	.0180
190	-6.18	$+.430$	.729	.70	$-.029$	.000841	5.1	.0043
195	-1.18	$+.082$	.546	.60	$+.054$	.002916	4.1	.0120
200	$+3.82$	$-.266$	.353	.28	$-.073$	.005329	4.4	.0234
205	$+8.82$	$-.614$	.193	.10	$-.093$	.008649	6.4	.0554
210	$+13.82$	$-.962$	.087	.12	$+.033$	.001089	12.6	.0137
215	$+18.82$	-1.310	.032	.06	$+.028$	.000784	32.2	.0252

$$\Sigma = .1520$$

$$\chi^2 = 15.20 \qquad P = .037$$

$$\xi = \frac{\overset{h_g}{(.0649)}\overset{L_g}{(204.33)} + \overset{h_l}{(.0696)}\overset{L_l}{(196.18)}}{.0649 + .0696}$$

$$= \frac{\overset{h_g}{13.261} + \overset{h_l}{13.645}}{.1345} = \frac{26.906}{.1345} = \mathbf{200.12}$$

$$DL_g = L_g - \xi = \mathbf{4.21} \qquad DL_l = \xi - L_l = \mathbf{3.93}$$

$$DL_m = \frac{L_g - L_l}{2} = \mathbf{4.07} \qquad \text{Weber ratio} = \frac{DL_m}{\xi} = \mathbf{.020}$$

$$IU = L_g - L_l = \mathbf{8.15}$$

4. Normal Interpolation and the Normal Graphic Method.— These processes have already been described and are to be followed out in the same manner here. The distance of every stimulus from L is found in terms of sigma units. In the one case the median and the values of $+1\sigma$ and -1σ are interpolated; in the other case a best-fitting line is drawn by inspection and the same values are read off the diagram. The value of xi can be observed in the graphic method, but it cannot be easily located by interpolation. The values as obtained by these methods for our illustrative problem may be seen in Table 32.

5. Culler's Phi-process.—Culler and others have severely criticized the Urban limens as being entirely too much at the mercy of O's attitude. The size of the DL is to a very great extent influenced by O's willingness or unwillingness to give 'doubtful' judgments. The more doubtful judgments O gives, the larger his IU and his DL's. This is reasonable when we consider that, the less sensitive the O, the more doubtful judgments he will give and the larger his DL will be. But this is not the whole story. Suppose that O is unwilling to give any doubtful judgments at all and guesses either 'greater' or 'less' even when he is in great doubt. With no doubtful judgments in the data, the two ogives would cross exactly on the 50 per cent level, and L_g would be equal to L_l. Notice, for example, the curves in Fig. 25. The DL reduces to zero, a truly absurd state of affairs. This is an extreme case, perhaps, but it can be seen from this example that the DL is highly dependent upon O's own attitude and upon his degree of self-confidence in his judgments. The Urban DL's therefore measure attitude as well as sensitivity.

There are various ways of avoiding this error. It is present, of course, in the linear interpolation method and in Spearman's method as well as in Urban's. Culler suggests that we take as the DL's the PE's of the ogive distributions. These may be readily obtained from h as found by Urban's process. DL_g is 7.35 and DL_l is 6.86 and the mean DL is 7.10. These values stand out in Table 32 as being decidedly higher than the other DL's. The PE's of these limens are PE's of PE and they can be found from the DL itself by the formula

$$PE_{PE} = \frac{.6745PE}{\sqrt{2n}} = \frac{.4769PE}{\sqrt{n}} = \frac{.2275}{h\sqrt{n}} \tag{86}$$

Culler points out (10, pp. 115 *ff.*) several advantages for his procedure: (1) The reliability of the limen is decidedly higher than for Urban's L, its PE being very much smaller. (2) It takes care of the 'doubtful' judgments by avoiding the error referred to above, in that (a) with a decrease in the 'doubtful' judgments h falls and the DL enlarges, "as in logic it should" (10, p. 117), and (b) with an increase in the 'doubtful' judgments, h increases and the DL grows smaller. (3) The DL and its PE are very easily computed from h. (4) The use and encouragement of doubtful judgments make for scientific caution on the part of O. The more cautious the O, the more doubtful judgments he will make, the higher will be *h*, and the smaller his *DL*, Culler argues.

But in criticism of Culler it may be said that the *DL* was designed primarily to measure sensitivity, not degree of scientific caution. The number of doubtful judgments depends upon other things besides the degree of scientific caution. It depends upon the assurance of *O* in his own judgments and in his predilection for guessing or not guessing. It is conceivable, also, that a large number of doubtful judgments are the result of laziness or of lack of attention rather than of scientific caution. Since Culler's *DL* is so dependent upon the number of doubtful judgments and since the latter are subject to so many influences other than sensitivity, the meaning of his *DL* is highly ambiguous.

Culler's and Urban's *DL*'s Inversely Related.—There is a curious inconsistency between the Culler *DL* and the Urban *DL* which leads to the conclusion that the two do not measure the same thing. Reference to Figs. 24*A* and *B* will illustrate this point. When *O*, either through high degree of sensitivity or through a negative set toward 'equal' or 'doubtful' judgments or for any of a number of reasons, fails to give many judgments in the intermediate category, Urban's *DL*'s are small and Culler's are large. As *O* gives more and more judgments in the equal or doubtful category, the Urban limens spread apart, indicating lowered sensitivity, whereas the steepness of the two ogives increases, indicating according to Culler's method increased discriminatory power or sensitivity. Surely two estimates which vary inversely, or even tend to do so, cannot be taken as equivalent measures of the same thing. The illustrations selected are perhaps overdrawn in order to prove a point. It is conceivable that there are factors which tend to make the *DL*'s of Urban and Culler correlate positively, just as there are obviously factors which tend to make them vary inversely. It is likely that the one gives results which will supplement the results obtained from the other and that a comparison of the two sets of results may help to analyze the controlling factors in the judgments of particular *O*s. For this reason both methods are described and recommended here.

Graphic Solution of Culler's *DL*.—It is hardly necessary to say that there is a graphic solution for Culler's *DL* if one wants quick approximations for the *DL*'s and their *PE*'s. This is accomplished in exactly the same way as with the normal graphic device described previously, except that we are interested more in the stimulus values at $+1PE$ and $-1PE$ than in the medians.   It may be more convenient in this case to translate the proportions into *PE* units from the mean rather than σ units as heretofore prescribed, since this yields a more direct solution.

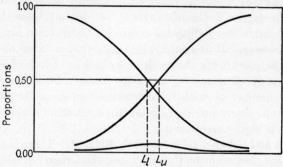

Fig. 24*A*.—Psychometric curves showing how, when the number of 'equal' or 'doubtful' judgments is reduced to a minimum, the Urban *DL*'s decrease toward the vanishing point and the Culler *DL*'s increase as the slopes of the ogives become lowered.

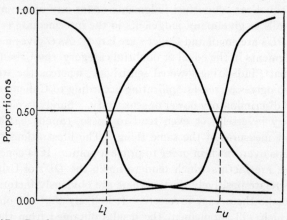

Fig. 24*B*.—Psychometric curves showing how, when the number of 'equal' or 'doubtful' judgments becomes unusually large, due either to poor sensitivity or to 'scientific caution,' Urban's *DL*'s become very large and Culler's become very small as the slopes of the ogives rise.

6. The Method of Right and Wrong Cases.—The method of right and wrong cases was the original form of the constant method and it dates from Fechner. The latter did away entirely with the troublesome 'd' judgments by dividing them equally between the judgments 'g' and 'l.' If we do this, our two ogives have exactly the same precision, and h, the measure of precision, may be used as the indicator of sensitivity. Fechner so used it. This is quite a different approach to the measurement of sensitivity from the concept of the *DL* as defined by Müller. If one wants a comparable measure of the *DL* from the method of right and wrong cases, the *PE* of the distribution is found, and it can be computed directly from h. In terms of 'correct' judgments, it is that *R*-difference which is correctly observed 75 per cent of the time.

The method of right and wrong cases may or may not permit *O* to give '*d*' judgments. This highly controversial question, as to the relative merits of two or three categories of judgments, will be left for fuller discussion later. Regardless of whether two or three are permitted, we may always treat the data as if only two had been used, as Fechner did. But no one now would divide the '*d*' judgments equally between the other two categories. We know from the very thorough work of Warner Brown (7) that, when *O* is forced to guess, even with differences as small as .2 gr., more right than wrong judgments will be given. Judgments of differences below the limen may differ only quantitatively from those for supraliminal differences. The best assumption is that the '*d*' judgments would have been divided proportionately between '*g*' and '*l*' had *O* been forced to guess. *O*'s guesses are therefore more likely to be right than wrong, and the fact that he says 'doubtful' does not mean that he is half inclined toward '*g*' and half toward '*l*,' as Fechner and others believed.

If we treat our lifted-weight data according to this proposal, the distributions of proportions are those given in Table 30. The two ogives and the plotted points are represented in Fig. 25. The

TABLE 30.—PROPORTIONS OF JUDGMENTS WITH 'DOUBTFUL' JUDGMENTS APPORTIONED TO 'GREATER' AND 'LESS'

R	185	190	195	200	205	210	215
D	−15	−10	−5	0	+5	+10	+15
p_g	.052	.146	.200	.517	.846	.853	.934
p_l	.948	.854	.800	.483	.154	.147	.066

solution demands that we find the *R*-difference that has a proportion of exactly .75. We may proceed as follows: The first step is to find from the proportions just how far each *R*-difference extends from the standard in terms of *PE* units (using Table C). We have six *R*-differences and from each one we can get an estimation of what *R*-difference is proportional to exactly one *PE*. In Table 31, −15 gr. has a distance of −2.410*PE*. The number of grams equivalent for one *PE* is therefore −15/−2.410, or 6.22 gr., which appears in column 5 of the table. In the same way five other estimations of the *PE* are computed. The mean of these six estimates is 5.51,

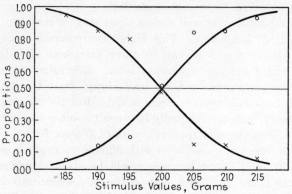

FIG. 25.—Psychometric functions for lifted weights with two categories of judgments.

which may be taken as the best estimate of the *R*-difference that will satisfy Jastrow's definition of the *DL* (34).[1]

Weighting the Observations.—It will be noticed that the six estimates of the *PE* differ from one another significantly. The range is from 3.31 to 6.72. This is due to the unreliability of the single observed proportions. The mean of the six is of course much more dependable than any one of them. But it will be recalled that the various proportions are themselves not equally reliable and should not possess equal weight in determining the final *PE*. It is reasonable to assume that the Müller-Urban weights should apply here, and our

[1] When there is an appreciable constant error in the *PSE* for the data, an alteration must be made in the procedure for computing the limen. The method as here presented assumes that the zero point of the *S*-scale coincides with the standard stimulus *S*. The median *L* of the psychometric curve may first be determined by linear interpolation, by normal interpolation, or by the normal graphic method. The differences *D* should then be obtained by (*R* − *L*) rather than by (*R* − *S*). The interpolated median in this case was 199.95, or so close to the standard *R* that little or no error is involved in computing the *DL*. However, as a general rule it is best to compute the differences *D* from the point of subjective equality, even if the constant error in the median is small.

next step has been to multiply each estimate of the *PE* by its corresponding Müller-Urban weight, using only two decimal places, as in column 7. The sum of column 7 is then divided by the sum of the weights, and the value of the *DL* finally estimated is 5.31. Its *PE* is like that of Culler's *DL*, the *PE* of a *PE*, or $.4769PE/\sqrt{n}$. The value of n in this case is again taken as 100, although this is open to criticism. Strictly, n ought to be the sum of the '*g*' and '*l*'

TABLE 31.—COMPUTATION OF THE DIFFERENCE LIMEN BY THE METHOD OF RIGHT AND WRONG CASES

R	D	p_q	S_{PE}	DL'	W	$W(DL')$
185	−15	.052	−2.410	6.22	.36	2.239
190	−10	.146	−1.562	6.40	.66	4.224
195	− 5	.200	−1.248	4.00	.77	3.080
205	+ 5	.846	+1.511	3.31	.68	2.251
210	+10	.853	+1.556	6.43	.66	4.244
215	+15	.934	+2.233	6.72	.42	2.820
			Σ	33.08	3.55	18.858
			DL	5.51		5.31

cases. If no '*d*' judgments had been permitted, this would have been true. If our assumption is correct—that, were *O* forced to guess for every '*d*' judgment, he would have thrown them proportionately into the other two classes—we should still be justified in saying that $n = 100$. This criticism also applies to the weighting procedure given above, for the Müller-Urban weights assume a constant n for all *R*-differences. In view of this criticism, it would be best either to permit no '*d*' judgments or else to repeat those observations giving '*d*' judgments until every '*g*' and '*l*' gives a constant value for n.

A Right-and-wrong-cases Limen by the Phi-process.—With two-category data, either genuine or artificial—and by artificial is meant data in which the '*d*' judgments have been divided—the best-fitting phi-gamma function may be obtained and the *DL* found from *h*. This is Urban's process, with Culler's modification, except that Culler's *DL* refers to the original distributions (in three-category data) whereas the present *DL* refers to the revised distributions. Since the two distributions are here exact reversals, only one task of fitting is required. The *DL* so obtained, like Culler's, has the advantage that its *PE* is small, but it also dispenses with the very troublesome uncertainties of the '*d*' judgments. It is therefore one of the most reliable and unambiguous measurements of sensitivity we have. It has the advantage over the procedure for the traditional method of right and wrong cases that a value for the *PSE* may be obtained. This is simply the median of the fitted curve.

TABLE 32.—SUMMARY OF THE LIFTED-WEIGHT LIMENS AND THEIR PROBABLE ERRORS

Process	L_g	PE	L_l	PE	DL_g	PE	DL_l	PE	DL_m	PE	PSE	IU
Linear interpolation..	204.67	.84*	196.56	.75*	3.77	....	4.33	....	4.05	....	200.89	8.10
Arithmetic mean.....	204.25	.69	196.80	.66	3.42	....	4.03	....	3.73	....	200.83	7.45
Urban process.......	204.33	.92	196.18	.86	4.21	....	3.93	....	4.07	....	200.12	8.15
Normal interpolation.	204.03	.82*	196.51	.67*	4.03	....	3.49	....	3.76	....	......	7.52
Normal graphic......	204.3	.86*	196.0	.82*	4.30	....	4.0	....	4.15	....	200.0	8.30
Culler process.......	......	....	....	....	7.35	.35	6.86	.33	7.10	....	200.12	
Culler graphic.......	......	....	....	....	6.9	.33*	6.5	.31*	6.7	.	200.0	
Right and wrong cases............	......	....	....	....	....	....	....	....	5.31	.25		
Right and wrong cases graphic......	......	....	....	....	6.2	.29*	6.3	.30*	6.25	.30*	200.0	
Right and wrong cases phi-process..	......	....	....	....	....	....	....	....	5.97	.28	199.84	

* The starred values must be considered merely as rough estimates.

A Graphic Solution for the Method of Right and Wrong Cases.— In this case the plot is between the *R* values on the abscissa and the values for S_{PE} as given in Table 31 on the ordinate. Both the upward-slanting and the downward-slanting lines should be drawn. The downward-slanting line is located from the *S* values corresponding to p_l in Table 30. The results have been tabulated for our illustrative problem in Table 32.

Choice of the Mathematical Process in Practice.—Suggestions as to the best processes to use in computing a limen were offered earlier in connection with the two-point limen problem. Those same suggestions also apply here. In addition, other comments are in order. First of all, it must be remembered that the results compiled in Table 32 represent at least three logically different measurements of sensitivity. There is the Müller *DL* which is presumed to have the same meaning as the *DL* found by the method of minimal changes. It is that *R*-difference which has a probability of .50 of being noticed. Sensitivity is measured by the interval of uncertainty, or by the width of the gap between the medians of the 'g' and 'l' distributions. There is the Culler DL, the PE of the ogive distributions of the 'g' and 'l' judgments. This is based upon the degree of confusion of either the 'g' or the 'l' judgments with the doubtful ones. The more rapid the *transition* from 'd' to either 'g' or 'l,' the lower the DL. Finally, there is the Fechner-Jastrow measurement of sensitivity, based logically upon the degree of confusion of the 'g' and 'l' judgments, in the ideal condition where there are no 'd' judgments. Under certain circumstances any two of the three DL's might be numerically the same. It is very doubtful whether with three-category data all three would ever exactly agree.

We can be guided to some extent by examining Table 32. Note that some methods yield no measurement of the interval of uncertainty IU. This is not a very serious defect, since the IU is usually equal to $2DL$ and so can be found from the DL; also it is probably as much a function of attitude as it is of sensitivity. Most methods yield a PSE, usually a very important constant to know, since it reveals constant errors and since its nearness to R_0 tells us how well the constant errors have been kept under control. Some methods give two measures of DL, namely, DL_g and DL_l. This is desirable since from Weber's law we would not expect them to be exactly equal. It is the experience of the writer, however, that the differences between DL_g and DL_l are so small as to be unreliable and that now one and now the other is the larger of the two, so that little significance can be attached to those differences. Some methods, again, yield a PE of the DL and others do not. Some give a PE of both DL_g and of DL_l and some do not. Some enable us to find a PE of L_g and L_l and others do not. Of all these PE's, the PE_{DL} is the most important to know. We usually want to compare two limens. And in order to test for significance of differences we must know their PE's. The procedures with right and wrong cases are the only ones that give us directly the PE_{DL}.

From all these considerations the writer is ready to make the following recommendations: The first choice would be the method of right and wrong cases, the constants to be computed by the Urban-Culler phi-process, *i.e.*, to secure data with only two categories of judgment, to fit them to the best phi-gamma function, and to take its PE as the DL. The next best procedure would be to use three-category data, but to divide the third category proportionately between '*g*' and '*l*.' As time-saving measures, either Jastrow's process for right and wrong cases, as extended above, or the graphic solution may be used. Among the other methods, with three-category data, Urban's phi-process is probably to be preferred to Culler's, mainly because the *DL* so found has a less indefinite meaning. It also has behind it much psychophysical tradition. There is a strong faith on the part of many that *O*'s attitude can be so controlled that he will maintain a constant criterion as to what is a positive judgment and what is mere guesswork. The limens from the same *O* might then be safely compared with one another, but the comparison of one *O*'s Urban-process limens with those of another is hardly to be taken seriously. Following these two processes would come in order: Spearman's mean, the normal graphic, normal interpolation, and finally linear interpolation. Further light will be thrown on the choice of method when the question of two versus three categories of judgments is discussed.

History of the Constant Methods

According to Titchener (43, II, p. 275), the fundamental idea of measuring sensitivity by means of the proportions of right, wrong, and doubtful judgments originated with Vierordt about 1852. The latter and his students were content merely to indicate psycho-logical differences by giving proportions. The establishment of right and wrong cases as a psychophysical method lies with Fechner, who between 1855 and 1859 devoted much time to the discrimination of weights, he alone making over 67,000 comparisons. He proposed to test Weber's law by finding for every standard weight that ΔR which would yield the same proportion of right cases. This assumption was to become more explicit years later with Cattell and his students and it is usually stated as follows: "Equally often noticed differences are equal unless always or never noticed." Fechner also furthered the method by pointing out that the distribution of right judgments is of the normal ogive form; in other words, it is an error function. He prepared a table giving for every p between .50 and 1.00 the corresponding value of $h\delta$, which he called t. Since $t = h\delta$ and δ is the R-difference, h simply equalled t/δ. The constant h was Fechner's measure of sensitivity.

Müller strenuously objected that we must distinguish between the precision of judgment and the traditional *DL*. He regarded h as merely a measure of the variability of the true *DL*. Fechner was unwilling to accept Müller's procedure, and maintained that the *DL* could be found from *h* and should be defined as the *PE* of the distribution of judgments. Müller refused to divide the equal and doubtful judgments between the 'rights' and the 'wrongs.' This emphasis upon the doubtful judgments required a change of name, since a doubtful judgment could be neither right nor wrong. The method was also illogical when dealing with an *R*-difference of zero, for in this case only the equal judgments could be right. Wundt proposed the name of the *method of three cases* (52, p. 189) or *Drei Hauptfälle*. Müller proposed the name of *Konstanzmethode* which has gained the popular preference.

The numerous difficulties presented by the doubtful judgments led to many efforts to eliminate them entirely, at least from the computation of the limen. Fechner is said to have proposed ignoring them, though he later rejected the idea, but Merkel and Kraepelin actually did ignore them (43, II, pp. 284 *f.*). Peirce and Jastrow went further and did not permit *O* to give them (34, p. 76) nor did Fullerton and Cattell (18, p. 12), thus initiating a method that has been called *right and wrong answers*. The limen, in this method, is that *R*-difference that is judged correctly 75 per cent of the time. Fullerton and Cattell prepared tables giving values of δ/PE for proportions between .50 and 1.00; from these values the *DL* can readily be found.

Subsequent history has already been indicated. Müller first suggested fitting the data to the normal ogive and finding the median of the latter, and he worked out his series of weights for the process (31). Urban added his contribution to the weights (46) in 1909. Boring reduced the least square solution to a convenient routine (2) and Rich constructed his checking tables to facilitate the process (35). Numerous studies have appeared within the last thirty years testing empirically the various procedures, the number and spacing of stimuli, the two versus three categories of judgment, and the relative merits of the different processes for computing limens. Very few of these can be mentioned specifically but the conclusions and the advice of many of them have been made to bear fruit indirectly in the present chapter. There is one controversial point which needs to be considered especially, and that is the question of the third category of judgments.

Equal versus Doubtful Judgments.—While the third-category judgments are often referred to as the 'equal' judgments, this is probably not the best name for them. Experience shows that two compared stimuli rarely if ever give the impression of exact equality. Even when O is instructed to judge 'equal' and does so, those judgments mean various things, such as "I don't know," "I wasn't attentive," "They are different but I don't know which one was greater," "Greater, but I'm not sure so I'll say equal," and the like. The third category therefore contains everything not 'g' or 'l.' The best report to ask for if a third category is to be used, is that of 'doubtful,' which recognizes the heterogeneity of that class of judgments.

Arguments for the Use of Two Categories.—The arguments for either two or three categories have been uttered by so many protagonists on both sides of the question that it is impossible to give due credit to every writer on the subject. Only a few references to writers will therefore be made. The list of arguments follows:

1. There is little doubt that two categories greatly simplify the treatment of results, and the computed constants have a less ambiguous meaning.

2. The judgment 'equal' comes from a variable impression of equality and in fact cases of actually experienced equality are so rare as to be almost negligible. (In reply it may be maintained that judgments of 'greater' or 'less' also issue from variable impressions, some differences being strongly experienced and some not.)

3. The judgment 'doubtful' is no judgment at all; it is evasive.

4. A third category permits O to avoid making a judgment when it is important that he should. In this connection recall that Müller's weights give more importance to proportions near .50.

5. O is kept in an alert, judicial attitude; he is not permitted to lapse into a "state of mild aboulia," as Brown (7) puts it.

6. The exclusion of a third category trains O to establish criteria for judging smaller differences.

7. In actual practice, Os who are impressed with the importance of giving 'e' judgments may have DL's twice as large as usual (13). Figure 24B shows what is likely to happen when O is overcautious about giving judgments of 'g' or 'l.'

8. Some Os have actually obtained DL's and IU's of zero because no 'e' judgments or 'd' judgments were given (13). In this connection refer to Fig. 24A.

9. In comparative studies, the results from the two-category method were found to be more reliable (24).

10. When the same Os used both methods, the great majority expressed a preference for the two-category method (24).

11. Judgments of '*d*' were found to result almost invariably from failure to follow instructions, most frequently from a lapse of attention (19).

12. Equality judgments require a longer time to make (25) and all judgments tend to require a longer time when the three-category procedure is used. According to George (19), reflection destroys attitude; the immediate judgment made under a passive attitude is best.

13. No matter how small the difference, even if it is as small as .2 with a 100-gr. standard, O is right more often than he is wrong if he guesses (7). Subliminal differences are merely quantitatively different from supraliminal differences, is the conclusion of Brown.

Arguments for the Use of Three Categories.—1. The two-category instruction places O under compulsion so that he cannot judge naturally.

2. O is forced to 'lie' about his experience in using two categories.

3. The three-category instruction is more exacting and forces O to be more cautious. The two-category plan trains O to become careless and unconscientious because it requires him to render a judgment even when his criteria for either '*g*' or '*l*' are absent.

4. No new mental standard is required (10, p. 111). O develops criteria for judgments '*g*' and '*l*' and when those criteria are absent he reports '*d*.' (However, when 'equality' is the intermediate category, there are *three* discriminations to make, '*g — e*,' '*e — l*,' and '*g — l*.')

5. The three-category method gives results with a higher precision (10, pp. 100–108) as measured by the steepness of the psychometric curves. (The fact that, when the precision rises, the Urban *IU* conversely indicates a *lowered* sensitivity, as is illustrated in Fig. 24, detracts from the weight of this argument.)

6. The three-category method gives two separate ogives for '*g*' and '*l*' whereas the two-category method arbitrarily forces the two to become identical in slope (10, p. 108).

7. It is sometimes argued that in the two-category method O will give proportionately greater attention to the small differences and hence an undue proportion of correct judgments for them. (If smaller differences increase O's attention, well and good. This greater attention will extend to the larger differences as well, for O

never knows whether the next difference to come will be large or small.)

8. Practiced *O*s can so control their attitudes that the criteria for '*d*' or '*e*' judgments will become constant (4).

9. George (19) recommends that *O* be permitted to give '*d*' judgments but that these be eliminated in the computation of the limens.

The writer is inclined to agree with the last recommendation. There are cases when, owing to a lapse of attention or of the proper attitude, *O* is in great doubt and he should be permitted to say 'doubtful.' *O* should be instructed to be alert to differences and to avoid judgments of '*d*' whenever he can truthfully do so. He should be informed that, if his attitude and attention are consistent and adequate, his 'guesses' are likely in the long run to be right more often than wrong. There may be cases of exact experienced equality, when *O* should be permitted to say 'equal.' Experience seems to show, in the face of strong arguments to the contrary, that the 'objective' attitude in which *O* judges and compares 'stimuli' is generally superior to the one in which he judges 'sensations.' Under the objective attitude *O* uses unconscious criteria and renders a 'guess' of '*g*' or '*l*,' even when his recognized conscious criteria are absent; his 'guesses' turn out to be legitimate judgments in the sense that their part of the psychometric function is consistent with and continuous with those parts which are obtained from conscious criteria.

Since, when the two-category instructions are used, the psychometric function, symbolizing the gradual transition of the proportion of judgments '*g*' or '*l*' from the smallest variable *R* to the greatest, is typically a good ogive, some form of the method of right and wrong cases would seem to be the best means of measuring the differential sensitivity. At least the elimination of the third-category judgments avoids the choice between two constant processes whose final measures are highly ambiguous. For the sake of convenience in using Urban's weights, it is best to repeat trials that yielded '*d*' or '*e*' judgments in order to attain a constant *n* for all stimulus pairs. Merely for the sake of preventing *O* from resorting to 'guessing' when he ought to be attentive, he should probably not be told that his '*e*' and '*d*' experiments will have to be repeated. The data then may be treated by the method of right and wrong cases or any of its variants. The retention of the third-category judgments and the solution of two psychometric functions is probably never justifiable unless the number of judgments is very great, perhaps 500 for every stimulus pair, or unless the range of equality is relatively large. In the latter event, the range of stimuli could be made greater, thus shortening the interval of uncertainty in terms of the step interval between stimuli. Many of those who have tried to uphold the best traditions in psychophysics will not agree with the advice presented here. But it would seem to the writer that, if we desire a measure of sensitivity that is uncontaminated, unambiguous, and widely applicable to all types of Os, we should follow the voice of experience as it has been interpreted in the last few paragraphs.

VARIATIONS OF THE CONSTANT METHODS

The Method of Single Stimuli.—A procedure which has become known as the **method of single stimuli** and which was recently called to our attention by Wever and Zener (49) under the name of the *method of absolute judgment* has received considerable attention of late.[1] In its extreme form, it consists in applying the variable stimulus without a standard with which to compare it. At the beginning of an experimental period O may be given a 3-min. practice period in lifting the standard, during which time he is supposed to establish an absolute impression of its weight. As each variable is presented later, O judges 'light,' 'intermediate,' or 'heavy' according as each weight impresses him (15). The distributions of 'light' and 'heavy' judgments are found to be normal ogives with somewhat lower precision than corresponding distributions by the usual constant method. Some investigators insert the standard at frequent intervals to help reestablish the absolute standard. Without this, however, the series itself tends to form a standard, more ambiguous or uncertain than a single weight would be, perhaps, but nevertheless a standard or background against which to compare each variable. The judgments are therefore not strictly 'absolute.' For this reason the tendency is to change the name of that of the *method of single stimuli*. This seems more appropriate and does

---

[1] The method of single stimuli has been known since the study of L. J. Martin and G. E. Müller, Zur Analyse der Unterschiedsempfindlichkeit, 1899, and it was revived in recent years by S. R. Truman and E. G. Wever in their study, The judgment of pitch as a function of the series, *Univ. Calif. Pub. Psychol.*, 1928, **3**, 215–223.

not prejudice the question as to whether the judgments are absolute or relative (48).[1]

The Method of Judgment Time.—As early as 1887 Cattell had proposed that a difference could be measured psychologically by the time of the reaction to that difference (51). Henmon (21) took up the suggestion in 1911 and found that this was very roughly true. A right judgment required less time than a wrong one and was less variable. The time also decreases regularly with the degree of assurance as reported by O. The motive behind these efforts seems to have been to get a purely objective indicator of observed differences in order to avoid dependence upon the verbally reported judgments of O. Kellogg (25) has more recently found that, if O does not know that his reaction times are being measured, the relationships are all the more significant. He is able to state the general law, "The psychometric time curves for all categories tend to be inversions of the psychometric relative frequency curves." That is, when O is unaware that his reaction time is being recorded, the time is an inverse function of the proportion of right judgments and the relation is roughly ogive in form. Certain irregularities, however, prevent the times alone from being dependable objective criteria of sensitivity.

Degrees of Confidence in Judging.—Fullerton and Cattell introduced a procedure whereby O could report his degree of assurance in each judgment. They found a positive relationship between the degree of confidence and the correctness of judgments. Others have also found that confidence correlates with accuracy. Brown (7) objects to this device, however, because it brings about a change of attitude and one can never be sure where O draws the line between different categories of confidence.

The Use of a Variable Standard.—Culler proposes the use of a variable standard stimulus, recommending that every weight in the series be compared with every other one. In the determination of a limen there can be computed as many pairs of limens as there are stimuli. He cites the following advantages: (1) A maximum

---

[1] Bressler (6) has recently introduced a variation in the method of single stimuli by asking O to judge in terms of stimulus values. For example, with a 100-gr. standard, as O lifts each weight he is to state its weight in grams. Reports of R values more than 100 are classed as 'g' judgments and reports of R values less than 100 as 'l' judgments. Reports of 100 are classed as 'e'. The data may be treated by any of the constant processes.

range of differences can be obtained with minimum equipment. (2) It guarantees some very high and some very low proportions. (3) It permits more very small *R*-differences and stimulates *O*'s caution. (4) It eliminates the error of 'absolute impression,' by which is meant a constant judgment tendency due to the repeated application of the same standard with every pair (10, p. 76). It will be recognized that this proposed variation is none other than the method of paired comparisons, a near cousin of the constant method.

Group Presentation of Stimuli.—As a time-saving device, Shaad and Helson (36) suggest that the same stimulus or stimulus pair need not be changed at every presentation. It is sometimes inconvenient, as in finding the two-point limen, to make a change in the apparatus after every trial. They have found that, either with the two-point limen technique or the lifted-weight experiment, the repetition of a stimulus from 10 to 25 times in succession makes no significant difference in the results. The best procedure, they concluded, was to warn *O* that the same stimulus might be given in succession, but to vary the number of repetitions in a group.

Using a Geometric Series of Stimuli.—Thurstone has pointed out that the phi-gamma hypothesis is in violation of Fechner's law or of any similar psychophysical law. The distribution of observed proportions of judgments should theoretically not be normally distributed if plotted against equal stimulus intervals on the abscissa. We ought, rather, to assume a *phi-log-gamma hypothesis*, using log *R* on the abscissa instead of *R*. This would mean the selection of equal logarithmic steps between stimuli as Galton proposed many years ago. When the Weber ratio is relatively large, perhaps 1:3 to 1:10, the error involved in the usual phi-gamma hypothesis is rather serious; when it is relatively small, 1:50 or less, the error is negligible. This notion of Thurstone's (42) has been substantiated by Lufkin (30), who found that the usual ogives are skewed negatively, as we should expect from Fechner's law. After all, however, Lufkin found that the normal ogive fitted the data about as well as any type of skewed curve. The reasons for Thurstone's proposal will be much clearer after a reading of his psychometric theories as reviewed in the next chapter.

The Method of Serial Groups.—This is a much abbreviated and mutilated method of right and wrong cases. It was first used by McDougall and by Stratton with primitive peoples and with children and its aim was to secure a quick measure of thresholds in studies of individual differences. Starting with a difference, for example, of two tactual points, that can readily be observed correctly, this stimulus would be applied 5 or 10 times in succession, alternated haphazardly with 'catch experiments' or *Vexierversuche*. The next smaller stimulus would then be applied in like manner and so on until a stimulus was reached below which less than 80 per cent of the judgments were correct. Stratton (38) gave as its advantages: (1) *O* knows of the *Vexierversuche* and is on his guard not to be 'caught.' (2) It eliminates the suggestibility involved in the method of limits. (3) Thresholds are determined by actually crossing them. (4) The principle of right and wrong cases is applied without elaborate computations.

Titchener (44) severely criticized the method on the following counts: (1) It is extremely unreliable owing to the very small number of trials. (2) Many times inversions occur and results are contradictory when the tests are repeated. (3) *E* has to decide for himself when sufficient preliminary trials have been made. These criticisms are serious in that ethnological comparisons have been made on the basis of just such limited tests of sensitivity. Thomson (39) defends the method and adds the suggestion for a *method of nonserial groups* in which, as the name implies, the magnitude of the stimulus is not changed in serial order. He lists as a further advantage that it does not discourage *O* who is bound to be right a large percentage of the times. It has certain disadvantages: (1) The limens are incomparable with others. (2) The 80 per cent point is less reliably determined than the 50 per cent point. (3) The use of 5 or 10 stimulations in a group does not permit a ready finding of the 75 per cent point. As a remedy for the latter, he advises the use of 4 or 8 stimulations in a group (40).

When the Limen Is Not the Median.—At certain times it is reasonable to reject the median of the ogive function as the limen. Brown (8) found in a study of the *RL* for taste, for example, that, owing to shifts of attitude from time to time and other uncontrollable central factors, the median was a highly variable quantity. He proposed, instead of the median, to take as the *RL* that point on the psychometric function where the curve was rising with greatest steepness. This would ordinarily be at the median, but when the curve is skewed this is not so. Brown actually found that points of steepest rise occur all the way from 5 to 80 per cent, with the majority of them between 42 and 62 per cent. Such *RL*'s were more constant from one time to another and under different conditions, such as a change in the range of stimuli.

The Method of 'Complete Series' or Vollreihenmethode.— Kirschmann (27) describes a process of computing the *DL* that is apparently more popular in Germany than here, known as the *Vollreihenmethode*. Three categories of judgments are permitted, and a wide range of stimuli is employed so that the lowest stimulus gives a proportion of .00 for judgments '*g*' and the highest gives a proportion of 1.00, and vice versa for the judgments '*l*.' The lower limen L_l is given by the formulas

$$L_l = R_0 + \left[\frac{\Sigma l}{n} + \frac{1}{2}\right]i \qquad (87a)$$

$$L_g = R_1 - \left[\frac{\Sigma g}{n} + \frac{1}{2}\right]i \qquad (87b)$$

where R_0 and R_1 = the R values at which p_g equals .00 and 1.00, respectively.

i = the class interval.

l and g = the numbers of judgments 'less' and 'greater,' respectively.

The *PSE* is obtained by eliminating the third category of judgments, either by dividing them equally, as did Fechner, or proportionately, as has been proposed in this chapter, and then applying the formula

$$PSE = R_1 - \left[\frac{\Sigma g}{n} + \frac{1}{2}\right]i \qquad (88a)$$

$$= R_0 + \left[\frac{\Sigma l}{n} + \frac{1}{2}\right]i \qquad (88b)$$

This is a short convenient method of computing the limens and the *PSE*, but the probable errors are determined with great difficulty, and the *DL*'s as found by this method are hardly comparable either in size or in meaning with those found by other procedures. For a fuller discussion of this method the reader is referred to Kirschmann's treatment of it (27, pp. 450 *ff.*).

APPLICATIONS OF THE CONSTANT METHODS

The range of usefulness of the constant methods within the field of psychophysics proper has already been mentioned at the

beginning of this chapter.   There is hardly a problem where their
principles cannot be applied in practice.   Outside the field of
psychophysics we already find appropriate adaptations of the
constant processes to the measurement of certain psychometric
constants, such as spans of apprehension and of memory, associative
recall, and finally mental-test procedures.

The Measurement of an Associative Limen.—The first of these
applications, suggested by Boring and Williams (50), was made to
the measurement of strength of memory impressions.   Once items
of material are committed to memory with certain associative
linkages—and this expression is used without prejudicing us to any
theory of association—we can at any time later find the probability
of the recall of that material.   The associative limen has been defined
as that strength of connection whose probability of an effective recall
is .5.   The point of half-learning would then be substituted for the
former Ebbinghaus standard of complete mastery.   The test of
recall might be in the form of paired associates, retained members,
or the method of prompting.   The percentage of successful reproductions is plotted against the number of repetitions or, as Williams (50)
suggested, against the logarithm of the number of repetitions.

The Spans of Apprehension and of Memory.—The application
to the measurement of the span of apprehension was first made by
Fernberger (14).   Exposing various numbers of objects, for example
from 4 to 15, it is usually found that the decrease in the proportion
of correct judgments of number follows the phi-gamma function
quite closely.   A very accurate limen of apprehension and its
probable error can thus be determined.   The limen of apprehension
becomes statistically defined as that number of objects which
when exposed momentarily has a probability of .5 of being observed
correctly.   The same condition holds for the memory span for digits
or letters, as demonstrated by Guilford and Dallenbach (20).   The
memory span, too, thus comes under the general definition of a
limen.

The Mental-age Level of a Test.—In establishing the age levels
of his various tests of intelligence, Binet adopted a rough and ready
standard.   Any test that could be passed by from two-thirds to
three-fourths of the children of a certain age should be placed at
that age level.   This obviously means that the average child of a
given age can do more than pass the tests at his age.   This is a
violation of the use of medians and means.   A five-year test should

be one that the average five-year-old child can pass, or one that 50 per cent of them can pass. Kreezer and Dallenbach (28) have shown that a simple test like that of grasping the meaning of opposition can be passed by more and more children of advancing years; the increase in the proportion passing the test is of the ogive form. A limen and its *PE* can be computed, and a logical and accurate age determination is then established for the test. This principle had been previously reached by Otis (33), but it has not as yet been generally applied. Related applications of it are to be found in the chapter on test methods.

Problems

1. In determining a tactual two-point limen by the constant method, the following proportions of judgments of 'two' were obtained, each stimulus being applied 100 times.

R, mm.	18	22	26	30	34
p	.05	.23	.55	.72	.91

    a. Compute the limen and its probable error by the various methods described in this chapter.

    b. In using the Urban constant process find the theoretical proportions and test the data for goodness of fit.

2. Find the median memory span from the following data:

R, digits	6	7	8	9	10	11	12
p	.93	.81	.68	.34	.21	.08	.05

3. The following data were obtained from a comparison of lifted weights, the standard being 100 gr. and each weight being compared with it 500 times.

R	88	91	94	97	100	103	106
Proportion:							
'Greater'........	.01	.03	.10	.29	.52	.66	.82
'Equal'.........	.07	.17	.27	.36	.26	.21	.13
'Less'...........	.92	.80	.63	.35	.22	.13	.05

    a. Compute the difference limens using the various appropriate variations of the constant method and the point of subjective equality, with tests of significance and goodness of fit.

  b. Find the same by means of Culler's process.

  c. Dividing the equality judgments proportionately into the 'greater' and 'less' categories, apply the method of right and wrong cases.

REFERENCES

1. BORING, E. G., The number of observations upon which a limen may be based, *Amer. J. Psychol.*, 1916, **27**, 315–319.

2. ———, Urban's tables and the method of constant stimuli, *Amer. J. Psychol.*, 1917, **28**, 280–293.

3. ———, A chart of the psychometric function, *Amer. J. Psychol.*, 1917, **28**, 465–470.

4. ———, The control of attitude in psychophysical experiments, *Psychol. Rev.*, 1920, **27**, 440–452.

5. ———, Is there a generalized psychometric function? *Amer. J. Psychol.*, 1924, **35**, 75–78.

6. BRESSLER, J., Judgment in absolute units as a psychophysical method, *Arch. Psychol.*, 1933, no. 152.

7. BROWN, W., The judgment of difference, *Univ. Calif. Pub. Psychol.*, 1910, **1**, no. 1.

8. ———, The judgment of very weak sensory stimuli, *Univ. Calif. Pub. Psychol.*, 1914, **1**, no. 3, 199–268.

9. BROWN, WM., and G. H. THOMSON, "The Essentials of Mental Measurement," Cambridge University Press, London, 1925.

10. CULLER, E., Studies in psychometric theory, *Psychol. Monog.*, 1926, **35**, no. 163, 56–137.

11. ———, Studies in psychometric theory, *J. Exper. Psychol.*, 1926, **9**, 271–298.

12. ———, Studies in psychometric theory, *J. Exper. Psychol.*, 1927, **10**, 463–477.

13. FERNBERGER, S. W., The effect of the attitude of the subject upon the measure of sensitivity, *Amer. J. Psychol.*, 1914, **25**, 538–543.

14. ———, A preliminary study of the range of visual apprehension, *Amer. J. Psychol.*, 1921, **32**, 121–133.

15. ———, On absolute and relative judgments in lifted weight experiments, *Amer. J. Psychol.*, 1931, **43**, 560–578.

16. ———, The use of equality judgments in psychophysical procedures, *Psychol. Rev.*, 1930, **37**, 107–112.

17. FRIEDLINE, C., The discrimination of cutaneous patterns below the two-point limen, *Amer. J. Psychol.*, 1918, **29**, 400–419.

18. FULLERTON, G. S., and J. McK. CATTELL, On the perception of small differences, *Pub. Univ. Penn., Phil. Series*, no. 2, 1892.

19. GEORGE, S. S., Attitude in relation to the psychophysical judgment, *Amer. J. Psychol.*, 1917, **28**, 1–37.

20. GUILFORD, J. P., and K. M. DALLENBACH, The determination of memory span by the method of constant stimuli, *Amer. J. Psychol.*, 1925, **36**, 621–628.

21. HENMON, V. A. C., The relation of the time of a judgment to its accuracy, *Psychol. Rev.*, 1911, **18**, 186–201.

22. IRWIN, F., Psychophysical measurement methods, *Psychol. Bull.*, 1935, **32**, 140–171.

23. KELLEY, T. L., "Statistical Method," The Macmillan Company, New York, 1924.
24. KELLOGG, W. N., An experimental evaluation of equality judgments in psychophysics, *Arch. Psychol.*, 1930, **17**, no. 112.
25. ————, The time of judgment in psychometric measures, *Amer. J. Psychol.*, 1931, **43**, 65–86.
26. KINCAID, M., An analysis of the psychometric function for the two-point limen with respect to the paradoxical error, *Amer. J. Psychol.*, 1918, **29**, 227–232.
27. KIRSCHMANN, A., Grundzüge der psychologischen Maszmethoden in Abderhalden's "Handbuch der biologischen Arbeitsmethoden," Abt. VI, Teil A, Urban und Schwarzenberg, Berlin, 1927.
28. KREEZER, G., and K. M. DALLENBACH, Learning the relation of opposition, *Amer. J. Psychol.*, 1929, **41**, 432–441.
29. LINDER, R. E., A statistical comparison of psychophysical methods, *Psychol. Monog.*, 1933, **44**, no. 199, 1–20.
30. LUFKIN, H. M., The best-fitting frequency function for Urban's lifted-weight results, *Amer. J. Psychol.*, 1928, **40**, 75–82.
31. MÜLLER, G. E., "Die Gesichtspunkte und die Tatsachen der psychophysischen Methodik," J. F. Bergmann, Wiesbaden, 1904.
32. NEWHALL, S. M., An interpolation procedure for calculating thresholds, *Psychol. Rev.*, 1928, **35**, 46–66.
33. OTIS, A. S., Some logical aspects of the Binet scale, *Psychol. Rev.*, 1916, **23**, 129–152, 165–179.
34. PEIRCE, C. S., and J. JASTROW, Small differences of sensation, *Mem. Nat. Acad. Sci.*, 1885, **3**, 75–83.
35. RICH, G. J., A checking table for the method of constant stimuli, *Amer. J. Psychol.*, 1918, **29**, 120–121, 232.
36. SHAAD, D. J., and H. HELSON, Group presentation in the method of constant stimuli as a time-saving device, *Amer. J. Psychol.*, 1931, **43**, 422–433.
37. SPEARMAN, C. The method of 'right and wrong cases' without Gauss' formulae, *Brit. J. Psychol.*, 1908, **2**, 227–242.
38. STRATTON, G. M., The method of serial groups, *Psychol. Rev.*, 1902, **9**, 444–447.
39. THOMSON, G. H., A comparison of the psychophysical methods, *Brit. J. Psychol.*, 1912, **5**, 203–241.
40. ————, An inquiry into the best form of the method of serial groups, *Brit. J. Psychol.*, 1913, **5**, 398–416.
41. ————, Fitting of frequency functions to Urban's lifted-weight results, *Amer. J. Psychol.*, 1929, **41**, 70–82.
42. THURSTONE, L. L., The phi-gamma hypothesis, *J. Exper. Psychol.*, 1928, **11**, 293–305.
43. TITCHENER, E. B., "Experimental Psychology," The Macmillan Company, New York, Vol. II, Pts. I and II, 1905.
44. ————, On ethnological tests of sensation and perception . . . in the reports of the Cambridge anthropological expedition to Torres Straits, *Proc. Amer. Phil. Soc.*, 1916, **55**, 204–236.

45. URBAN, F. M., "The Application of Statistical Methods to Problems of Psychophysics," Psychological Clinic Press, Philadelphia, 1908.
46. ———, Die psychophysischen Maszmethoden als Grundlagen empirischer Messungen, *Arch. ges. Psychol.*, 1909, **15**, 261–355; **16**, 168–227.
47. ———, Die Verallgemeinerung der Konstanzmethode, *Arch. ges. Psychol.*, 1931, **80**, 167–178.
48. VOLKMANN, J., The method of single stimuli, *Amer. J. Psychol.*, 1932, **44**, 808 *f*.
49. WEVER, E. G., and K. E. ZENER, The method of absolute judgment in psychophysics, *Psychol. Rev.*, 1928, **35**, 466–493.
50. WILLIAMS, H. D., On the calculation of an associative limen, *Amer. J. Psychol.*, 1918, **29**, 219–226.
51. WOODWORTH, R. S., Professor Cattell's psychophysical contributions, *Arch. Psychol.*, 1914, no. 30, 60–74.
52. WUNDT, WM., "Logik," Vol. II, F. Enke, Stuttgart, 1895.

PART II

PSYCHOLOGICAL SCALING METHODS

CHAPTER VII

THE METHOD OF PAIRED COMPARISONS

The methods of this section of the volume we refer to as the purely psychometric methods for the reason that the R values are usually unknown and it is merely the S values with which we have to deal. A truly psychophysical method deals with both the R values and their corresponding S values and attempts to relate them in some way. That is possible when the stimuli can be weighed or measured in objective terms. There are no objective measures for the agreeableness of a color or an odor or for the beauty of a rose or for the quality of a specimen of handwriting. Methods like that of paired comparisons enable us to assign rather accurate psychological values to such stimuli without knowledge of any corresponding R values.

THE LAW OF COMPARATIVE JUDGMENT

We are enabled to derive S values from data obtained by the method of paired comparisons because of the law of comparative judgment which was recently formulated by Thurstone (18). The germ of the idea is to be found in Cattell's principle that 'equally often noticed differences are equal unless always or never noticed.' Let us follow Thurstone's recent exposition of the law.

The Discriminal Process and Its Dispersion.—Assume, as we have before in Chapter IV, a physical continuum with its various R values, $R_1, R_2, R_3, \ldots, R_n$, and parallel with it a corresponding psychological continuum with its S values, $S_1, S_2, S_3, \ldots, S_n$, as in Fig. 26. Any stimulus on the physical continuum, when applied to an organism responsive to it, gives rise to a certain experience or reaction which is technically called a **discriminal process**. This term is neutral as to the question of whether the organism's response is one of consciousness or some effector adjustment. There is not a perfect one-to-one correlation between each stimulus R_i ard some discriminal process S_i. R_5, for example, does not always give rise to one and only one process S_5. Depending upon various 'chance'

217

conditions, it may give rise to S_4, S_3, or S_2, or to S_6, S_7, or S_8. The response to R_5 varies up and down the S-scale. The process most frequently associated with R_5 is denoted as S_5. This most frequent discriminal process for any given R is called the **modal discriminal process.** The frequencies for the other processes above and below S_5 are smaller the farther those processes lie from the mode. We can make the reasonable assumption that these frequencies form the usual normal distribution and this can be experimentally demonstrated. Such a distribution is called the **discriminal dispersion.** The unit of the scale, according to Thurstone, is the standard deviation of this discriminal dispersion.

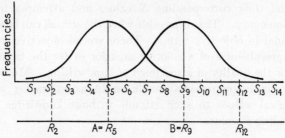

FIG. 26.—Discriminal dispersions of two stimuli.

Let us take another stimulus R_9 with its modal process S_9 and its discriminal dispersion as represented also in Fig. 26. The typical problem in the method of paired comparisons is to find the extent of the difference $S_9 - S_5$, knowing only what proportion of the times R_9 has been chosen as greater than R_5. It can be seen from the overlapping distributions that R_9 will not be judged greater than R_5 all the time. As the S for the former is varying up and down the scale, the S for the latter is also varying according to the laws of chance. At any given comparison R_9 may give rise to S_7, for example, and R_5 may give rise to S_8. The judgment will be that R_9 is less than R_5. On very rare occasions both stimuli might give rise to one and the same discriminal process and then the judgment should be 'equal.' But such occasions are extremely rare. Usually one or the other S is just sufficiently higher in the scale and can be judged 'greater.' In the method of paired comparisons equality judgments are not permitted, or if given at all the trial is repeated.

Distribution of the Observed Differences.—So, as the two stimuli are repeated again and again, the psychological difference is continually changing, becoming larger and smaller, now positive and now negative. The frequencies of these differences themselves will form a normal distribution curve as is shown in Fig. 27. Here the shaded area of the curve represents the proportion of judgments $R_b > R_a$ and the unshaded area represents that proportion of the judgments which is negative, *i.e.*, $R_b < R_a$, the total area under the curve being taken as unity; $p_{b>a}$ (the probability that R_b appears greater than R_a) plus $p_{b<a}$ (the probability that R_b appears less than R_a) equals 1.00. The mean of the distribution is equal to the

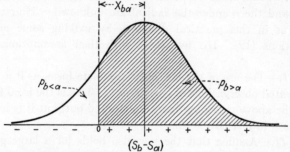

Fig. 27.—Distribution of the scale separations of two stimuli A and B.

psychological scale separation between S_b and S_a, the zero point of the scale being arbitrarily placed at the modal discriminal process of the lesser of the two stimuli. The scale separation $(S_b - S_a)$ is therefore given by the deviate on the abscissa of the distribution of differences, a quantity called X_{ba}. Knowing $p_{b>a}$, we as usual deduct .50, giving the proportion of the area (shaded) between the mean $(S_b - S_a)$ and zero. By resort to the tables the corresponding deviate can be obtained. If $p_{b>a}$ is .85, for example, X_{ba} is 1.036. The unit of this distribution is the standard deviation of the differences. The scale separation between S_b and S_a is therefore $X_{ba}\sigma_{\text{diff.}}$ or $1.036\sigma_{\text{diff.}}$.

The sigma of a difference is related to the sigmas of the two original measures by formula (36), page 59. So it follows that

$$S_b - S_a = X_{ba}\sqrt{\sigma_b^2 + \sigma_a^2 - 2r\sigma_b\sigma_a} \tag{89}$$

where S_b and S_a = the scale values for the two stimuli R_b and R_a, respectively.

X_{ba} = the deviate corresponding to the proportion of judgments R_b greater than R_a.

σ_b and σ_a = the standard deviations of the dispersions made by R_b and R_a on the psychological continuum.

r = the correlation between the discriminal deviations of R_b and R_a during the same judgment.

Applications of the Law of Comparative Judgment.—It would seem at first sight that formula (89), which is a mathematical statement of the law of comparative judgment, could not be used in a practical way. From our experimental data we know only the proportions of judgments of one stimulus as judged greater than another. From these proportions only X_{ba} can be obtained. The sigmas and the r under the radical are unknown. Thurstone has helped us in this practical difficulty by making some necessary assumptions (19). His five cases with their assumptions are as follows:

Case I.—The use of the law in its complete form, as it applies to the repeated observations of one subject. This is the ideal form for which the above reasoning has been worked out, but it is incapable of solution in just that form.

Case II.—Assume that the law also holds for a large group of Os who judge each pair of stimuli only once. This carries the assumption that the discriminal dispersions of the single stimuli will be normal in form as they are for a single individual.

Case III.—Assume that r equals zero, that there is no correlation between the evaluations of two stimuli when being compared. Presumably r would be positive when some factor causes the two to vary to some extent in the same direction up or down the scale at the same time. And r would be negative when some factor causes them to vary in opposite directions while being shown together for comparison. Contrast effects would give a case of negative correlation; mutual enhancement or degradation would give a case of positive correlation. This elimination of r makes possible a solution of scale separations since the sigmas in formula (89) can be closely estimated. The abbreviated law is then written in the form,

$$S_b - S_a = X_{ba}\sqrt{\sigma_b^2 + \sigma_a^2} \tag{90}$$

Case IV.—Assume that the discriminal dispersions are approximately equal. The law then reduces to the form,

$$S_b - S_a = .707 \, X_{ba}(\sigma_b + \sigma_a) \tag{91}$$

Discriminal dispersions will be equal when stimuli are equally unambiguous or equally easy to judge. One sample of hand-writing or a drawing or an English composition might be more difficult to judge than another because of contaminating factors and because of a multiplicity of criteria. Stimuli such as lifted weights, lines, or other more objective materials, in which the few relevant criteria can be isolated with relative ease, may be assumed to have nearly equal dispersions. Since the sigmas must be estimated for Case IV as well as for Case III, however, there is but little more labor in using the more accurate computation of S values with formula (90).

Case V.—One last assumption is made for the simplest solution of all, the assumption that all the discriminal dispersions are equal. Letting $\sigma_a = \sigma_b$, the law can be stated:

$$S_b - S_a = X_{ba}\sqrt{2\sigma_b^2}$$
$$= X_{ba}\sigma_b\sqrt{2}.$$

And letting σ_b become the unit of the scale,

$$S_b - S_a = X_{ba}\sqrt{2} \tag{92}$$

The Relation to the Method of Constant Stimulus Differences.— It is easy to point out close relationships to the constant processes that were described in the chapter just preceding. The technique of paired comparisons itself is equivalent to Culler's proposal of the constant method with a variable standard. Comparing each stimulus with every other one is equivalent to making every stimulus in turn a standard. If the phi-gamma hypothesis can be applied to comparative judgments in the constant method, there is no reason why it cannot be likewise applied to paired comparisons—with one important difference. In the constant method, the phi-gamma function is assumed to be the mathematical relationship between the R values and their corresponding proportions of judgments 'g' or 'l.' According to Thurstone and the logic of the law of comparative judgment, that relationship holds between $S(= \log R)$ and the proportions and not between R and p. The last statement assumes Fechner's law, or that S is proportional to $\log R$. We need not assume Fechner's law, but from the law of comparative judgment it follows that the ogive relationship holds between S and the observed proportions. It should be added that this discussion assumes

Thurstone's Case V, in which the discriminal dispersions are equal and $r = 0$.

These facts are shown graphically from data obtained by the method of paired comparisons (see Fig. 28). Seven weights, ranging from 185 to 215, were compared with one another 200 times each by the same O. The S values were computed according to Case V (9). These S values are given along the X-axis in Fig. 28. The corresponding observed proportions are plotted against the S values for each weight in turn as a standard. It is perhaps clearer from this diagram how from every observed proportion we can

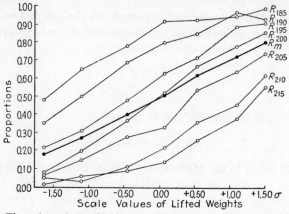

Fig. 28.—The ogive relationship between a given scale value and the proportions of choices of a weight of that value as compared with other weights.

predict the S value for every stimulus. Seven predictions are possible for every stimulus. The seven differ slightly from one another, but their means are the best S values for the stimulus in question. The heavy line near the center of the family of ogives is drawn at the means of the proportions. Its use will be discussed later.

HISTORY OF THE METHOD OF PAIRED COMPARISONS

Origin of the Method.—The method of paired comparisons is derived from Fechner's *method of choice* or *Wahlmethode*. In the latter a number of stimuli were exposed simultaneously in a haphazard arrangement and O was to select the one he liked best. This procedure met with numerous objections. Certain stimuli tended to be chosen because of their positions rather than because of any intrinsic values of the stimuli themselves. Some stimuli of a series were never chosen and so could not be discriminated. When the number of judges was small and the number of stimuli large, often no two chose the same stimulus. The method of paired comparisons grew out of these dissatisfactions with the method of choice. Fechner (5) himself first suggested the presentation of pairs of stimuli for judgment, but did little work with the method. Witmer (30) employed it in 1894 and criticized it on the score that it took too much time. Cohn (4) reports its use in the same year and defends it as being the simplest and best of the methods for measuring feeling tone. He permitted equality judgments, dividing them equally between '*g*' and '*l*.' He may be credited with the first attempt at a systematic presentation of stimuli.

Titchener recommended the use of the method in his first manual of psychology (26) and gave Cohn's schematic arrangement for the order of presentation of the pairs, an arrangement which is open to the objection that the same stimulus is used twice in succession. This is not good procedure in making affective judgments since the affective reaction adapts so quickly. Titchener (27) used the method with tones of different pitch and with metronome beats of different frequencies in his ingenious experiments on Wundt's tridimensional theory of feeling. Kowalewski (13) improved upon the order of presentation of stimuli, avoiding the error of repeating stimuli in immediate succession which was present in Cohn's and Titchener's procedures. Martin (14) was the first to point out the relation between the method and that of constant stimuli, but she did not proceed to devise a way of computing scale values. She proposed a variation which she called the *serial method;* this will be described among the other variations of paired comparisons.

The Nature of the Aesthetic Judgment.—Since the method is most often applied to the evaluation of feeling tone, or some other aesthetic aspect of the stimulus, and since much of the criticism for and against the method has dealt with the aesthetic judgment, it is necessary to discuss that topic here. Bullough (3) in 1908 led the attack against the method of paired comparisons, maintaining that the comparative judgment is entirely out of place in aesthetic evaluations. The comparative attitude, he maintained, is entirely opposed to the aesthetic attitude. The aesthetic attitude is above all, "noncomparative, individualizing, isolating, and in a sense absolute," he says (3, p. 412). Gordon (7) rejected paired comparisons in aesthetics for similar reasons. "It so quickly exhausts the aesthetic reaction," she comments. She proceeded, however, to use the ranking method, which is even more subject to the same criticism.

Valentine (29), although prejudiced against paired comparisons at the beginning of a study with musical intervals, came to the conclusion that it is fully as reliable and satisfactory as a rating-scale method that involves absolute judgments. In addition, his Os found paired judgments more objective than absolute judgments. Nakashima (15), who made a detailed introspective study of the affective judgment and the factors that control it, came to the conclusion that "affective judgments may be and usually are as direct and immediate as the sensory judgments of psychophysics" (15, p. 178). He also found that the most favorable attitude for a reliable judgment is a passive, listless one. This checks very well with the findings concerning judgments of a sensory type as reported in the preceding chapter.

Mathematical Development in Handling Paired Comparisons.— While credit for the final rationalization of the method of computing scale values from paired comparisons belongs to Thurstone, three others may be mentioned as having taken steps in the right direction. Thorndike (17) in preparing his handwriting scale first used the method of equal-appearing intervals. The final scale values were determined by a paired comparison of neighboring samples. The scale separation between them was based upon the assumption that 'equally often noticed differences are equal, unless always or never noticed.' Thurstone (20) has now shown that this principle is not always true. It holds only when the discriminal dispersions in question are equal. Two pairs of stimuli having two unequal scale separations between the members of the pairs might still give equal proportions of judgments, or two pairs having two equal scale separations might give unequal proportions if the discriminal dispersions are not equal. To proceed as Thorndike did is to assume that the dispersions are all equal, which is equivalent to Thurstone's Case V.

Hillegas (11) took one step beyond Thorndike when he defined as the unit of his scale for English compositions the PE of the distribution. Two specimens were regarded as one unit apart when the one was preferred to the other 75 per cent of the time. This unit is the PE of the distribution of differences and is $\sqrt{2}$ times as large as the *PE* of the discriminal dispersion. Garth (6) followed Hillegas in evaluating color preferences for different races. Whereas Hillegas was merely interested in selecting samples of compositions at equal intervals on the scale, Garth assigned numerical scale values for all the stimuli, and was perhaps the first on record to do so.

EXPERIMENT IX. A MEASURE OF RACIAL PREFERENCES

Problem.—To evaluate the preferences of a group of subjects for nine racial or national groups by the method of paired comparisons.

Materials.—Record sheets with paired lists of races.

Procedure:

1. Choose the names of nine foreign races or national groups which will probably have a wide range as to desirability or undesirability in the judgment of the average student.

2. Pair every race with every other one, making up the $n(n-1)/2$ customary pairs. Since n is 9, there will be 36 such pairs. Place the pairs in a prearranged scheme, seeing that no race is repeated twice in succession or in any rhythmical pattern and that every race appears an equal number of times on the right and left. The arrangement on the page should be somewhat as follows:[1]

German—Italian	Chinese—English	Greek—Russian
Russian—Spanish	Turk—French	Italian—Mexican

3. Prepare carefully a set of instructions for *O*, to be placed at the top of the page of paired names. Define clearly the chief criterion for making the choices: desirability for admission to American citizenship, desirability as close neighbors, intermarriage, or any similar specification.

4. Administer the experiment to at least 100 *O*s who are rather homogeneous as to age, education, and culture. This number of *O*s will do for demonstration purposes, but not less than 200 *O*s is a desirable number for experimental purposes.

5. It is well to secure from the *O*s information as to their own racial origins. Questions should be asked as to the race of the father's father and mother and the mother's father and mother. The scale values may later be compared with the national origins of the *O*s.

THE COMPUTATION OF SCALE VALUES

Finding the Observed Proportions.—The cooperation of several members of the class is required since the labor of tabulation is tedious and time consuming. The main initial task is to find the proportions of judgments each race received as compared with every other one. Such a table of proportions is given below, the data being adapted from one of Thurstone's studies (22).

---

[1] Ideal orders of presentation and schemes for working out orders for varying numbers of stimuli are prepared by Ross (16).

TABLE 33.—PROPORTIONS OF THE TIMES THAT THE NATIONALITY GIVEN AT THE TOP OF THE COLUMN WAS PREFERRED TO THOSE AT THE LEFT

	English	Scotch	French	Swedish	Italian	Russian	Greek	Mexican	Turk
English.....	.500	.278	.114	.122	.030	.038	.008	.008	.004
Scotch......	.722	.500	.357	.201	.076	.079	.030	.008	.000
French......	.886	.643	.500	.389	.222	.068	.013	.013	.013
Swedish.....	.878	.799	.611	.500	.200	.201	.084	.059	.026
Italian......	.970	.924	.778	.800	.500	.372	.163	.084	.046
Russian.....	.962	.921	.932	.799	.628	.500	.350	.261	.090
Greek.......	.992	.970	.987	.916	.837	.650	.500	.340	.213
Mexican....	.992	.992	.987	.941	.916	.739	.660	.500	.254
Turk........	.996	1.000	.987	.974	.954	.910	.787	.746	.500
Σ_p	7.898	7.027	6.253	5.642	4.363	3.557	2.595	2.019	1.146
M_p	.878	.781	.695	.627	.485	.395	.288	.224	.127

The proportion for each nationality as compared with itself is assumed to be .500, as indeed it would have been had the *O*s been asked to make this judgment. Each column is totaled in order to find out which nationality has the greatest sum. This one is placed at the left of the table and the others are arranged in rank order for convenience. The means of the proportions will be used later in a short-cut process of computing scale values.

Translating the Proportions into Standard Measurements.— The second major step is to translate the proportions into standard measurements, or *X*-distances, by means of Table E in the Appendix. These values correspond to the X_{ba} of the law of comparative judgment [see formula (89)]. For the illustrative problem they are given in Table 34. The average scale value of each stimulus will now be computed by means of three of Thurstone's procedures.

Solution with Case V.— The law of comparative judgment according to Case V is $S_b - S_a = X_{ba}\sqrt{2}$. From the table of X values we can find several estimates for each scale separation. For example, the separation $S_1 - S_2$ is given directly, but it is also to be found by the following relations:

$$(S_1 - S_3) - (S_2 - S_3) = S_1 - S_2,$$
$$(S_1 - S_4) - (S_2 - S_4) = S_1 - S_2,$$
$$(S_1 - S_5) - (S_2 - S_5) = S_1 - S_2,$$

and so on. It will be seen that these pairs of values appear in columns 1 and 2 of Table 34. The differences d_{12} can therefore be found by subtracting all numbers in column 2 from the corresponding ones in column 1. For example, in the third line of Table 34,

TABLE 34.—SCALE SEPARATIONS IN TERMS OF STANDARD DEVIATIONS OF THE DIFFERENCES BETWEEN EACH PAIR OF NATIONALITIES

Nationality	1	2	3	4	5	6	7	8	9
1. English.....	.000	− .589	−1.206	−1.165	−1.881	−1.774	−2.409	−2.409	−2.652
2. Scotch......	.589	.000	− .366	− .838	−1.433	−1.412	−1.881	−2.409	*
3. French.....	1.206	.366	.000	− .282	− .765	−1.491	−2.226	−2.226	−2.226
4. Swedish....	1.165	.838	.282	.000	− .842	− .838	−1.379	−1.563	−1.943
5. Italian.....	1.881	1.433	.765	.842	.000	− .327	− .982	−1.379	−1.685
6. Russian....	1.774	1.412	1.491	.838	.327	.000	− .385	− .640	−1.340
7. Greek......	2.409	1.881	2.226	1.379	.982	.385	.000	− .412	− .796
8. Mexican....	2.409	2.409	2.226	1.563	1.379	.640	.412	.000	− .662
9. Turk.......	2.652	*	2.226	1.943	1.685	1.341	.796	.662	.000

* When $p = 1.00$ or when $p = .00$ the scale separations are indeterminate.

$S_1 - S_3$ is 1.206 and $S_2 - S_3$ is .366. From the first example just mentioned, $(S_1 - S_3) - (S_2 - S_3)$, we have $1.206 - .366 = .840$, which is one estimate of $S_1 - S_2$. The difference

$$(S_1 - S_4) - (S_2 - S_4)$$

is $1.165 - .838 = .327$, another estimate of $S_1 - S_2$. We can thus obtain eight estimates of $S_1 - S_2$, if columns 1 and 2 are complete, and the mean of these estimates is probably a better measure of that scale separation than any one of them. These differences appear in column 1 of Table 35. Notice that the difference .589 appears only once. It is numerically the same whether we are dealing with $(S_1 - S_2)$ or $(S_2 - S_1)$, and it is therefore used only once in finding the mean of the differences.[1] Notice also that the last three differences are missing from column 1. This is because one or both of the X values concerned in these differences are greater than 2σ, and hence are relatively unreliable. No difference coming from a p greater than .977 or less than .023 (X is then greater than 2.00σ) should be used in finding an unweighted mean of the differ-

[1] An exception to this rule is the rare case in which every stimulus is also judged as compared with itself and p_{kk} is not assumed to equal .50. Such a case can occur with lifted weights or other stimuli whose identity can be kept from O.

ences.[1] The reason for this will be clear in the solution of a weighted mean which is illustrated on the following page.

Once the means of the differences are found, as at the bottom of Table 35, the next step is to multiply them by $\sqrt{2}$ in order to make the unit of the scale the σ of the discriminal dispersion. The final step is to assign a value of .000 to the smallest scale value by adding the successive differences to obtain the final scale values for all the stimuli. These nine values will be seen in Table 36.

TABLE 35.—DIFFERENCES BETWEEN EACH S VALUE AND ITS NEAREST NEIGHBOR, AND THE UNWEIGHTED MEANS OF THE DIFFERENCES

R	d_{12}	d_{23}	d_{34}	d_{45}	d_{56}	d_{67}	d_{78}	d_{89}
1	.....	.617	−.041	.716	−.107	.....	.....	.....
2	.589	......	.472	.595	−.021	.469	.....	.....
3	.840	.366	......	.483	.726	.....	.....	.....
4	.327	.556	.282	.....	−.004	.541	.184	.380
5	.448	.668	−.077	.842	......	.655	.397	.306
6	.362	−.079	.653	.511	.327	.....	.255	.701
7	.....	......	......	.397	.597	.385	.....	.384
8	.....	......	......	.184	.739	.228	.412	.....
9	.....	......	......	.258	.344	.545	.134	.662
Σ_d	2.566	2.128	1.289	3.986	2.601	2.823	1.382	2.433
M_d	.513	.426	.258	.498	.325	.471	.276	.487
$\sqrt{2}M_d$	.725	.602	.365	.704	.460	.666	.390	.689

Weighting the Observed Differences.—As in the constant process, proportions deviating very far from .50 should have less influence in determining the mean of the differences here, just as they had less weight in determining the DL. Thurstone (23) describes the weighting process in detail in a recent study on the measurement of opinion. The Müller-Urban weights which were used in the constant process can be readily adapted here. The weight of a difference, d_{ba}, is given by the formula

$$W_{ba} = \frac{1}{\dfrac{1}{w_{ak}} + \dfrac{1}{w_{bk}}} \tag{93}$$

[1] If Table 34 were complete, with no vacancies as at X_{92} and X_{29}, and if there were no values greater than 2.000, then the scale values could be obtained directly from the means of the columns. Each M_x should be multiplied by $\sqrt{2}$ and a new zero point should be adopted in order to eliminate negative scale values.

where w_{ak} and w_{bk} are the Urban weights corresponding to the proportions p_{ak} and p_{bk}, respectively, the subscript k being used to stand for any other stimulus. As an illustration, the weighted mean of the differences d_{12} is worked out in Table 37.

TABLE 36.—SUMMARY OF THE SCALE VALUES FOUND BY ALL THE METHODS EMPLOYED

Race	Case V		Case IV	Case III	
	Un-weighted	Weighted	Un-weighted	Un-weighted	Weighted
English..........	4.601	4.862	5.176	5.267	5.422
Scotch...........	3.876	4.112	4.021	4.051	4.214
French...........	3.274	3.488	3.415	3.429	3.592
Swedish..........	2.909	3.043	3.088	3.119	3.167
Italian..........	2.205	2.287	2.377	2.401	2.442
Russian..........	1.745	1.772	1.910	1.935	1.949
Greek............	1.079	1.087	1.302	1.326	1.310
Mexican..........	.689	.699	.906	.928	.914
Turk.............	.000	.000	.000	.000	.000

TABLE 37.—DIFFERENCES BETWEEN S_1 AND S_2, AND THEIR WEIGHTED MEAN

	p_{1k}	p_{2k}	d_{12}	w_{1k}	w_{2k}	$1/w_{1k}$	$1/w_{2k}$	$1/W_{12}$	W_{12}	$W_{12}d_{12}$
2	.722	.500	.589	.881	1.000	1.1351	1.0000	2.1351	.4684	.27589
3	.886	.643	.840	.578	.952	1.7301	1.0504	2.7805	.3596	.30206
4	.878	.799	.327	.600	.771	1.6667	1.2970	2.9637	.3374	.11033
5	.970	.924	.448	.247	.457	4.0486	2.1882	6.2368	.1603	.07181
6	.962	.921	.362	.292	.468	3.4247	2.1368	5.5615	.1798	.06509
7	.992	.970	.528	.090	.247	11.1111	4.0486	15.1597	.0660	.03485
8	.992	.992	.000	.090	.090	11.1111	11.1111	22.2222	.0450	.00000

$$\Sigma \quad 1.6165 \quad .86003$$
$$M_d \qquad\qquad .532$$
$$\sqrt{2}M_d \qquad\qquad .752$$

The advantage of using weighted means is now clearer. The weights for the differences vary from .4684 down to .0450. When the proportions exceed .970, the weight falls in the vicinity of .1000, which emphasizes the importance of dropping those differences when obtaining an unweighted mean. However, in this problem the unweighted means are so very close to weighted means that the tedious process of weighting seems not worth the extra time and effort. The scale values as obtained from weighted average differences will be found in Table 36.

Testing the Scale Values.—The best test of whether Case V, or any of the assumptions made by Thurstone, fits the observed data is to start with the final scale values and work backward to the theoretical proportions demanded by them. The discrepancies between the theoretical and observed proportions tell the story. Taking the scale values from column 1 of Table 36, for example, the first step is to find the theoretical X values by the formula

$$X'_{ba} = \frac{(S_b - S_a)}{\sqrt{2}} \tag{94}$$

which is derived directly from formula (92).[1] These theoretical X values are given in Table 38.

TABLE 38.—THEORETICAL X VALUES FROM SCALE VALUES OBTAINED WITH CASE V, UNWEIGHTED MEANS

	1	2	3	4	5	6	7	8
2	.513							
3	.939	.426						
4	1.197	.684	.258					
5	1.695	1.182	.756	.498				
6	2.020	1.507	1.081	.823	.325			
7	2.491	1.978	1.552	1.294	.796	.471		
8	2.767	2.254	1.828	1.570	1.072	.747	.276	
9	3.254	2.741	2.315	2.057	1.559	1.234	.763	.487

The 36 theoretical proportions may now be found from these values by the use of Table B. These proportions are given in Table 39.

The discrepancies between p and p' may now be found by comparing Table 39 with Table 33 and finding the differences. These discrepancies are given in Table 40.

---

[1] As a short cut here, one may make use of the mean differences M_d to be found in the next-to-the-bottom row of Table 35, adding them by two's, three's, and four's as is necessary. For example $(S_1 - S_3)/\sqrt{2}$ is equal to $M_{d12} + M_{d23} = .513 + .426 = .939$. $(S_1 - S_4) = M_{d12} + M_{d23} + M_{d34} = .513 + .426 + .258 = 1.197$.

TABLE 39.—THEORETICAL PROPORTIONS OBTAINED FROM THE SCALE VALUES CALCULATED BY CASE V

	1	2	3	4	5	6	7	8
2	.696							
3	.826	.665						
4	.884	.753	.602					
5	.955	.881	.775	.691				
6	.978	.934	.860	.795	.627			
7	.994	.976	.940	.902	.787	.681		
8	.997	.988	.966	.942	.858	.773	.609	
9	.999	.997	.990	.980	.940	.891	.777	.687

TABLE 40.—DISCREPANCIES BETWEEN THE OBSERVED AND THEORETICAL PROPORTIONS ASSUMING CASE V

	1	2	3	4	5	6	7	8
2	.026							
3	.060	.022						
4	.006	.046	.009					
5	.015	.043	.003	.109				
6	.016	.013	.072	.004	.001			
7	.002	.006	.047	.014	.050	.031		
8	.005	.004	.021	.001	.058	.034	.051	
9	.003	.003	.003	.006	.014	.019	.010	.059

From Table 40 we see that the maximum discrepancy is .109, the mean discrepancy is .027, and the median is .014. The seriousness of any discrepancy is best decided from the PE of the observed proportion to which it corresponds. p_{45} is .800, and its PE is .018 ($N = 239$). The discrepancy (.109) is therefore at least six times PE_p; it is certainly too large to be ignored. In fact, any discrepancies larger than .080 are probably significant of a poor correspondence between theory and fact. The value .080 is chosen because it is four times the PE_p when $p = .750$. Only one discrepancy in Table 40 exceeds this criterion, so the scale values may be regarded on the whole as valid. Any *significant* discrepancies might be expected to disappear if Case IV or Case III were used, bringing into the estimation of the scale values the sigmas of the discriminal dispersions. If the discrepancies do not then become insignificant, Case II must be assumed and r in formula (89) cannot be zero.

If the scale values from column 2 of Table 36 are used, in other words, those found from the weighted means of the differences computed by Case V, the discrepancies are scarcely any smaller. Their mean is .028 and the maximum is .097, which is still over five times its PE_p. The relative merits of weighted versus unweighted scale values are seen in a comparison of these discrepancies with those above. A few relatively large discrepancies make it important to try Cases IV and III.

Solution with Case IV.—A solution with either Case III or Case IV requires the estimation of the standard deviations of the dispersions. Thurstone (24) has provided a method for approximating these sigmas. The steps in estimating σ_1, for example, are as follows:

1. Find V_1, which is the standard deviation of all the scale separations from S_1. It is the σ of the distribution of the nine values in column 1 of Table 34. Find V_k likewise for every column.

2. Find $\Sigma(1/V_k)$, or the sum of all the reciprocals of these standard deviations.

3. Find a constant value a by the formula

$$a = \frac{2n}{\Sigma \dfrac{1}{V_k}} \tag{95}$$

where n = the number of stimuli.

4. Find σ_1 by the general formula

$$\sigma_k = \frac{a}{V_k} - 1 \tag{96}$$

The most expedient solution for V_1, and for any other V_k, is to square all the X values (X_{ka} in Table 34), find the sums of the squares for each column, and solve for V, as one solves for any σ of a distribution, by formula (9): $\sigma = \sqrt{\dfrac{\Sigma X^2}{n} - M_x^2}$. For our illustrative problem, $\Sigma(1/V_k) = 8.671$ and $a = 2.076$. The various sigmas [applying formula (96)] are found to be : 1.45, .90, .74, 1.01, .75, 1.05, .89, .97, and 1.24, for the nationalities 1 to 9, respectively. The unit of the sigmas is their mean. Their sum is consequently equal to n, which serves as a check upon the computation of the sigmas. In this case, $\Sigma\sigma_k = 9.00$ exactly.

In Case IV $S_b - S_a = .707X_{ba}(\sigma_b + \sigma_a)$. The simplest arrangements consist of (1) a table giving the values for $(\sigma_b + \sigma_a)$; (2) a table giving $.707(\sigma_b + \sigma_a)$; and finally (3) a table with

$$.707X_{ba}(\sigma_b + \sigma_a).$$

The latter corresponds exactly in meaning with Table 34, which was obtained by Case V. A table of the differences is then computed, corresponding to Table 35 of the solution by Case V.[1] Either weighted or unweighted means of the differences may then be computed. For the illustrative data the writer has computed only unweighted means, and the resulting scale values are given in Table 36. In order to test the superiority of Case IV over Case V, theoretical proportions were computed from the final scale values. The theoretical X values are first computed by the formula

$$X'_{ba} = \frac{(S_b - S_a)}{.707(\sigma_b + \sigma_a)} \qquad (97)$$

and from these the theoretical proportions are obtained. When this was done for the illustrative problem, the mean discrepancy was .019, with a maximum of .084. The results are apparently better than with Case V, even when the means are weighted in the latter case.

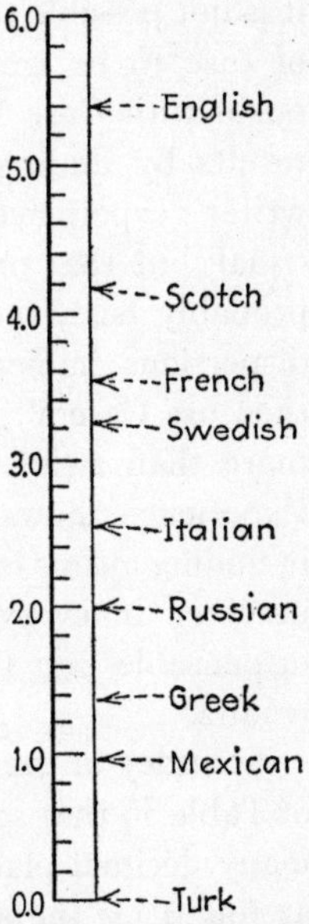

Solution by Case III.—Having estimated sigmas of the dispersions, one may as well employ the more accurate methods of computation offered by Case III. $S_b - S_a = X_{ba}\sqrt{\sigma_b^2 + \sigma_a^2}$. Three convenient tables for the solution of these differences give the values of: (1) $\sigma_b^2 + \sigma_a^2$, (2) $\sqrt{\sigma_b^2 + \sigma_a^2}$, and (3) $X_{ba}\sqrt{\sigma_b^2 + \sigma_a^2}$. A fourth table of scale differences, d_{12}, d_{23}, d_{34}, etc., is prepared. As before, weighted or unweighted means of the differences may be computed. The final scale values for our problem on nationalities are given in columns 4 and 5 of Table 36. The test

Fig. 29.—Graphic representation of the scale values of the nine nationalities.

---

[1] The arithmetic labor may be reduced in this problem by delaying the multiplication by .707, omitting step (2), until the means of the scale separations have been found.

of these scale values is the same as before. The theoretical X values are found by the formula

$$X'_{ba} = \frac{(S_b - S_a)}{\sqrt{\sigma_b^2 + \sigma_a^2}} \qquad (98)$$

The mean discrepancy with unweighted averages is .021, with a maximum of .088; with weighted averages the mean is .020, with a maximum of .084. Case III here proves to be no better than Case IV, but this would not always be so.

Choice of the Case to Use.—At the present stage of our experience with the modes of computing scale values from paired comparisons, it is not possible to lay down any hard and fast rules as to the choice of case to be employed in any given situation. One can always begin with Case V, as described in this chapter, and then test the results by finding the size of the discrepancies. It has been the writer's experience that the discriminal dispersions are rarely exactly equal, but that on the other hand they do not differ widely. It is probably best, therefore, to estimate the sigmas of the discriminal dispersions immediately. If the sigmas are practically identical, then use Case V. If they are nearly the same, with the largest no more than twice the smallest, then Case IV is usually adequate. Experience shows that the differential weighting of the differences in finding means is time wasted. A judicious choice of the differences involved in every unweighted mean makes such weighting easily dispensable and the results are closely comparable with weighted results.

Accuracy of the Scale Values.—It is evident from an examination of Table 36 that scale values as usually computed are not accurate to many decimal places. The scale values, weighted and unweighted, as found by the same case, usually differ significantly beyond the second decimal place and may be regarded as strictly accurate only to the first decimal place. The addition of more decimal places during the process of computation is perfectly possible but it gives merely an appearance of delicacy of measurement that is highly misleading. Mere manipulation of figures adds nothing by way of accuracy to data that are not perfectly accurate to begin with. However, sufficient decimal places must be kept during the computations so that none of the accuracy already present will be lost. Proportions and X values should be computed to three decimal places when the number of judges is relatively large. In the end, the third decimal place should very properly be dropped from the scale values.

Variations of the Method

The chief objection to the method of paired comparisons is that it takes too much time and is wearying to the judges. When the number of stimuli becomes relatively large—and any number greater than 15 would be regarded as relatively large for paired comparisons —the task of judging pairs of stimuli becomes long and irksome. Not only is the task long for the judges; it is also very long for the investigator. The number of pairs is $n(n-1)/2$, and even with no more than 20 stimuli there are about 190 pairs, 190 judgments, 190 proportions, and 190 deviates to look up in the tables and deal with thereafter. There are ways of shortening the tasks of either the judges or the investigator or of both.

Reducing the Number of Pairs of Stimuli.—There is nothing sacrosanct about pairing each stimulus with every other one in the series. To do so probably does tend to emphasize the unity of the continuum in question in the minds of the judges. And yet some stimuli in long series are so far apart psychologically that the proportions of judgments approach 1.00; hence the differences are so unreliable as to be useless for the computation of scale values. Therefore, not every stimulus is a good standard with which to compare all the stimuli of the series. It is often a proper procedure to select from all the stimuli a limited number to become the standards for the scale. These should be chosen at approximately equal intervals along the scale and they should be among the least ambiguous of the lot. In a series of seven lifted weights the writer found (9) that the number of standards could be reduced to three or five without serious loss in accuracy of the results.

A very practical device is suggested by Uhrbrock and Richardson (28). A list of the names of 45 supervisors whom they wished to evaluate was broken up into four groups (A, B, C, and D) of 10 each and an additional group (K) of 5 'key' men. Within each group of 10, each man was compared with every other man. Every man in groups A, B, C, and D, was compared with every one of the 5 'key' men in group K. Thus the number of pairs was reduced from a possible 990 to only 390.

The suggestion of Uhrbrock and Richardson still leaves a very large number of judgments to be made. A greater saving might be made by taking a cue from Thorndike. Having established the approximate rank order of his samples from the method of equal-appearing intervals—any other rough method will do—he obtained paired comparisons between neighboring pairs of stimuli. This plan might be extended somewhat, pairing every stimulus with a limited number of its neighbors on either side. Since scale separations coming from proportions near .500 carry the greatest weight in fixing the final scale values, the proportions from relatively close neighbors are what we want. Proportions from remote pairs of stimuli carry little weight and may very well be eliminated from consideration. This plan would give us a few more reliable differences, d_{12}, d_{23}, etc., from which to find a final mean scale separation between neighbors and thus the total scale.

Reducing the Labor of Computation.—The author (8) has suggested a means whereby the labor of computing scale values may be very materially reduced even when a complete pairing of the stimuli has been used. The essential part of this process consists in finding the mean of the proportions of judgments for every stimulus as compared with every other one *as well as* with itself. This has been done in Table 33. The means of the columns are given at the bottom of the table. The deviates corresponding to these mean proportions are now found from the usual table. For the sake of illustration, the mean proportions and their deviates are given here in Table 41.

TABLE 41.—MEANS OF THE PROPORTIONS OF JUDGMENTS GREATER FOR EVERY STIMULUS AND THEIR CORRESPONDING DEVIATES

Stimulus	1	2	3	4	5	6	7	8	9
Mean proportion	.878	.781	.695	.627	.485	.395	.288	.224	.127
X value	1.165	.776	.510	.324	−.038	−.266	−.559	−.759	−1.141
SV	2.306	1.917	1.651	1.465	1.103	.875	.582	.382	.000

The advantage, from the point of view of economy of effort, is at once apparent. Only n proportions need be dealt with instead of $n(n-1)/2$, and, once the deviates are found, they can be immediately translated into positive scale values by shifting the zero point to the lowest stimulus in the series. A still greater saving can be made in tallying the judgments. The mean proportions can be found without calculating the $n(n-1)/2$ single proportions at all.

We need merely tally the total number of times any stimulus is chosen in all its comparisons and then apply the formula

$$M_p = \frac{C + \dfrac{N}{2}}{nN} \tag{99}$$

where C = the total number of choices given to a stimulus.

$\quad N$ = the number of judges.

$\quad n$ = the number of stimuli.

The correction $N/2$ in the numerator is for the assumed number of choices the stimulus would have received if it had been compared with itself. This makes clearer the theory underlying the short-cut method proposed here. It is assumed that the standard is a composite of all the stimuli in the series and that M_p is the proportion of the times any given stimulus is chosen in preference to that standard.

From one point of view this procedure is much like that in the *method of single stimuli* described in the preceding chapter. Although the judgments in the latter method are called 'absolute,' actually no stimulus is judged or can be judged except on the background of residual impressions of all the stimuli in the series, and it is judged primarily in comparison with the one just preceding. If the order of presentation of stimuli is controlled so that each stimulus follows every other one equally often, the method of single stimuli approaches that of paired comparisons. In the method of paired comparisons, contrariwise, although we ask for comparative judgments, O cannot help judging each stimulus on the background of the residual impressions of all others in the series; to that extent he renders an 'absolute' judgment. If the ogive relationship holds for the one case, it should hold for the other, and scale values on the X-axis should be approximately correct when found from the mean proportions.

The validity of the process just proposed may be seen in Fig. 30 where the scale values from this method are plotted against those obtained from Case III (weighted means) appearing in the last column of Table 36. The plot is clearly linear within a range of five units on the scale at least, and the correlation is so very close that the short-cut method, even from the standpoint of valid relative scale values, would seem justified. It has been tested and found valid on previous occasions (9).

The most serious objection to the short-cut method is the uncertainty of the unit. There is, so far as the writer knows, no theoretical basis for defining the unit. It is neither the sigma of the average discriminal dispersion nor the sigma of the difference between the two stimuli. If the above analogy to the method of single stimuli holds, then the unit is the sigma of the difference between every stimulus and the mean scale value of them all. So long as we deal with a single set of stimuli and want merely their relative scale positions, the uncertainty of the unit is not a serious matter; thus

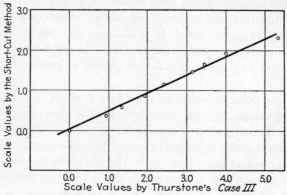

FIG. 30.—The relationship between scale values as obtained from the short-cut process and those obtained from Thurstone's Case III.

for most practical purposes the problem of the unit need not cause serious concern.

The Serial Method.—The **serial method** was first proposed by Martin (14, p. 147) but seems not to have been applied until 1929 by Beebe-Center (1). The method consists in presenting the stimuli in serial order and asking for a judgment of 'p' (pleasant), 'u' (unpleasant), or 'd' (doubtful). No suggestion was made for computing scale values. Martin went directly from this to a rating-scale procedure without taking the expected step of finding the proportion of 'p' judgments for each stimulus and translating this into sigma units. The procedure would be simpler if no 'd' judgments were permitted, but, if they are to be permitted, they could be eliminated from the computations as was suggested in connection with the constant process.

The advantage of this method over ordinary paired comparisons, at least in dealing with affective and aesthetic values, is that an absolute zero point can be established. It is the indifference point of the affective scale. Paired comparisons with the foregoing modes of computing scale values do not enable us to find this point for any series of stimuli. The serial method, as proposed here, would not be adequate to deal with a whole series of stimuli in all cases, since there are obviously some stimuli that would be judged '*p*' (or '*u*') either always or never. The unit of the scale would also be somewhat uncertain. It is very probable that the larger the number of judges, or the more heterogeneous they are with respect to the attribute being judged, the larger the unit would become and the smaller the apparent scatter of the scale values. That is true, however, but to a lesser extent, with scale values from paired comparisons. But it is urged here that the serial method be tried and that it be used to supplement paired comparisons in order to find the real zero points of the scale values.

The Method of Balanced Values.—A more complicated but well-rationalized method of finding scale values with reference to a real zero point has been described by Horst (12). It may be called the **method of balanced values.** In addition to asking for paired comparisons, as in the form, "I would rather have S_1 than S_2," Horst asks for judgments of the type, "If I could have S_1, I would be willing to take S_9." In the former case, S_1 and S_2 are relatively near together on the continuum so that neither is preferred to the other 100 per cent of the time. In the latter case, the two are on opposite sides of the indifference point, which is taken as the absolute zero, S_1 being pleasant and S_9 being unpleasant. The two are sufficiently well balanced to avoid proportions of positive responses equal to 0 or 1.00. When the two are equidistant from zero, $p = .50$. When $p < .50$, then $S_1 + S_9$ is a negative value, S_9 being more unpleasant than S_1 is pleasant. When $p > .50$, then $S_1 + S_9$ is a positive value, with S_1 more pleasant than S_9 is unpleasant. From the scale separations and differences obtained from the two types of judgments, a least square solution gives scale values with reference to the indifference point. The method of balanced values is not described in detail here because it still lacks empirical tests to determine its general applicability; it is much more laborious than the serial method which was mentioned in the preceding paragraph.

Applications of Paired Comparisons

The range of applicability of the method of paired comparisons is so great that not all the specific uses can be referred to here. In general, it can be applied whenever stimuli can be presented in pairs, either simultaneously or in succession. Its chief use up to the present time has been in the determination of affective values and of aesthetic values; colors, designs, rectangles, musical intervals, nationality preferences, and the like have been the favorite stimuli. Opinions on such questions as prohibition, war, religion, and the like can be treated and evaluated by this method, although the handling of such material in paired comparisons becomes at times a bit awkward. The application to the evaluation of individuals on some trait of personality or character, or on their value to a certain industry, as Uhrbrock and Richardson have already done, would seem to have great possibilities. It might replace the less accurate and less valid methods of rating scales, where more exacting practical or experimental work needs to be done. It might very well serve as the criterion of validity against which to check any of the less accurate or less dependable methods of evaluating stimuli, either persons or things, attributes or opinions, wherever the results of those less reliable methods are held in question.

The Method of Similar Reactions (Similar Attributes)

Another type of scaling device deserves to be mentioned, and, since it is based upon probabilities, it is more closely allied to paired comparisons than to any other scaling method. This device is known as the **method of similar reactions** or the **method of similar attributes.** It has been rationalized by Thurstone (25) and it was recommended as a tool for securing scale values of propositions reflecting social attitudes. A large number of individuals are asked to endorse all the propositions to which they agree in a list pertaining to a single topic, for example, opinions pertaining to war. One proposition might be, "War is thoroughly rooted in human nature," and another, "War stirs man to heights of unselfishness." If the two opinions stand close together on the continuum representing a favorable versus an unfavorable attitude toward war, an individual who endorses one will be very likely to endorse the other. Out of a large number of subjects, a high percentage will react positively to both. If two other statements are widely separated on the scale, only a small proportion of those who endorse the one will also endorse the other. In other words, the greater the proportion of 'similar reactions' to two propositions, the nearer together they are on the scale. From the probability of a similar reaction to two items can be computed the scale separation between them. With scale separations computed between each item and every other one, the remaining task is much like that for paired comparison data.

Unfortunately, if two propositions or items have scale differences of an irrelevant nature, other than a difference restricted to the fundamental dimension or continuum in question, the method is unfitted to cope with the problem. For example, the writer (10) attempted to evaluate the degree of introversion or extroversion of the reactions to items of a typical questionnaire. Scale separations could be found between every item and every other one, but, after the final average scale differences were obtained, the discrepancies between them and the experimentally determined scale separations were entirely too large. The reason is, of course, that the individual scale separations between pairs of items do not lie along the same linear continuum. The test items represented several different dimensions of personality. Wherever a single dimension can be shown to apply, the method of similar reactions may be used. But at present there is no preliminary test to determine whether or not this is the case. Only the test of internal consistency after the deed will tell, and, if the test of consistency fails, it is then too late. For this reason space is not given here to describe the method of similar reactions in detail. It is expected that the difficulty will be overcome and that this device may be added to the as yet limited repertory of scaling methods.

Problems

1. Seven weights were compared with one another by the same individual, as in the method of paired comparisons, making 200 judgments of every pair. The table shown on page 242 gives the proportions of the judgments of 'greater' for the stimulus at the top of the table as compared with each stimulus at the side. The stimuli are designated by the physical weight in grams.

    a. Compute the psychological scale values for the seven weights, assuming Case V, both with and without weighted observations.

    b. Estimate the standard errors of the dispersions for the seven stimuli and, if necessary, assume Cases IV and III and compute the scale values accordingly.

    c. Compute scale values by means of the author's short method.

	185	190	195	200	205	210	215
185	.48	.65	.78	.92	.93	.95	.99
190	.35	.50	.69	.80	.85	.97	.94
195	.22	.31	.48	.63	.72	.89	.91
200	.08	.20	.37	.52	.67	.78	.86
205	.07	.15	.28	.33	.54	.64	.74
210	.05	.03	.11	.22	.36	.46	.62
215	.01	.06	.09	.14	.26	.38	.56

References

1. BEEBE-CENTER, J. G., The law of affective equilibrium, *Amer. J. Psychol.*, 1929, **41**, 54–69.
2. ———, "The Psychology of Pleasantness and Unpleasantness," D. Van Nostrand Company, Inc., New York, 1932.
3. BULLOUGH, E., The 'perceptive problem' in the aesthetic appreciation of single colours, *Brit. J. Psychol.*, 1908, **2**, 406–462.
4. COHN, J., Experimentelle Untersuchungen über die Gefühlsbetonung der Farben, Helligkeiten und ihrer Combinationen, *Phil. Stud.*, 1894, **10**, 562–603.
5. FECHNER, G. T., Zur experimentalen Aesthetik, *Abhandl. math. phys. Classe d. K. Sächs. Ges. d. Wiss.*, 1871, **9**, 555–635.
6. GARTH, T. R., Color preferences of 559 full blood Indians, *J. Exper. Psychol.*, 1922, **5**, 392–418.
7. GORDON, K., Esthetics of simple color arrangements, *Psychol. Rev.*, 1912, **19**, 352–363.
8. GUILFORD, J. P., The method of paired comparisons as a psychometric method, *Psychol. Rev.*, 1928, **35**, 494–506.
9. ———, Some empirical tests of the method of paired comparisons, *J. Gen. Psychol.*, 1931, **5**, 64–76.
10. ———, An examination of a typical test of introversion-extroversion by means of the method of similar reactions, *J. Soc. Psychol.*, 1933, **4**, 430–443.
11. HILLEGAS, M. B., A scale for the measurement of quality in English composition, *Teach. Coll. Rec.*, 1912, **13**, no. 4.
12. HORST, P., A method for determining the absolute affective value of a series of stimulus situations, *J. Educ. Psychol.*, 1932, **23**, 418–440.
13. KOWALEWSKI, A., Studien zur Psychologie des Pessimismus, *Grenzfragen des Nerven und Seelenlebens*, 1904, **24**.
14. MARTIN, L. J., An experimental study of Fechner's principles of aesthetics, *Psychol. Rev.*, 1906, **13**, 142–219.
15. NAKASHIMA, T., Contributions to the study of the affective processes, *Amer. J. Psychol.*, 1909, **20**, 157–193.
16. ROSS, R. T., Optimum orders for the presentation of pairs in the method of paired comparisons, *J. Educ. Psychol.*, 1934, **25**, 375–382.
17. THORNDIKE, E. L., Handwriting, *Teach. Coll. Rec.*, 1910, **11**, no. 2.

18. THURSTONE, L. L., Psychophysical analysis, *Amer. J. Psychol.*, 1927, **38** 368–389.

19. ———, A law of comparative judgment, *Psychol. Rev.*, 1927, **34**, 273–286.

20. ———, Equally often noticed differences, *J. Educ. Psychol.*, 1927, **18**, 289–293.

21. ———, The method of paired comparisons for social values, *J. Abn. and Soc. Psychol.*, 1927, **21**, 384–400.

22. ———, An experimental study of nationality preferences, *J. Gen. Psychol.*, 1928, **1**, 405–424.

23. ———, The measurement of opinion, *J. Abn. and Soc. Psychol.*, 1928, **22**, 415–430.

24. ———, Stimulus dispersions in the method of constant stimuli, *J. Exper. Psychol.*, 1932, **15**, 284–297.

25. ———, Theory of attitude measurement, *Psychol. Rev.*, 1929, **36**, 222–241.

26. TITCHENER, E. B., "Experimental Psychology," The Macmillan Company, New York, Vol. I, Pt. I, 1901.

27. ———, Ein Versuch die Methode der paarweisen Vergleichung auf die verschiedenen Gefühlsrichtungen anzuwenden, *Phil. Stud.*, 1902, **20**, 382–406.

28. UHRBROCK, R. S., and M. W. RICHARDSON, Item analysis, *Person. J.*, 1933, **12**, 141–154.

29. VALENTINE, C. W., The method of comparison in experiments with musical intervals, *Brit. J. Psychol.*, 1914, **7**, 118–135.

30. WITMER, L., Zur experimentellen Aesthetik einfacher räumlicher Form-verhältnisse, *Phil. Stud.*, 1894, **9**, 96–144, 209–263.

31. WOODWORTH, R. S., Professor Cattell's psychophysical contributions, *Arch. Psychol.*, 1914, no. 30, 60–74.

CHAPTER VIII

THE METHOD OF RANK ORDER

ORDER-OF-MERIT METHOD

The method of rank order has been one of the most popular and one of the most practical of the psychometric methods. Its appeal has consisted largely in the ease with which a relatively large number of stimuli can be judged with reference to one another, and also in its wide range of applicability. Any stimuli that can be manipulated in any manner so as to place them in serial order can be treated with this method, whether they be lifted weights, names of scientists, artistic designs, beliefs, advertisements, or jokes. Stimuli that have been ranked by a number of judges can be placed in a final 'pooled' rank order. More than that, definite scale values can now be assigned to the stimuli. The method bears some superficial resemblance to that of equal-appearing intervals on the one hand and to paired comparisons on the other. It resembles the former in that the stimuli are arranged by O along some continuum. It is different in that there is only one stimulus in a class and the intervals between stimuli are not necessarily equal; in fact the intervals are usually not equal. The resemblance to paired comparisons is much more fundamental, in that each stimulus can be compared with all the rest, all of them being present for simultaneous observation. Any stimulus R_k may be said to be judged greater than all stimuli placed lower in the list, $R_l, R_m, R_n, \ldots, R_z$, and judged less than all those placed higher in the list, $R_j, R_i, R_h, \ldots, R_a$. There is this slight difference, however, in that paired comparisons give opportunity for deviations from a strict rank order. The method of rank order enforces upon a judge a certain internal consistency which at times may be artificial.

EARLY HISTORY OF THE METHOD

Its Origin.—Credit for the origin of the method of rank order is often given to Cattell, and it is in a sense a child of the Columbia

Psychological Laboratory.   The first published report which features the method is a study of belief by Sumner (22).   Twenty-five propositions were to be placed in order for the degree of belief or disbelief by 130 subjects.   The earliest mention of evaluating stimuli by ranking them, however, was made by Witmer in 1894 (25). Witmer referred to it as his *method of regular arrangement*.   Galton had evaluated human traits even earlier (8).   Cattell's first study with the method consisted of the arrangement of 211 shades of black, white, and gray (3).   He was primarily interested in the average error of displacement of the samples, which he found to range from 6 to 11.5 steps.   In 1906 Cattell (4) made the first application to the evaluation of human traits in his study of men of science.   A thousand scientists having been chosen in a preliminary experiment, the men in each scientific field were ranked by 10 from that field. The average of the 10 ranks given to each scientist measured his merit as a scientist.   The implicit assumption in this practice is that each rank position marks a unit on the psychological scale.

Early Applications.—Others immediately applied the method in similar studies.   Wells (24) attempted to evaluate the leading American writers.   Besides measuring general merit, he tried to secure ratings of 10 specifically defined traits.   Hollingworth (14) followed with evaluations of advertising appeals.   Strong (19, 20) had advertisements rated for attention value, persuasiveness, and memory value.   Strong deserves special mention here because of the suggestion that the final scale values be the median of the ranks rather than the mean.   This is in line with the mode of computing scale values from the method of equal-appearing intervals.   It tends to overcome the end effect in both methods.

Other Applications.—To cite only a few additional applications in order to show the variety of materials that can be so handled, the studies of Downey, Fernald, Kuper, Gordon, and Brogan may be mentioned.   Downey (6) had samples of handwriting ranked for degree of similarity to a standard sample.   Fernald (7) studied ethical judgments of delinquents by asking them to rank 10 offenses. Kuper (18) studied the interests of children by asking them to rank pictures.   Gordon (10) demonstrated the use of the method in aesthetics in a study of oriental rug patterns, showing that pooled ranks have a high degree of reliability.   Brogan (2) demonstrated its applicability to experimental ethics by asking large numbers of students to put in rank order for degree of wrongness 16 common unethical practices.

EXPERIMENT X. SCALE VALUES FROM RANK ORDERS

Problem.—To determine the psychological scale values for a series of related stimuli by the method of ranking.

Materials.—Select 20 to 25 stimuli belonging to the same continuum, such as samples of handwriting; playing–card designs; names of books, magazines, radio programs, or songs; advertisements; words; picture postcards; or anything that can be readily manipulated by the judges.

Procedure:

1. Provide ample table space upon which the stimuli may be spread out and viewed simultaneously.

2. Prepare and write out a set of instructions for O to follow, defining with care the particular continuum along which the stimuli are to be arranged in order from highest to lowest.

3. O is to reread the instructions whenever in doubt as to the nature of the judgments he is to make.

4. O is to avoid being impressed with the appearance of the series as a whole and is to make frequent recourse to paired comparisons.

5. When satisfied with the final arrangement, E records the rank order of each stimulus, giving the highest numerical value to the highest or best stimulus and a value of 1 to the lowest in the series.

6. After several days O is to repeat the judgments under the same instructions as before.

7. At least 10 judges should be asked to rank the same set of stimuli twice in the same manner.

COMPUTATION OF SCALE VALUES

For the sake of a simple illustration, the set of data in Table 42 may be used. The stimuli were 12 samples of handwriting judged for quality by 10 Os. A rank of 12 means the best sample in the lot and a rank of 1 the poorest.

The Mean- and Median-rank Orders.—Following the traditional method of Cattell, we would compute the mean rank for each stimulus. It must be remembered that the means merely represent rank positions and they are usually not to be regarded as scale values on a linear scale. They rarely give us more than a final rank order representing the pooled judgments of a number of Os. The same may be said for the medians of the ranks, although the latter may give a somewhat better relative rating of the stimuli near the ends of the series owing to the cancellation of the end effect. The means and medians will give approximate linear scale values when the distribution of stimuli is of the rectangular type or approaches the rectangular type. This means that the stimuli are about evenly scattered over a certain range of the continuum in question, with no bunching at any place. When the stimuli are normally distributed, as they often are, there is a bunching of values near the middle of the range, and the means or medians of the ranks do not represent scale values.

TABLE 42.—THE RANKS ASSIGNED TO TWELVE SAMPLES OF HANDWRITING BY TEN DIFFERENT JUDGES

O	A	B	C	D	E	F	G	H	I	J	K	L
1	12	8	11	10	9	6	5	4	7	1	2	3
2	11	12	10	9	7	8	6	4	1	3	5	2
3	10	11	12	9	7	8	6	5	3	4	1	2
4	9	12	11	10	8	7	4	3	5	6	2	1
5	12	10	11	9	4	7	8	1	6	2	5	3
6	11	10	7	12	6	5	9	8	1	4	2	3
7	12	11	9	7	10	8	6	3	4	5	1	2
8	12	8	10	11	9	7	6	4	5	2	3	1
9	11	12	9	8	10	7	4	6	3	5	2	1
10	12	11	9	10	7	8	6	5	4	1	3	2
Σ_r	112	105	99	95	77	71	60	43	39	33	26	20
M_r	11.2	10.5	9.9	9.5	7.7	7.1	6.0	4.3	3.9	3.3	2.6	2.0
Mdn_r	11.5	10.8	10.0	9.5	7.5	7.25	5.9	4.2	4.0	3.5	2.25	2.0

Linear Scale Values for Normally Distributed Stimuli.—In many cases we know that ranks cannot stand for units on a scale since the objects ranked fall into a normal distribution or approximately so. This would be true, for example, if the objects ranked are human individuals who are being rated for some trait or characteristic and if the group is reasonably large, being composed of more than 20 individuals selected at random. It might even be true of samples of handwriting or of any other product of human performance. If a normal distribution is the case, individuals near the center of the range are actually nearer together in the trait than are those at the two extremes, as Fig. 31 will demonstrate. The base line represents an ordinary linear scale such as we have at the base line of any distribution curve, and it is arbitrarily divided into 10 units. It can readily be seen that the samples ranking 1 and 2 at the lower end of the scale are much farther apart than any two near the center of the scale.

Hull (17, pp. 382 *ff.*) has proposed a device by which, assuming a normal distribution of the samples ranked, we can translate the assigned ranks into scale values on the base line of the normal distribution curve. He has assumed that the usual series of stimuli fall within plus or minus 2.5σ from the mean, or within a total range of

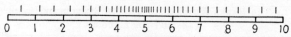

FIG. 31.—The spacing of stimuli along a continuum when the distribution is normal.

5σ units. This 5-point scale is subdivided into a 10-point scale, each unit being .5σ. Each rank assigned to a stimulus is translated into a *per cent position* by means of the formula

$$Pc = \frac{(r - .5)100}{n} \qquad (100)$$

where r = the assigned rank.

n = the number of stimuli ranked.

If there are 12 stimuli, as in our illustrative problem, for example, the per cent position for a rank of 12 would be 95.83. This means that, assuming a normal distribution for our 12 samples,[1] any sample ranking in the 12th place would belong at the 95.83th place in 100 specimens, or it would be better than 95.83 per cent of the lot. The other per cent positions can be located in the same manner, although it is perhaps easier to find $100/n$, which is 8.33 in this problem, and to deduct that amount successively until the per cent position of rank 1 is found.

In translating the per cent positions into scale values, a convenient table, which has been prepared by Hull, can be used.[2] It is reproduced, with one unimportant revision, in Table 43. The 12 per cent positions for our illustrative problem can be easily found. One decimal place is sufficient and so no interpolations are needed. The rank positions of Table 42 have been translated into scale values as given in Table 44. The means of the scale values are then

---

[1] This would rarely or never be assumed in practice with only 12 specimens.

[2] Hull's method of finding the per cent position corresponds with Galton's proposal to translate ranks into *centesimal gradations* or *centesimal grades* (8, pp. 53 *f.*).

TABLE 43.—HULL'S TABLE FOR TRANSMUTING PER CENT POSITIONS INTO SCALE VALUES ON A LINEAR SCALE OF 10 POINTS[1]

Per cent position	Scale value	Per cent position	Scale value	Per cent position	Scale value
.09	.1	22.32	3.5	83.31	6.9
.20	.2	23.88	3.6	84.56	7.0
.32	.3	25.48	3.7	85.75	7.1
.45	.4	27.15	3.8	86.89	7.2
.61	.5	28.86	3.9	87.96	7.3
.78	.6	30.61	4.0	88.97	7.4
.97	.7	32.42	4.1	89.94	7.5
1.18	.8	34.25	4.2	90.83	7.6
1.42	.9	36.15	4.3	91.67	7.7
1.68	1.0	38.06	4.4	92.45	7.8
1.96	1.1	40.01	4.5	93.19	7.9
2.28	1.2	41.97	4.6	93.86	8.0
2.63	1.3	43.97	4.7	94.49	8.1
3.01	1.4	45.97	4.8	95.08	8.2
3.43	1.5	47.98	4.9	95.62	8.3
3.89	1.6	50.00	5.0	96.11	8.4
4.38	1.7	52.02	5.1	96.57	8.5
4.92	1.8	54.03	5.2	96.99	8.6
5.51	1.9	56.03	5.3	97.37	8.7
6.14	2.0	58.03	5.4	97.72	8.8
6.81	2.1	59.99	5.5	98.04	8.9
7.55	2.2	61.94	5.6	98.32	9.0
8.33	2.3	63.85	5.7	98.58	9.1
9.17	2.4	65.75	5.8	98.82	9.2
10.06	2.5	67.48	5.9	99.03	9.3
11.03	2.6	69.39	6.0	99.22	9.4
12.04	2.7	71.14	6.1	99.39	9.5
13.11	2.8	72.85	6.2	99.55	9.6
14.25	2.9	74.52	6.3	99.68	9.7
15.44	3.0	76.12	6.4	99.80	9.8
16.69	3.1	77.68	6.5	99.91	9.9
18.01	3.2	79.17	6.6		
19.39	3.3	80.61	6.7		
20.83	3.4	81.99	6.8		

[1] Adapted from Hull's table (16). Those who compare Table 43 with Hull's original table will find that the scale values have been reversed here. This is because Hull regards a rank of 1 as the highest in a series whereas, in this chapter, 1 is regarded consistently throughout as the lowest rank.

computed and these appear at the bottom of the table. These are probably not accurate beyond the first decimal place and so are not given beyond that point. With a larger number of stimuli and a greater number of judges, a second decimal place might be significant.

TABLE 44.—LINEAR SCALE VALUES OBTAINED BY HULL'S METHOD FROM THE RANKS GIVEN IN TABLE 43

O	A	B	C	D	E	F	G	H	I	J	K	L
1	8.3	5.6	7.3	6.6	6.1	4.8	4.4	3.9	5.2	1.7	2.7	3.4
2	7.3	8.3	6.6	6.2	5.2	5.6	4.8	3.9	1.7	3.4	4.4	2.7
3	6.6	7.3	8.3	6.2	5.2	5.6	4.8	4.4	3.4	3.9	1.7	2.7
4	6.1	8.3	7.3	6.6	5.6	5.2	3.9	3.4	4.4	4.8	2.7	1.7
5	8.3	6.6	7.3	6.2	3.9	5.2	5.6	1.7	4.8	2.7	4.4	3.4
6	7.3	6.6	5.2	8.3	4.8	4.4	6.1	5.6	1.7	3.9	2.7	3.4
7	8.3	7.3	6.1	5.2	6.6	5.6	4.8	3.4	3.9	4.4	1.7	2.7
8	8.3	5.6	6.6	7.3	6.1	5.2	4.8	3.9	4.4	2.7	3.4	1.7
9	7.3	8.3	6.1	5.6	6.6	5.2	3.9	4.8	3.4	4.4	2.7	1.7
10	8.3	7.3	6.1	6.6	5.2	5.6	4.8	4.4	3.9	1.7	3.4	2.7
Σ	76.1	71.2	66.9	64.8	55.3	52.4	47.9	39.4	36.8	33.6	29.8	26.1
M	7.6	7.1	6.7	6.5	5.5	5.2	4.8	3.9	3.7	3.4	3.0	2.6

Scale Values Assuming a Composite Standard.—The treatment about to be proposed is based on the writer's process for dealing with paired comparisons (see page 236). The basic assumption again is that each stimulus is judged in comparison with the group as a whole. The group as a whole then becomes a composite standard CS, with which every stimulus is compared. It is from the proportions of judgments given to every stimulus as compared with the CS that linear scale values are derived. This is even more reasonable in the ranking method than with paired comparisons, since in the ranking method the whole series of stimuli is laid out for observation and each stimulus is placed according to its position in the entire scheme. Since the writer's procedure was first adapted to paired comparisons, let us approach its application to ranked data in the same manner, assuming for the moment that we are dealing with comparative judgments.

If in a series of ranked stimuli a given specimen R_k is assigned to the 15th place, then R_k may be said to have secured preference over

14 other stimuli which fell in ranks lower than 15. But if R_k is considered as having been compared with itself, it deserves an additional one-half choice, or a total of 14.5 choices. To generalize, any assigned rank r_i means a total of $(r_i - .5)$ choices for the R_k so ranked. If there are N judges, the total number of choices becomes $\Sigma(r_i - .5) = \Sigma r_i - .5N$. The probability that R_k will be chosen as greater than the CS is the total number of choices which R_k receives, given by $\Sigma r_i - .5N$, divided by the total number of comparisons in which R_k appears. R_k appears for comparative judgment by each judge as many times as there are stimuli, or n times. Its total number of appearances is theoretically nN. The probability that R_k is judged greater than the CS is therefore given by the formula

$$P_{R_k > CS} = \frac{\Sigma r_i - .5N}{nN} \tag{101}$$

For illustrative data in Table 42, the proportions are derived as in Table 45. The next step is to look up the deviates corresponding to those proportions and finally to make all the scale values positive by placing the zero point arbitrarily at the lowest scale value.

TABLE 45.—DETERMINING SCALE VALUES FROM RANKED DATA USING THE PROPORTIONS OF PREFERENCES FOR EACH STIMULUS

	A	B	C	D	E	F	G	H	I	J	K	L
Σr_i	112	105	99	95	77	71	60	43	39	33	26	20
$\Sigma r_i - .5N$	107	100	94	90	72	66	55	38	34	28	21	15
$P_{R_k > CS}$	.89	.83	.78	.75	.60	.55	.46	.32	.28	.23	.175	.125
$X_{R_k CS}$	1.23	.95	.77	.67	.25	.13	−.10	−.47	−.58	−.74	−.93	−1.15
SV	2.38	2.10	1.92	1.82	1.40	1.28	1.05	.68	.57	.41	.22	.00

Solution Assuming the Law of Comparative Judgment.—We may assume with Thurstone that ranked data yield comparative judgments and that they can be reduced to the same form as data obtained from paired comparisons. Four stimuli, B, D, A, C, ranked in the order given yield six comparative judgments: $B > D$, $B > A$, $B > C$, $D > A$, $D > C$, and $A > C$.[1] From repeated

---

[1] In a similar manner, we can conceive of judgments by equal-appearing intervals as comparative judgments; they may be treated statistically as such in order to derive scale values. This would avoid the issue as to whether the observed intervals are actually equal.

judgments of the same series of stimuli we can determine the proportion of the time each stimulus is preferred to every other stimulus (23). From Table 42, for example, we can tabulate those proportions, which appear in Table 46.

TABLE 46.—PROPORTIONS OF THE TIMES THAT EACH STIMULUS AT THE TOP OF THE COLUMNS WAS JUDGED GREATER THAN EVERY ONE AT THE SIDE

	A	B	C	D	E	F	G	H	I	J	K	L
A	...	.4	.2	.2	.0	...	...	...	...	...	..	..
B	.6	...	.4	.3	.2	.0	.0	.0	...	...	..	..
C	.8	.6	...	.3	.2	.0	.1	.1	.0	...	..	..
D	.8	.7	.7	...	.2	.1	.0	.0	.0	.0	.0	..
E	1.0	.8	.8	.8	...	.4	.2	.1	.1	.0	.1	.0
F	...	1.0	1.0	.9	.6	...	.2	.1	.1	.0	.0	.0
G	...	1.0	.9	1.0	.8	.8	...	.1	.2	.2	.0	.0
H	...	1.0	.9	1.0	.9	.9	.9	...	.5	.3	.2	.1
I	...	...	1.0	1.0	.9	.9	.8	.5	...	.6	.2	.2
J	...	...	...	...	1.0	1.0	.8	.7	.4	...	.5	.3
K	...	...	...	...	.9	1.0	1.0	.8	.8	.5	..	.4
L	...	...	...	...	1.0	1.0	1.0	.9	.8	.7	.6	..
SV	5.2	4.7	4.4	4.1	3.2	3.0	2.4	1.6	1.4	1.0	.4	.0

Thurstone's Case V has been assumed, and unweighted means of the differences are obtained as described in the preceding chapter (see pages 226 ff.). The resulting scale values are given in the last row of Table 46. The unit is the standard error of the discriminal dispersions of the samples of handwriting, all dispersions assumed to be equal. Any other of Thurstone's procedures for computing scale values, Case IV or Case III, could be used. Such limited data as we have here do not justify any attempts at greater mathematical accuracy than that afforded by Case V.

A Device for Extracting Proportions from Ranked Data.—The tabulation of the proportions of paired judgments from Table 42 was not a difficult process. But when there are many stimuli, more than 20, for example, and numerous judges, perhaps 300, the task becomes enormous. This would mean the tabulation of 300 times 190 items. Thurstone has suggested a process by means of which the proportions may be approximated with less effort (23). The first step consists in tabulating the proportions of the judges who place each stimulus in each rank position. Such a table, based upon our illustrative data, would resemble Table 47.

TABLE 47.—PROPORTIONS OF THE JUDGES WHO PLACED EACH STIMULUS IN EACH OF THE RANK POSITIONS

Rank	A	B	C	D	E	F	G	H	I	J	K	L
1	..	..	..	..	..	..	..	.1	.2	.2	.2	.3
2	..	..	..	..	..	..	..	.0	.0	.2	.4	.4
3	..	..	..	..	..	..	..	.2	.2	.1	.2	.3
4	..	..	..	..	.1	..	.2	.3	.2	.2	.0	..
..	..	..	..	..	..	..	..	..	..	..	..	..
5	..	..	..	..	.0	.1	.1	.2	.2	.2	.2	..
6	..	..	..	..	.1	.1	.5	.1	.1	.1	..	..
7	..	..	.1	.1	.3	.4	.0	.0	.1	..	..	..
8	..	.2	.0	.1	.1	.4	.1	.1	..	..	..	..
..	..	..	..	..	..	..	..	..	..	..	..	..
9	.1	.0	.3	.3	.2	..	.1	..	..	..	..	..
10	.1	.2	.2	.3	.2	..	..	..	..	..	..	..
11	.3	.3	.3	.1	..	..	..	..	..	..	..	..
12	.5	.3	.1	.1	..	..	..	..	..	..	..	..

The proportions we are looking for are given by the formula

$$p_{b>a} = \Sigma(p_{ai} \times p_{b>i}) + \frac{1}{2}\Sigma(p_{ai} \times p_{bi}) \qquad (102)$$

where $p_{b>a}$ = the proportion of judgments B greater than A.

p_{ai} = the proportion of judgments placing A in rank i.

p_{bi} = the proportion of judgments placing B in rank i.

$p_{b>i}$ = the proportion of judgments placing B in a rank higher than i.

As an illustrative problem let us find $p_{c>d}$, the proportion of judgments of C greater than D. We can find p_{ci} and p_{di} directly from Table 47, and $p_{c>i}$ is also readily found from the same source. The work is conveniently tabulated as shown in Table 48.

The proportion $p_{c>d}$ which we were seeking is estimated as .59, whereas by actual count of the cases it is .70. The approximation would have been much closer with the usual more extensive data.[1] The remaining proportions must be estimated in a similar manner, involving as many tables similar to Table 48 as there are pairs

[1] Thurstone (23) gives a formula which is said to give a closer approximation than does formula (102).

of stimuli. This number of pairs as in paired comparisons is $n(n-1)/2$, unless some of the proportions are zero or one, as will sometimes be the case.

TABLE 48.—THE COMPUTATION OF THE PROPORTION OF JUDGMENTS PLACING STIMULUS C HIGHER THAN STIMULUS D

Rank	Stimulus D	Stimulus C			
	p_{di}	p_{ci}	$p_{c>i}$	$p_{di} \times p_{c>i}$	$p_{di} \times p_{ci}$
7	.1	.1	.9	.09	.01
8	.1	.0	.9	.09	.00
9	.3	.3	.6	.18	.09
10	.3	.2	.4	.12	.06
11	.1	.3	.1	.01	.03
12	.1	.1	.0	.00	.01

$$\Sigma\ .49 \qquad\qquad .20$$

$$\Sigma(p_{di} \times p_{c>i}) = .49 \qquad\qquad \frac{1}{2}\Sigma = .10$$

$$\frac{1}{2}\Sigma(p_{di} \times p_{ci}) = .10$$

$$\overline{\rule{2cm}{0pt}}$$

$$p_{c>d} = .59$$

An Evaluation of the Five Procedures.—Of the five processes for finding scale values from ranked data, that of Thurstone's is based upon safest logical grounds. The unit is a defined quantity, being the standard error of the discriminal dispersion of the average stimulus in the series. The most valid logical objection that can be offered is that the pseudo-comparative judgments yielded by ranked data are not valid substitutes for the true comparative judgments that would be obtained from paired comparisons. On the other side of the ledger is the greater internal consistency that is imposed upon comparative judgments when taken from ranked data. The second best process is probably that of the writer. Like Thurstone's method, it does not assume a normal distribution of the stimuli. The spacing of stimuli along the continuum will almost invariably form a linear relationship with that spacing obtained by Thurstone's process. The chief weakness of the composite standard method is that the size of the unit varies from one set of data to another. This is a handicap on some occasions. The logic upon which this method is based is better founded than that for applying it to paired comparisons, in that each stimulus can be compared, and is compared, with the series as a whole.

When the number of stimuli is as great as 30 and when the items being ranked are human individuals, Hull's method is very properly applied. When the stimuli are not individuals, or the products of individuals, the assumption of normal distribution must always be supported with evidence. There is some logical support for the assumption that human creations, such as handwriting, drawings, designs, advertisements, and the like, should be normally distributed in the same way that all samples of performance or tests are so distributed. There is even a possibility that materials not necessarily in the form of human products tend to approximate a normal distribution as a result of the act of human observation. Hollingworth's **law of central tendency** would seem to indicate this. The law states that a series of stimuli which vary over a continuum are misjudged toward the center of the range. For example, in a series of squares the larger ones tend to be underestimated and the smaller ones overestimated.

This fact, taken together with a peculiarity of judgment to be discussed later, leads one to wonder whether or not the average observer has a habitual set to force stimuli belonging to a single series in the direction of a normally distributed array. Be that as it may, whether the stimuli are human individuals or the products of human craft or whether they are of nonhuman origin, a normal distribution is hardly safely assumed with less than 20 stimuli in the series. This was done with the 12 stimuli above merely for the sake of demonstration. As it actually turned out, the scale values obtained by Hull's procedure bear an almost perfect linear relationship with those from Thurstone's method.

When the number of stimuli is small, less than 20, let us say, and the number of judges is also small, the mean or median rank of each stimulus gives roughly its relative scale position in the series, and no more extensive calculations need be undertaken. Empirically it can be shown, as with the illustrative problem above, that the mean- or median-rank positions sometimes bear a close linear relationship to the scale values from Thurstone's method, the median ranks giving a closer approximation than the mean ranks. This would be true, as was said before, when the distribution of stimuli approaches a rectangular form. If the number of judges is relatively large, more than 50, for example, even though the number of stimuli be small, the two most accurate procedures are justly employed. In fact the writer's CS method may be used with profit whenever the product nN is greater than 200. Thurstone's method is probably not used with profit unless N alone is as large as 100.

Combining Incomplete Sets of Ranks.—It sometimes happens, especially in ranking human individuals according to some trait, that not every observer is able to judge all the items to be ranked. Each judge ranks only those whom he feels competent to evaluate. This is somewhat disturbing to the smooth functioning of the devices for computing scale values, but it requires only a few adjustments, some of which will be illustrated. A very simple problem with 12 stimuli and only 5 judges will be used. Table 49 contains the incomplete sets of ranks. Only one stimulus, A, was known by all the judges and placed in a rank position by them all. No judge placed all 12 individuals to be ranked.

TABLE 49.—INCOMPLETE SETS OF RANK POSITIONS ASSIGNED TO 12 INDIVIDUALS BY 5 JUDGES

Judge	A	B	C	D	E	F	G	H	I	J	K	L	N
1	8	6		7		5		4		3	1	2	8
2	6	5				4			3	2		1	6
3	8	9	7	6	5		4		2	1	3		9
4	8		7		6	4	5	3	2		1		8
5	9	8	7	6	5		4	3			2	1	9
Σ	39	28	21	19	16	13	13	10	7	6	7	4	40
N	5	4	3	3	3	3	3	3	3	3	4	3	
M_r	7.8	7.0	7.0	6.3	5.3	4.3	4.3	3.3	2.3	2.0	1.8	1.3	
Mdn_r	8.0	7.0	7.0	6.3	5.3	4.3	4.3	3.3	2.3	2.0	1.5	1.3	

The means and medians of the ranks are in very close agreement. According to Garrett (9), the means of the ranks give a more valid final rank order than any of the more elaborate time-consuming devices for combining incomplete set of ranks.

The combination of incomplete ranks demands one adjustment in the writer's CS method. This is due to the fact that the product nN varies from one stimulus to another. The value of nN can be obtained for each stimulus from the last column of Table 49. For stimulus A, nN is 40, or the sum of all the values in the last column.

For stimulus B, nN is 32, summing all the N's except that for the fourth judge, who did not rank stimulus B at all. The others are given in Table 50, row 2.

TABLE 50.—SOLUTION OF SCALE VALUES FROM INCOMPLETE RANKS BY THE COMPOSITE STANDARD METHOD

	A	B	C	D	E	F	G	H	I	J	K	L
$\Sigma r_i - .5N$	36.5	26.0	19.5	17.5	14.5	11.5	11.5	8.5	5.5	4.5	5.0	2.5
Nn	40	32	26	26	26	22	26	25	23	23	34	23
$P_{R_k>cs}$	.91	.81	.75	.67	.56	.52	.44	.34	.24	.20	.15	.11
X_{R_kcs}	1.34	.88	.67	.44	.15	.05	$-.15$	$-.41$	$-.71$	$-.84$	-1.04	-1.23
SV	2.6	2.1	1.9	1.7	1.4	1.3	1.1	.8	.5	.4	.2	.00

The solution with Hull's method presents no really new problem. Every rank is converted into a per cent position, and from Table 43 into a score on the 10-point scale. The only things to be kept in mind are that n of formula (100) will vary from one judge to another and that this involves extra computations not encountered when the sets of ranks are complete and n is constant. The solution with Thurstone's process is no different, except that his convenient device for estimating the proportions $p_{b>a}$ cannot be adapted to incomplete ranks and individual judgments must therefore be tabulated, making a tedious, time-consuming task.

SOME PECULIARITIES OF HUMAN JUDGMENTS

The Law of Central Tendency.—Certain peculiarities of human judgments that appear in a number of the psychometric methods seem to have made themselves felt most strikingly in the order-of-merit procedure. Hollingworth's *law of central tendency* (15, pp. 44 *ff.*) has already been mentioned; a tendency for stimuli in a series to bunch themselves near the center of the range, as if approaching a normal distribution in their spacing. This proclivity of a group of stimuli superimposes itself upon the observed differences as postulated by Thurstone's law of comparative judgment. Scale values would seem to be altered owing to the mere presence of other stimuli. Even the complete law of comparative judgment with its coefficient of correlation between pairs of judgments may not be adequate to cover the intricate interplay of dynamic forces at work within the series. The law of central tendency probably falsifies the true scale values of stimuli. They have one psychological value when seen alone or in one context and a different value when seen in another context.

Variability of Different Parts of the Series.—It has been quite commonly found that, when the variability of the rank position of a stimulus is calculated in terms of ranks, stimuli near the center of the scale have a greater dispersion than those near the ends. This may be due in part to the end effect and in part to the normal distribution, apparent or real, of the series of stimuli. If the ranks near the ends of the series are phenomenally farther apart than those near the center, certainly the dispersions, given in terms of rank positions, will be greater near the middle of the scale. If Hull's method is applied and the normal distribution is thus allowed for, the true variabilities can be estimated and compared. Only when the normal distribution is allowed for can we be sure whether the variabilities near the center of the range are really greatest. The writer has proposed elsewhere (12) another way of making this allowance for normally distributed stimuli when dealing with proportions of judgments $R_k > CS$. Theoretically the variability in any part of the scale should be proportional to the probable error of a proportion, or $PE_p = .6745\sqrt{pq/N}$. Any deviations from these theoretical variabilities would tell us in what part of the scale variability is really greatest.

The Mean Variability and the Number of Steps.—A very curious phenomenon has been reported by several investigators. When the mean variability of all the stimuli has been computed, it has often been found to approximate one-fifth the number of steps in the scale. This holds true, apparently, whether the data are ranked—and there are as many steps as there are ranks—or whether the method of equal-appearing intervals is used. This phenomenon would divide the total range of stimuli into about six PE units (15, pp. 112 f.). This is a further indication that a series of stimuli observed as a whole conforms to a normal distribution. As more direct evidence of this normal tendency, Strong supplies the following facts (21). He had asked 25 students to arrange 50 advertisements in piles at "just noticeable intervals" without specifying the number of piles. The number of piles ranged from 6 to 37. Each subject was then told to give a numerical value to each pile on a scale from 0 to

100. The distribution of the assigned scores approximated the normal form in spite of the fact that a sorting according to equal-appearing intervals had been the original aim.

Judgments of Similarity and of Difference.—Some controversy has arisen over the question as to which are more convenient and which are more valid, judgments of similarity or judgments of difference. Would it be better to ask *O* to rank a set of stimuli on the basis of resemblance to some fixed standard or on the basis of difference from that standard? Hollingworth (15, pp. 68–84) reached several conclusions on this problem—conclusions based upon intercorrelation of the obtained ranks. Judgments of similarity were more self-consistent, and the variability from one judge to another was less. Introspections suggested greater ease, confidence, and naturalness in judging similarity. But with increased practice the rank orders for judgments of difference and similarity did approach one another. Different criteria were used in the two cases. Judgments of similarity were based more upon general impressions whereas judgments of difference were based more upon details. This is probably why the latter type of judgment has more room for variations. The detailed criteria can more easily shift from one time to another.

Validity as a Function of the Number of Judges.—The question is often raised as to whether the pooling of judgments from a number of observers really increases the validity of the final scale values. Students of aesthetics especially are often of the opinion that the combined judgments of the masses should count for little as compared with the judgments of a single 'expert.' A partial answer to this fixed idea of students of aesthetics is given by Gordon (11). Ten lifted weights were ranked by 200 judges once each. The judgments were pooled by fives, tens, twenties, and fifties. The means of the ranks were then correlated with the actual weights of the stimuli. The average validity coefficient for one judge at a time was .41; for five judges at a time, .68; ten judges, .79; twenty judges, .86; and fifty judges, .94. There is not the slightest doubt that pooled judgments of weights approach the truth more closely as the number of judges increases. That this would also be true for judgments of beauty or of affective value does not follow immediately from this study. This point is difficult to establish in view of the lack of any objective criteria of beauty or of affective value. The writer is confident that the validity of aesthetic judgments does increase with the number of judges in some manner not unlike that which Gordon found with lifted weights.

Comparison with Other Methods

Compared with Paired Comparisons.—From the standpoint of ease and economy of time on the part of the judges, the ranking method is far superior to paired comparisons. It is obviously much easier to rank 20 stimuli than to judge 190 pairs. The dynamic interrelations apparently existing throughout any series of stimuli, although probably present to some extent in paired comparisons, are of great significance in ranked judgments. The favorable and unfavorable aspects of these influences have already been pointed out. As for the scale positions obtained from the two methods, the one type is equally as valid as the other. This fact is borne out by Barrett (1) who concluded that the results from both are extremely valid when the scale values are correlated with objective criteria. Since she used the rank-difference method of correlation, a method that depends upon rank positions, the issue is left somewhat uncertain as to which of the two methods gave the more valid results. Hevner (13) found that the two methods give almost identical results with samples of handwriting, the ranking method giving a better showing when tests of internal consistency are applied.

Compared with Rating-scale Methods.—When evaluating 40 jokes for the degree of humor, Conklin and Sutherland (5) found rating-scale methods superior to the method of ranking. The former gave a higher self-correlation and a smaller variability in the scale values. No data are available for comparing the two methods with other types of stimuli. The rating-scale methods, however, have certain practical advantages over both paired comparisons and ranked judgments. Rating methods can be applied with stimuli, like odors, which cannot be presented either simultaneously or in quick succession but which must be presented alone. Furthermore, rating methods furnish absolute zero points for scales whereas both the other two methods fail to do so. It is to the rating-scale methods that we turn in the next chapter.

Problem

1. Compute scale values for the 12 stimuli, using the various processes described in this chapter.

THE RANKS ASSIGNED TO 12 MUSICAL SELECTIONS BY 20 DIFFERENT JUDGES

O	A	B	C	D	E	F	G	H	I	J	K	L
1	12	11	9	8	6	7	10	5	3	2	4	1
2	12	10	7	6	11	4	8	9	5	2	1	3
3	11	12	8	5	6	10	9	4	2	3	1	7
4	12	9	11	10	8	4	7	6	5	1	2	3
5	12	10	11	7	5	9	4	8	6	2	3	1
6	11	8	12	6	10	4	7	5	9	2	3	1
7	12	10	11	7	9	8	5	6	2	4	3	1
8	12	9	11	8	6	5	4	3	10	2	7	1
9	12	10	11	8	6	4	7	9	5	2	3	1
10	11	12	8	9	7	5	10	6	3	1	2	4
11	12	10	11	7	9	4	5	3	6	2	8	1
12	11	7	9	10	12	8	4	5	3	2	1	6
13	12	10	11	7	4	9	8	5	3	2	6	1
14	12	11	9	10	6	8	5	9	1	3	4	2
15	12	6	11	8	7	10	9	5	3	4	2	1
16	11	12	8	10	7	6	5	4	3	9	2	1
17	12	8	11	5	10	9	7	6	3	2	4	1
18	11	12	10	8	6	9	4	3	2	7	1	5
19	12	10	8	6	9	11	5	1	7	4	3	2
20	12	11	9	10	6	4	8	5	7	2	3	1

REFERENCES

1. BARRETT, M., A comparison of the order of merit method and the method of paired comparisons, *Psychol. Rev.*, 1914, **21**, 278–294.
2. BROGAN, A. P., Moral valuations about men and women, *Internat. J. Ethics*, 1925, **35**, 105–124.
3. CATTELL, J. McK., The time of perception as a measure of differences in intensity, *Phil. Stud.*, 1902, **19**, 63–68.
4. ———, A statistical study of American men of science, *Science, N. S.*, 1906, **24**, 658–665.
5. CONKLIN, E. S., and J. W. SUTHERLAND, A comparison of the scale of values method with the order of merit method, *J. Exper. Psychol.*, 1923, **6**, 44–57.
6. DOWNEY, J., Preliminary study of family resemblance in handwriting, *Univ. Wyo. Psychol. Bull.*, 1910, no. 1, 1–51.
7. FERNALD, G. G., The defective delinquent class differentiating tests, *Amer. J. Insan.*, 1912, **68**, 523–594.
8. GALTON, F., "Inquiries into Human Faculty and Its Development," Macmillan & Company, Ltd., London, 1883.
9. GARRETT, H. E., An empirical study of the various methods of combining incomplete order of merit ratings, *J. Educ. Psychol.*, 1924, **15**, 157–171.

10. GORDON, K., A study of esthetic judgments, *J. Exper. Psychol.*, 1923, **6**, 36–43.

11. ——, Group judgments in the field of lifted weights, *J. Exper. Psychol.*, 1924, **7**, 398–400.

12. GUILFORD, J. P., Racial preferences of a thousand American university students, *J. Soc. Psychol.*, 1931, **2**, 179–204.

13. HEVNER, K., An empirical study of three psychophysical methods, *J. Gen. Psychol.*, 1930, **4**, 191–212.

14. HOLLINGWORTH, H. L., Judgments of persuasiveness, *Psychol. Rev.*, 1911, **18**, 234–256.

15. ——, Experimental studies in judgment, *Arch. Psychol.*, 1913, no. 29.

16. HULL, C. L., The computation of Pearson's *r* from ranked data, *J. Appl. Psychol.*, 1922, **6**, 385–390.

17. ——, "Aptitude Testing," World Book Company, Yonkers, 1928.

18. KUPER, G. M., Group differences in interests of children, *J. Phil., Psychol., and Sci. Method*, 1912, **9**, 376–379.

19. STRONG, E. K., The relative merits of advertisements, *Arch. Psychol.*, 1911, no. 17.

20. ——, Psychological methods as applied to advertising, *J. Educ. Psychol.*, 1913, **4**, 393–404.

21. ——, Application of the 'order of merit method' to advertising, *J. Phil., Psychol., and Sci. Method*, 1911, **8**, 600–606.

22. SUMNER, F. B., A statistical study of belief, *Psychol. Rev.*, 1898, **5**, 616–631.

23. THURSTONE, L. L., Rank order as a psychophysical method, *J. Exper. Psychol.*, 1931, **14**, 187–201.

24. WELLS, F. L., A statistical study of literary merit, *Arch. Psychol.*, 1907, **1**, no. 7.

25. WITMER, L., Zur experimentellen Aesthetik einfacher räumlicher Formverhältnisse, *Phil. Stud.*, 1894, **9**, 96–144.

CHAPTER IX

RATING-SCALE METHODS

The rating-scale methods have enjoyed a vigorous growth along two rather independent lines within psychology. Experimental psychology, on the one hand, resorted to these procedures at times when paired comparisons or the ranking method would have been too laborious, impractical, or ill-advised. On the other hand, rating devices have become the favorite tools for the evaluation or quantitative judgment of traits of personality and character. Their uses in industrial and other fields of applied psychology have over-shadowed the applications of all other evaluative methods based upon personal judgments.

General Description and Purpose of Rating Scales.—The essence of all forms of rating devices is the same. Some particular psychological continuum is defined as univocally as it can be under the circumstances, be it affective values of odors, strength of belief or of persuasiveness, the vividness of an image, or such personal qualities as leadership and tactfulness; certain landmarks or guideposts are supplied along this continuum to aid a judge in the evaluations of samples that can be placed on that continuum. The guideposts may be in terms of descriptive phrases to which numerical (or letter) values are assigned; we then speak of a **numerical rating scale** or of the **scale of values method.** The guideposts may be given in terms of actual samples, for example, handwriting specimens that have been evaluated previously by one of the other psychometric methods; we may then speak of a **scale of standards** or of a **standard scale.** Thorndike's handwriting scale and his drawing scale are good examples of this type. The *man-to-man* scale that was used in the army falls into this class. Very frequently a straight horizontal line is drawn to represent the continuum in question and descriptive terms are attached at intervals along the way from the one extreme to the other. The judge merely checks with pencil that point on the continuum where he believes the sample should fall. This type is called the **graphic rating scale.** A less frequently used type may be called the **defined-group scale.** This is more like the numerical rating scale, except that no numerical values are assigned, and the judge is given instructions as to what proportions of the samples should be expected to fall in each group. There are minor variations of these four main groups, a number of which will be illustrated in the discussion to follow.

HISTORY OF RATING SCALES

Origin of Rating Scales.—There seems to be little doubt that the first rating scale employed in a psychological problem was that of Galton, used in the evaluation of the vividness of images (17, p. 93). Galton had previously collected many descriptions of images from a large number of individuals. He had also been much impressed with the application of the normal distribution curve to the quantitative description of human traits and the convenient division of a distribution into four quartiles and eight octiles. His rating scale for images possessed eight steps or octiles, with a ninth added for very rare cases. Rating devices were known, however, before Galton's scale for imagery. Titchener (54) reports that such scales had been used to describe the weather. As early as 1805 the British Navy had used estimates of wind velocities on a 12-point scale, zero representing no wind at all and 12 a hurricane. The latent idea behind the scale was that these 12 steps should represent equal sense distances. The earliest bath thermometers were calibrated according to sense distances with descriptive terms. A temperature scale for the weather was used daily by some 30 observers during a period of several months. This scale possessed 20 points, 20 being called "intolerably hot" and 1 "unbearably cold." There was also a scale for estimating "mugginess," zero representing bright, brisk, or stimulating weather and 10 points the muggiest or most enervating weather. Galton's own early associations with the infant science of meteorology may have acquainted him with the possibilities of rating methods in tackling the problems of human nature.

Extending the Applications of the Rating Methods.—Not all the applications of rating methods can be mentioned here. Their first use, as nearly as can be determined in each type of psychological problem, is of historical interest. Among these first uses were judgments of aesthetic values. In 1895 Major (33) used the *method of single stimuli* or, as he called it, the *method of isolated exposure,* for the evaluation of the affective value of colors. In

1905 Martin asked for judgments of the comic on a five-point scale (35). Keith, in 1906, used a seven-point scale for judgments of agreeableness of odors (26). This use of ratings has continued up to the present time as, for example, in studies by Kenneth (27) and Young (58, 59). The rating of stimuli as to degree of persuasiveness or as to degree of belief had a relatively early beginning and continues to the present time. The studies of Hollingworth (21) and others on advertisements and of Lund (32) on belief testify to this fact. Conklin has been almost alone in applying the methods of rating to problems of genetic psychology (7).

Probably the first to secure ratings of human abilities was Karl Pearson (40) who in 1906 devised a seven-point scale for estimating intelligence. This application received its greatest impetus during the World War when psychologists were called upon to devise methods of rating the efficiency of officers. The result was the invention of the *man-to-man* scale, which has usually been credited to Scott (45). The experiences gained with this scale and the critical studies made of it by Rugg (44) and others have done much to demonstrate the great practical usefulness, the limitations and errors involved, and the sphere of applicability to the ratings of human traits. Without any doubt, rating-scale methods have made their place secure in industrial practice and in the educational field. From the standpoint of theoretical psychology, also, the ratings of human traits and actions are now indispensable. This is true particularly in the studies of personality and in child psychology.

EXPERIMENT XI. A STUDY OF BELIEF

Problem.—To determine the degree of correlation between belief and desire.

Material.—Set of 25 propositions. The list suggested here has been adapted from Lund (32.)

1. Ratings of the propositions for belief.
   a. Secure the cooperation of at least five subjects.
   b. Provide them with the following list of propositions together with the numerical scale for belief. Instruct *O* to indicate with a number the strength of his belief or disbelief in each proposition. The judgments are to be placed in the parentheses at the left.
   c. Scale of belief:
      9. Belief allowing for no doubt.
      8. Very strong belief.
      7. Fairly strong belief.
      6. Slight belief.

5. Neither belief nor disbelief.

4. Slight disbelief.
3. Fairly strong disbelief.
2. Very strong disbelief.
1. Disbelief allowing for no doubt.

( ) 1. The world is becoming better.................................. ( )
( ) 2. A democracy is the best form of government................... ( )
( ) 3. A black cat crossing one's path causes bad luck............... ( )
( ) 4. The higher forms of life were derived from lower forms through
          a process of evolution....................................... ( )
( ) 5. The whale swallowed Jonah................................. ( )
( ) 6. Atoms exist.. ( )
( ) 7. Shakespeare wrote *The Merchant of Venice*.................... ( )
( ) 8. Christianity is losing its influence in this country.............. ( )
( ) 9. There are other human minds besides your own................ ( )
( ) 10. Only the good die young..................................... ( )
( ) 11. The sun will rise tomorrow morning........................... ( )
( ) 12. There is life on other heavenly bodies......................... ( )
( ) 13. Our republic will exist 100 years from now..................... ( )
( ) 14. All men should have equal political rights...................... ( )
( ) 15. Death ends personal existence................................ ( )
( ) 16. Morality is a man-made institution............................ ( )
( ) 17. Two plus two equals four..................................... ( )
( ) 18. Spirits of the departed can communicate with the living......... ( )
( ) 19. The earth travels around the sun.............................. ( )
( ) 20. Animals have feelings similar to our own...................... ( )
( ) 21. Landscape paintings may yield as much satisfaction as the finest
          natural scenery.. ( )
( ) 22. The golden rule is a practical guide in business relations......... ( )
( ) 23. The dinosaur once existed.................................... ( )
( ) 24. Lincoln was an honest and upright man........................ ( )
( ) 25. Slander is morally wrong..................................... ( )

2. Ratings of the propositions for desirability.
    a. At another time ask the same *O*s to rate the same 25 propositions as to
       desirability. The scale of desirability, given below, has no relation
       whatever to the truth or validity of a proposition. Let *O* decide in each
       case how strongly he wishes that the proposition were true. Place these
       judgments in the parentheses at the right. Needless to say *O* must not
       have access to his judgments of belief at this time.
    b. Scale of desirability:
       9. Desirable beyond question.
       8. Very desirable.
       7. Quite desirable.
       6. Somewhat desirable.

       5. Indifferent; neither desirable nor undesirable.

       4. Somewhat undesirable.
       3. Quite undesirable.

2. Very undesirable.

1. Undesirable beyond question.

Results:

1. With a limited number of *O*s, find for each one a coefficient of correlation (rank-difference method will do, see page 339) between the ratings for belief and the ratings for desire.

2. Pool the ratings for all the *O*s, finding for every proposition the mean rating for belief and for desire. Correlate the two sets of ratings. Compare with the mean correlation of the individual *O*s.

3. Find correlations between several pairs of individual ratings for belief (or for desire) selected at random.

4. Form two pools of judgments, using the same number of *O*s in each pool, for belief (or desire), and correlate the two pools. Compare this correlation with the mean correlation between sets of individual ratings. Interpret these and all other results.

THE CONSTRUCTION OF RATING SCALES

The Number of Steps or Points to Be Used.—Certain problems of scale construction are met in the setting up of any type of scale and some problems are peculiar to each type alone. The number of scale divisions is something that has to be decided for all scales. In a survey of 54 teacher-rating scales, Boyce (3) found that some of them had as few as 2 steps or divisions, while others had as many as 7, with 4 the most popular number. Conklin (7) found from 2 to 20 steps had been used in various types of scales. Scott's man-to-man scale had 5 main divisions which were to be subdivided into 3 each, making a total of 15. The most finely graded scale to the knowledge of the writer is Lund's (32) scale for estimating degrees of belief, which contains 21 steps.

The decision as to the optimal number of steps in any scale is largely an empirical matter. If we use too few steps, the scale is obviously a coarse one and we lose much of the efficiency of *O*'s judicial powers. We do not ordinarily measure to the nearest foot when it is almost as easy to measure to the nearest inch. On the other hand, we can grade the scale so finely that it is beyond *O*'s limited powers to discriminate between one step and the next. One would never attempt to estimate length to the hundredth of a millimeter with the naked eye. The fineness will depend also upon the willingness of *O* to make the effort required for fine discriminations. It depends therefore upon the raters, their ability to discriminate, and their motivation in making the ratings.

Fortunately we have some empirical evidence bearing on the choice of the number of steps. Conklin (7) concluded after an analysis of some 23,000 judgments that for untrained Os the maximum number of steps should be *five* for a single scale and *nine* for a double scale. A *single scale* is one which extends from zero to the maximum, whereas a *double scale* extends through zero with opposite qualities as the extremes of the continuum. Symonds (50) maintains that the degree of reliability one wishes in the final ratings should decide the matter. He concluded that for rating human traits *seven* is the optimal number. More than seven classes yielded an increase in reliability that hardly paid for the trouble. Less than seven led to an appreciable loss in reliability. Fewer points may be used, he advises (52, p. 79), if the trait is rather obscure and if the raters are untrained and only moderately interested, or if a number of aspects of the same thing are rated and the ratings are pooled. More than seven points may be used profitably if the trait is very objective, or if the raters are trained and enthusiastic.

The Percentage of the Cases in Each Class.—A rater may be helped to reach a more valid set of ratings of a group of individuals if he is given some notion of the number of cases that might be expected to fall within each class. This practice also helps to put the ratings of different judges on a more equitable basis. It helps the experimenter to unearth the constant tendencies of the various raters. It is usually safe to assume that any trait that is rated has a normal distribution in a fairly large unselected group. If we further assume that in a random group of 40 individuals the range is 5σ and that in a random group of 185 individuals the range is 6σ, the following percentages suggested by Symonds (52, p. 81) will serve as a good guide.

TABLE 51.—PERCENTAGE OF CASES NORMALLY EXPECTED TO FALL WITHIN THE VARIOUS CLASSES OF RATINGS

Classes	Three		Four		Five		Six		Seven	
N	40	185	40	185	40	185	40	185	40	185
1	20	16	11	7	7	4	5	2	4	2
2	60	68	39	43	24	24	15	14	10	8
3	20	16	39	43	38	44	30	34	22	23
4			11	7	24	24	30	34	28	34
5					7	4	15	14	22	23
6							5	2	10	8
7									4	2

The Man-to-man Scale.—As applied to military purposes, five qualities were selected for rating: (1) physique, (2) intelligence, (3) leadership, (4) personal qualities, and (5) general value to the service. Each superior officer was asked to write down the names of 12 to 25 officers whom he knew very well. He was then asked to arrange them in rank order for each one of the five traits. The highest man in each list was then chosen as the top position in that scale and the lowest in rank as the lowest point on the scale. The middle man occupied the third point on the scale, and two men midway between the extremes and the median were chosen for the second and fourth positions. The scale with its five landmarks was then complete, and O could place any officer who came up for his judgment on the scale by merely comparing him with the five key men already selected. A certain officer's 'yardstick' for leadership might look as follows:

Leadership: Initiative, force, self-reliance, decisiveness, tact, ability to inspire men and to command their obedience, loyalty, and cooperation.

Highest	Captain Spence	15
High	Lieutenant Moore	12
Middle	Captain Travers	9
Low	Lieutenant Johns	6
Lowest	Lieutenant Conrad	3

The advantages that have been claimed for the man-to-man scale are three:

1. It gets away from the mere assignment of abstract numbers to an individual's traits.

2. A rather permanent 'yardstick' is set up. O's standards will therefore not shift from day to day.

3. If all judges use the same men in their 'yardsticks,' the ratings of different judges will be comparable in absolute amount.

Disadvantages often pointed out are:

1. In practice, two judges' scales are rarely exactly alike, even if they know the same men.

2. The distances between men on the scale are not necessarily equal.

3. Overestimation and underestimation of an individual are still possible when the scale is used.

4. The original scales are very difficult to make, and the student of psychophysical method will see that they are very crudely made.

5. The whole procedure is cumbersome and its use in industry has been dropped or replaced by simpler devices.

In defense of the method it may be pointed out that the man-to-man scale is not unlike the handwriting and drawing scales now used in educational practice. It is more objective in the sense that there are definite stimuli with which to compare the new samples. It is subjective, however, in the sense that each judge must make and use his own original scale; hence in practice it cannot compare in validity with educational scales.

Graphic Rating Scales.—The graphic type of rating scale is by far the most popular and on the whole the most satisfactory. Freyd (15) lists several advantages over other types of scales:

1. It is simple and easily grasped.
2. It is interesting and requires little outside motivation.
3. It can be quickly filled out.
4. It frees the rater from the use of direct quantitative terms.
5. Ratings can be as finely discriminated as the rater chooses. (The fineness of the scale can of course exceed O's powers of discrimination, and hence this seeming advantage is partly an illusion. The advantage is also often lost in scoring by the use of a crude scoring device.)
6. It requires no master or standard scale, as does the man-to-man scale.
7. The fineness of scoring can be altered as desired; one may introduce 5 steps or 100 as one chooses.

There are no disadvantages that apply to the graphic type of scale alone. Constant errors and difficulties applying to ratings in general will be discussed later.

As examples of graphic scales consider the following, the first being reproduced from Laird's *Personal Inventory C2*.

In social conversation how have you been? | talkative | an easy talker | talked when necessary | preferred listening | refrained from talking

The second sample is a form very frequently employed:

Is he slow or quick thinking?

| Extremely slow | Sluggish Plodding | Thinks with ordinary speed | Agile-minded | Exceedingly rapid |

Still a third form:

Industry. Consider energy and application to duties day in and day out.	Lazy	Indiffer-ent	Average application	Indus-trious	Unusually energetic

Experience has shown that certain arrangements of the line and certain descriptive material give best results. Certain other rules improve the reliability of the ratings. All these rules and suggestions are listed below.

Rules for the Construction of Graphic Scales:

1. Each trait should occupy a page by itself. This rule is rarely observed. When numbers of individuals are to be rated, it is far better that all of them be rated in one trait before going on to the next.

2. The line should be at least 5 in. long but not much longer, so that it can be easily grasped as a whole.

3. The line should have no breaks or divisions. A broken line may suggest a discontinuous variable.

4. The 'good' and 'poor' ends should be alternated in random order so as to avoid a constant motor tendency to check at one side of the page.

5. Introduce each trait with a question to which the rating gives an answer, that is, "How has he responded when praised?"

6. Use three or five descriptive adjectives—two extremes and one or three intermediates.

7. The descriptive phrases should be in small type with considerable white space between them.

8. Only universally understood descriptive terms should be used, avoiding slang and other colloquial expressions.

9. Decide beforehand upon the probable extremes of ability (or of the trait) to be found in the group or groups in which the scale is to be used.

10. The end phrases should not be so extreme in meaning as to be avoided by the raters.

11. Have the extreme phrases set flush with the ends of the lines.

12. The average or neutral phrase should be at the center of the line.

13. Descriptive phrases need not be evenly spaced. The meaning of the intermediate ones should be nearer the middle one than the extremes.

14. In the scoring use a stencil which divides each line into several sections to which numerical values are assigned.

15. The divisions of the scoring stencil need not be equal; they may be made to conform to the distribution of ratings.

16. Do not require any finer distinctions in rating than are used in scoring. If anything, the scoring units may be smaller than the rating units.

Errors in Rating and How to Correct Them

Constant Errors Common to All Raters.—Raters are human and they are therefore subject to all the errors to which humankind must plead guilty. One constant tendency that many raters have in common is to rate all individuals whom they know above the average in certain traits, usually the desirable ones. This is the **error of leniency.** If the extent of this error has been determined for any trait—and this can be done by an examination of the distribution of ratings in any trait—appropriate corrections may be made in the construction of the scale. The spacing of the adjectives or phrases can be altered to force a more normal distribution, as in the following sample:

Physical health:

poor	fair	good	very good	excellent

Another constant error to which all judges alike tend to fall victim is the **error of central tendency.** Judges are inclined to hesitate to give extreme judgments and so tend to displace individuals in the direction of the mean of the total group. This is perhaps more common in rating individuals whom the judges do not know very well. It is for this reason that a recommendation was made above in connection with graphic scales that the intermediate descriptive phrases be made nearer in meaning to the middle than to the extremes of the scale. In a similar manner in the numerical type of scale, the strength of the descriptive adjectives may be adjusted so as to counteract the error of central tendency. Greater differences in meaning may be introduced between steps near the ends of the scale than between steps near the center.

The Personal Equation in Ratings.—Aside from these common errors, there are many individual differences in tendencies to overrate or underrate individuals in traits as compared with the average ratings of all the judges. These tendencies can be determined by obtaining a mean rating for every individual a rated in a given trait and by using these means as the standards or norms from which individual differences in raters may be calculated. Let these mean ratings be called r_{ma}. Let the rating by any one judge k for any given individual in the same trait be called r_{ka}. The difference $r_{ka} - r_{ma}$ is that judge's deviation from the norm in that particular trait and for that particular individual. The **total error** (TE) that judge k makes in rating a group of individuals in a trait may be obtained from the formula

$$TE = \frac{\Sigma|r_{ka} - r_{ma}|}{N} \tag{103}$$

in which N is the number of individuals rated. It will be seen that the deviations of all this judge's ratings from the means are summated, disregarding algebraic signs. The TE is the mean deviation of all k's ratings from the norms or standards.

Any rater's tendency to overestimate or underestimate in judging a trait is given by the formula

$$SE = \frac{\Sigma(r_{ka} - r_{ma})}{N} \tag{104}$$

in which SE stands for the **systematic error**. In this case the deviations of k's ratings from the means are summed algebraically. Any judge's ratings can be corrected for his systematic error in any trait. If his SE is positive, he is inclined to overestimate in the trait and his ratings should be reduced by the amount of his SE. If his SE is negative, the reverse is true.

But individual judges differ from one another and from the means not only in overestimating and underestimating traits. They also differ in the degree of scatter which they give to a group of individuals in any trait. As usual, the amount of scatter or dispersion may be indicated by means of the standard deviation. If the distribution of individuals in the trait is properly assumed to be normal, once we know the mean rating and the sigma of the distribution of ratings that have been assigned by each judge, we may translate all the ratings into common terms, in a distribution having a common mean and a common sigma. We may choose, if we wish, the mean and sigma of any one of the judges, or we may arbitrarily choose a new mean and a new sigma.

Translating Ratings into a Common Distribution.—Perhaps the simplest method of transforming ratings of different judges into a uniform scale is to divide the range into five parts. Following the plan of Paterson (39), one would then place certain percentages of the individuals in the five classes: 10 per cent in the lowest (and highest), 20 per cent in the two next classes, and 40 per cent in the middle class. This would be done for every rater's judgments. All the distributions are therefore made comparable. These percentages may be varied to conform to Symonds's suggestions as given in Table 51, if it is so desired.

Hull (24, p. 397) gives a more accurate plan of translating ratings into a common distribution. Following his own notations, letting M = the mean of the original distribution.

$\quad \sigma$ = the standard deviation of the distribution.

$\quad X$ = a given individual's rating in that distribution.

$\quad M'$ = the mean of the new distribution.

$\quad \sigma'$ = the sigma of the new distribution.

$\quad X'$ = the same individual's rating in the new distribution.

$$X' = K + SX \qquad (105)$$

where

$$S = \frac{\sigma'}{\sigma}$$

and

$$K = M' - SM.$$

It seems doubtful whether the validity of pooled ratings is sufficiently increased by the adjustments just described to justify the labor involved. Conrad (9) found after thorough studies with the Army rating scale that the adjustments did not increase the validity of the combined ratings at all. In the rating of intelligence of nursery-school children the adjustments increased the coefficients of validity only .017 points on the average (10). Apparently, so far as the validity of combined ratings is concerned, adjustments are not worth the trouble. But there are cases in which we want one rater's judgments put into comparable terms with those of others, and so the above methods of adjustment are still useful.

The Halo Effect.—A constant error to which every judge falls victim is called the **halo effect**. First mentioned by Wells (57), the error was given its name by Thorndike (53). In the words of

Rugg (44, p. 37), "We judge our fellows in terms of a general mental attitude toward them; and there is, dominating this mental attitude toward the personality as a whole, a like mental attitude toward particular qualities." One result of the halo effect is to force the rating of any trait in the general direction of the *general impression* of the individuals rated and to that extent to make the ratings of some traits less valid. Another result is to introduce a spurious amount of positive correlation between the traits that are rated. Because of this fact, ratings in which the halo effect has not been in some way cancelled out or held constant should never be used in an attempt to find the intercorrelation of traits. The halo effect is not unlike the stimulus error of psychophysics. It constitutes an irrelevant criterion with which judgments are contaminated. Perhaps it can never be fully avoided, but experience has shown us where it is most likely to be found and we can therefore know where to suspect its influence and where to avoid it. According to Symonds (51) it is most prevalent:

1. In a trait that is not easily observable.
2. In a trait that is not frequently singled out or discussed.
3. In a trait not clearly defined.
4. In a trait involving reactions with other people.
5. In a trait of high moral importance. This involves the so-called traits of character.

According to Knight (52, p. 113), acquaintance increases the halo effect.

A Logical Error in Rating.—Newcomb (38) points out an error in rating whose effect is not unlike the halo effect. This error is due to the fact that judges are likely to give similar ratings in traits that seem logically related in the minds of the raters. We may therefore call it a **logical error.** When several raters estimated the proneness of each of 30 boys to certain types of behavior, the intercorrelations of the traits averaged .493. When objective records were kept by these same raters, based upon observed behavior, the intercorrelations averaged only .141. The difference is attributed to "logical presuppositions in the minds of the raters" (38, p. 289). Like the halo effect, this error increases the intercorrelation of traits, but for a different reason. In the halo effect it is the apparent coherence of qualities in the same individual, whereas in the logical error it is the apparent logical coherence of various traits irrespective of individuals. The latter error can be avoided in part by calling for judgments of objectively observable actions rather than abstract, and hence overlapping, traits.

Additional Facts Concerning Judges.—A wealth of experience with rating scales has taught us much about judges and their peculiarities aside from those already mentioned. These additional peculiarities are listed below. In each case an attempt is made to refer to the investigator who deserves credit for making the suggestion.

1. Individuals differ in the capacity to judge others, but there is no such thing as a general judicial capacity (Hollingworth, Wells).

2. Raters disagree because they observe the individuals in different types of situations (Remmers, Plice, Arlett, Dowd, Webb).

3. Two ratings by the same judge are no more valid than one (Slawson). The reason for this is apparently that a rater repeats the same constant errors a second time, and the means of his ratings therefore deviate just as far from the truth as do the single judgments.

4. Judges do much better if interested in the ratings they make (Conrad).

5. Judges should have sufficient time for making the ratings (Conrad).

6. The judges should have similar educational and professional backgrounds (Conrad).

7. The ability of any judge to rate a specified trait should be determined (Conrad). The correlation of his ratings with a pool of ratings by others is the accepted test.

8. The good judge of self is more intelligent and more observing than the good judge of others (Adams).

9. The good judge of self tends to be happier, less irritable, more sympathetic and generous, and more courageous than the good judge of others (Adams).

10. The good judge is not necessarily self-consistent (Hollingworth), nor is the self-consistent judge necessarily a good judge (Slawson).

11. For certain admirable traits there is a positive correlation between possession and the ability to judge. The reverse of this is true in general for undesirable traits (Hollingworth).

12. One who knows himself best also judges others better in certain traits (Hollingworth).

13. Raters should be carefully trained by discussing the distribution of abilities, describing the scale, cautioning against errors such as the halo effect, central tendency, overrating, prejudice, and the logical error.

14. Judges tend to rank themselves in a group less accurately than they rank others (Shen). This is largely due to the systematic errors of the rater.

15. Judges tend to overestimate themselves in most traits and to underestimate themselves in few (Shen).

16. Judges do not always overestimate themselves in desirable traits (Shen).

17. There are individuals who overestimate themselves in all traits and others who underestimate themselves in all traits. (Shen).

18. Men are more lenient in their ratings than women (Hart, Olander).

19. Judges rate their colleagues, fellow students, or fellow teachers higher than they rate others (Cattell, Remmers, Plice).

20. Self-ratings are too high on desirable traits and too low on undesirable traits (Hollingworth, Shen, Hurlock).

21. There is a tendency to overrate members of the same sex as compared with members of the opposite sex (Kinder).

22. In self-ratings, superior individuals underestimate themselves and inferior individuals overrate themselves, the latter having the greater error (Hoffman).

23. Parents overrate their children as a rule, but they may underestimate very superior children.

24. Personally selected judges, selected by those who are to be rated, tend to rate an individual higher than he rates himself (Uhrbrock).

25. The assurance of a judge is of some importance. Judgments of which he is very sure are much more reliable than ordinary ratings (Cady).

26. Ratings may be influenced by the judges knowing the purpose for which they are to be used. To avoid this error, ratings should be secured with the judges in ignorance of their use and if possible at a time in advance of the situation demanding their use (Paterson).

27. Different judges use different criteria in judging the same trait. For this reason it is sometimes desirable to ask the rater to state the basis upon which his own judgments are made.

Concerning Differences between Traits.—The recommendations given so far have applied more specifically to constant errors in the judges, the personal equation, and other common errors that occur no matter what traits are being rated. There are also certain facts that apply to some traits and not to others. Some traits are more easily observed and judged than others. Some are more objective and different judges are more likely to agree upon them than they do upon other more subjectively estimated traits. The experiences of various investigators will now be summarized briefly. Hollingworth (22) found close agreement among raters upon the following traits: *efficiency, originality, perseverance, quickness, judgment, clearness, energy,* and *will.* There was fair agreement upon *mental balance, breadth, leadership, intensity, reasonableness, independence, refinement, physical health,* and *emotions.* There was poor agreement upon such traits as *courage, unselfishness, integrity, cooperativeness, cheerfulness,* and *kindliness.* Shen (47) found the best agreement upon *scholarship, leadership,* and *intelligence* and the poorest agreement upon *judicial sense, punctuality,* and *tact.* Miner (37) found good agreement for the traits of *energy, leadership, general ability,* and *reliability.*

A few rules concerning traits can be gleaned from experience:

1. Traits should be described univocally, objectively, and specifically (Paterson, Kingsbury).

2. A trait which is to be rated should not be a composite of a number of traits that vary independently (Freyd). This rule is as yet impossible to apply, since we have no scientific analysis of personality into independent variables.

3. Each trait should refer to a single type of activity or to the results of a single type of activity (Paterson).

4. Traits should be grouped according to the accuracy with which they can be rated (Paterson).

5. In describing traits, avoid the use of general terms such as 'very,' 'extreme,' 'average,' or 'excellent' (Freyd).

6. Traits should be judged on the basis of past or present accomplishments rather than upon what the raters regard as future promise (Paterson).

7. In self-ratings there is no trait in which all individuals overestimate or all underestimate themselves.

8. Finally, do not use scales for traits on which reliable or more objective data can be obtained (Paterson). It would be absurd to depend upon ratings of health when medical records are obtain-

able, or to use ratings on intelligence when mental tests are available.

The Reliability and Validity of Ratings.—As elsewhere, the reliability of measurements is determined by a self-correlation; repeated sets of measurements are correlated with each other. Repetition in the case of ratings means ratings obtained from additional comparable judges. The validity pertains to the truth of the ratings—how nearly they represent evaluations of the trait in question. This can be determined only if some outside criterion of the same trait is available. It is rarely possible to obtain such a criterion. Ratings themselves have very often been used as the outside criterion against which to check the validity of a new test of ability or of personality. The best type of outside criterion, for either ratings or test scores, is, of course, some measure of actual behavior.

The reliability and validity of ratings increase with the number of judges. According to Rugg (44), one should use the pooled ratings of not less than three independent judges. Symonds (52, p. 96) demands at least eight judges. According to Bradshaw (4), with the average trait a reliability coefficient of .80 may be obtained with 5 to 22 judges; a reliability of .90 may be obtained with 10 to 50 judges; and a reliability of .95 may be obtained with 21 to 106 judges. Much depends upon the particular trait and the manner of securing the ratings. The reliabilities should be determined for each set of conditions and the degree of reliability desired will determine the number of judges required.

Furfey (16) has shown that the reliability of a rating scale may be increased by subdividing a trait into a number of sub-traits and asking the same judge to rate the subdivisions. A pooling of such ratings gives somewhat the same effect as pooling the judgments of different raters. The average intercorrelation of 18 sub-traits he found to be .475 and .437 for two judges. The reliabilities of the 18 pools were .945 and .936, respectively. To what extent these correlations are due to halo effect and to the logical error, we do not know. But if a single judge is to repeat his ratings of a trait, it is necessary to redefine the trait in order that his pooled ratings shall give an increased reliability.

GENERAL EVALUATION OF RATING METHODS

As compared with their nearest rivals, paired comparisons and the method of rank order, the rating-scale methods have certain definite advantages and the results often compare very favorably with those accurate methods. The advantages may be listed as follows:

1. Ratings require much less time than either paired comparisons or ranking methods.

2. The procedure is far more interesting to the judges, especially if graphic methods are employed.

3. Rating-scale methods have a much wider range of application.

4. They can be used with psychologically naive judges who have had a minimum of training.

5. They can be used with large numbers of stimuli. Even the method of ranking becomes difficult and irksome when there are more than 30 to 40 stimuli.

6. Some investigators in experimental aesthetics maintain that the best judgments are made when stimuli are presented singly, that comparative judgments destroy the aesthetic attitude (see page 223).

7. Ratings give absolute scale values in the sense that a zero point is directly located.

8. The objection that ratings are subject to many constant errors is met by proof to the contrary that pooled ratings somehow eliminate the force of those errors and by the fact that certain corrections may be made if necessary to take account of those errors.

Certain empirical studies made to compare the different scaling methods also demonstrate the worth of ratings. Symonds (51) concludes that under ordinary conditions ratings give results as reliable as those obtained from the ranking method. Conklin and Sutherland (8) in a study of jokes found that ratings gave smaller mean deviations, in other words, were less variable from one judge to another, than did rankings. The reliability of the ratings was given by a coefficient of .79 as compared with a reliability of .73 for rankings. Since the humor of a joke may so quickly wear off with repetition, one can readily see why single presentations should give more stable results. Marsh and Perrin (34), in a study of the validity of ratings, correlated them with more objective criteria. The judges observed the subjects while they performed certain tasks and then made their judgments without knowing the test scores. The ratings for intelligence correlated .78 with test scores. A like coefficient for the aiming test was .36; for a card-sorting test it was .68. Judgments of head size correlated with actual size to the extent of .76. No comparison can be made here with other scaling devices, paired comparisons, or ranking, but the coefficients indicate several conclusions. Ratings of some human traits and performances have a satisfactory degree of validity. The degree of validity of ratings varies for different traits, as we should expect. Finally, ratings lack sufficient validity to be used as final criteria against which to gauge the validity of mental tests.

Problems

1. The following table presents the ratings assigned to 40 different colors by five judges who were asked to evaluate them on a nine-point scale for affective value. Each rating is a mean (to the nearest unit) of five judgments.

Color	A	B	C	D	E	Color	A	B	C	D	E
1	7	4	6	2	5	21	7	5	6	4	5
2	8	4	7	2	7	22	5	3	6	5	5
3	8	4	8	6	5	23	2	2	6	3	2
4	7	5	7	3	4	24	6	4	7	6	5
5	5	2	7	3	4	25	6	6	7	6	7
6	3	1	6	3	2	26	7	7	9	8	6
7	4	3	6	3	6	27	6	8	7	7	6
8	3	3	6	5	4	28	6	6	6	6	6
9	6	5	8	4	7	29	5	2	4	5	6
10	4	6	7	6	6	30	5	4	6	5	5
11	5	5	7	5	4	31	5	3	6	3	3
12	7	7	9	7	9	32	6	4	7	4	5
13	8	7	9	8	8	33	7	4	6	5	6
14	7	8	8	7	8	34	7	4	6	4	7
15	7	8	8	6	8	35	6	4	5	5	7
16	7	7	8	7	6	36	7	5	7	7	7
17	7	7	7	5	7	37	5	6	7	7	7
18	4	6	6	2	7	38	7	7	8	6	9
19	7	5	8	4	6	39	7	7	7	5	7
20	7	4	7	5	4	40	8	4	7	6	7

a. Find the average scale value for every color.
b. Find the total error, TE, for every judge and also his systematic error, SE.
c. Adopting judge E as the standard, translate the ratings of the other judges into comparable terms.

REFERENCES

1. ADAMS, H. F., The good judge of personality, *J. Abn. and Soc. Psychol.*, 1927, **22**, 172–181.
2. ARLETT, A. H., and C. E. DOWD, Variability among a group of judges in rating character traits in children, *Psychol. Bull.*, 1926, **23**, 617–619.
3. BOYCE, A. C., Methods of measuring teachers' efficiency, *Fourteenth Yearbook Nat. Soc. Stud. Educ.*, 1915, Pt. II.
4. BRADSHAW, F. F., The American Council on Education rating scale, *Arch. Psychol.*, 1930, no. 119.
5. CADY, V. M., The estimation of juvenile incorrigibility, *J. Delinq. Monog.*, 1923, no. 2.
6. CATTELL, J. McK., "American Men of Science," 2d ed., pp. 537–596, Science Press, New York, 1910.
7. CONKLIN, E. S., The scale of values method for studies in genetic psychology, *Univ. Ore. Pub.*, 1923, **2**, no. 1.
8. CONKLIN, E. S., and J. W. SUTHERLAND, A comparison of the scale of values method with the order of merit method, *J. Exper. Psychol.*, 1923, **6**, 44–57.
9. CONRAD, H. S., The bogey of the "personal equation" in ratings of intelligence, *J. Educ. Psychol.*, 1932, **23**, 147–149.
10. ———, The personal equation in ratings: I. An experimental determination, *J. Genet. Psychol.*, 1932, **41**, 267–293.
11. ———, The personal equation in ratings: II. A systematic evaluation, *J. Educ. Psychol.*, 1933, **24**, 39–46.
12. DALLENBACH, K. M., The measurement of attention, *Amer. J. Psychol.*, 1913, **24**, 465–507.
13. DORCUS, R. M., Some factors involved in judging personal characteristics, *J. Appl. Psychol.*, 1926, **10**, 502–518.
14. DOWNEY, J., The imaginal reaction to poetry, the affective and the esthetic judgment, *Univ. Wyo. Psychol. Bull.*, 1911, no. 2.
15. FREYD, M., The graphic rating scale, *J. Educ. Psychol.*, 1923, **14**, 83–102.
16. FURFEY, P. H., An improved rating scale technique, *J. Educ. Psychol.*, 1926, **17**, 45–48.
17. GALTON, F., "Inquiries into Human Faculty and Its Development," Macmillan & Company, Ltd., London, 1883.
18. GEISSLER, L. R., The measurement of attention, *Amer. J. Psychol.*, 1909, **20**, 473–529.
19. HART, H., and E. OLANDER, Sex differences in character as indicated by teachers' ratings, *School and Soc.*, 1924, **20**, 381–382.
20. HOFFMANN, G. J., An experiment in self-estimation, *J. Abn. and Soc. Psychol.*, 1923, **18**, 43–49.
21. HOLLINGWORTH, H. L., Judgments of persuasiveness, *Psychol. Rev.*, 1911, **18**, 234–256.
22. ———, "Judging Human Character," D. Appleton-Century Company, Inc., New York, 1922.
23. HUGHES, W. H., General principles and results of rating trait characteristics, *J. Educ. Method*, 1925, **4**, 421–431.
24. HULL, C. L., "Aptitude Testing," World Book Company, Yonkers, 1928.

25. HURLOCK, E. B., A study of self-ratings by children, *J. Appl. Psychol.*, 1927, **11**, 490–502.

26. KEITH, J. A. H., The mutual influence of feelings, *Harvard Psychol. Stud.*, 1906, **2**, 141–157.

27. KENNETH, J. H., An experimental study of affects and associations due to certain odors, *Psychol. Monog.*, 1927, **37**, no. 171.

28. KINDER, V. S., Through our own looking glass, *School and Soc.*, 1925, **22**, 533–536.

29. KINGSBURY, F. A., Analyzing ratings and training raters, *J. Person, Res.*, 1922, **1**, 377–383.

30. KNIGHT, F. B., and R. H. FRANZEN, Pitfalls in rating schemes, *J. Educ. Psychol.*, 1922, **13**, 204–213.

31. LINDSAY, E. E., Personal judgments, *J. Educ. Psychol.*, 1921, **12**, 413–415.

32. LUND, F. H., Emotional and volitional determinants of belief, *J. Abn. and Soc. Psychol.*, 1925, **20**, 63–81, 174–196.

33. MAJOR, D. R., On the affective tone of simple sense-impressions, *Amer. J. Psychol.*, 1895, **7**, 57–77.

34. MARSH, S. E., and F. A. C. PERRIN, An experimental study of the rating scale technique, *J. Abn. and Soc. Psychol.*, 1925, **19**, 383–399.

35. MARTIN, L. J., Psychology of aesthetics, *Amer. J. Psychol.*, 1905, **16**, 35–118.

36. ———, An experimental study of Fechner's principles of aesthetics, *Psychol. Rev.*, 1906, **13**, 142–219.

37. MINER, J. B., Evaluation of a method for finely graduated estimates of abilities, *J. Appl. Psychol.*, 1917, **1**, 123–133.

38. NEWCOMB, T., An experiment designed to test the validity of a rating technique, *J. Educ. Psychol.*, 1931, **22**, 279–289.

39. PATERSON, D. G., Methods of rating human qualities, *Ann. Amer. Acad. Pol. and Soc. Sci.*, 1923, **110**, 81–93.

40. PEARSON, K., On the relationship of intelligence to size and shape of head, *Biometrika*, 1907, **5**, 105–146.

41. PERRIN, F. A. C., Physical attractiveness and repulsiveness, *J. Exper. Psychol.*, 1921, **4**, 203–217.

42. REMMERS, H. H., and M. J. PLICE, Reliability of ratings at Purdue University, *Indus. Psychol.*, 1926, **1**, 717–721.

43. REMMERS, H. H., N. W. SHOCK, and E. L. KELLY, An empirical study of the validity of the Spearman-Brown formula as applied to the Purdue rating scale, *J. Educ. Psychol.*, 1927, **18**, 187–195.

44. RUGG, H. O., Is the rating of human character practicable? *J. Educ. Psychol.*, 1921, **12**, 425–438, 485–501; 1922, **13**, 30–42, 81–93.

45. SCOTT, W. D., R. C. CLOTHIER, and S. B. MATHEWSON, "Personnel Management," McGraw-Hill Book Company, Inc., New York, 1931.

46. SHEN, E., The influence of friendship upon personal ratings, *J. Appl. Psychol.*, 1925, **9**, 66–88.

47. ———, The reliability coefficient of personal ratings, *J. Educ. Psychol.*, 1925, **16**, 232–236.

48. ———, The validity of self-estimates, *J. Educ. Psychol.*, 1925, **16**, 104–107.

49. SLAWSON, J., The reliability of judgments of personal traits, *J. Appl. Psychol.*, 1922, **6**, 161–171.

50. SYMONDS, P. M., On the loss of reliability in ratings due to coarseness of the scale, *J. Exper. Psychol.*, 1924, **7**, 456–461.

51. ———, Notes on rating, *J. Appl. Psychol.*, 1925, **9**, 188–195.

52. ———, "Diagnosing Personality and Conduct," D. Appleton-Century Company, Inc., New York, 1931.

53. THORNDIKE, E. L., A constant error in psychological ratings, *J. Appl. Psychol.*, 1920, **4**, 25–29.

54. TITCHENER, E. B., The psychophysics of climate, *Amer. J. Psychol.*, 1909, **20**, 1–14.

55. UHRBROCK, R. S., Rating tendencies of personally selected judges, *J. Educ. Psychol.*, 1932, **23**, 594–603.

56. WEBB, E., Character and intelligence, *Brit. J. Psychol. Monog. Suppl.*, 1915, no. 3.

57. WELLS, F. L., A statistical study of literary merit, *Arch. Psychol.*, 1907, no. 7.

58. YOUNG, P. T., The constancy of affective judgment to odors, *J. Exper. Psychol.*, 1923, **6**, 182–191.

59. ———, Studies in affective psychology, *Amer. J. Psychol.*, 1930, **42**, 17–27.

PART III

CORRELATION AND TEST METHODS

CHAPTER X

THE ELEMENTS OF CURVE FITTING

THE PROBLEMS OF FUNCTIONAL RELATIONSHIPS

In the preceding chapters our chief concern has been with the measurement of a single variable at a time. A mean and a standard deviation, or some equivalent measures, were the typical end results of our labors. But usually science demands more than that for an answer to its many questions. Science is typically interested in relationships between variables. In its efforts to predict one phenomenon from another it must determine how the one depends upon the other. It seeks to find cause and effect; it wants to know the independent and the dependent variable, and how a certain change in the one is accompanied by a corresponding change in the other. Whenever possible, this relationship is stated in quantitative terms. This can be done when both cause and effect are continuously variable and subject to measurement. A functional relationship between two variables can then be determined and it can often be expressed in the form of a mathematical equation.[1] The mathematical equation, aside from being the scientist's ideal shorthand method of expressing a relation between two phenomena, is often the tool whereby he is able to make far-reaching deductions. It is important, then, that the individual whose ambitions tend in the direction of scientific research should have at his command at least a minimum working knowledge of mathematical functions.

The Two-fold Problem in Functional Relationships.—The problem of fitting empirical data to a mathematical function divides itself naturally into two parts. First, there is the problem of the choice of type of mathematical function to be used. Will the data fit a straight line, a parabola, or a cubic, or will they require a logarithmic function to describe best the relationship between the two variables? Second, there is the final checkup to determine

---

[1] At this point the student may do well to review the section of Chapter III that deals with the concept of mathematical functions (pp. 79 ff)

whether the data fit the chosen function reasonably well. This is the problem of correlation proper.[1] If the amount of correlation is low, it may be because the improper function has been assumed and some other function should be chosen,[2] or it may be that the experimental control has been poor or has been impossible to attain. In the latter case additional independent variables have not been held constant or at least have not been taken into account. When a dependent variable has several determining causes and when all except one cannot be held constant while measuring the effects of that one, we still have recourse to the techniques of partial and multiple correlation.

For example, success in a college subject depends to some extent upon intelligence, degree of motivation, previous preparation, and amount of time available for the study of that subject. If we measure all these factors separately, no single one might correlate more than .50 with the record made in that subject, because of the contamination of the other factors which vary more or less at random. By means of partial correlation methods we can hold constant one or more independent variables while determining the net effects of another independent variable. By means of the multiple correlation technique we can determine the combined causal effect of several independent variables upon the dependent variable, and we can furthermore estimate the relative importance of each in affecting the dependent variable. Partial and multiple correlations thus constitute a third major problem in the analysis of functional relationships. In this chapter we shall deal almost exclusively

---

[1] Too often, psychologists in particular have overlooked the first problem and have jumped to the second without realizing it. The correlation between two sets of psychological data is often so low that it is difficult to decide what type of relationship probably holds. The simplest assumption is a straight-line function, which assumption is usually made more often implicitly than explicitly. Nor do many psychologists stop to consider whether their measuring scale is a linear one, possessing equal units throughout, or whether it is logarithmic or some other type of scale, with unequal numerical units. The literature is strewn with coefficients of correlation that are absolutely meaningless and useless when taken at their face value; worse still, they are actually misleading because the source from which they came and the assumptions underlying their computation are unknown or ignored.

[2] A relatively high correlation, on the other hand, does not necessarily mean that the best mathematical function has been chosen. Some other assumption might give an even higher coefficient of correlation. The degree of correlation will, however, indicate which of two curves fits the data better.

with the first problem—that of determining the type of functional relationship between two variables and of deriving a mathematical equation for the relationship where that is desired. In the two chapters immediately following we shall deal more with the degree of dependence found between two variables and we shall consider how one variable can depend simultaneously upon several.

Determining the Type of Relationship

As an illustrative problem, let us take a set of data obtained from a single O who was asked to reproduce horizontal straight lines of various lengths. The standard lengths varied from 20 mm., by steps of 10 mm., to 350 mm. Sixty experiments were performed, in each of which O made 50 reproductions of a standard line, as in the method of average error of Chapter II. The mean and the PE of each distribution of 50 lines were computed. We therefore have 60 pairs of measurements, which are given in Table 52 in the order in which they were completed.

TABLE 52.—Data Giving the Relation between Lengths of Lines Reproduced and the Probable Errors of the Distributions of
Reproductions, in Millimeters

Length of line	PE of distri- bution	Length of line	PE of distri- bution	Length of line	PE of distri- bution	Length of line	PE of distri- bution
20	1.5	40	2.5	350	12.4	320	11.5
40	3.0	80	5.1	260	10.4	270	10.5
210	9.0	240	9.6	100	5.4	150	7.6
180	8.4	200	9.5	130	7.2	140	7.6
330	12.2	340	10.1	150	8.0	100	5.5
300	11.2	350	11.4	150	8.2	120	6.4
190	8.7	210	9.5	90	5.1	120	7.6
200	11.9	250	12.3	60	5.2	80	4.4
300	11.9	280	11.4	90	6.6	110	6.1
290	11.2	310	12.9	270	11.6	300	11.1
200	10.5	250	9.3	220	8.8	250	10.1
160	9.0	170	8.4	30	2.7	60	4.1
50	4.4	330	11.6	30	2.4	50	3.9
100	6.8	70	4.9	230	9.5	240	9.8
150	7.0	180	7.3	300	10.8	350	11.1

Plotting the Correlation Diagram.—What is the functional relationship between a given standard line and the average error of O's reproductions, measured in terms of the PE? According to Weber's law we should expect a straight-line relationship, with a formula of the general form $PE = KR$. The first step in determining this relationship naturally is to plot the points in a system of coordinates, with the independent variable R on the X-axis and the dependent

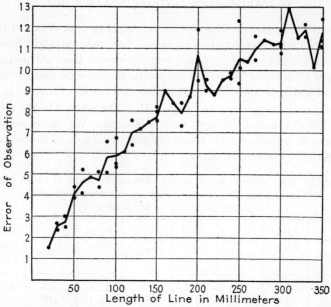

FIG. 32.—Correlation diagram showing the relation between the length of line reproduced and the PE of the distribution of reproductions.

variable PE on the Y-axis. The plot of the points appears in Fig. 32. Such a plot is known as a **correlation diagram** or **scatter diagram.** It is quite obvious from the plot in Fig. 32 that the PE is an increasing function of R. Before we assume that the relationship is linear, however, it is well to examine the trend of the points more carefully. This we can do by the use of averages.

Discovering Trends by Means of Averages.—In our illustrative problem the same stimulus value was sometimes employed in a number of sets of 50 observations. We can get a clearer notion of the trend of the curve if for every R value we compute an average PE, as has been done in Table 53. There the R values are arranged

TABLE 53.—DATA GIVING THE RELATION BETWEEN LENGTHS OF LINES REPRODUCED AND THE PROBABLE ERRORS OF THE DISTRIBUTIONS

Length of line, mm.	Probable errors for each length	Average *PE* for each length
20	1.5	(1.5)
30	2.4, 2.7	2.55
40	2.5, 3.0	2.75
50	3.9, 4.4	4.15
60	4.1, 5.2	4.65
70	4.9	(4.9)
80	4.4, 5.1	4.75
90	5.1, 6.6	5.85
100	5.4, 5.5, 6.8	5.90
110	6.1	(6.1)
120	6.4, 7.6	7.00
130	7.2	(7.2)
140	7.5	(7.5)
150	7.0, 7.6, 8.0, 8.2	7.70
160	9.0	(9.0)
170	8.4	(8.4)
180	7.3, 8.4	7.85
190	8.7	(8.7)
200	9.5, 10.5, 11.9	10.63
210	9.0, 9.5	9.25
220	8.8	(8.8)
230	9.5	(9.5)
240	9.6, 9.8	9.70
250	9.3, 10.1, 12.3	10.57
260	10.4	(10.4)
270	10.5, 11.6	11.05
280	11.4	(11.4)
290	11.2	(11.2)
300	10.8, 11.1, 11.2, 11.9	11.25
310	12.9	(12.9)
320	11.5	(11.5)
330	11.6, 12.2	11.90
340	10.1	(10.1)
350	11.1, 11.4, 12.4	11.63

in serial order and the average *PE* values that correspond to them appear in the last column. Whenever there is only one measurement of the *PE* for a given *R* value, the 'average' *PE* is placed in a parenthesis. The broken line which wends its way upward through the series of points in Fig. 32 is based upon these averages. The graphic relationship between *R* and *PE* is still not without inversions. Because of this fact it cannot reasonably be taken as the true functional relationship between *R* and *PE*. But it does give an idea of what the true relation probably is. In view of the general upward trend of the scatter of dots, we should expect that the true relation involves an increase in *PE* for every increase in *R*. Since none of the average *PE* values in Table 53 are based upon more than four measurements, none of them can be any too reliable as averages. All are subject to fluctuations due to errors of sampling.

In order to increase the reliability of averages, it is necessary to extend the number of measurements in each class. That can be accomplished by grouping the data into broader classes. Instead of finding the average *PE* for each single *R* value, we group several *R* values together and find the mean of the several corresponding *PE* values. This grouping is rather arbitrary. We need to leave enough classes so as not to destroy the real trend of the curve and yet group a sufficient number of observations in each class to insure some degree of reliability for the averages. In this problem we may form seven groups, letting the class interval for the *R* values be 50 mm. Instead of letting the midpoints of the *R* intervals represent those intervals, we find the actual mean of the *R* values in every one of those intervals. This gives us seven pairs of values and seven points that we can now plot on the correlation diagram. The results of the computations are to be found in Table 54 and the seven points are plotted in Fig. 33, being connected by the heavy lines.

The rectangles that appear in the region of each point in Fig. 33 represent the extents of the standard errors of the means. The standard errors of the means were obtained according to formulas (17*b*) and (17*c*) of Chapter II. Interpreting them as applying to this particular problem, we may say that these sigmas indicate the probable·limits within which two-thirds of similar means would fall. To take a particular case, when *R* is 37.1 mm., two-thirds of the means of the *PE* values corresponding to it, if obtained under comparable conditions, would probably lie within the limits of 2.91 ± .46 mm. Or, if we wished to turn the prediction about, for a *PE* of 2.91, we should expect the mean *R* to be within the limits of 37.1 ± 5.2 mm. The dotted lines in Fig. 33 are drawn connecting

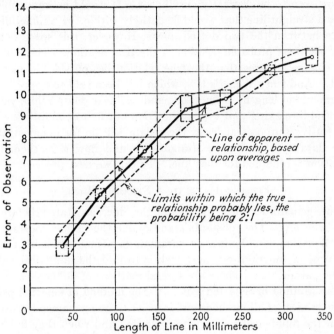

Fig. 33.—The trend of the average relationship between length of line and its *PE*.

TABLE 54.—Relation between the Average Length of Line Reproduced and the Average *PE* of the Distribution of Reproductions, with Standard Deviations of the Averages

Class limits	N	Average length	σ_M	Average PE	σ_M
10– 59	7	37.1	5.2	2.91	.46
60–109	10	83.0	5.2	5.31	.28
110–159	9	135.6	6.0	7.29	.26
160–209	8	185.0	6.3	9.21	.60
210–259	9	233.3	6.6	9.77	.38
260–309	9	285.6	5.8	11.12	.21
310–359	8	335.0	6.3	11.65	.36

the corners of the rectangles and according to Ezekiel (2, pp. 48 *f.*) the chances are two to one that the true relationship between *R* and PE lies somewhere between the dotted lines. This gives us a still more exact idea of the true shape of the curve. The trend is now seen to be distinctly curvilinear. It would be impossible to draw a straight line that would lie entirely within the confines of the space between the two dotted lines. However, this space defines only the most probable position of the true relation. There is still one chance in three that the true relation lies outside, in part, at least. And since Weber's law, which has been said to apply to the judgments of lengths of lines, demands a linear relationship, we are justified in making that type of function our first assumption. For illustrative purposes at least, these data will do for demonstrating how data are fitted to a straight line and how a mathematical equation is obtained for that line. To this we next proceed.

FITTING DATA TO A STRAIGHT LINE

The general formula for a straight line, as stated before, is $Y = a + bX$. The constants a and b, like the similar constants in any equation, are known as **parameters**. Once we have chosen the type of function, our next task is to find the numerical values of the parameters. There are several methods of doing this.

The Method of Selected Points.—The **method of selected points** is the crudest of all methods and is never to be recommended except when the number of points is very limited and when they fall very close to a straight line, or under less favorable circumstances when only the roughest approximation is wanted. Any two points are sufficient to determine the location of a straight line. Any two of the observed points that seem most representative may be selected and the line drawn through them, or any two new points may be placed where it seems reasonable to do so. The values of parameters a and b can be readily found, since a is the Y-intercept and b is the slope of the line and is equal to $(Y - a)/X$. Any selected point with its Y and X values would suffice for finding b from this formula.

The Graphic Method.—The **graphic method of curve fitting** has been proposed in earlier chapters in connection with previous problems. It consists in using a thread or a transparent lined ruler and adjusting the thread or line until it comes nearest to the greatest number of points or until it seems to represent the total slope and position best. The line is then drawn and the parameters are found as in the last-mentioned procedure. Like the first method, it can be used to advantage only when the points fit the line very closely.

Hardly any two observers would extend the line in exactly the same position nor would the same observer do so on two different occasions. It would be next to impossible to use the graphic method with the present illustrative problem.

The Method of Successive Differences.—The **method of successive differences** makes use of the fact that in a straight-line function a given numerical change in X is paralleled by a corresponding numerical change in Y. If we may designate a given change in X as dX and the corresponding change in Y as dY, then the ratio dY/dX is constant. Furthermore, we know that the ratio dY/dX measures the slope of the line and is therefore equal to the parameter b. This may be stated as a mathematical relationship as follows:

$$b = \frac{Y_2 - Y_1}{X_2 - X_1} = \frac{dY}{dX}$$

in which X_2 and X_1 are any two chosen values of X selected from the data, X_2 being greater than X_1, and Y_2 and Y_1 are the observed Y values corresponding to them.

We might proceed to find all the X differences in Table 52 and all the Y differences corresponding to them, and then the ratios or b values corresponding to them. The b of the final line would be a mean of all those ratios. It is more expedient and perhaps just as accurate, if the function is really linear, to deal with only a few differences. For this purpose we can use the averages of Table 54. They are repeated in Table 55 with the differences and their ratios.

TABLE 55.—AVERAGE INCREASES IN PE CORRESPONDING TO COMPARABLE INCREASES IN R AND THE RATIOS OF THOSE INCREASES AT SUCCESSIVE PARTS OF THE R-SCALE

X (R)	Y (PE)	dX $(X_2 - X_1)$	dY $(Y_2 - Y_1)$	dY/dX (b)
37.1	2.91			
		45.9	2.40	.052
83.0	5.31			
		52.6	1.98	.038
135.6	7.29			
		49.4	1.92	.039
185.0	9.21			
		48.3	.56	.011
233.3	9.77			
		52.3	1.35	.026
285.6	11.12			
		49.4	.53	.011
335.0	11.65			
M 185.7	8.23	....	....	.029

The ratios indicate what the slope of the line would have been, had it been drawn through each successive pair of points. The increase in Y for a corresponding increase in X is seen to vary considerably, from .011 to .052. In general, the ratios decrease with increasing values of X, which verifies the suspicion that the relationship is not really linear. But we have assumed for the present a straight-line relation, and so we proceed to find the parameters b and a. The most probable b by this method is the mean of the ratios in the last column of the table. This mean is .029. Knowing b, we can find a by means of the relation $a = Y - bX$. Substituting for Y and X the means of the Y values and X values, we have

$$a = 8.23 - (.029)(185.7)$$
$$= 8.23 - 5.39$$
$$= 2.84.$$

The equation for which we are looking is therefore

$$Y = 2.84 + .029X.$$

The Method of Averages.—The previous method depended upon the seven points which were obtained by using averages. The present method carries the same principle a step farther. It reduces the data to two main groups and finds by means of averages just two points, which are all that we need for locating a line. The reasoning involved, however, and the approach are somewhat different. We begin by assuming that every pair of X and Y values furnishes us with information that helps in the finding of parameters. We can substitute in the general equation $Y = a + bX$ any pair of values for X and Y; for example, to use the first pair of values from Table 53, we may say that $1.5 = a + 20b$. Using the second pair of values, $2.4 = a + 30b$. The parameters a and b are the unknowns for which we are looking. Elementary algebra teaches that, if we have two equations and two unknowns, we have sufficient information to find those unknowns. The two equations may be solved simultaneously and values for a and b may be determined which will satisfy both equations. So we could continue, finding values for a and b from every combination of such equations taken two at a time. That tedious process is unnecessary. What we do is to group the data into two large pools, preferably the one group at the lower end of the R values and the other at the upper end as in Table 56, which gives some of the equations.

TABLE 56.—EQUATIONS FOR THE SOLUTION OF PARAMETERS a AND b BY THE
METHOD OF AVERAGES

Group I	Group II
$1.5 = a + 20b$	$8.7 = a + 190b$
$2.4 = a + 30b$	. . . .
$2.7 = a + 30b$	. . . .
$3.0 = a + 40b$	$10.1 = a + 340b$
. . . .	$11.1 = a + 350b$
. . . .	$11.4 = a + 350b$
$8.4 = a + 180b$	$12.4 = a + 350b$
$\Sigma\ 172.2 = 30a + 3000b$	$321.8 = 30a + 8140b$
$M\ \ 5.74 = a + 100b$	$10.73 = a + 271.3b$

We next find the two means of the two groups of equations, which
appear at the bottom of Table 56. These are the two simultaneous
equations which when solved will give the two parameters. Subtracting equation I from equation II,

$$10.73 = \not{a} + 271.3b$$
$$5.74 = \not{a} + 100.0b$$

$$4.99 = \qquad 171.3b$$
$$.0291 = b$$
$$a = Y - bX.$$

Substituting for Y and X the means of equation I,

$$a = 5.74 - (.0291)(100)$$
$$= 5.74 - 2.91$$
$$= 2.83.$$

The equation by this method, $Y = 2.83 + .029X$, is very close
to that found by the previous method. This would naturally
be true since the two methods have so much in common. In this
method, as compared with the preceding one, we have only 2 averages and 1 pair of differences instead of 14 averages and 7
pairs of differences. The Y difference is 4.99 and the X difference
is 171.3. The ratio is just what was found for b in the preceding
solution.

The Method of Least Squares.—In the preceding method we
grouped the many equations into two pools and found their sums
and means in order to solve for a and b. In the **method of least
squares** we are able to reach the same goal by keeping the data in

one pool and by dealing with the sums and means of all the equations taken together.   The resulting line of best fit is defined as *that line from which the sum of the squares of the deviations is a minimum.* This is the *principle of least squares.*   When we say "deviations," we mean the deviations in the Y values from the best-fitting line.

But we have two unknowns, a and b, and it is impossible to find those parameters without having two equations, for there must be as many equations as there are unknowns.   Grouping the data in one pool gives us only one equation.   Whence comes the other? This cannot be fully explained to the nonmathematical student, since a bit of differential calculus is involved.   Let it suffice here to say that the other **normal equation** (for that is the technical term applied to the two equations we need) is obtained in the following manner: Every equation (such as those appearing in Table 56), which comes from a single pair of Y and X values, is multiplied through by the value of X in that equation.   For example, the first equation in Table 56, which reads $1.5 = a + 20b$, would then become $30 = 20a + 400b$, X being equal to 20 in this equation.   The second equation would read $72 = 30a + 900b$; the third would be $81 = 30a + 900b$; and so on.   From the sums of these equations we derive the other normal equation.   In general terms, the two normal equations are

(A) $$\Sigma(Y) = Na + \Sigma(X)b$$
(B) $$\Sigma(XY) = \Sigma(X)a + \Sigma(X^2)b \tag{106}$$

Here we deal with sums rather than averages as in the previous method, although even there we might just as well have dealt with sums; the result would have been the same.

In finding all the known values in the two normal equations, it is not necessary to write out all the equations as they appear in Table 56; that would be a waste of paper and ink.   It is convenient to prepare a work sheet similar to Table 57, with columns for the following items: X, Y, X^2, Y^2, and XY.   The item of Y^2 is included, not because it is needed in finding the parameters, but because it will be necessary to know $\Sigma(Y^2)$ if we want to compute the sigma of the Y distribution or the coefficient of correlation, as we usually do.   The other headings will be explained later.   It will be noted that in the first column we have reduced the numerical size of the X values by dropping the last zero.   This is for the purpose of keeping the numerical values small in the process of squaring and in

TABLE 57.—WORK SHEET FOR THE METHOD OF LEAST SQUARES. THE INDE-
PENDENT VARIABLE *X* IS THE LENGTH OF LINE REPRODUCED AND THE
DEPENDENT VARIABLE *Y* THE *PE* OF THE DISTRIBUTION
OF REPRODUCTIONS[1]

X	Y	X^2	XY	Y^2	Y'	Y'^2	z	z^2
2	1.5	4	3.0	2.25	3.51	12.3201	−2.01	4.0401
3	2.7	9	8.1	7.29	3.80	14.4400	−1.40	1.9600
3	2.4	9	7.2	5.76	3.80	14.4400	−1.10	1.2100
4	3.0	16	12.0	9.00	4.08	16.6464	−1.58	2.4964
4	2.5	16	10.0	6.25	4.08	16.6464	−1.08	1.1664
5	4.4	25	22.0	19.36	4.37	19.0969	− .47	.2209
5	3.9	25	19.5	15.21	4.37	19.0969	+ .03	.0009
6	4.1	36	24.6	16.81	4.65	21.6225	− .55	.3025
6	5.2	36	31.2	27.04	4.65	21.6225	+ .55	.3025
7	4.9	49	34.3	24.01	4.94	24.4036	− .04	.0016
....	....	....	....	....	....	....	......	......
....	....	....	....	....	....	....	......	......
15	8.2	225	123.0	67.24	7.22	52.1284	+ .98	.9604
16	9.0	256	144.0	81.00	7.50	56.2500	+1.50	2.2500
17	8.4	289	142.8	70.56	7.79	60.6841	+ .61	.3721
18	7.3	324	131.4	53.29	8.08	65.2864	− .78	.6084
18	8.4	324	151.2	70.56	8.08	65.2864	+ .32	.1024
....	....	....	....	....	....	....	......	......
....	....	....	....	....	....	....	......	......
30	11.2	900	336.0	125.44	11.50	132.2500	− .30	.0900
30	11.9	900	357.0	141.61	11.50	132.2500	+ .40	.1600
31	12.9	961	399.9	166.41	11.78	138.7684	+1.12	1.2544
32	11.5	1024	368.0	132.25	12.07	145.6849	− .57	.3249
33	11.6	1089	382.8	134.56	12.35	152.5225	− .75	.5625
33	12.2	1089	402.6	148.84	12.35	152.5225	− .15	.0225
34	10.1	1156	343.4	102.01	12.64	159.7696	−2.54	6.4516
35	11.1	1225	388.5	123.21	12.93	167.1849	−1.83	3.3489
35	11.4	1225	399.0	129.96	12.93	167.1849	−1.53	2.3409
35	12.4	1225	434.0	153.76	12.93	167.1849	− .53	.2809
Σ 1114	494.0	26518	10836.6	4602.00	494.23	4546.1910	44.23	59.8447
M 18.57	8.23	.....	....	....	8.24	....	.737	
σ 9.861	2.985	.....	....	....	2.814	....	1.007	

[1] Some of the data have been omitted from the table in order to save space. The sums
refer to the complete table.

finding the **cross-products** (XY values). This is a process of 'coding,' which is legitimate and useful. We need only make the proper adjustments in the final answers.

Table 57 gives only enough of the data and their *extensions* to illustrate the least square procedure. The sums of the columns are the significant values. From them we can set up the two normal equations. They are as follows:

$$494 = 60a + 1114b.$$
$$10836.6 = 1114a + 26518b.$$

The solution of these equations has been reduced to a routine formula in the following manner: Let us start from the generalized equations (A) and (B) which are given in formula (106). In order to solve for b, the coefficients of a must be made identical. Equation (A) must be multiplied through by the constant $\Sigma(X)$ and equation (B) by the constant N. The result is

(A') $\Sigma(X)\Sigma(Y) = N\Sigma(X)a + \Sigma(X)\Sigma(X)b.$
(B') $N\Sigma(XY) = N\Sigma(X)a + N\Sigma(X^2)b.$

Finding the difference, $(B') - (A')$,

$$N\Sigma(XY) - \Sigma(X)\Sigma(Y) = N\Sigma(X^2)b - (\Sigma X)^2 b.$$

Transposing and collecting terms,

$$[N\Sigma(X^2) - (\Sigma X)^2]b = N\Sigma(XY) - \Sigma(X)\Sigma(Y)$$
$$b = \frac{N\Sigma(XY) - \Sigma(X)\Sigma(Y)}{N\Sigma(X^2) - (\Sigma X)^2} \tag{107a}$$

Dividing through by N,

$$b = \frac{\Sigma(XY) - N(M_x)(M_y)}{\Sigma(X^2) - N(M_x)^2} \tag{107b}$$

As before, a is found by the general formula

$$a = M_y - (M_x)b \tag{108}$$

In our illustrative problem,

$$b = \frac{10836.6 - 9171.9}{26518.0 - 20683.3}$$
$$= \frac{1664.7}{5834.7}.$$

$$b = .285.$$
$$a = 8.23 - (18.57)(.285)$$
$$= 8.23 - 5.29$$
$$= 2.94.$$

The equation of the best-fitting line by least squares is therefore $Y = 2.94 + .285X$. This is given in terms of the coded X values of Table 57, in which $X = R/10$. In terms of the original R values, the equation is $PE = 2.94 + .0285R$. This enables us to say that, for every millimeter a line increases in length, the uncertainty of reproductions increases by .0285 mm., when this uncertainty is measured by the PE of the distribution of reproductions. Thus the parameter b tells us how many units Y is increasing for every increase of one unit in X. In this case Y increases 2.85 per cent as fast as X. Or, interpreting in terms of Weber's law, we may say that the Weber ratio is .0285 or 2.85 per cent.

Testing the Goodness of Fit

By means of the equation that has just been obtained one may next predict the most probable Y for any chosen X value. How accurate will such predictions be? There are several ways in which this question can be answered. The most direct indicator, perhaps, is the **standard error of the estimate,** which is designated by the symbol σ_{yx}. Like all standard errors, this value tells us the limits within which two-thirds of the Y values lie. In this case it indicates the amount of dispersion expected about the predictions made from given values of X. The other customary indicator of goodness of fit when linear functions are involved is the **coefficient of correlation.** The two are mathematically related, the one being derivable from the other. Either can be computed from the original data or from the discrepancies that we find between the predicted Y values and the corresponding observed Y values. We shall follow the latter course first.

Finding the Discrepancies.—Most of the points, naturally, deviate somewhat from the best-fitting line, as may be seen in Fig. 34. It is the vertical or Y deviations that we are interested in, for they represent our failures to predict by means of the function we have adopted. In order to find the numerical amount of these discrepancies, or *residuals* as they are sometimes called, we first compute the predicted Y values, using the equation of the best-fitting line. These appear under the heading of Y' in Table 57.

Note that the sum of the Y' values in Table 57 is 494.23, or practically the same as the sum of the actual Y values. This is a good indication that the computations thus far have been correct. The discrepancy of +.23 is due to the accumulation of errors in the second decimal place. The Y' values have all been squared in order to find the sigma of their distribution, which appears at the end of column 6 in Table 57.

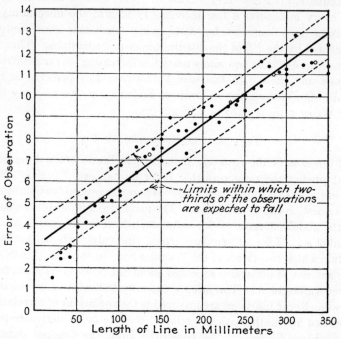

Fig. 34.—The line of best fit for the line-drawing data as determined by the method of least squares.

The discrepancies, which we designate by the letter z, are equal to $Y - Y'$. They are listed in column 8 of Table 57. Like the Y values, they are in terms of millimeters as the unit of measurement. Very few of them are greater than 1 mm., although two of those listed are larger than 2 mm. They are naturally both negative and positive, and the algebraic sum of them should be zero. Since we are interested in the size of them rather than in their direction, disregarding signs, we find the absolute mean of them to be .737. This value is equivalent to the familiar average deviation. The standard deviation of the discrepancies is identical with σ_{yx}, the standard error of the estimate.

The Standard Error of the Estimate.—The standard error of the estimate is thus obtained directly from the squares of the discrepancies. The discrepancies themselves are really deviations about a changing average, an average which is the line of best fit. Recall that, when deviations themselves are used, $\sigma = \sqrt{\Sigma x^2/N}$. Thus the formula for finding σ_{yx} is

$$\sigma_{yx} = \sqrt{\frac{\Sigma z^2}{N-1}} \tag{109}$$

The subscript of σ here indicates that Y is being estimated from X. The use of $(N - 1)$ in place of the usual N is recommended for all except very large samples (2, p. 114). In the illustrative problem,

$$\sigma_{yx}^2 = \frac{59.8447}{59}$$
$$= 1.014317.$$
$$\sigma_{yx} = 1.007.$$

A region 1.007 mm. above and below the line of best fit should include two-thirds of all the observed points. In Fig. 34 lines are drawn parallel with the line of best fit and at vertical distances of 1 mm. from it. It will be noticed that only 15, or one-fourth, of the observed points actually fall outside those limits. A few of the points that are outside the limits, however, tend to deviate very markedly from the best line. Some of these deviations are no doubt due to the true nonlinearity of the relationship. At both ends of the scatter diagram the points deviate negatively. Only within the range from $R = 50$ to $R = 330$ is the assumption of linearity very reasonable. Any general psychophysical law of any breadth of applicability should fit the data over a wider range of stimulus values.

The Coefficient of Correlation as a Measure of Goodness of Fit.— In some relationships the variations in the dependent variable are entirely determined, or accounted for, by variations in the independent variable. For example, the volume of a sphere is entirely determined by its diameter. There is no variation in volume of spheres that is independent of variations of their diameters. The correlation between the diameters and the volumes of spheres is perfect. These remarks apply to 'ideal' spheres. Such is not the case in other functional relationships. No one could maintain that the *PE* of the distribution of lines is 100 per cent determined by the length of line. Other factors, chiefly within the observer, make for variable and constant errors which destroy a perfect relationship. A coefficient of correlation can be used to indicate the extent to which the variation in one variable determines the observed variation that we find in the other variable. To this extent it tells us how important the one variable is as a determining factor of the other. The standard error of estimate tells us how reliable our predictions are; the coefficient of correlation tells us how strong the relationship is, or to what extent one phenomenon determines another.

As usual we measure variability in terms of sigma, the standard deviation. The total variability in the *PE* values is indicated by a sigma of 2.985 (see Table 57). How much of this variability may be attributed to the length of line reproduced? When we predict *PE* from *R* (or *Y* from *X*), we have begun to answer this question. The degree of variability of the predictions *Y'* (see Table 57) shows to what degree *R* is determining *PE*. The sigma of the predicted *PE* values is 2.814. Compared with the sigma of the observed *PE* values, the variability is smaller. On the whole, the scatter of the predicted *PE* values from their mean is somewhat narrower than that of the observed *PE* values. The line of best fit (also called the **line of regression**) slopes upward less steeply than we might expect. The poorer the agreement between prediction and observation, the greater the discrepancy between σ_y and $\sigma_{y'}$ will be. The strength of the agreement is therefore measured by the ratio of $\sigma_{y'}$ to σ_y. This ratio is the coefficient of correlation. We may state our first formula for the coefficient of correlation,

$$r_{yx} = \frac{\sigma_{y'}}{\sigma_y} \tag{110}$$

The notation r_{yx} indicates that *Y* and *X* are the variables correlated and that we are dealing with the regression of *Y* upon *X*. The correlation r_{xy} would mean that *X* is the dependent variable and *Y* is the independent variable. The *value* of *r* would, however, be the same. The *r* taken alone tells us nothing about causal relationships except concerning their strength. Which factor is cause and which is effect we must decide for ourselves.

In our problem of this chapter,

$$r_{yx} = \frac{2.814}{2.985}$$
$$= .943.$$

Assuming that the true relationship between R and PE is linear, the strength of the relationship is shown by a coefficient of .943. The variability of the predicted PE values is 94.3 per cent of the variability of the observed PE values. If the relationship between two variables is complete, so that Y can be predicted from X without error, the variability of the predicted Y' values would be equal to that of the observed Y values and the ratio would be 1.00. When the line has an upward slope, this ratio is given a positive sign; when the slope is downward, r is negative. If there is no real relationship between Y and X, the predictions of Y' would all be identical. Then $\sigma_{y'}$ would be zero and r would be zero. When r equals zero there is a complete absence of correlation.

The Coefficient of Determination.—"But just how large is a correlation of .943?" is a question that a beginner in correlation methods may very properly ask. There are several ways of judging the significance of a coefficient of correlation. Certain it is that the coefficient does *not* give the percentage of relationship. It would be improper to say from our coefficient of .943 that the PE is determined to the extent of 94.3 per cent by R or even to say that there is 94.3 per cent of agreement between an R and its PE. But the percentage of determination of Y by X can be estimated from r_{yx} under certain conditions if there is a true causal relationship. The latter proviso can be decided only from the logic of the experimental situation. If we can assume that both X and Y are built up of a number of simple elements, mutually independent and equally variable, and if we can assume in addition that *all* the factors present in X are also present in Y, but that Y has some additional elements in it not found in X, then the percentage of determination of Y by X is given by r_{yx}^2. In terms of a formula,

$$d_{yx} = r_{yx}^2 \tag{111}$$

in which d_{yx} is the symbol for the **coefficient of determination**. The use of r_{yx}^2 as a measure of the percentage of determination of Y by X seems more reasonable if another statistical concept is introduced in this connection, namely, the concept of **variance**. The variance in a set of measurements is the square of the standard deviation. If we denote variance by V, then $V_x = \sigma_x^2$. Recalling that r_{yx} is the ratio of $\sigma_{y'}$ to σ_y, then d_{yx} is the ratio of $\sigma_{y'}^2$ to σ_y^2. *The coefficient of determination is therefore the ratio of the variance in the predicted values to that in the observed values.*

In the line-drawing problem we might assume that the *PE* of a distribution of lines is dependent upon all the elements that go into the variation in length of lines plus extraneous factors not present in the lines themselves. If this assumption is safe, then the extent to which length determines the average error of reproduction is r^2, or $.943^2$, which is $.8892$. If a linear relation is the true one, then the variability of reproduction of lines in this experiment was about 89 per cent due to length of line alone. The remaining determination of 11 per cent came from extraneous factors.

When applied with caution and with all due regard for the logic of the problem at hand, the coefficient of determination is another very useful statistical tool. Its validity always depends upon whether or not the necessary assumptions can reasonably be made. Taken alone, d_{yx} merely means that proportion of the elements determining Y which is made up of the total mass of elements that determine X. Wherever these conditions do not prevail, the proportion of elements in common to Y and X is not given by r_{yx}^2.

The Relation of r to σ_{yx}.—It is possible, as was indicated before, to derive r from σ_{yx} or vice versa. σ_{yx} may be found from r by means of the formula

$$\sigma_{yx} = \sigma_y \sqrt{1 - r_{yx}^2} \qquad (112)$$

Using the r_{yx} which we have already found, namely, $.943$, σ_{yx} is estimated as follows:

$$\sigma_{yx} = 2.985\sqrt{1 - .943^2}$$
$$= 2.985\sqrt{1 - .889249}$$
$$= 2.985\sqrt{.110751}$$
$$= (2.985)(.3328)$$
$$= .994.$$

If σ_{yx} is already known and we wish to estimate from it the correlation coefficient r_{yx}, we may use the relation

$$r_{yx}^2 = \frac{\sigma_y^2 - \sigma_{yx}^2}{\sigma_y^2} = 1 - \frac{\sigma_{yx}^2}{\sigma_y^2} \qquad (113)$$

Using the σ_{yx} which was obtained directly from the z values,

$$r_{yx}^2 = 1 - \frac{1.014317}{8.910225}$$
$$= 1 - .113838$$
$$= .886162.$$
$$r_{yx} = .941.$$

It will be noticed that σ_{yx} and r_{yx}, as estimated by means of formulas (112) and (113), do not quite coincide with the corresponding values computed more directly from Table 57. This may be expected, owing to the fact that $(N - 1)$ is used in formula (109) instead of the customary N, as in finding an ordinary standard deviation, and owing to the accumulation of errors in computation as nonsignificant figures frequently enter.

The Computation of r from the Cross-products.—There is still another way of computing r without first finding σ_{yx} or $\sigma_{y'}$, or without finding the predicted Y values at all. This is accomplished by using the cross-products XY and the sigmas of the distributions, σ_x and σ_y; this is known as Pearson's **product-moment method** of correlation. The r values already found are equivalent to product-moment coefficients. They were merely calculated in a different manner from the one now to be explained. The present method may be employed even before the line of best fit and its parameters have been determined. The coefficient of correlation is found from the cross-products by means of the formula

$$r_{yx} = \frac{\Sigma(XY) - N(M_x)(M_y)}{N\sigma_x\sigma_y} \tag{114}$$

If, instead of using the actual measurements X and Y, we were to reduce them to deviations from the mean, x and y, the Pearson product-moment coefficient formula reduces to

$$r_{yx} = \frac{\Sigma(xy)}{N\sigma_x\sigma_y} \tag{115}$$

Using the data obtainable from Table 57,

$$r_{yx} = \frac{10836.6 - 9171.9}{60(2.985)(9.861)}$$
$$= \frac{1664.7}{1766.1051}$$
$$= .943.$$

Correction of r and σ_{yx} for the Numbers of Variables and Observations.—As computed by the methods thus far, both σ_{yx} and r are slightly in error if the number of observations is rather small, and they need a small amount of adjustment before we can apply them to the whole range of phenomena, of which the observed data are merely representative samples. σ_{yx} is inclined to be too small and r too large. With a small number of observations, less than 30, for example, σ_y and σ_x are likely to be too small as compared with the sigmas of the two theoretical distributions of X and Y, with infinitely large numbers of samples in each. If we wish our conclusions, which are based upon limited samples of all the possible cases in the 'universe' of lengths of line R and their dispersions PE, to be applicable to that whole universe, we must adjust our coefficients accordingly. This adjustment takes into account the number of **degrees of freedom** in our data. As explained by Ezekiel (2, p. 121), "A straight line would exactly fit any two observations with no residuals at all. When a straight line is fitted to ten observations, there are only eight 'degrees of freedom' in determining the values a and b, as the 'freedom' of two of these observations is used up in the determination. As a consequence of these conditions, the $\sigma_{y'}$ tends to be larger than it should be, and σ_y tends to be too small. Hence the quotient $\sigma_{y'}/\sigma_y$ tends to be too large, on the average. Also, since $\sigma_{y'}$ tends to be too large, σ_z tends to be too small, and hence the observed standard error of the estimate also needs correction." The corrected standard error of the estimate is in general

$$_c\sigma_{yx}^2 = \sigma_{yx}^2\left(\frac{N-1}{N-m}\right) \tag{116a}$$

or

$$_c\sigma_{yx}^2 = \frac{N\sigma_z^2}{N-m} \tag{116b}$$

where m = the number of variables.

$N - m$ = the number of degrees of freedom.

The general correction for r, the coefficient of correlation, is

$$_c r_{yx}^2 = 1 - (1 - r_{yx}^2)\left(\frac{N-1}{N-m}\right) \tag{117}$$

in which m is the number of variables. For linear equations m is two. A simple rule to follow is to make m equal to the number of parameters in the equation to which the observations are being adjusted. A linear equation has two parameters; nonlinear equations or linear equations involving more than two variables have more than two. If the expression to the right of "$1 - $" in formula (117) is greater than 1.00, $_c r$ is taken to be zero. Applying these formulas to the σ_{yx} and the r_{yx} which have been found for our illustrative problem,

$$_c\sigma_{yx}^2 = 1.007\left(\frac{59}{58}\right)$$
$$= (1.007)(1.01724)$$
$$= 1.011137.$$
$$_c\sigma_{yx} = 1.012.$$
$$_c r_{yx}^2 = 1 - (1 - .943^2)\left(\frac{59}{58}\right)$$
$$= 1 - (1 - .889249)(1.01724)$$
$$= 1 - (.110751)(1.01724)$$
$$= 1 - .112660$$
$$= .887340.$$
$$_c r_{yx} = .942.$$

It will be seen that, with a correlation as high as this one and with N as great as 60, the correction makes practically no difference. The original uncorrected constants, σ_{yx} and r, could have been taken to represent the situation with respect to the whole universe of observations from which they come. When either r or N is small, however, the correction makes a drastic revision in those constants. The interpretation of $_c r$ and $_c\sigma_{yx}$ is given by Ezekiel (2, p. 122) as follows: If $_c r$ is .80 or higher, then the chances are even that the true correlation in the universe in question is either higher or lower than $_c r$. But if $_c r$ is lower than .60, then the chances are between 60 and 70 out of 100 that the true correlation is at least as high as $_c r$. As for the interpretation of $_c\sigma_{yx}$ the odds are even that the true $_c\sigma_{yx}$ is no greater than $_c\sigma_{yx}$.

FITTING NONLINEAR FUNCTIONS

Whenever the correlation diagram, such as that in Fig. 32, shows a distribution of points that is quite apparently nonlinear, it is worth while to investigate types of relationships other than straight lines. Here one may proceed in two directions. One course would be to select a type of mathematical function for which an equation can be written.   In this we can be guided empirically by observing the shape of the scatter diagram, or we can rationalize our experimental problem and the variables concerned and be guided by our logical conclusions.   The other path is to waive any mathematical formulation for the relationship and to plot a freehand curve.   In the latter case our interest is a purely practical one; we merely want to predict values of Y from X.   In the former case our motive is a more theoretical one; we wish to establish a more general law and to follow up its implications.   A mathematical formulation enables us to make predictions, to be sure, and, if the true relationship does conform to an equation, all the better.   The predictions would thus be more accurately and expeditiously made.   But if the true relation conforms to no known mathematical equation, we do actual violence to the facts by forcing them into an artificial mold and the predictions may be even less accurate.   The nonmathematical fitting process will be discussed very briefly first.

Expressing a Relation by a Freehand Curve.—This is a graphic method which, by a trial-and-error process, draws a curve that seems to represent best the trend in the scatter diagram.   One might proceed with the original scatter of points and attempt to draw the line freehand through them.   This would be a very arbitrary method, however, and would possess insufficient validity. It would be much better to begin by grouping the data as was done in Table 54 and in Fig. 33.   With the 60 points thus reduced to 7, the task is much easier.   With the two dotted lines drawn as they are in Fig. 33 to enclose the most probable position of the true relation, further guidance is obtained.   The data might be regrouped into other pools, giving additional points between the seven of Fig. 33.   One could then resort to a smoothing process much like that described for distribution curves in Chapter III, page 89.   A freehand curve might be drawn through the average points a number of times and the several curves made into a composite or average.   The value of such a curve, as was said before, is purely practical.   Having it, one can then predict for any value of X the most probable value of Y, *but only for values of X lying between the ends of the curve, i.e.,* no extrapolated values may be estimated.

If it is desired to know something about the accuracy of the predictions, one may proceed now as with predictions from a best-fitting straight line.   The Y' values are all predicted by the graphic method; the z values are found and σ_{yx} can be computed.[1] It may often be found that the errors of estimate are smaller from such predictions than if a mathematical function is assumed. But if Nature habitually favors simple mathematical relationships rather than complex and even nonmathematical ones, then the observed relation may be an actual distortion of the truth, due to errors of

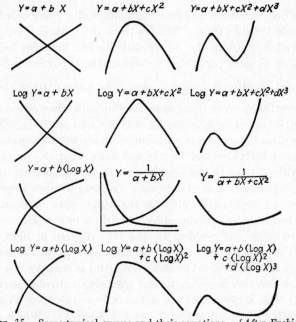

FIG. 35.—Some typical curves and their equations. (*After Ezekiel.*)

measurement, and this superiority of nonmathematical predictions is merely an illusion. Scientists are prone to keep faith in the fundamental rationality of phenomena and to assume mathematical functions, at least as first approximations to the truth. On the other hand, the 'truth' in biological or psychological data is often so involved with a number of determining factors interacting in complicated ways that rational formulations are exceedingly difficult to make.

Selecting the Type of Nonlinear Function.—The curves displayed in Fig. 35 are typical mathematical functions and they offer a

---

[1] The procedure for this follows that presented in the sections below rather than that given above in connection with the testing of linear assumptions.

sufficient variety of relationships to take care of many a problem. The general equation is given with each one. At the top of the chart are found, besides the already very familiar linear function, the simple parabola $Y = a + bX + cX^2$, which has typically one maximum or one minimum value, and the cubic parabola

$$Y = a + bX + cX^2 + dX^3,$$

with its one maximum and one minimum and a point of inflection somewhere between them. Besides these three, there is the hyperbola which appears in the center with its two branches becoming asymptotic to some particular X value and some particular Y value. Its general equation is $Y = \dfrac{1}{a + bX}$. The lower parts of the chart show what happens to those same relationships when either Y or X (or both) is translated into (log Y) or (log X), respectively. The use of logarithms in connection with curve fitting will be demonstrated shortly. A little study of Fig. 35 will show what the introduction of logarithms does to the simpler functions. Remember that, in general, logarithms tend to decrease differences between large values as compared with small values in the same scale. This accounts for all the distortions produced by logarithms in Fig. 35.

Returning to our problem on the reproduction of lines, which type of curve in Fig. 35 would seem most likely to fit the nonlinear distribution of points? The observed trend is concave downward. There are two curves especially that seem similar to our distribution in form. One is given with the equation $Y = a + b(\log X)$ and the other with the equation $(\log Y) = a + b(\log X)$. Which shall it be? Could it in reality belong in neither class? This possibility must be considered. The data are not very extensive since no lines longer than 350 mm. were used. We may have just a branch of some type of parabola to deal with. There are at least six examples of branches of curves that are concave downward in Fig. 35.

The logic of the experimental problem itself must come to the rescue. Is it at all likely that, if lines longer than 350 mm. were used, the trend of the PE values of the distribution would take a turn and actually decrease in average value for very long lines? No one, of course, knows. There is a practical limit beyond which this problem could not be fairly extended. The lines must not be so long that they extend beyond the field of vision or even too far into the periphery where form perception is uncertain; again a device for reproducing lines of great length would be out of the question. It is not conceivable that the average error of observation of lines should actually decrease as the limits of the visual field are approached. Weber's law, or any similar psychophysical law, assumes a continuous increase in the PE as R increases. We are thrown back, then, upon the two logarithmic functions. Can logic guide us any further in our choice?

It might be appropriate to ask at this point whether the author's nth power law might not be invoked, or Cattell's square root law. In either case a function of the form $Y = KR^n$ is assumed. Cattell's law has behind it the logic which has already been presented in Chapter IV (page 137). It has against it much empirical evidence that psychophysical data do not fit the square root law. The power law, with its variable n, promises to satisfy a wide variety of data because of its generality. Further than this, it may be maintained that some type of function is needed that will pass through the origin. It is probably meaningless to speak of a line of zero length. But if there were such a line to be reproduced, theoretically the PE of the distribution should be zero also. A function of the type $PE = KR^n$ is bound to pass through the origin because of the absence of the parameter a. Such a function does not seem to be represented in Fig. 35, but in reality it is included there. Suppose we take the logarithms of both sides of the general equation $Y = KX^n$. We then have $(\log Y) = (\log K) + n(\log X)$. If for the moment we substitute a for $(\log K)$ and b for n, we have $(\log Y) = a + b(\log X)$, which appears in Fig. 35. Let us make some further substitutions. Let $(\log Y)$ become $\overline{Y}$ and let $(\log X)$ become $\overline{X}$. The equation then becomes $\overline{Y} = a + b\overline{X}$, which the reader recognizes as a linear equation.

In order to test our decision to fit the data to the equation $(\log Y) = a + b(\log X)$ instead of the equation $Y = a + b(\log X)$, the thing to do is to make a preliminary plot of the two functions. Translate all the X and Y values into $(\log X)$ and $(\log Y)$, respectively. Plot the Y values against the $(\log X)$ values and in another diagram plot the $(\log Y)$ values against the $(\log X)$ values. This has been done in Fig. 36. The one giving the plot more nearly in the form of a straight line wins the test. In this case, although neither is strictly a linear plot, that giving $(\log Y)$ against $(\log X)$ is distinctly more linear. This is the one leading to the power law, if that final form is preferred to a logarithmic equation.

An equation of the type $(\log PE) = a + b(\log R)$ means that an absolute change in the *logarithm* of R is accompanied by b times that many units of change in the *logarithm* of PE. Since an *absolute* change in the *logarithm* of a number means a constant *percentage*

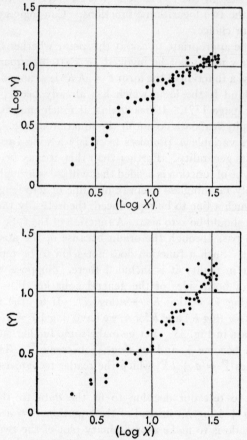

Fig. 36.—Tests of linearity when logarithms of X and Y are plotted.

of change in the number itself, we can say that a certain proportional change in length of a line is accompanied by a given proportional change in the errors of observation, no matter whether we are dealing with long or short lines. It is interesting in this connection that economists (2, p. 105) see in the relation between changes in prices and corresponding changes in consumption the same type of relationship. No matter whether prices are high or low, a proportional change in price is accompanied by a proportional change in consumption of a commodity. Consumption is a function of prices to some power n. Since the expenditure of money for commodities depends upon the judgments of values, psychologically this phenomenon may be closely related to judgments of lines or of any material such as is employed in psychophysical experiments. This line of thinking may at least make more reasonable, if it does not entirely rationalize, the use of the power law to express the true relation between PE and R.

Least-square Solution of a Nonlinear Function.—When the logarithms of both X and Y values have been found, the tasks of fitting those data to a straight line, finding the parameters, and testing the fit are essentially the same as in the previous example when an actual linear assumption was made. The data are extended in part in Table 58. The usual $\bar{X}^2$ values, $\bar{Y}^2$ values and $\bar{X}\bar{Y}$ values are computed and the two normal equations are set up as in the previous example. From the normal equations, we find by using formula (107) that

$$b = \frac{65.692058 - 62.064635}{89.440470 - 83.686841}$$
$$= \frac{3.627423}{5.753629}$$
$$= .6305$$

and

$$a = .87587 - (.6305)(1.18101)$$
$$= .87587 - .74463$$
$$= .13124.$$

The equation for the logarithmic curve is therefore

$$(\log Y) = .13124 + .6305 (\log X).$$

We want the equation finally in the form $Y = KX^n$. We began by taking logarithms of both sides, obtaining

$$(\log Y) = (\log K) + n(\log X).$$

Comparing this with the equation we found by solving the normal equations, we find that $(\log K)$ corresponds to .13124 and n corresponds to .6305. Taking the antilogarithms of both sides of the

TABLE 58.—WORK SHEET FOR FITTING THE DATA FROM REPRODUCTION OF LINES TO AN EQUATION OF THE FORM

$(\text{Log } Y) = a + b(\text{Log } X)$

(R) X	(PE) Y	(log X) X̄	(log Y) Ȳ	X̄²	Ȳ²	XY	.6305 (log X) + .13124 Ȳ'	Y'	(Y − Y') z''	(z'')²
2	1.5	.3010	.1761	.090601	.031011	.053006	.32102	2.09	− .59	.3841
3	2.4	.4771	.3802	.227624	.144552	.181393	.43205	2.70	− .30	.0900
3	2.7	.4771	.4314	.227624	.186106	.205821	.43205	2.70	.00	.0000
4	2.5	.6021	.3979	.362524	.158324	.239576	.51086	3.24	− .74	.5476
4	3.0	.6021	.4771	.362524	.227624	.287262	.51086	3.24	− .24	.0576
5	3.9	.6990	.5911	.488601	.349399	.413179	.57195	3.73	+ .17	.0289
5	4.4	.6990	.6435	.488601	.414092	.449807	.57195	3.73	+ .67	.4489
6	4.1	.7782	.6128	.605595	.375524	.476881	.62190	4.19	− .09	.0081
6	5.2	.7782	.7160	.605595	.512656	.557191	.62190	4.19	+1.01	1.0201
7	4.9	.8451	.6902	.714194	.476376	.583288	.66408	4.61	+ .29	.0841
15	8.2	1.1761	.9138	1.383211	.835030	1.074720	.87277	7.46	+ .74	.5476
16	9.0	1.2041	.9542	1.449857	.910498	1.148752	.89043	7.77	+1.23	1.5129
17	8.4	1.2305	.9243	1.514130	.854330	1.137351	.90707	8.07	+ .33	.1089
18	7.3	1.2553	.8633	1.575778	.745287	1.083700	.92271	8.37	−1.07	1.1449
18	8.4	1.2553	.9243	1.575778	.854330	1.160274	.92271	8.37	+ .03	.0009
33	12.2	1.5185	1.0864	2.305842	1.180265	1.649698	1.08865	12.26	− .06	.0036
34	10.1	1.5315	1.0043	2.345492	1.008618	1.538085	1.09685	12.50	−2.40	5.7600
35	11.1	1.5441	1.0453	2.384245	1.092652	1.614048	1.10480	12.73	−1.63	2.6569
35	11.4	1.5441	1.0569	2.384245	1.117038	1.631959	1.10480	12.73	−1.33	1.7689
35	12.4	1.5441	1.0934	2.384245	1.195524	1.688319	1.10480	12.73	− .33	.1089
Σ		70.8605	52.5521	89.440470	48.555593	65.692058		492.03	+1.81	42.8175
M		1.1810	.8759						.03	
σ		.3097	.2051							.852

equation, we have[1]

$$Y = 1.353(X)^{.6305}.$$

In Table 58, Y is the PE in terms of millimeters and X is the length of line, or R, in terms of centimeters. In other words, $X = R/10$, if R is also to be given in terms of millimeters. Substituting PE and R in the above equation, we have

$$PE = 1.353\frac{R^{.6305}}{10^{.6305}}.$$

Simplifying the equation,

$$PE = 1.353\frac{R^{.6305}}{4.271}$$

or

$$PE = .3167R^{.6305}$$

which gives the functional relationship between PE and R when both are in terms of millimeters. In either case, whether Y is in terms of centimeters or millimeters, the value of n remains the same. Since we are not sure that n is significant to four places, we might rather say $PE = .317R^{.63}$. Remembering in this type of relationship that for a certain *proportional* increase in X there is a corresponding *proportional* increase in Y, the value .63 tells how rapidly the one is advancing as compared with the other. The proportional increase in Y is about 63 per cent as rapid as the proportional increase in X.

The Index of Correlation.—As in the case of linear equations, the closeness of fit of the observed points to the assumed function may be estimated by means of the standard error of the estimate or by means of a measure of correlation. The product-moment method of correlation was designed for linear relationships, but it can be made to apply to any relation that can be reduced to linear form. The correlation is then not between Y and X, but between Y and (X), *i.e.*, between Y and some function of X. The strength of agreement between Y and $f(X)$ is measured by the **index of correlation,** which is expressed by the symbol $p_{y \cdot f(x)}$, or by p_{yx}. In the above problem, the linear relationship exists between Y and X^n. The

[1] The student should remember that, to find the product of two numbers, we add logarithms; thus, reversing the process, when two logarithms are summed, their antilogarithms are multiplied.

strength of the correlation p_{yx} may be found by correlating the log Y and log X values.   Using the cross-products (and formula 114)

$$p_{yx} = \frac{65.692058 - 62.064635}{60(.3097)(.2051)}$$
$$= \frac{3.627423}{3.811168}$$
$$= .952.$$

In correcting the index of correlation for the number of observations and the number of variables, formula (117) is used, but the value for m is always greater than 2 because it takes more than two points to determine the position of a nonlinear function.   In this problem, m equals 3.   There are in reality three parameters, a, b, and n.   There appear to be only two because $a = 0$.   The correction is therefore found as follows:

$$_c p_{yx}^2 = 1 - (1 - .905923)\left(\frac{59}{57}\right)$$
$$= 1 - (.094077)(1.035)$$
$$= .9026303.$$
$$_c p_{yx} = .950.$$

This correlation is barely higher than that for the linear assumption, which was .943.   When r is above .90, however, a very small numerical change is highly significant, much more so than when r is less than .90.

The Index of Determination.—For the linear function it was assumed that the percentage of determination of Y by X was measurable by r_{yx}^2, the coefficient of determination.   If the logarithmic function which was later assumed is the correct one, and if the same conditions of determination hold as were assumed to hold before, *i.e.*, that Y is determined by all the factors in X plus some additional ones, then the percentage of determination of Y by X is $(.952)^2$, or 90.63 per cent.   To distinguish it from the coefficient of determination, p_{yx}^2 is called the **index of determination.**   It should be remembered that the uncorrected p, like the uncorrected r, refers to the empirical data at hand, and p^2 therefore refers to determination limited to the observed cases.   Since $_c p$, like $_c r$, refers to the probable correlation of the whole universe of phenomena from which the data were drawn, then $_c p^2$ is 90.26.   The percentage of determination of PE by R, in general under conditions comparable to those in the experiments reported here, is therefore 90.26 per cent.

Standard Error of the Estimate for Nonlinear Functions.—This constant is found in just the same manner as with linear data. It may be found from p_{yx} by means of formula (112). It is symbolized as $\sigma_{y \cdot f(x)}$. If p is .952, then

$$\begin{aligned} \sigma_{y \cdot f(x)} &= \sigma_y \sqrt{1 - p_{yx}^2} \\ &= 2.985\sqrt{1 - .906304} \\ &= 2.985\sqrt{.093696} \\ &= (2.985)(.3061) \\ &= .914. \end{aligned}$$

This standard error is also obtainable from the discrepancies z'', which are presented in part in Table 58, squared and summed to find $\sigma_{y \cdot f(x)}$. By this method,

$$\begin{aligned} \sigma_{y \cdot f(x)}^2 &= \frac{42.8175}{59} \\ &= .725712. \\ \sigma_{y \cdot f(x)} &= .852. \end{aligned}$$

The corrected standard error is

$$\begin{aligned} {}_c\sigma_{yf \cdot (x)}^2 &= (.725712)(1.035) \\ &= .751112. \\ {}_c\sigma_{y \cdot f(x)} &= .867. \end{aligned}$$

The standard error of the estimate, as obtained from the discrepancies z'', even when corrected, is noticeably smaller than that which was computed from the index of correlation $p_{y \cdot f(x)}$. The former is probably nearer the truth, since it deals with the actual predictions and their deviations from the observed values. The latter is undoubtedly more conservative. Both are noticeably smaller than the corresponding sigmas of the estimate obtained when a linear assumption was used. In Fig. 37 dotted lines have been drawn at .90 mm. above and below the best-fitting curve, showing the range within which two-thirds of the predicted observations should fall. Only 14 of the 60 observations actually lie outside those limits.

Fitting Other Nonlinear Functions.—As in the problem just illustrated, every nonlinear equation that is assumed must be transformed into linear form before the method of least squares can be applied. This frequently requires the use of logarithms, as in the above problem, and it also often involves more than two parameters. A hyperbola of the form $Y = 1/(a + bX)$ can be made linear by taking reciprocals of both sides, giving $1/Y = a + bX$.

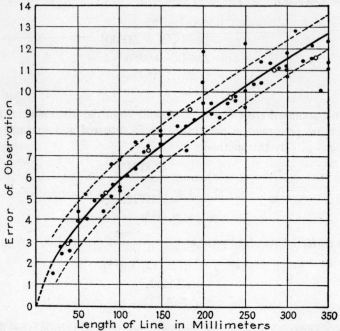

FIG. 37.—Best-fitting curve of the form $PE = K(R^n)$ for the line-drawing data.

An equation of the type $Y = a + (b/x)$ becomes linear if transformed into $Y = a + b(1/X)$. $Y = X/(a + bX)$ can become $X/Y = a + bX$.[1]

The student may recall that in the chapter on the constant methods, in which psychophysical judgments were fitted to the normal ogive curve, tables of the normal probability integral were used. For every observed value of p, the proportion of judgments of a certain category, the corresponding gamma was found. In so doing, the relation between p and R was made linear. It was

---

[1] For more details and for transforming more complicated equations into linear form, see references to Huntington's and Running's accounts (3, 6).

assumed that p is the ϕ-function of gamma, and the ϕ-function is the ogive curve. Gamma is equal to $h(R - L)$, the distance of R from the limen in terms of h. The two normal equations (including Urban's weights) are

$$\Sigma\gamma W = h(\Sigma xW) - hL(\Sigma W)$$
and $$\Sigma x\gamma W = h(\Sigma x^2W) - hL(\Sigma xW),$$

which when solved simultaneously reduce to

$$h = \frac{(\Sigma W)(\Sigma x\gamma W) - (\Sigma xW)(\Sigma\gamma W)}{(\Sigma W)(\Sigma x^2W) - (\Sigma xW)(\Sigma xW)},$$

an expression that is similar to formula (107b).

The fitting of data to parabolas presents a somewhat different problem. In the quadratic equation $Y = a + bX + cX^2$ there are three unknowns to be found and this requires three normal equations. In the cubic $Y = a + bX + cX^2 + dX^3$ there are four unknowns, requiring four normal equations. It is customary in these cases to treat each power of X as a new independent variable, as if the equations were $Y = a + bX + cZ$,

$$Y = a + bX + cZ + dQ,$$

and so on. With more than one independent variable we have problems in multiple correlation, a subject to which we turn in Chapter XII.

Uses and Limitations of Equations

Empirical versus Rational Equations.—One may assume a given type of function, find the best-fitting curve of that type with its parameters, and obtain a fairly high coefficient of correlation, yet the curve and its equation may still be meaningless so far as any truth of nature is concerned. The fact that data fit a given type of curve almost to perfection is no final proof that the phenomena for which the data stand are related in just that way. It is necessary to remember the distinction between empirical and rational equations. The former are merely descriptive. An empirical equation becomes a shorthand expression which tells a great deal about the data and their relationships. It is practically useful in making predictions, but it means nothing beyond that. One is not even justified in making predictions beyond the two limits of the observations already made. In the case of rational equations, however, the nature of the phenomena and the variables involved are well thought out and logical reasons are given to support the type of equation selected. Certain deductions in the form of hypotheses can be made and tested. Predictions may then be made by extrapolation beyond the limits of the observed data. There is, to be sure, a certain risk in this, because many quantitative laws hold true only within certain limits. Beyond those limits other factors sometimes enter to change the relationship. Thus, rational equations also have their limitations. Empirical equations may lead occasionally to rationalization once they are experimentally verified. The distinction between empirical and rational equations is therefore far from complete.

As an example of the distinction between the two types of equations, let us take Thurstone's attempts to find a universal type of equation for the learning curve. First attempts (7) led to an empirical equation of the form

$$Y = \frac{L(X + P)}{(X + P) + R}$$

where Y = the degree of attainment, measured in the number of
successful acts per unit of time.

X = the number of practice acts since the beginning of formal practice.

R = the rate of learning, a constant for each individual.

L = the limit of practice, in acts per unit of time.

P = the previous practice, in comparable practice units.

This equation takes account of the obvious variables in learning, but there is no adequate logical basis for relating those variables in just that way. Furthermore, this equation fails to describe all varieties of learning curves. It is hyperbolic in form and applies to those curves which rise sharply at first and approach a limit, with negative acceleration. It does not apply to curves that start with a positive acceleration and an inflection point, nor does it apply to curves in which there are 'plateaus.' One suspects from this that the problem of learning has not been thoroughly rationalized. This Thurstone proposes to do in presenting a more recent generalized learning equation (8). The rational learning equation reads as follows:

$$\frac{2p - 1}{\sqrt{p - p^2}} = \frac{kt}{\sqrt{m}} + z_0$$

where p = the proportion of successful acts per unit of time.

t = the practice time.

k = a learning constant of the individual.

m = the complexity of the task.

z_0 = the value of z when $p = p_0$, and p_0 is p when $t = 0$.

This formulation assumes for simple homogeneous tasks an S-shaped curve with an inflection point at $p = .50$, when the task is half learned. When the task is a composite of two homogeneous ones, the one easy and the other difficult, there will be a plateau because the simple element is mastered in a short time and the second rise is for the more rapid phase of learning the difficult one. When several elementary tasks are combined, the point of inflection of the learning curve is shoved downward toward the beginning of the curve. If enough different elements are present, the inflection point may be entirely missing. Thus the rational equation covers most varieties of learning curves.[1]

Some Other Examples of Psychological Functions.—Although the phenomena with which psychology deals are very intricate and variable, many problems have been such that the quantitative data could be described in the form of equations, empirical for the most part. A few examples will now be presented. The well-known law of retention handed down to us from Ebbinghaus has been put into the form

$$R = \frac{K}{(\log t)C}$$

where R = the percentage retained.

t = the time.

K and C = constants.

The relation between the length of a series of items to be memorized and the time required to master them has been known as a definite progression since Ebbinghaus's classical experiments. Recently Thurstone has provided two general empirical equations to describe this relationship (9). One reads

$$T = \frac{c}{k}n\sqrt{n - a}$$

---

[1] For a complete logical account and the assumptions upon which this equation is based, the reader is referred to Thurstone's own presentation (8).

where T = the time required to master the material.

c = the degree of mastery required.

k = a learning constant for the particular learner.

n = the number of items in the list.

a = the span of apprehension of the learner.

In terms of the number of repetitions R,

$$R = \frac{c}{k}\sqrt{n - a}.$$

Examples thus far mentioned refer either to learning and memory or to psychophysical experiments. Bousfield (1) has recently applied an equation in the field of motives, in particular to the reactions of chicks and cats to food. The amount of food eaten at any given moment after the starting point can be predicted by the formula

$$f = c(1 - e^{-mt})$$

where c = a constant for the particular animal and stands for the upper limit or the total amount of food the animal would consume during the time of feeding.

e = the base of the natural system of logarithms.

m = a 'coefficient of voracity' and determines the speed of eating.

t = the time.

From this equation can be deduced the relation

$$R = m(c - f)$$

in which R stands for the rate of eating. In this form it means that the rate of eating at any moment is a product of the animal's voracity and the amount of food yet to be consumed in order to reach satiety. To measure an animal's voracity we need only transform the above equation to read

$$m = \frac{R}{c - f}.$$

The usefulness and significance of these few illustrations should be so apparent that it should strike one as strange that psychologists have not more generally taken fuller advantage of quantitative formulations and have not exacted greater service of that handmaiden of all sciences, mathematics, and above all, that there have been so few attempts to seek rationalized laws. If this chapter has done something to convince the student of the need of a greater emphasis upon quantitative laws in psychology, the author will feel that it has served its purpose well.

Some Additional Useful Formulas

In some problems it is convenient to use the following formulas in place of the ones already given in this chapter:

$$b = \frac{\Sigma(xy)}{\Sigma x^2} \tag{118}$$

$$\sigma_{yx}^2 = \frac{(\Sigma x^2)(\Sigma y^2) - (\Sigma xy)^2}{N \Sigma x^2} \tag{119}$$

$$b_{yx} = r\frac{\sigma_y}{\sigma_x} \tag{120}$$

$$r = b_{yx}\frac{\sigma_x}{\sigma_y} \tag{121}$$

$$\sigma_{y'} = r\sigma_y \tag{122}$$

$$Y = M_y + r\left[\frac{\sqrt{\Sigma Y^2 - (\Sigma Y)M_y}}{\sqrt{\Sigma X^2 - (\Sigma X)M_x}}\right](X - M_x) \tag{123}$$

Problems

1. The data shown in the table on page 326, adapted from Lashley,[1] give the number of errors made in learning a maze as a function of the percentage of cortical destruction in 37 rats.

     a. Plot correlation diagrams similar to Figs. 32 and 33, using the data presented on page 326.

     b. Assume a linear function and find the best-fitting line by the various methods described on pages 294 *ff.*

     c. Find the coefficient of correlation and the standard error of the estimate. (*Hint:* Code the values, using the nearest whole numbers for percentage of destruction. The numbers of errors may be rounded to tens or to the nearest hundreds, or they may be divided by 50 or 25 or any other convenient constant. In the final regression equation the original unit must be restored.)

     d. If it seems wise, assume some nonlinear function, adjust the data to it by the method of least squares, and find an index of correlation. Compare with the results from the linear assumption.

2. Using the scale values that were obtained from the data in Problem 2, page 164, assume Fechner's law and also an *n*th power law. Test the goodness of fit of the data to the two laws and determine the parameters of the two functions.

[1] K. S. Lashley, "Brain Mechanisms and Intelligence," 1929, 36.

Percentage of destruction	Errors	Percentage of destruction	Errors	Percentage of destruction	Errors
1.5	5	22.6	332	32.0	193
4.6	51	22.8	534	34.8	645
6.0	126	23.0	183	39.8	617
7.3	92	23.9	621	41.5	546
7.9	112	24.8	388	44.8	809
8.0	82	24.9	206	44.9	386
8.4	43	25.3	147	53.3	682
9.1	65	26.9	752	54.9	761
11.2	165	27.6	309	57.6	593
16.1	397	27.9	444	65.3	2,287
16.4	338	29.5	331	66.4	1,048
18.1	163	30.6	501	69.5	1,423
				81.2	1,330

REFERENCES

1. BOUSFIELD, W. A., Certain quantitative aspects of chickens' behavior towards food, *Amer. J. Psychol.*, 1934, **46**, 456–458.
2. EZEKIEL, M., "Methods of Correlation Analysis," John Wiley & Sons, Inc., New York, 1930.
3. HUNTINGTON, E. V., Curve-fitting by the method of least squares and the method of moments, in Rietz's "Handbook of Mathematical Statistics," Houghton Mifflin Company, Boston, 1924.
4. LIPKA, J., "Graphical and Mechanical Computation," John Wiley & Sons, Inc., New York, 1918.
5. MERRIMAN, M., "Elements of the Method of Least Squares," Macmillan & Company, Ltd., London, 1877.
6. RUNNING, T. R., "Empirical Formulas," John Wiley & Sons, Inc., New York, 1917.
7. THURSTONE, L. L., The learning curve equation, *Psychol. Monog.*, 1919, **26**, no. 114.
8. ———, The learning function, *J. Gen. Psychol.*, 1930, **3**, 469–493.
9. ———, The relation between learning time and length of task, *Psychol. Rev.*, 1930, **37**, 44–53.
10. TREMMEL, E. E., and C. C. WEIDEMANN, A machine method of calculating the Pearson correlation coefficient, *Univ. Neb. Pub.*, 1930.
11. WELD, L. D., "Theory of Errors and Least Squares," The Macmillan Company, New York, 1926.

CHAPTER XI

SIMPLE CORRELATION METHODS

In the preceding chapter our interest was chiefly in the finding of functional relationships that exist between two variables, whether those relationships stand for any real, causal connections or whether we wish merely to use them for the practical purpose of prediction. The concept of correlation and the coefficient of correlation were introduced in connection with tests of goodness of fit. A high correlation was taken to indicate that a reasonably good assumption had been made and to indicate in addition that other variables than the two in question had been experimentally well controlled. The emphasis in this chapter will be placed upon the degree of relationship between two variables. Since the degree of relation between two sets of measurements indicates to what extent we may predict one variable from another, correlation methods find their greatest practical application in connection with mental tests. These applications will be brought out in a later chapter on mental-test methods.

The problem of correlation is especially important in psychology for the very reason that the variables of human reaction are so numerous and so inextricably interwoven that we cannot isolate them logically before an experiment nor can we control them completely if we do isolate them. In the physical sciences the problem of correlation is unimportant because the variables, such as time, space, mass, temperature, and potential, are relatively few in number and to a high degree are experimentally controllable. Correlations for data in the physical sciences would yield coefficients very close to 1.00. In contrast with this, biological, psychological, and social data yield extremely few correlations above .90 and many as low as zero. Low coefficients of correlation, if accurately determined, however, may be extremely useful. They not only point to the presence of variables that were entirely overlooked or unsuspected before, but in more recent years they are also used to analyze data in order to find out what the fundamental variables are and

327

to what extent those variables enter into various psychological reactions. This statement refers to a recently developed, very useful, statistical tool known as **factor analysis,** a subject which will be treated in the final chapter.

THE PRODUCT-MOMENT METHOD

Pearson's product-moment method of computing a coefficient of correlation was introduced in the preceding chapter, together with the necessary formulas. The procedure that was followed there may be called the 'long' method. It involved squaring the X values and Y values, finding the XY values and their sums. With more than 30 pairs of measurements that type of procedure becomes too costly in time and effort. We usually resort to a short method which involves grouping the data into a few class intervals and the use of guessed averages. That short procedure will now be outlined step by step. For this purpose we shall use a set of data obtained from two psychological tests, a color-naming test and a directions test. In the former each subject was given a sheet of squares of five colors arranged in haphazard order. The score is the time required to name 50 squares, plus a small correction for errors. In the latter method, a sheet of printed directions was given which the subject was required to follow. The time is again given in seconds. In this correlation problem we are dealing with a 'population' rather than with a set of data obtained from the reactions of a single observer. We wish to determine whether an individual difference in color naming is likely to carry with it a corresponding individual difference in reading and following directions.

Constructing the Scatter Diagram.—A scatter diagram is prepared similar to that in Table 59. The X variable is placed along the top and the Y variable along the side. We have little choice of dependent and independent variables when dealing with two mental tests, so we may arbitrarily call one X and the other Y. We next choose the step intervals for the two variables, observing the same rules that were proposed for this in an earlier chapter (page 31). The number of classes will ordinarily lie between 9 and 16. The limits of the intervals are written in the table as in the illustration. Ordinarily, small numerical values are placed at the left and lower ends of the scales, corresponding with the usual system of X and Y coordinates. The sizes of the intervals, i_x and i_y, are written at the top and side, as are the names of the variables.

TABLE 59

X-color-naming test time, seconds

Y-directions test time, seconds $i_y = 20$

$i_x = 2$

	20–21	22–23	24–25	26–27	28–29	30–31	32–33	34–35	36–37	38–39	40–41		fy'	y'	fy'	fy'²	Σf(x'y') +	Σf(x'y') −
280–299							1			1			2	+7	14	98	35	
260–279													0	+6	0	0		
240–259							2			1			3	+5	15	75	40	
220–239					1		1			1			3	+4	12	48	20	4
200–219					1		2	1					4	+3	12	36	36	
180–199					1		1	1	1	1			5	+2	10	20	26	2
160–179		1		1		1	1		1				5	+1	5	5	4	6
140–159							2	1	1	2			6	0				
120–139		2	1	2	3	3	3	2			1		17	−1	−17	17	18	12
100–119		2	2	3	5	2		1					15	−2	−30	60	50	4
80–99	1	2	2	3	1				1				12	−3	−36	108	90	9
60–79		3	3										6	−4	−24	96	60	
40–59		1		1									2	−5	−10	50	30	
fx'	1	8	8	15	11	8	7	8	5	6	3							
x'	−5	−4	−3	−2	−1	0	+1	+2	+3	+4	+5							
fx'	−5	−32	−24	−30	−11		7	16	15	24	15							
fx'²	25	128	72	60	11		7	32	45	96	75							

$80 = N$

$\Sigma fy' = -49$

$\Sigma fy'^2 = 613$

$\Sigma fx' = -25$

$\Sigma fx'^2 = 551$

$\Sigma x'y' = +372$

The tabulation now begins. A tallying process is by far the safest and most convenient procedure. For every pair of measurements a single tally is placed in the table. It must be located in the proper square, the X value being sought at the top of the table to determine the proper column and the Y value being sought at the side of the table in order to find the proper row. When all the pairs of measurements have been represented by tally marks, the tallies in every square are counted.

The next step is to compute the frequencies of the columns and rows separately. The frequencies of the rows, $f_{y'}$, are recorded in the column with that heading. The frequencies of the columns are likewise recorded in the row labeled $f_{x'}$. The subscripts y' and x' indicate that deviations from a guessed average are to be used. One next finds the sum of the $f_{y'}$ values and also the sum of the $f_{x'}$ values. The two should of course be identical and equal to N, the number of cases, and they should be recorded in the place provided at the intersection of the row and column in which the frequencies appear. Should the sums here not agree, an error has been made in adding or counting tallies. The counting and summing of tallies therefore have a definite check. The tallying process, however, has no such check and it is often wise to repeat the tallying a second time, independently of the first, in order to avoid any errors.

Computing the Standard Deviations.—The formula for the product moment r as given previously [formula (115)] is

$$r_{xy} = \frac{\Sigma(xy)}{N\sigma_x\sigma_y}$$

when true deviations from the mean are used. When deviations from a guessed average are used and when the data are given in terms of class intervals, the formula is altered to read

$$r_{xy} = \frac{\dfrac{\Sigma(x'y')}{N} - (c'_x)(c'_y)}{(\sigma'_x)(\sigma'_y)} \tag{124}$$

in which c'_x and c'_y are the *corrections* required by the use of guessed averages.

Formula (124) requires that we know the standard deviations of X and Y and also the cross-products.[1] The finding of the standard

[1] It is not necessary that the two distributions represented in a correlation diagram be normal (13, p. 172). But, in addition to a linear relationship, if a

deviations is not a new task for the student. One chooses a guessed average *GA* for *X* and one for *Y* that is near the center of the range of scores. In Table 59, the *GA* for *X* is 31, or the midpoint of the interval extending from 30 to 31.99. The *GA* for *Y* is 150, or the midpoint of the interval 140 to 159.99. Heavy lines are drawn so as to set those intervals off from the others. The class intervals are next numbered in row *x'* and column *y'*. Row *fx'* and column *fy'* are next filled in, followed by row *fx'²* and column *fy'²*. These rows and columns are summed with the results recorded in the places appropriate for them. The routine calculation of the corrections (c'_x and c'_y) and the two sigmas (σ'_x and σ'_y) may then be carried out as in Table 60. Since the coefficient of correlation may be computed directly from these values, which are in terms of the class interval as the unit, one need not find σ_x and σ_y, and c_x and c_y, unless one wishes also to find the standard errors of the estimate or the regression equations.

Computing the Product Moments and *r*.—The term 'moment' as applied here has a similar meaning as when used in the expression 'moments of force' in physics. We can think of every case tallied in Table 59 as having two moments of force, an *X* moment and a *Y* moment, both of which are 'pulling' to a certain extent in the *X* direction and in the *Y* direction and helping to determine the final position of the straight line that is to represent the relation between *X* and *Y*. A single case having an *X* value of +5 in Table 59 and a *Y* value of +3 is exerting its share toward pulling the line of best fit into its own quadrant of the table and specifically through the point (+5, +3). The product of the two moments is +15, which we can properly call the product moment of that particular case. We can similarly determine the product moments for all the squares in the table. The product moment of any square is its *x'* value multiplied by its *y'* value. The product moment of each square may be entered in the upper left-hand corner of that square. It is hardly necessary to point out that the product moments in the upper right and lower left quadrants of the table will have positive values and those in the upper left and lower right will have negative values.

Pearson *r* is to be computed, the scatter diagram should be *homoscedastic*. By homoscedasticity it is meant that the dispersions of the columns and rows should have approximately equal standard deviations. Any distributions that depart markedly from this condition are questionable material from which to compute a Pearson *r*.

But there are a number of cases in many of the squares, and each case should have as much weight as any other one. The next step is to multiply each product moment by the frequency of its square.

TABLE 60

X = color-naming test	Y = directions test

$$c_x' = \frac{\Sigma fx'}{N} = \frac{-25}{80} = -.3125 \qquad c_{\overline{x}}'^2 = .097656 \qquad c_x = (c_x')i = -.625$$

$$c_y' = \frac{\Sigma fy'}{N} = \frac{-49}{80} = -.6125 \qquad c_{\overline{y}}'^2 = .375156 \qquad c_y = (c_y')i = -12.25$$

$$\sigma_x' = \sqrt{\frac{\Sigma fx'^2}{N} - c_x'^2} = \sqrt{\frac{551}{80} - .097656} = \sqrt{6.789844} = 2.606$$

$$\sigma_y' = \sqrt{\frac{\Sigma fy'^2}{N} - c_y'^2} = \sqrt{\frac{613}{80} - .375156} = \sqrt{7.287344} = 2.700$$

$$\sigma_x = (\sigma_x')i = (2.6057)(2) = 5.211$$
$$\sigma_y = (\sigma_y')i = (2.6997)(20) = 53.99$$

$$r_{xy} = \frac{\dfrac{\Sigma x'y'}{N} - (c_x')(c_y')}{(\sigma_x')(\sigma_y')} = \frac{\dfrac{372}{80} - (-.3125)(-.6125)}{(2.606)(2.700)}$$

$$= \frac{4.6500 - .1914}{7.0362} = \frac{4.4586}{7.0362} = .634$$

$$PE_r = .6745\frac{1 - r^2}{\sqrt{N}} = .6745\frac{1 - .401956}{\sqrt{80}} = .6745\left(\frac{.598044}{8.944}\right) = .045$$

$$M_x = GA_x + c_x = 31.00 - .625 = 30.375$$
$$M_y = GA_y + c_y = 150.00 - 12.25 = 137.75$$

$$Y = (r)\left(\frac{\sigma_y}{\sigma_x}\right)(X - M_x) + M_y Y = (.634)\left(\frac{53.99}{5.211}\right)(X - 30.375) + 137.75$$
$$Y = (.634)(10.36)(X - 30.375) + 137.75$$
$$Y = 6.57X - 61.81$$
$$X = (r)\left(\frac{\sigma_x}{\sigma_y}\right)(Y - M_y) + M_x X = (.634)\left(\frac{5.211}{53.99}\right)(Y - 137.75) + 30.375$$
$$X = (.634)(.0965)(Y - 137.75) + 30.375$$
$$X = .0612Y + 21.95$$

$$\sigma_{xy} = \sigma_y\sqrt{1 - r_{xy}^2} = 5.2114\sqrt{.598044} = (5.2114)(.773) = 4.028$$
$$\sigma_{yx} = \sigma_x\sqrt{1 - r_{xy}^2} = 53.994\sqrt{.598044} = (53.994)(.773) = 41.737$$

These products, $f(x'y')$, are then summed for every row, keeping the positive and negative ones separated for the sake of convenience, and they are recorded in the last two columns of Table 59. Their algebraic sum is then found for the $\Sigma(x'y')$, which we need for the use of formula (124). The solution of r_{xy} is carried out in Table 60, and it is found to be $+.634$.

The Reliability of a Coefficient of Correlation.—A coefficient of correlation, like any statistical constant, is not a fixed, unchangeable quantity. It is subject to the customary errors of measurement that appear in the original data from which r is computed. Repeated experiments would give a varying coefficient of correlation. It is desirable to know within what range any obtained coefficient will fluctuate if repeatedly calculated from comparable sets of data. As in finding the reliability of any statistical constant, it is the customary assumption that coefficients of correlation fluctuate above and below the obtained one according to the law of normal distribution. The reliability is then indicated by the *PE* of that distribution. The *PE* of r is given by the formula

$$PE_r = .6745\frac{1 - r^2}{\sqrt{N}} \tag{125}$$

The *PE* of an index of correlation (see page 317) is similarly

$$PE_p = .6745\frac{1 - p^2}{\sqrt{N - m}} \tag{126}$$

in which m is as usual the number of parameters (see page 294). For our coefficient of .634, when N equals 80,

$$PE_r = .6745\frac{1 - .401956}{8.944} = .045.$$

Given the usual interpretation, we may say that, in repeated determinations of r_{xy} under comparable conditions, half the r values would lie between $.634 \pm .045$, or between .589 and .679. The chances are 993 in 1000 that similarly obtained r's would lie between .454 and .814, which are the limits of $4PE_r$ from .634. The general rule is that an r must be at least four times its *PE* in order to be significant. When r is very low, it should be more than four times its *PE* to be indicative of any correlation at all.[1]

---

[1] Fisher (8, p. 170) recommends the formula $\sigma_r = \dfrac{1 - r^2}{\sqrt{N - 1}}$, and Ezekiel (7, p. 256) is more conservative with the formula $\sigma_r = \dfrac{1 - r^2}{\sqrt{N - 2}}$. Both insist that these formulas give accurate estimates only if N is very large and if r is moderate or small.

These rules have in mind the probability that *r* may be greater than zero. Obviously, an *r* of .15 with a *PE* of .10 is only 1.5*PE* removed from zero, and according to Table C there would be 156

TABLE 61.—PROBABLE ERRORS OF THE COEFFICIENT OF CORRELATION FOR VARIOUS VALUES OF *r* AND OF N[1]

Number of measures	Correlation coefficient *r*						
	0.0	0.1	0.2	0.3	0.4	0.5	0.6
20	.1508	.1493	.1448	.1373	.1267	.1131	.0965
30	.1231	.1219	.1182	.1121	.1035	.0924	.0788
40	.1067	.1056	.1024	.0971	.0896	.0800	.0683
50	.0954	.0944	.0915	.0868	.0801	.0715	.0610
70	.0806	.0798	.0774	.0734	.0677	.0605	.0516
100	.0674	.0668	.0648	.0614	.0567	.0506	.0432
150	.0551	.0546	.0529	.0501	.0463	.0413	.0352
200	.0477	.0472	.0458	.0434	.0401	.0358	.0305
250	.0426	.0421	.0409	.0387	.0358	.0319	.0272
300	.0389	.0386	.0374	.0354	.0327	.0292	.0249
400	.0337	.0334	.0324	.0307	.0283	.0253	.0216
500	.0302	.0299	.0290	.0274	.0253	.0226	.0193
1000	.0213	.0211	.0205	.0194	.0179	.0160	.0137
	0.65	0.7	0.75	0.8	0.85	0.9	0.95
20	.0871	.0769	.0660	.0543	.0419	.0287	.0147
30	.0711	.0628	.0539	.0444	.0342	.0234	.0120
40	.0616	.0544	.0467	.0384	.0296	.0203	.0104
50	.0551	.0486	.0417	.0343	.0265	.0181	.0093
70	.0466	.0411	.0353	.0290	.0224	.0153	.0079
100	.0391	.0345	.0294	.0242	.0187	.0128	.0066
150	.0318	.0281	.0241	.0198	.0153	.0105	.0054
200	.0275	.0243	.0209	.0172	.0133	.0091	.0047
250	.0246	.0218	.0187	.0154	.0118	.0081	.0042
300	.0225	.0199	.0170	.0140	.0108	.0074	.0038
400	.0195	0172	.0148	.0122	.0094	.0064	.0033
500	.0174	.0154	.0132	.0109	.0084	.0057	.0029
1000	.0123	.0109	.0093	.0077	.0059	.0041	.0021

[1] From Garrett (10, p. 171), by permission of the publisher.

chances in 1000 for an *r* that is less than zero under similar circumstances. In a like manner we could find the probability that an *r* would be less than a certain amount. By finding the difference between two *r* values, the *PE* of the difference, and the critical ratio, we could estimate the probability that one r is significantly greater than another.[1]

Fisher's Test of the Significance of r.—The use of PE_r to indicate the reliability of an obtained r has been very seriously questioned by Fisher. He maintains (8, pp. 170 *ff.*) that the distribution of r is not normal except when r is moderate or small (less than .70, for example) and when N is very large. With very small samples he points out that r is likely to be in error as compared with the true r, so that a PE_r which is based upon a small obtained r, is likewise often in error. The student will recall that, in Ezekiel's correction of the obtained r to find the most probable true r (see page 308), when N is small the change made by formula (117) is relatively large. So when N is less than 100, which will be true in a majority of the problems with which the average student has to deal, it is recommended that a different test of significance of r be used.

We should not fail to take into consideration, when we obtain a certain value of r, the possibility that unless r is very large it might have arisen purely by chance. Let us suppose a zero correlation with 25 cases. The PE_r by formula (125) is then $.6745/\sqrt{25}$, or .135. Let us assume that there really is no correlation between the two variables. Yet, by the proper selection of cases we should expect one-fourth of the coefficients so obtained to be greater than $+.135$; we should expect 89 in 1000 to be greater than $+.270$, and even 22 in 1000 to be greater than $+.405$, the latter being $3PE$ from zero. Were we to obtain an r of $+.40$ with 25 cases, we could not be absolutely sure that this result is not in reality due to chance. Fisher's method takes the approach that has just been indicated by this paragraph. His test of significance tells *the probability that an r as large as we have obtained could arise by random sampling from an uncorrelated population.*

It is unnecessary here to go into the details of Fisher's method. In Table K are given the lower limits for r that may be considered significant for varying numbers of cases. The value in lighter print in each case is considered the least significant r; the one in heavier print is considered the least r that is *very* significant. By 'significant' it is meant that the probability that such a coefficient of correlation will arise from an uncorrelated population is .05, or 5 chances in 100; by 'very significant' is meant a similar probability of .01,

---

[1] For a discussion of the critical ratio and the test of significance of a difference see pages 58 *ff.*

or 1 chance in 100. In the first column of Table K appear the various degrees of freedom (see page 308), or N minus the number of variables. The other columns are headed by the numbers of variables. In the case of the r that we have found between the two mental tests, .634, the number of degrees of freedom is 78 and the number of variables is 2. We do not find exactly 78 in column 1 of Table K, but we may use 80 which is given there, or we may interpolate. In the second column we find that with 80 degrees of freedom a coefficient of .217 (or higher) would be significant, and one of .283 would be very significant. Our coefficient of .634 is undoubtedly very significant. There is less than 1 chance in 100 that it could have arisen if there were no true correlation.

The Two Regression Equations.—In the preceding chapter the regression equation of the form $Y = a + bX$ was found directly from the data before r was obtained. It is also possible, *after r has been found*, to use it in finding not only the equation for the regression of Y upon X but also the equation for the regression of X upon Y. It is sometimes desirable to work out both regressions. The two formulas are:

$$Y = (r_{yx})\left(\frac{\sigma_y}{\sigma_x}\right)(X - M_x) + M_y \qquad (127a)$$

$$X = (r_{xy})\left(\frac{\sigma_x}{\sigma_y}\right)(Y - M_y) + M_x \qquad (127b)$$

From Table 60 it will be seen that for our mental-test problem the two equations reduce to

$$Y = 6.57X - 61.81,$$

and

$$X = .0612Y + 21.95.$$

The two regression lines are sketched lightly in Table 59. They intersect at the means of the two distributions and they would do so regardless of the value of r. The higher r is, the more nearly the two lines approach one another. When $r = 1.00$ the two lines become identical. When $r = 0$ they are at right angles to each other.

Notice that the coefficient of X, which we shall designate as b_{yx}, is equal to $(r_{yx})(\sigma_y/\sigma_x)$. The coefficient of Y in the second regression equation is equal to $(r_{xy})(\sigma_x/\sigma_y)$. These values are called the **regression coefficients,** b_{yx} being the one for the regression of Y

upon X and b_{xy} being the one for the regression of X upon Y. In terms of formulas they are

$$b_{yx} = (r_{yx})\left(\frac{\sigma_y}{\sigma_x}\right) \tag{128a}$$

$$b_{xy} = (r_{xy})\left(\frac{\sigma_x}{\sigma_y}\right) \tag{128b}$$

The former tells the average change in Y for a unit change in X. From the numerical value of b_{yx} we may say that for every second increase in time for performing the color-naming test there is an average change of 6.57 sec. in performing the directions test. The latter, b_{xy}, tells how rapidly X changes for one unit of change in Y. It appears from the numerical value of b_{xy} that, for every second the time increases in the directions test, the time for doing the color-naming test increases by .0612 sec.

In the two equations (128a, 128b) $r_{yx} = r_{xy} = .634$. When r is zero, then the regression coefficient is zero and the regression equations reduce to $Y = M_y$ and $X = M_x$. That is, when there is no correlation, the most probable Y value for *any* X value is M_y, and the most probable X value for *any* Y value is M_x. When $r = 1.00$ in either equation, notice that b becomes the ratio of the two standard deviations. Then any score that is so many sigmas above or below the mean in the one distribution corresponds to a score that is exactly the same number of sigmas above or below the mean in the other distribution. Since r is really the variable part of the regression coefficient, it alone is the important factor in determining the slope of the regression line. The other part merely reduces the two measurements to a common unit, the sigma of the distribution.

The Beta Coefficients.—If the X measurements and Y measurements are given in terms of standard measures, then r becomes the slope of the regression line. In this case, however, it is known as *beta*, the **standard regression coefficient**. The two regression equations would then read

$$\frac{Y - M_y}{\sigma_y} = \beta_{yx}\left(\frac{X - M_x}{\sigma_x}\right), \quad \text{or} \quad z'_y = \beta_{yx}z_x$$

and

$$\frac{X - M_x}{\sigma_x} = \beta_{xy}\left(\frac{Y - M_y}{\sigma_y}\right), \quad \text{or} \quad z'_x = \beta_{xy}z_y$$

where $z_y' = $ the predicted standard scores in Y.

$z_y = $ the actual standard scores in Y.

z_x' and z_x have corresponding meanings.

In both cases beta equals r (this is true only in simple correlation problems of two variables), which is .634 in the illustrative problem. Thus either X or Y, when measured in terms of standard scores, is increasing only .634 times as rapidly as its covariable, also measured in terms of standard scores. The relation of the β coefficients to the b coefficients is given by the formulas

$$\beta_{yx} = b_{yx}\left(\frac{\sigma_x}{\sigma_y}\right) \tag{129a}$$

$$\beta_{xy} = b_{xy}\left(\frac{\sigma_y}{\sigma_x}\right) \tag{129b}$$

The use and significance of beta coefficients will become more apparent in dealing with partial and multiple correlations. They have no practical use in simple correlations, except of course as r itself is useful, for they are identical with r. The meaning of a beta coefficient, however, lends significance to the relation between r and the ordinary regression coefficients.

The Standard Errors of the Estimates.—The concept of the standard error of the estimate was introduced in the preceding chapter. The same concept applies here. The only new aspect here is that we have two regressions instead of one and each regression has its own standard error of the estimate. Adapting the formula for the sigma of the estimate, which was given as formula (112) to the two regressions, we have

$$\sigma_{yx} = \sigma_y\sqrt{1 - r_{yx}^2} \tag{112a}$$
$$\sigma_{xy} = \sigma_x\sqrt{1 - r_{xy}^2} \tag{112b}$$

While the quantity beneath the radical is the same for both, the one formula contains σ_y and the other σ_x. When these are solved, as in Table 60, we find the equations leading to a σ_{yx} of 4.028 and to a σ_{xy} of 41.737. It should be noticed that in both cases (see Table 60) the original sigmas of the distributions X and Y are reduced by the same amount, namely, to 77.3 per cent of their original size, since the two original sigmas are multiplied by .773. From this fact we can say that, because of a correlation of .634 between Y and X, the variability of observed values about our predictions is approximately 77 per cent as great as the variability of those same observations about their mean. Thus, if we had the choice of predicting any particular Y value either from the knowledge of the mean of the Y values or from the knowledge of the corresponding X value, we would reduce our error of prediction to about 77 per cent by choosing the latter basis of prediction. That amount of reduction in error of prediction is certainly not very great, but it is helpful. The point to be emphasized here is that the expression $\sqrt{1 - r^2}$ gives the ratio of σ_{yx} to σ_y.

Reliability of a Regression Coefficient.—The reliability of b_{yx} is given by its standard error, which is found by the formula

$$\sigma_{b_{yx}} = \frac{\sigma_{yx}}{\sigma_x \sqrt{N}} = \frac{\sigma_y}{\sigma_x} \sqrt{\frac{1 - r_{xy}^2}{N}} \tag{130}$$

The reliability of b_{xy} is found by a similar formula for $\sigma_{b_{xy}}$, interchanging variables X and Y throughout formula (130). In the problem of Table 60,

$$\sigma_{b_{yx}} = \frac{4.028}{(5.211)(8.944)} = \frac{4.028}{46.607} = .086.$$

b_{yx} is 6.57, which is more than 76 times its standard error and it is therefore highly significant. The chances are two to one that b_{yx} lies between 6.48 and 6.66.

The Method of Rank Differences

Of several substitute or short-cut methods for finding an estimate of r, the rank difference method is by far the most commonly employed. The essential steps are to convert the X values and the Y values into two sets of ranks, to find the differences between corresponding pairs of ranks, and to square the differences. The coefficient to be calculated is ρ (rho), which is found by using the formula

$$\rho = 1 - \frac{6\Sigma d^2}{N(N^2 - 1)} \tag{131}$$

The Computation of Rho.—To illustrate, let us use the following data consisting of 12 pairs of values, the one member of the pair being the Army Alpha score made by a student and the other his grade in a psychology course. We first assign a rank order to each individual in the first variable, in this case his grade in psychology. It is immaterial whether we assign rank 1 to the highest score or to the lowest. To be consistent with the procedure recommended for the ranking method in an earlier chapter, we should assign rank 1 to the lowest grade in column 1. That is a grade of 55. The grade of 62 ranks second, 67 ranks third, and 68 ranks fourth. All runs smoothly until the grade of 82 is reached. There are two cases of this value. One would normally be seventh and the other eighth. Not knowing which is really higher, if either, we call them both 7.5 in rank; in other words we give them the median value of the two ranks 7 and 8. The next higher case is ranked 9. In column 2 there are three scores of 150, coming with ranks 6, 7, and 8. We call them all 7 and proceed with the next higher score by calling it 9. In the end, there must be a rank equal to N for the highest value in each column.

Having the two columns of ranks, we next find their differences. The differences are then squared as in the last column. Their sum is 97.50. We now have all the required information to use formula (131).

TABLE 62.—AN ILLUSTRATIVE TABLE FOR SOLVING A CORRELATION BY THE RANK DIFFERENCE METHOD

Grade in psychology	Army Alpha score	R_1	R_2	d	d^2
75	140	5	4	1	1.00
82	135	7.5	3	4.5	20.25
94	167	12	11	1	1.00
62	150	2	7	5	25.00
85	170	10	12	2	4.00
77	155	6	9	3	9.00
84	145	9	5	4	16.00
55	120	1	1	0	0.00
67	150	3	7	4	16.00
82	150	7.5	7	0.5	0.25
90	164	11	10	1	1.00
68	129	4	2	2	4.00

$$\Sigma d^2 = 97.50$$

$$\rho = 1 - \frac{6(97.50)}{12(143)}$$

$$= 1 - \frac{585.00}{1716}$$

$$= 1 - .341$$

$$= .659$$

Finding the Pearson *r* Equivalent to ρ.—The computation of ρ is based upon the assumption that the differences between any two neighboring ranks at any part of the same scale are equal. This assumption is obviously false. A correction for this, based upon the more reasonable assumption that the measurements are normally distributed, is supplied by Pearson. It gives an equivalent Pearson *r* by the relation

$$r_\rho = 2 \sin\left(\frac{\pi}{6}\rho\right).$$

The correction is very slight, being greatest when *r* and ρ are near .50. The following brief table will suffice to make all the transformations usually needed.

TABLE 63.—TABLE FOR CONVERTING ρ INTO *r* BY PEARSON'S FORMULA

ρ	*r*	ρ	*r*	ρ	*r*	ρ	*r*
.05	.052	.30	.313	.55	.568	.80	.813
.10	.105	.35	.364	.60	.618	.85	.861
.15	.157	.40	.416	.65	.668	.90	.908
.20	.209	.45	.467	.70	.717	.95	.954
.25	.261	.50	.518	.75	.765	1.00	1.000

Since in the rank difference method we usually deal with coefficients from relatively small numbers of cases, coefficients that are none too reliable in themselves, we are hardly justified in retaining more than two decimal places. This being true, it will be seen from Table 63 that, when ρ is below .10 or above .95, there would be no correction to find *r*; between .36 and .75 the correction is +.02; at all other points it is +.01.

The Reliability of the Rank Difference Coefficient.—The coefficient ρ is statistically less reliable than the Pearson *r*, and so the r_ρ that is estimated from it is also less reliable. The *PE* of r_ρ is given only approximately by the relation

$$PE_{r_\rho} = .7063\frac{(1 - r_\rho^2)}{\sqrt{N}} \tag{132}$$

In the above problem

$$PE_{r_\rho} = (.7063)\frac{(1 - .458329)}{(3.464)}.$$

$$PE_{r_\rho} = (.7063)\frac{(.541671)}{(3.464)}$$

$$= .133.$$

Aids in the Computation of Rho.—One frequently has a large number of ρ coefficients to calculate in a single investigation and the saving of time when N is relatively small is probably its most attractive feature. Further time saving may be accomplished in several ways. One device that is useful when N is constant for a number of problems is to revise formula (131) to read

$$\rho = 1 - \Sigma d^2 \left[\frac{6}{N^3 - N} \right].$$

The quantity within the bracket will remain constant for any given value of N. Only Σd^2 varies from problem to problem. Cureton (2) has worked out values for $\frac{6}{N^3 - N}$ when N varies from 10 to 50 and those values are given in Table 64.

TABLE 64.—VALUES OF $\frac{6}{N^3 - N}$ FOR DIFFERENT VALUES OF N

N	$\left[\dfrac{6}{N^3 - N}\right]$	N	$\left[\dfrac{6}{N^3 - N}\right]$	N	$\left[\dfrac{6}{N^3 - N}\right]$	N	$\left[\dfrac{6}{N^3 - N}\right]$
10	.00606	20	.000752	30	.000222	40	.0000938
11	.00455	21	.000649	31	.000202	41	.0000871
12	.00350	22	.000565	32	.000183	42	.0000810
13	.00275	23	.000494	33	.000167	43	.0000755
14	.00220	24	.000435	34	.000153	44	.0000705
15	.00179	25	.000385	35	.000140	45	.0000659
16	.00147	26	.000342	36	.000129	46	0000617
17	.00123	27	.000305	37	.000119	47	.0000578
18	.00103	28	.000274	38	.000109	48	.0000543
19	.000877	29	.000246	39	.000101	49	.0000510
						50	.0000480

When a large number of ρ coefficients must be computed, a device suggested by Toops (20) will be of great service. This consists in the construction of a **nomograph** or graphic chart. For a description of this device the reader is referred to Toops's own account.[1]

---

[1] A slightly simpler correlation method based upon the differences between ranks is known as Spearman's *footrule method*, or the *method of gains*. Its coeffi-

A GENERAL METHOD FOR NONLINEAR CORRELATIONS

In the preceding chapter, when data were fitted to a nonlinear function, an index of correlation p_{yx} was found which indicated the amount of correlation between Y and $f(X)$ or between the predicted Y values and the observed Y values. This involved the assumption of some type of mathematical function, or else the drawing of a freehand curve through the scatter diagram, the predictions of Y from X, and perhaps also the calculation of the discrepancies of the predicted Y values from the observed Y values, before an index of correlation could be computed. There are many instances, although they compose a small minority, in which the scatter diagram shows a nonlinear trend and we wish to know the strength of the connection between two variables without having any interest in the type of regression. For this purpose there is a very general method of correlating the two variables without having recourse to least squares or even to any attempts at predicting Y from $f(X)$. The statistical constant used in this connection is called the **correlation ratio** and it is designated by the symbol η (eta).

The Correlation Ratio.—Note the scatter diagram in Table 65. The general drift of the points is from upper left to lower right and superficially it might seem that the relationship is linear. To show that it is not exactly linear, however, proceed to find the means of the different columns, or *Y-arrays*, which are represented by circlets, and it is clear that we have a nonlinear trend. How significant is the trend?

If there were no definite trend, no correlation of any kind between X and Y, the means of the arrays would on the whole approach the mean of all the Y values, falling along a horizontal line at the level of M_y, which is at 74.30. A maximum correlation would be obtained when the scatter of the means of the arrays is as large as possible (within the limits of the variability of the Y values themselves) above and below M_y. The degree of scatter of these means of the arrays is measured by the sigma of their distribution. The ratio of this sigma to σ_y gives the amount of correlation. If we think of every mean of an array as the best prediction of Y from the

---

cient R requires a very radical correction in order to find the equivalent Pearson r. The method is used to a less extent than the rank difference method described here. A good account of the method is given by Garrett (10, p. 193).

corresponding X value of that array, then what we are doing in reality is comparing the sigma of the predicted Y values with the original sigma of the Y values. We have seen before that

$$r_{yx} = \sigma_{y'}/\sigma_y$$

[see page 304, formula (110)]. In fact, η_{yx} is the ratio of the sigma of the predicted Y values to the sigma of the observed values. When the relationship is linear,

$$\eta_{yx} = r_{yx}$$

There is a difference, however, between the predictions of Y here and in the previous chapter. In the previous chapter we insisted upon a continuous function, either graphic or one found from the method of least squares—a function without inversions. In the present method the means of the arrays vary from one column to the next. The trend is not necessarily free from inversions. Thus, in this method, because the 'predictions' of each array are independent of any particular assumed trend, it is possible to obtain a higher degree of correlation. The η coefficient may be expected to yield the maximum amount of correlation that the scatter of the data will permit. The only limitations to this lie in the fact that the data are grouped arbitrarily and the means of the arrays are found from those arbitrary groupings. In general, the grouping should be coarse enough not to permit too many inversions, for inversions are probably due to chance factors. Nor should an η coefficient be computed unless N is relatively large, so that there can be a sufficient number of classes and so that the means of the arrays shall be reasonably reliable.

The solution of η_{yx} is illustrated in Tables 65 and 66. The essential steps are as follows:

1. Find the sum and the mean of each Y-array. These are listed under n and Y'' in Table 66. The symbol Y'' is used instead of Y' in order to distinguish those two types of prediction.

2. Find the deviation of every Y'' from the mean. These are listed as $(Y'' - M_y)$ in Table 66. The mean is 74.3 in our present problem.

3. Square the deviations, finding $(Y'' - M_y)^2$.

4. Weight each deviation by multiplying by the corresponding n in each array. Recall that the Y'' values are in reality predictions for given values of X. It is only reasonable that we should make as

many predictions in an array as there are individual cases, hence the reason for finding $n(Y'' - M_y)^2$.

TABLE 65

X-simple auditory reaction time

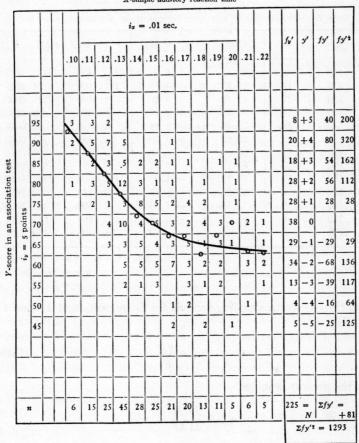

Y-score		$i_x = .01$ sec.												f_y'	y'	fy'	fy'^2
		.10	.11	.12	.13	.14	.15	.16	.17	.18	.19	20	.21	.22			
95		3	3	2											8	+5	40	200
90		2	5	7	5		1								20	+4	80	320
85				2	3	.5	2	2	1	1		1	1		18	+3	54	162
80		1		3	5	12	3	1	1		1		1		28	+2	56	112
75				2	1	3	8	5	2	4	2		1		28	+1	28	28
70					4	10	4	5	3	2	4	3	2	1	38	0		
65				3	3	5	4	3	5		3	1		1	29	−1	−29	29
60					5	5	5	7	3	2	2		3	2	34	−2	−68	136
55						2	1	3		3	1	2		1	13	−3	−39	117
50								1	2				1		4	−4	−16	64
45								2		2	1				5	−5	−25	125
n		6	15	25	45	28	25	21	20	13	11	5	6	5	225 = N	$\Sigma fy'$ = +81		
															$\Sigma fy'^2 = 1293$			

(Y-score in an association test, $i_y = 5$ points)

5. Find the sum of the weighted, squared deviations and divide by N to find their mean. In this step we are finding $\sigma_{y''}$, the standard error of the predicted Y values. In terms of a formula,

$$\sigma_{y''} = \sqrt{\frac{\Sigma[n(Y'' - M_y)^2]}{N}} \tag{133}$$

in which n is the frequency of an array.

In this particular problem, $\sigma_{y''} = 7.691$. The correlation ratio is given by the formula

$$\eta_{yx} = \frac{\sigma_{y''}}{\sigma_y} \qquad (134a)$$

TABLE 66.—WORK SHEET FOR THE SOLUTION OF A CORRELATION RATIO

X	n	Y''	$(Y'' - M_y)$	$(Y'' - M_y)^2$	$n(Y'' - M_y)^2$
.100	6	93.33	$+19.03$	362.1409	2172.8454
.110	15	88.83	$+14.53$	211.1209	3166.8135
.120	25	83.50	$+ 9.20$	84.6400	2116.0000
.130	45	77.28	$+ 2.98$	8.8804	399.6180
.140	28	72.86	$- 1.44$	2.0736	58.0608
.150	25	70.50	$- 3.80$	14.4400	361.0000
.160	21	67.74	$- 6.56$	43.0336	903.7056
.170	20	67.25	$- 7.05$	49.7025	994.0500
.180	13	63.27	-11.03	121.6609	1581.5917
.190	11	67.95	$- 6.35$	40.3225	443.5475
.200	5	72.50	$- 1.80$	3.2400	16.2000
.210	6	64.17	-10.13	102.6169	615.7014
.220	5	64.50	$- 9.80$	96.0400	480.2000

$$\Sigma[n(Y'' - M_y)^2] = 13309.3339$$
$$\sigma_{y''}^2 = 59.1526$$
$$\sigma_{y''} = 7.691$$

and there is a corresponding formula for the regression of X upon Y, namely,

$$\eta_{xy} = \frac{\sigma_{x''}}{\sigma_x} \qquad (134b)$$

In the present problem,

$$\eta_{yx} = \frac{7.691}{11.85} = .649.$$

The algebraic sign of η will naturally be positive in all cases. Whether the relationship that it represents is a positive one or negative will have to be decided by the investigator and the appropriate sign can then be attached. The downward trend in Table 65 suggests a negative correlation and so η would normally receive a negative sign here. But this often depends also upon the arrangement of the numerical scores. In the reaction time test a small numerical score indicates a 'good' performance, and so the two abilities represented are really positively correlated. Our conclusion should be that there is a positive correlation between reaction time and the association test. We might therefore more properly leave η with a positive sign.

Correction of the "Raw" Eta.—Because of errors introduced by the process of grouping the data (especially when N is not large and when the number of arrays is large), the obtained η is probably too large. Pearson's correction for the "raw" η is approximated by the formula[1]

$$_c\eta^2 = \frac{\eta^2 - \dfrac{(\kappa - 3)}{N}}{1 - \dfrac{(\kappa - 3)}{N}} \tag{135}$$

in which κ (kappa) is the number of arrays. In the present problem,

$$_c\eta^2 = \frac{.4212 - \dfrac{(13 - 3)}{225}}{1 - \dfrac{(13 - 3)}{225}}$$

$$= \frac{.4212 - .0444}{1 - .0444}$$

$$= \frac{.3768}{.9556}$$

$$= .394307.$$

$$_c\eta = .628.$$

The reliability of a correlation ratio is given by its probable error, which is the same as the PE of r as in formula (125).

$$PE_\eta = .6745\frac{1 - \eta^2}{\sqrt{N}} \tag{136}$$

For the corrected η just found,

$$PE_\eta = .6745\frac{1 - .394384}{\sqrt{225}}$$

$$= .6745\frac{.605616}{15}$$

$$= .027.$$

[1] The correction becomes less as the number of groups or classes decreases. With three classes $\kappa - 3$ would be zero and no correction would result. However, it is still wise to use a relatively large number of classes since another error of grouping enters when κ becomes small (13, p. 242).

A Test of Linearity.—How much greater is the nonlinear correlation than a linear Pearson r would have been? We determine this, not by comparing η_{yx} with r_{yx}, but by comparing the squares of those two constants. The test of linearity is given by ζ (zeta) when

$$\zeta = \eta^2 - r^2 \tag{137}$$

The Pearson r_{yx} for the same data was found to be .549. Applying the test,[1]

$$\zeta = .394384 - .301401$$
$$= .092983, \text{ or } .093.$$

The question now arises as to whether a ζ of .093 is great enough to be significant. Tests of significance of differences demand the comparison of those differences with their standard errors or probable errors. Formulas have been given for the standard error of ζ. They are very elaborate and even then they are of doubtful validity (13, p. 239). The simplest approximation is

$$\sigma_\zeta = 2\sqrt{\frac{\zeta}{N}} \tag{138}$$

In the present problem,

$$\sigma_\zeta = 2\sqrt{\frac{.092983}{225}}$$
$$= 2\frac{.305}{15}$$
$$= .0406.$$

Thus, ζ is 2.29 or .093/.0406 times its standard error. This quantity the student will recognize as a critical ratio, and from it we can find the probability of a positive difference, which in this case would be about 989 in 1000.

A much simpler test, which is probably adequate in most cases, is known as Blakeman's test. By this test a regression is said to be linear if

$$N(\eta^2 - r^2) < 11.37 \tag{139}$$

---

[1] Ordinarily the uncorrected η is used in computing ζ. However, this gives a zeta that is probably too large whereas the corrected η gives a zeta that is too small. The use of the corrected η therefore gives the more conservative indication of nonlinearity.

In this problem, $225(.093) = 20.92$, which leads definitely to the inference that the regression is nonlinear.

CORRELATIONS BASED UPON DATA GROUPED IN CLASSES OR CATEGORIES

Not infrequently one or both of the variables that we wish to correlate are not continuously variable or, even if they are continuously variable, we may be unable to obtain varying measurements of them. One or both of the variables may be capable only of being classified into two or more distinct classes. For example, if we wished to correlate color of hair with color of eyes, we should have to resort to the classification of the individuals into a few discrete categories. There are ways of taking care of just such incomplete measurements. We begin with the case in which one variable has been measured as a continuous variable and the other has been treated as if the individual cases fell into two distinct classes or categories.

The Biserial Coefficient of Correlation.—Let us consider the following specific problem: Ninety-five men had been asked in a personality inventory to answer the question, "Are you inclined to act on the spur of the moment without thinking things over?" The same 95 men had been given the cube-fluctuation test, in which the characteristic rate of fluctuation for each man was determined. According to a particular theory there should be a negative correlation between the rate of fluctuation and the trait implied by an affirmative answer to the above question. All that the subjects could do with the question was to reply by saying "Yes" or "No." It is unlikely from what we know about the distribution of any personal characteristic that men fall into two separate and distinct categories with respect to the tendency to "act on the spur of the moment without thinking things over." Were they allowed to give graduated estimations of themselves, the distribution of responses might reasonably be of the normal form. The estimates of this variable have been forced into two classes by the nature of the experiment. The biserial r may be computed when the two classes are really two qualitatively different classes, as well as when they merely represent coarsely grouped data. Table 67 presents the data as they are prepared for the computation of a biserial r, and the necessary steps are demonstrated there.

TABLE 67.—WORK SHEET FOR THE COMPUTATION OF A BISERIAL r

Fluctuations per minute....	5	10	15	20	25	30	35	40	45	50	55	60	65	70	n	n/N	
Yes distribution............	1	8	7	4	4	2	4	2			1			1	34	.358	p
No distribution............	6	17	14	9	8		2	2	1		1	1			61	.642	q
Total distribution..........	7	25	21	13	12	2	6	4	1	0	2	1	0	1	95	1.000	

The formula for the biserial r is

$$\text{biserial } r = \frac{M_p - M_q}{\sigma_t} \times \frac{pq}{y} \qquad (140)$$

where M_p = the mean of the one distribution.

　　　M_q = the mean of the other.

　　　p = the proportion of cases in the one distribution.

　　　q = the proportion in the other.

　　　σ_t = the standard deviation of the total distribution.

　　　y = the ordinate of the normal distribution curve for the corresponding values of p and q, when p and q as usual represent areas under the normal curve.

For the present problem,

$$\text{biserial } r = \frac{25.30 - 20.55}{12.665} \times \frac{.229836}{.3734}$$

$$= \frac{4.75}{12.665} \times \frac{.229836}{.3734}$$

$$= \frac{1.091721}{4.7291}$$

$$= .231.$$

The standard error of the biserial r is given approximately by

$$\sigma_{\text{biserial } r} = \frac{\dfrac{\sqrt{pq}}{y} - r^2}{\sqrt{N}} \qquad (141)$$

In this particular problem,

$$\sigma_{\text{biserial } r} = \frac{\dfrac{.4794}{.3734} - .0534}{\sqrt{95}}$$

$$= \frac{1.2838 - .0534}{9.747}$$

$$= \frac{1.2304}{9.747}$$
$$= .126$$

and

$$PE_r = (.6745)(.126) = .085.$$

Thus the biserial r is not quite three times its PE and therefore might have occurred by chance. It should be added that a biserial r should not be computed unless the graduated series of measurements is reasonably normally distributed and unless N is relatively large—preferably when N is greater than 50. Another important condition is that the cases be not too unevenly divided between the two distributions, particularly when N is small.

Tetrachoric Correlation.—At times the data in both variables are forced into two categories, or naturally belong in two. This gives a fourfold classification, or a **tetrachoric** table. For example, let us take the responses of 930 subjects to two following questions from a personality inventory, in which the responses were to be either "Yes" or "No":

1. Do you like to confide in others?
2. Do you express such emotions as delight, sorrow, anger, and the like readily?

In finding a tetrachoric coefficient of correlation, the assumption is made that the two variables in reality have normal distributions but that the measurements are forced into two classes for each variable. We can make this reasonable assumption for the responses to the two questions above. The tetrachoric table is prepared as in Table 68, the general form being given at the left.

TABLE 68.—FOURFOLD CLASSIFICATION OF SAMPLES PREPARED FOR THE CALCULATION OF A TETRACHORIC COEFFICIENT OF CORRELATION

Variable 1

	+	−	Total
+	a	b	$a + b$
−	c	d	$c + d$
Total	$a + c$	$b + d$	N

Question 1

	Yes	No	Total
Yes	374	167	541
No	186	203	389
Total	560	370	930

The next step is to transform the frequencies into proportions, as in the two diagrams in Table 69, the one at the left being the generalized form. From this point the computation of a tetrachoric *r* is long and tedious if one must apply Pearson's lengthy formula without any additional aids. Fortunately, Thurstone and his associates (19) have prepared a set of diagrams that enable us to solve a

TABLE 69.—TETRACHORIC TABLES IN WHICH CELL FREQUENCIES ARE GIVEN IN TERMS OF PROPORTIONS

Variable 1

		+	−	Total
Variable 2	+	α	β	p
	−	γ	δ	q
	Total	p'	q'	

Question 1

		Yes	No	Total
Question 2	Yes	.402	.180	.582
	No	.200	.218	.418
	Total	.602	.398	1.000

tetrachoric *r* in a very few minutes, once the data are put into the above form. For this reason Pearson's formula is not given here; the reader who has occasion to find tetrachoric coefficients is urged to use Thurstone's excellent diagrams. The tetrachoric *r* for the data in Table 69, as computed from Thurstone's diagrams, was found to be .340. From the preponderance of cases in categories *a* and *d* we give this *r* a positive sign. The standard error of a tetrachoric *r* is to be found only through a discouragingly long process and there are as yet no simplified graphic methods for estimating it. Kelley (13, p. 254) gives the necessary formulas for this as well as Pearson's formula for finding r_t. For those to whom Thurstone's diagrams for finding r_t are unavailable, there are other ways of finding an equivalent Pearson *r* from fourfold tables. These methods will be described next.

Correlation of a Fourfold Point Surface.—If the real nature of the variables is discrete, *i.e.*, if the cases fall into two qualitatively different groups, like blue and brown eyes, for example, we have to deal with a fourfold *point surface*. Suppose we wish to find the correlation between fathers and sons as to eye color and we limit our cases to definitely blue-eyed and brown-eyed individuals. From Yule we may borrow the data (24, p. 70) of Table 70, using only the blue and brown categories.

The correlation of point distributions is given by the formula

$$\phi = \frac{\alpha\delta - \beta\gamma}{\sqrt{pqp'q'}} \tag{142}$$

in which the symbols have the same significance as in Table 69.   The coefficient is designated by ϕ in order to distinguish it from the

TABLE 70.—FOURFOLD TABLES OF POINT DISTRIBUTIONS USED IN THE SOLUTION OF PHI

Father's Eye Color

	Blue	Brown	Total
Blue	194	30	224
Brown	56	109	165
Total	250	139	389

(Son's Eye Color)

Father's Eye Color

	Blue	Brown	Total	
Blue	.499 α	.077 β	.576	p
Brown	.144 γ	.280 δ	.424	q
Total	.643	.357	1.000	
	p'	q'		

(Son's Eye Color)

ordinary r, which applies only to continuous variables.   From the above problem,

$$\phi = \frac{.139720 - .011088}{\sqrt{.0560619}}$$

$$= \frac{.128632}{.2368}$$

$$= .543.$$

The correlation between fathers and sons for eye color thus seems well within the range of the familiar correlations between close relatives in physical traits.   In actual practice, of course, we should have categories for gray eyes and for hazel eyes, as Yule has when presenting his data.   There are other methods for correlating 3×3 fold and 4×4 fold tables.   Yule's data were reduced to a 2×2 fold table here for the purpose of illustrating the computation of the ϕ coefficient.   Such examples of point distributions are rarely met and the assumption of such a distribution should always be carefully scrutinized to make sure that it is not actually continuous.   The ϕ coefficient may be employed toward the solution of r in a fourfold table of the continuous type of variable, but it must undergo radical adjustments before it is equivalent to the ordinary r.   These transformations of ϕ into an equivalent r will be described later.

Relationships in Terms of Probability.—In the preceding example, dealing with the eye color of fathers and sons, we can raise the simple question as to the probability that such a fourfold classification would arise by chance if there really were no correlation between eye colors of fathers and sons. To take a simplified case, let us suppose that 60 per cent of the fathers are blue-eyed and also 60 per cent of the sons; in round numbers those percentages are not very far from the truth as represented in Table 70. In either case

TABLE 71.—CORRELATION BETWEEN CONDITIONS OF ATTENTION AND ATTENTIVE RESPONSE

			Condition			
			Right	Left	Total	Proportions
Greater Clearness	Right	M_{AB}	153	40	193	.467
		t_{AB}	95.8	97.2		
		$d_{AB} = M_{AB} - t_{AB}$	57.2	−57.2		
		$d^2{}_{AB}$	3271.84	3271.84		
		$d^2{}_{AB}/t_{AB}$	34.15	33.64		
	Left	M_{AB}	52	168	220	.533
		t_{AB}	109.2	110.8		
		$d_{AB} = M_{AB} - t_{AB}$	−57.2	57.2		
		$d^2{}_{AB}$	3271.84	3271.84		
		$d^2{}_{AB}/t_{AB}$	29.97	29.51		
		Total	205	208	413	
		Proportions	.496	.504	...	1.000

the remaining 40 per cent are brown-eyed. What then is the probability that any two individuals, father and son, would both be blue-eyed if there were no correlation? The probability of a combined event or of a repeated event is the product of the probabilities of the two separate events; in this case, .6 × .6, or .36. Likewise, the probability that both father and son would have brown eyes is .4 × .4, or .16. The probability of a blue-eyed father and a brown-eyed son (or vice versa) is .6 × .4, or .24. The sum of the probabilities, .36 + .16 + .24 + .24, equals 1.00.

We are not primarily interested in the proportions of cases to be expected in the four cells, but we are interested in the deviations of the proportions actually found in the cells from the expected proportions. Let us take as an illustrative problem some data obtained from experimental psychology. The experimental problem was to find the effectiveness of certain supposed 'factors of attention' upon the observer, including such factors as size, novelty, isolation, and repetition. The material was exposed tachistoscopically with the stronger condition now on the right and now on the left. O was to report which part of the material was most compelling or 'attributively clear.' From 413 such observations the data were classified in four categories as in Table 71. The correlation between the externally controlled factors of attention and the resulting reaction of O will reveal to what extent the outside conditions were effective, the remainder of the determining factors presumably being due to internal conditions or to additional outside incidental factors.

Let each cell frequency be given the general symbol of M_{AB}. The expected or theoretical frequency of a cell is given the symbol of t_{AB}. It is the differences between the actual and the theoretical cell frequencies in which we are interested. If the expected frequencies coincide with the obtained frequencies, then the cases are distributed as if by pure chance and there is no correlation. The greater the deviations between the observed and theoretical frequencies, in other words, the greater the deviation from a chance classification, the stronger the correlation. The theoretical cell frequencies are to be found by the formula

$$t_{AB} = Npq \tag{143}$$

In Table 71 the values of p are given in the last column and those of q in the last row, and N is 413. The theoretical frequency of the upper left cell is $(413)(.467)(.496) = 95.8$. A short cut would consist in using the totals (either of the rows or of the columns) multiplied by the corresponding q or p. For example, the same t_{AB} might be found by the product $(193)(.496)$ or by $(205)(.467)$. It is probably more accurate to use the latter procedure, and multiplying both ways gives a check. Another short cut in the case of a fourfold table is to compute only one t_{AB}. The remaining ones can then be readily found by deducting this t_{AB} from the sums of the row and column in which it appears.

Having the values for t_{AB}, the next step is to find the *cell divergence*, or d_{AB}. In terms of a formula the cell divergence is

$$d_{AB} = M_{AB} - t_{AB} \tag{144}$$

Each cell divergence is then squared and divided by its corresponding t_{AB}. These ratios, of d_{AB}^2 to t_{AB}, are then summed, giving our old familiar chi square:

$$\chi^2 = \Sigma\left[\frac{d^2{}_{AB}}{t_{AB}}\right] = \Sigma\left[\frac{(M_{AB} - t_{AB})^2}{t_{AB}}\right] \tag{145}$$

In the illustrative problem,

$$\chi^2 = 127.27.$$

We could now proceed to use χ^2 in much the same way as heretofore to find the Pearson coefficient P. In this instance P would give us the probability that there would occur a classification as extreme as the one we have, if there really were no correlation. Reference to Table D will show that a χ^2 of 127.27 is highly significant. There is less than 1 chance in 100 that a departure from the theoretical frequencies could be as large as the ones that were found. In using Table D, when dealing with a fourfold classification, n should be taken as 1, since there is only one degree of freedom in that type of fourfold table, says Fisher (8, p. 89). This follows from the fact that, once the frequency of a single cell is fixed, the remaining cells are determined by the totals in the rows and columns. In general, if there are κ (kappa) rows and λ (lambda) columns in a classification table, then $n = (\kappa - 1)(\lambda - 1)$.

The Mean Square Contingency.—While the use of χ^2 tells us the probability that there is a lack of independence between two variables, it does not tell us just how strong the dependence is. From χ^2 can be derived a coefficient, however, which does indicate something about the strength of the correlation and which can eventually lead to a coefficient that is equivalent to the more familiar r. From χ^2 we can find very directly the **mean square contingency** by the formula

$$\phi^2 = \frac{\chi^2}{N} \tag{146}$$

In the last illustrative example

$$\phi^2 = \frac{127.27}{413}$$
$$= .308160.$$
$$\phi = .555.$$

The ϕ thus obtained is, in the case of a fourfold table, numerically equivalent to the ϕ obtained by formula (142). In fact one can find the value of ϕ, and hence of ϕ^2, from the fourfold table without calculating the expected frequencies at all, by the use of formula (142). If χ^2 is wanted directly from the fourfold table, this formula can be slightly altered to read

$$\chi^2 = \frac{N(ad - bc)^2}{(a + b)(c + d)(a + c)(b + d)} \tag{147}$$

Omit the term N from this formula and ϕ^2 is likewise obtained directly from the frequencies.

The Coefficient of Contingency.—In order to obtain a coefficient that is comparable with r, we must translate ϕ into a **coefficient of contingency** by the relation

$$C = \sqrt{\frac{\phi^2}{1 + \phi^2}} = \sqrt{\frac{\chi^2}{N + \chi^2}} \tag{148}$$

C is comparable with r and in fact becomes identical with it under the four following conditions: (1) The variables are of the continuous type; (2) N is large; (3) the number of classes is sufficient to overcome errors of grouping; (4) the distributions are normal. If the first two conditions are satisfied, two corrections can be made to overcome the lack of the second two. The first is a correction in the mean square contingency for the numbers of categories. If there be κ rows and λ columns, then the corrected ϕ^2 is

$$_c\phi^2 = \phi^2 - \frac{(k - 1)(\lambda - 1)}{N} \tag{149a}$$

or

$$_c\phi^2 = \frac{\chi^2 - (\kappa - 1)(\lambda - 1)}{N} \tag{149b}$$

The other correction is made in C, but never in ϕ, and in C only when the distributions are of continuous variables. It is known as the **correction for class index** (13, p. 266). It is necessary because in grouping the distribution of a continuous variable into broad categories the full weight of its variance is lost and the correlation between this variable and any other will be correspondingly reduced. In grouping we really correlate means of groups rather than individual pairs of measurements. The correlation between the class means and the original ungrouped measurements would be less than perfect, and the coarser the grouping the lower would be this correlation. The correlation between a variable X and its class means is designated by r_{xX} and that between a variable Y and its class means is known as y_{yY}. The correction for C is then given by the formula

$$_mC = \frac{C}{r_{xX}r_{yY}} \tag{150}$$

Now we apply these corrections to our attention problem and find a coefficient of contingency that will be equivalent to r. Condition 1 may be assumed, though not with absolute certainty. Although the stronger factor of attention was sometimes right and sometimes left, the degree of objective difference differed somewhat from exposure to exposure, depending upon the content and upon how successfully the difference was brought out by the experimenter in preparing the materials. The differential response of O was undoubtedly continuously variable. Although he was to report 'right' or 'left' according as the one or the other was more compelling, his differences were clearly not all the same and often he resorted to reports of 'equal.' The 'equal' reports have been neglected here, although they need not have been discarded, for the methods used here can take care of any combination of numbers of rows and columns. Condition 2 is satisfied, for N is relatively large, so we may now proceed. First we find the $_c\phi^2$ coefficient corrected for numbers of cells, from formula (149a),

$$_c\phi^2 = .308160 - \frac{1 \times 1}{413}$$
$$= .308160 - .002421$$
$$= .305739.$$
$$_c\phi = .553.$$

This correction is trivial when there are only two columns and rows and when N is very large. Next, we find the coefficient of contingency from $_c\phi^2$. From formula (148) we find that

$$C = \sqrt{\frac{.305739}{1.305739}}$$
$$= \sqrt{.234150}$$
$$= .484.$$

The correction for class index requires some further assumptions and calculations, namely, in connection with r_{zX} and r_{yY}. These correlations with the class means will differ according as the distributions are normal, rectangular, or of some other type. Kelley (13, p. 268) has prepared a series of values for these correlations for varying numbers of categories and for different types of distribution. His values are reproduced in Table 72.

TABLE 72.—VALUE OF r_{zX}, THE CORRELATION BETWEEN CLASS MEANS AND MEASUREMENTS, FOR DIFFERENT NUMBERS OF GROUPS AND FOR DIFFERENT TYPES OF DISTRIBUTION[1]

Number of classes	Equal ranges, normal distributions	Equal sub-frequencies, normal distribution	Equal ranges, rectangular distribution	Equal ranges, any distribution
2	.798	.798	.707	.589
3	.872	.891	.816	.842
4	.923	.928	.866	.915
5	.949	.947	.894	.946
6	.964	.959	.913	.963
8	.979	.972	.935	.979
10	.986	.979	.949	.987

[1] The term 'equal ranges' in the heading of the table means that the measurements in both variables taken singly have a range of 5.6σ, which is generally true when N is 100 or larger.

The writer has found that, in most problems similar to the foregoing, a normal distribution seems to be nearest the truth, judging by the values of r_{zX} and r_{yY} when actually worked out.[1] Under the assumption of normal distributions, the corrected C is then

$$_mC = \frac{.484}{(.798)(.798)}$$
$$= \frac{.484}{.6368}$$
$$= .760.$$

[1] The method of solving r_{yX} and r_{xY} may be found in Kelley's presentation (13, p. 168).

When a tetrachoric r is found for the same data, $r_t = .793$. This means that the corrected C is not far from a better recognized estimate of r and that the correction has not been too drastic.

The Reliability of the Coefficient of Contingency.—In order to find the standard error of either ϕ or C, a new statistical constant ψ^3 (psi cubed) must be computed. Using the same data and many of the same constants already found in Table 71, ψ^3 can be computed from the formula

$$\psi^3 = \frac{1}{N}\Sigma\left[\frac{d_{AB}^3}{t_{AB}^2}\right] \tag{151}$$

We already know the ratios of d_{AB}^2/t_{AB} from Table 71, and so it is convenient to restate the formula in the form

$$\psi^3 = \frac{1}{N}\Sigma\left[\frac{d_{AB}^2}{t_{AB}} \times \frac{d_{AB}}{t_{AB}}\right].$$

This involves the finding of the ratios d_{AB}/t_{AB}, which appear in Table 73.

TABLE 73.—COMPUTATION OF THE ψ^3 FUNCTIONS

	RR	RL	LR	LL
d_{AB}/t_{AB}	.597	— .588	— .524	.516
d_{AB}^2/t_{AB}	34.15	33.64	29.97	29.51
d_{AB}^3/t_{AB}^2	20.388	−19.790	−15.704	15.227

$$\psi^3 = \frac{.121}{413}$$
$$= .000293$$

The standard error of C is given by the relation

$$\sigma_c^2 = \frac{1}{N}\left[\frac{\dfrac{\psi^3}{\phi^2} + 1 - \phi^2}{(1 + \phi^2)^3}\right] \tag{152}$$

The term ϕ^2 in this formula is the uncorrected ϕ^2. With the data from the attention problem,

$$\sigma_c^2 = \frac{1}{413}\left[\frac{\dfrac{.000293}{.308160} + 1 - .308160}{(1 + .308160)^3}\right]$$

$$= \frac{1}{413} \left[\frac{.000951 + .691840}{(1.308160)^3} \right]$$

$$= \frac{1}{413} \left[\frac{.692791}{2.2386} \right]$$

$$= \frac{.309475}{413}$$

$$= .0007493.$$

$$\sigma_c = .0274$$

and

$$PE_c = (.6745)(.0274)$$
$$= .0185.$$

This, it must be remembered, is the index of reliability for the uncorrected C. The PE of the corrected C should be increased by correction in direct proportion as the corrected C, or

$$PE_{mc} = \frac{PE_c}{r_{zx}r_{yy}} \qquad (153)$$

$$= \frac{.0185}{(.798)(.798)}$$

$$= .029$$

With this we may consider our contingency problem complete. The correlation of .760 with a PE of .029 is certainly significant. And if we can make the assumption that all the elements that went into the experimental material for controlling attention are entirely included in the determining factors of O's attention, a very fair assumption in this case, then $(.760)^2$, or $.5776$, gives the proportion of the determining factors of O's attention represented in the objective material, or at least in that aspect of the material which enabled the experimenter to say that the stronger factor was sometimes left and sometimes right.

INTERPRETATIONS OF COEFFICIENTS OF CORRELATION

It has been said before that the coefficient of correlation is not to be regarded as a percentage. The question of the importance of a certain value of r often arises. This is not to be answered by the probable error of r, or by giving the result of any other test of significance. All that these tests of significance can do is tell us the likelihood that there is a real relationship and within what approximate limits we may expect the degree of true relationship to fall. We might have two coefficients, one of .60 and one of .85, both having approximately the same probable error, both therefore about equally accurate as measures of relationship. But we still would not know how much closer the relationship is in the latter than in the former. The importance of a coefficient will vary according to the purpose for which it is going to be used. If it is to be used to indicate the accuracy of prediction, that is one thing. If it is to be used to indicate the percentage of factors that are common to two variables, that is another thing. A number of ways of interpreting the coefficient of correlation will be discussed next.

Interpretation of r in Terms of the Coefficient of Alienation.— It will be recalled that the standard error of the estimate is obtained by the formula $\sigma_{yx} = \sigma_y \sqrt{1 - r_{yx}^2}$. The key to the whole formula is the expression $\sqrt{1 - r_{yx}^2}$. If r is equal to 1.00, then this expression is zero and σ_{yx} is zero. The error of prediction is nil. If on the other hand r is zero, then the expression is equal to 1.00 and $\sigma_{yx} = \sigma_y$. In this case, the errors of prediction of Y are as great as the errors could be without any knowledge of X to help in predicting Y. The expression $\sqrt{1 - r^2}$ is known as the **coefficient of alienation,** and it measures the absence of relationship just as r measures its presence. It is given the single notation of k. In Table 74 are to be found values of k corresponding to values of r.[1] When r is .10, k is .995; when r is 30, k is still very large, namely .954. Thus while r is small and even moderate in size, the lack of relationship, as indicated by k, reduces very slowly as r increases. It requires an r of .886 to give a k of .500. From this point of view an r of .866 is one-half of a perfect correlation. It requires an r of this size to reduce the errors of prediction by one-half as shown by the formula for the standard error of the estimate. When k is known, the formula for the standard error of the estimate becomes $\sigma_{yx} = (\sigma_y)k$. This line of interpretation should make the student cautious in placing great faith in predictions based upon an r even moderate in size.

The Index of Forecasting Efficiency.— A somewhat clearer criterion of r is known as the **index of forecasting efficiency.** This tells us directly the percentage of reduction in the errors of prediction for a given r. The complete formula is

$$E = 100\left[1 - \sqrt{\frac{N-1}{N-2}(1 - r^2)}\right] \qquad (154)$$

---

[1] A much more complete table of r and k is Table L of the Appendix.

When N is very large, above 100, for example, the ratio of $(N - 1)$ to $(N - 2)$ becomes approximately equal to 1 and the formula reduces to

$$E = 100 \left(1 - \sqrt{1 - r^2}\right).$$

TABLE 74.—INDICATORS OF THE IMPORTANCE OF COEFFICIENTS OF CORRELATION

r_{xy}	Coefficient of alienation, k_{xy}	Percentage reduction in errors of prediction of Y from X, $100(1 - k_{xy})$	Percentage of causal factors measured, $100r_{xy}^2$
.00	1.000	0.0	0.00
.05	.999	.1	0.00
.10	.995	.5	1.00
.15	.989	1.1	2.25
.20	.980	2.0	4.00
.25	.968	3.2	6.25
.30	.954	4.6	9.00
.35	.937	6.3	12.25
.40	.917	8.3	16.00
.45	.893	10.7	20.25
.50	.866	13.4	25.00
.55	.835	16.5	30.25
.60	.800	20.0	36.00
.65	.760	24.0	42.25
.70	.714	28.6	49.00
.75	.661	33.9	56.25
.80	.600	40.0	64.00
.85	.527	47.3	72.25
.90	.436	56.4	81.00
.95	.312	68.8	90.25
.98	.199	80.1	96.00
.99	.141	85.9	98.00
.995	.100	90.0	99.00
.999	.045	95.5	99.80

Using the symbol k for its appropriate substitute,

$$E = 100(1 - k).$$

The values of E for various values of r are given in the third column of Table 74.   Notice that it requires an r greater than .40 to reduce the percentage of errors more than 10 per cent.   It requires an r as large as .65 to reduce the errors by 24 per cent.   It is a striking fact that the forecasting efficiency increases very slowly for low and moderate values of r and very rapidly for values of r above .90. Hull (12, p. 275) remarks that most psychological tests correlate with their criterion (the thing we wish to measure) less than .70, at which value of r the forecasting efficiency is 28.6 per cent.   Tests with a **coefficient of validity**[1] less than .50 are practically useless, except in distinguishing between extreme cases, since at that value of r the forecasting efficiency is only 13.4 per cent.   If a regression equation is to be used for predictive purposes, it would seem of limited value unless r is .50 or above.

The Percentage of Overlapping Elements or Factors.—More than once we have used r^2, or d_{yx}, to denote the percentage of determination of Y by X, assuming that all the elements determining X were included within the greater number of elements determining Y. Let us begin with a more general case.   Assume that X is determined by two sets of elemental, simple factors, the two sets being called A and C, and that Y is likewise determined by sets B and C.   The factors are assumed to be independent and like 'coins' in that by chance they may add or deduct from the 'score' in X or Y.   It can be demonstrated (13, p. 190) that under these conditions the correlation between X and Y is equal to

$$r = \frac{n_c}{\sqrt{n_a + n_c}\sqrt{n_b + n_c}}$$

in which n_a, n_b, and n_c are the number of factors in sets A, B, and C, respectively.   In the accompanying diagram (Fig. 38A) X is determined by nine factors, four A's and five C's, and Y is determined by eleven factors, six B's and five C's.   The correlation between X and Y is therefore

$$r = \frac{5}{\sqrt{(9)(11)}} = \frac{5}{9.95} = .502.$$

It will be observed that this formula for r is the ratio of the number of common factors in X and Y to the geometric mean of the total

---

[1] By the *coefficient of validity* is meant the correlation between a test and some better established measure of the same trait which the test was designed to measure.

numbers of factors in X and Y. If the total number of factors in X exactly equals the total number in Y, in other words, if $n_a = n_b$, then the correlation is

$$r = \frac{n_c}{n_a + n_c}.$$

For the example illustrated in Fig. 38B, where $n_a = n_b = 4$ and $n_c = 5$,

$$r = \frac{5}{4 + 5} = \frac{5}{9} = .556.$$

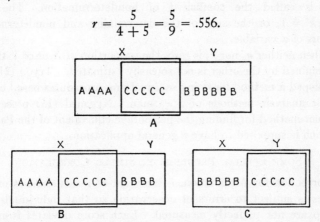

FIG. 38.—Three cases of overlapping variables, showing how the correlation between variables depends upon the proportion of common elements.

Finally, when $n_a = 0$ and all the determining factors of Y are included in n_c,

$$r = \frac{n_c}{\sqrt{n_c(n_b + n_c)}}.$$

In Fig. 38C, n_b is 5 and n_c is also 5, so

$$r = \frac{5}{\sqrt{5(5 + 5)}} = \frac{5}{7.071} = .7071.$$

The third and last case is the one in which we are justified in computing a coefficient of determination and in which r^2 gives the percentage of determination of X by Y. Squaring the above formula,

$$r^2 = \frac{n_c^2}{n_c(n_b + n_c)} = \frac{n_c}{n_b + n_c}$$

which gives the ratio of the common factors to the total number of factors. In the above numerical example,

$$r^2 = \tfrac{5}{10} = (.7071)^2 = .50.$$

Half the determining factors of X are the total determining factors in Y, as Fig. 38C shows. From this point of view, an r of .7071 may be called one-half of a perfect correlation. A list of values of r^2 is given in Table 74 to compare with the other tests of significance of r. If r^2 measures the percentage of determination, k^2, which equals $1 - r^2$, measures the amount of nondetermination and is called the **coefficient of nondetermination.** The sum $r^2 + k^2 = 1$, or the sum of the determining and nondetermining factors of a variable.

When neither n_a nor n_b is zero, the proportion of X or of Y that is determined by the other is not so easily estimated. Tryon (21) has developed a method for doing so, involving procedures based on the factor analysis methods of Spearman. Nygaard (15) presents a simpler method for finding the percentage equivalent of the Pearson r which is supposed to have a general application.

Some Special Problems in Simple Correlation

Correction for Attenuation.—Every set of measurements or test scores is subject to errors of observation so that individuals of a group are not perfectly measured. Each score deviates from the true score for that individual. The scores of any test are fallible. Yet it is these fallible scores that we correlate to find the relationship between two tests or variables. The net effect of errors of measurement is to lower the degree of correlation. Since the errors help to make up the raw scores and yet are uncorrelated, they make up a part of the factors which the two tests do not have in common, and thus they reduce or *attenuate* the apparent degree of relation. If we wish to know the true correlation between two variables, we must make some correction for this attenuation in the raw coefficient.

The amount of attenuation present in any set of test scores is indicated by the coefficient of reliability of that test. The latter is obtained by means of a self-correlation. The test is repeated, an alternative form is given to the same individuals, or the test items of a single test are divided into two equivalent pools and two scores are obtained from the half-tests. In the following, let $r_{\infty\omega}$ stand for the true correlation between X and Y when ∞ is a true score (see p. 411) in Y and ω is a true score in X. Since tests X and Y must be administered twice each in order to obtain their coefficients of reliability, let tests 1 and I be the two applications of X, and 2 and II be the two applications of Y. Then r_{1I} is the reliability coefficient of X, r_{2II} is the reliability coefficient of Y, and r_{12} is the intercorrelation of the first applications of X and Y. The simplest formula for the correction for attenuation is

$$r_{\infty\omega} = \frac{r_{12}}{\sqrt{r_{1I}r_{2II}}} \qquad (155)$$

or, in other words, it is the raw coefficient divided by the geometric mean of the two coefficients of reliability. Let $r_{12} = .55$, $r_{1I} = .94$, and $r_{2II} = .85$. The true correlation is

$$r_{\infty\omega} = \frac{.55}{\sqrt{(.94)(.85)}} = \frac{.55}{.894} = .615.$$

But since each test was administered twice, there are other possibilities of obtaining intercorrelations, namely, r_{1II}, r_{2I}, and $r_{1\,II}$. We might similarly find the geometric mean of these four; the formula then becomes

$$r_{\infty\omega} = \frac{\sqrt[4]{r_{12}r_{1II}r_{2I}r_{1\,II}}}{\sqrt{r_{1I}r_{2II}}} \qquad (156)$$

If in addition to the above intercorrelation, $r_{1II} = .62$, $r_{2I} = .47$, and $r_{1\,II} = .54$, then

$$r_{\infty\omega} = \frac{\sqrt{(.55)(.62)(.47)(.54)}}{\sqrt{(.94)(.85)}} = \frac{.5424}{.894} = .607.$$

Cureton and Dunlap (3) have shown, however, that this formula gives an underestimation of the true correlation. The same formula, altered so as to use the arithmetic mean of the four intercorrelations in the numerator, although also underestimating the true r, is nearer the truth. Revising the formula accordingly,

$$r_{\infty\omega} = \frac{r_{12} + r_{1II} + r_{2I} + r_{1\,II}}{4\sqrt{r_{1I}r_{2II}}} \qquad (157)$$

Using the same data as before,

$$r_{\infty\omega} = \frac{.55 + .62 + .47 + .54}{\sqrt{(.94)(.85)}} = \frac{.545}{.894} = .610.$$

Hull (12, p. 243) points out that "correlations should always be computed on the basis of the most accurate measures available."

It is a well-established principle in mental testing that longer tests are more reliable than shorter ones; thus intercorrelations of long tests, as well as their reliability coefficients, are more accurately determined than those for shorter tests. He therefore recommends that for the intercorrelation of X and Y we use the sums of the scores of the two applications, $(1 + \text{I})$ for X and $(2 + \text{II})$ for Y. While we need to keep the applications 1, I and 2, II separate for the sake of finding the self-correlations, by means of a formula we can predict the reliability coefficient of the double test from that of its two components.[1] The improved correction formula then becomes

$$r_{\infty\omega} = \frac{r_{(1+\text{I})(2+\text{II})}}{\sqrt{\dfrac{2r_{1\text{I}}}{1 + r_{1\text{I}}}} \sqrt{\dfrac{2r_{2\text{II}}}{1 + r_{2\text{II}}}}} \tag{158}$$

For example, in the same problem as above, $r_{(1+\text{I})(2+\text{II})} = .576$ and the coefficients of reliability of the short tests are as before. The solution is

$$r_{\infty\omega} = \frac{.576}{\sqrt{\dfrac{1.88}{1.94}} \sqrt{\dfrac{1.70}{1.85}}} = \frac{.576}{.944} = .610.$$

While the last formula is undoubtedly the best one to use, the others may be used with justification when the circumstances favor them. The only difference between this formula and the previous ones is that it deals with longer and therefore more reliable tests.

There are times in practical tests when we are justified in correcting for attenuation only in one of the variables. Suppose that we are attempting to establish the validity of a test by correlating it with some chosen criterion. For example, we have a test that is supposed to measure and to predict artistic talent of a certain type and we have samples of the artistic work of the tested individuals—samples that have been evaluated for excellence. Neither the test nor the criterion scores are perfectly reliable. By means of the above correction formulas we can estimate the true correlation between the two. But the test as a practical tool of prediction is still as unreliable as ever and predictions based upon it would be in error to the extent of its unreliability. As for the unreliable criterion scores, however, unless we correct for their fallibility we shall have an inadequate notion of the real worth of the test as a predicting instrument.

[1] This is known as the Spearman-Brown prophecy formula (see page 418).

We should correct for the attenuation in the criterion scores alone. Dunlap and Cureton (4) provide the formula for doing this. Using the same type of notation as before, the formula is

$$r_{\infty 2} = \frac{r_{2(1+\mathrm{I})}}{\sqrt{\dfrac{2r_{\mathrm{II}}}{1 + r_{\mathrm{II}}}}} \tag{159}$$

in which tests 1 and I are two independent sets of criterion scores and 2 is one set of test scores. Such a corrected r gives the correlation to be expected with a perfect criterion. In the above illustrative example we may assume that tests 1 and I are the criterion scores. Then

$$r_{\infty 2} = \frac{.562}{\sqrt{\dfrac{1.88}{1.94}}} = \frac{.562}{.985} = .571.$$

It should be added that in all the above formulas it is assumed that the standard deviations of the repeated sets of test scores are equal, $\sigma_1 = \sigma_{\mathrm{I}}$ and $\sigma_2 = \sigma_{\mathrm{II}}$. If these conditions are not satisfied, then the corrected coefficients are correspondingly in error.[1]

Average Intercorrelation.—On some occasions an investigator wishes to know the average correlation between several pairs of variables without caring especially to know what the individual r values are. This happens most often in connection with the use of rating-scale or ranking methods. Such a procedure means a great saving in effort when reliability coefficients are desired for a test that has been repeated several times or for a test of which several forms have been given. In either case there are several ways of pairing the sets of scores in obtaining a self-correlation. This is more easily done with ranked data than with raw scores. If a stands for the number of different rank orders of N measurements, the average rank-order coefficient is given by a formula suggested by Kelley (13, p. 218)

$$\bar{r}_{pq} = 1 - \frac{a(4N + 2)}{(a - 1)(N - 1)} + \frac{12\Sigma S^2}{a(a - 1)N(N^2 - 1)} \tag{160}$$

in which S stands for the sum of the ranks assigned to each sample.

[1] The standard error of a corrected $r_{\infty 2}$ may be computed according to formulas given by Kelley (13, p. 209).

As an illustration, let us take the judged ranks of 12 samples of handwriting from Table 42, page 247. The rankings of the first five judges will suffice. The ranks of each sample are summed and then squared in the last two columns of the table.

TABLE 75.—RANKS ASSIGNED BY FIVE JUDGES TO 12 SAMPLES OF HANDWRITING ARRANGED FOR COMPUTING AN AVERAGE INTERCORRELATION

Sample	1	2	3	4	5	S	S^2
A	12	11	10	9	12	54	2016
B	8	12	11	12	10	53	2809
C	11	10	12	11	11	55	3025
D	10	9	9	10	9	47	2209
E	9	7	7	8	4	35	1225
F	6	8	8	7	7	36	1296
G	5	6	6	4	8	29	841
H	4	4	5	3	1	17	289
I	7	1	3	5	6	22	484
J	1	3	4	6	2	16	256
K	2	5	1	2	5	15	225
L	3	2	2	1	3	11	121

$$a = 5 \qquad N = 12 \qquad\qquad \Sigma S^2 = 15696$$

$$\bar{r}_{pq} = 1 - \frac{(5)(50)}{(4)(11)} + \frac{(12)(15696)}{(5)(4)(12)(143)}$$

$$= 1 - \frac{250}{44} + \frac{3924}{715}$$

$$= .806$$

When the data have not been transformed into ranks, an average intercorrelation may still be computed, although the task is not quite so simple. When the means and the standard deviations of all the distributions are equal or approximately equal, then the following formula, also provided by Kelley (13, p. 217), may be employed:

$$\bar{r}_{pq} = \frac{\dfrac{\sigma_a^2}{\sigma^2} - a}{a^2 - a} \tag{161}$$

where a = the number of series combined.

σ_a = the standard deviation of the combined test scores, in which the a scores have been totaled for each individual.

σ = the standard deviation of any one distribution or of the pool of the total number (Na) of scores.

When the means and sigmas are not equal, a method devised by Edgerton and Toops (6) may be employed.

The Correlation of Interchangeable Variables.[1]—There are problems in which the two sets of measurements are interchangeable, as, for example, in the correlation of measurements of twins or siblings. Of each pair we cannot say which shall be the Y measurement and which shall be the X measurement. We could arbitrarily select one of each pair as Y and the other as X. This would give one coefficient of correlation. But had we reversed some of the pairs, the correlation would perchance be different. There are many possible arrangements of the pairs, each giving its own coefficient of correlation. The mean of all these coefficients is the best correlation. It is not necessary to rearrange the data in all possible combinations and to compute all possible coefficients of correlation. The thing to do, with ungrouped data, is to pool all the measurements into two duplicate distributions having $2N$ individuals, treating each individual in turn as an X and a Y, so that $\Sigma X = \Sigma Y$ and $\Sigma X^2 = \Sigma Y^2$. The formula for r, as presented by Furfey (9) is

$$r_i = \frac{4N\Sigma XY - (\Sigma X + \Sigma Y)^2}{2N(\Sigma X^2 + \Sigma Y^2) - (\Sigma X + \Sigma Y)^2} \qquad (162)$$

If deviations from the mean, x and y, are used in place of X and Y, a formula suggested by Goodenough (11) applies,

$$r_i = \frac{\dfrac{\Sigma xy}{N}}{\sigma^2} \qquad (163)$$

where σ = the standard error of the combined data, including the $2N$ measurements.

Σxy = the sum of the products of only the N pairs.

If grouped data are used, and a guessed average, then $c'_x = c'_y$ and $c'_x c'_y = c'^2$. The formula then becomes

$$r = \frac{\dfrac{\Sigma x'y'}{N} - c'^2}{\sigma'^2} \qquad (164)$$

[1] This corresponds to the 'intraclass' correlation of Fisher (8, p. 190).

Perhaps the simplest device for finding the correlation between interchangeable variables is to be obtained from the standard error of the differences between the pairs.   Recall that the formula for the σ of a difference is given by the relationship

$$\sigma_d = \sqrt{\sigma_1^2 + \sigma_2^2 - 2r\sigma_1\sigma_2}.$$

Squaring both sides,

$$\sigma_d^2 = \sigma_1^2 + \sigma_2^2 - 2r\sigma_1\sigma_2.$$

Solving for r,

$$2r\sigma_1\sigma_2 = \sigma_1^2 + \sigma_2^2 - \sigma_d^2.$$

$$r = \frac{\sigma_1^2 + \sigma_2^2 - \sigma_d^2}{2\sigma_1\sigma_2} \tag{165}$$

Formula (165), it may be said, can be used in place of the usual product-moment formula and at a saving of time when the sigmas of the two distributions and the sigma of the differences are already known.[1]   As applied to interchangeable variables, since we have made double use of every measurement by placing it in both the X and the Y distributions, $\sigma_1 = \sigma_2$, so that

$$r_i = \frac{2\sigma^2 - \sigma_d^2}{2\sigma^2} = \frac{\sigma^2 - \dfrac{\sigma_d^2}{2}}{\sigma^2} = 1 - \frac{\sigma_d^2}{2\sigma^2} \tag{166}$$

in which σ is the standard error of the pool of $2N$ measurements.

Correlation of Initial Values with Gains.—In the rather special problem in which it is desired to know the correlation between the initial status in a task and the amount of gain due to practice, a false notion of the true correlation will arise from the raw correlation between initial scores and the gains.   This can be shown to be due to the unreliability of the measures of initial status and of the gains. The raw correlation will ordinarily be negative.   This is reasonable, because the individual who by errors of measurement obtains a score too high in the initial test will show a corresponding under-estimation when his gain is computed, and one who is underestimated at the beginning will be likely to show an unwarranted amount of gain.   A formula for giving the true correlation between initial scores and gains is presented by Thomson (17, 18),

[1] The reader is referred to an article by Symonds (16), in which 52 varieties of formulas for computing the Pearson r are given.

$$r_{ag} = \frac{\sigma_z r_{xz} - \sigma_x r_{xx}}{\sqrt{r_{xx}(r_{xx}\sigma_x^2 + r_{zz}\sigma_z^2 - 2\sigma_x\sigma_z r_{xz})}} \tag{167}$$

where a = a true initial value.

g = a true gain.

r_{ag} = their true correlation.

x = the measured initial value.

r_{xx} = its reliability coefficient.

z = the measured final value.

r_{zz} = its reliability coefficient.

r_{xz} = the correlation between x and z.

σ_x and σ_z = the sigmas of initial and final values.

The Correlation of Averages.—It has been shown (22) that the correlation between means $(r_{\overline{xy}})$ is equal to the correlation between single measurements (r_{xy}). This is strictly true only when the samples are taken at random. If the data are biased, for example, with members of one group resembling one another more closely than they resemble the members of other groups, as in classes that have been sectioned for differences in ability, then the correlation of means will be slightly altered, sometimes higher and sometimes lower than the true correlation.

Correlation in Heterogeneous Samples.—When the population from which the data are obtained is very heterogeneous as to age, sex, race, training, and similar factors, the resulting correlation may be correspondingly in error. Any third factor, such as age, is likely to increase the apparent correlation between two tests if both tests are positively (or negatively) correlated with that third factor. Because in most psychological tests an older child makes a higher score than a younger child, any two tests will seem to have some correlation even when they really have nothing in common. If the third factor correlates positively with one test and negatively with the other, the effect would be to reduce any real amount of correlation; thus two variables that really have something in common might appear to have very little.

There are three ways of meeting this situation. One may, if possible, select homogeneous populations—groups of one sex, groups of constant ages, or groups homogeneous as to training, etc. A second solution is the use of partial correlation methods. This solution can be applied when the third factor also is measurable and when its correlations with the two experimental variables can be obtained. These methods are to be described in the following chapter. When neither of these two solutions is convenient, a device suggested by May (14) can be applied. This enables us to find the correlation between large groups that are heterogeneous in their make-up and still to correct for any disturbing effect that the heterogeneity has upon the correlation. The essential feature of the method is to divide the total number of individuals into as many homogeneous subgroups as is necessary, and then to apply the formula

$$r_{\xi_1 \xi_2} = \frac{r_{12}\sigma_1\sigma_2 - r_{m_1 m_2}\sigma_{m_1}\sigma_{m_2}}{\sqrt{\sigma_1^2 - \sigma_{m_1}^2}\sqrt{\sigma_2^2 - \sigma_{m_2}^2}} \tag{168}$$

where r_{12} = the correlation of all cases taken together in one scatter diagram.

$r_{m_1 m_2}$ = the correlation between the means of the subgroups when each is weighted by its own N.

σ_1 and σ_2 = the sigmas of the entire population.

σ_{m_1} and σ_{m_2} = the sigmas of the subgroup means.

Spurious Correlations.—When coefficients of correlation are either raised or lowered by the intrusion of additional factors, as in the above examples, we speak of **spurious correlation.** A coefficient that is spuriously high is more serious than one that is spuriously too low, especially if we are placing our faith in the validity of predictions whose reliability is indicated by the size of r. In either case, however, the extent of the true relationship is falsified unless the proper steps are taken to correct the coefficient.

Spurious correlations are caused by a number of circumstances. Two sets of measurements having in common the same multipliers or divisors, which vary from pair to pair, will have a spuriously high correlation. For example, if each child's mental age in two tests is divided by his chronological age to find his IQ, and the IQ's of the two tests are then correlated, r is spuriously high. This is known as a *spurious index correlation.* The IQ, or a percentage, or any other type of index, should never be correlated with another variable until one is certain that the correlation is uninfluenced by the mere manipulation of numbers. The same test scored in two different ways is likely to exhibit a spurious correlation between those scores.

Another instance of spuriously high correlation is found when the parts of a test are correlated with the whole test, including the part, or when the ratings of one judge are correlated with the pool of ratings of which his judgments are a part. A part test containing 20 items in a total test of 100 items would theoretically have one-fifth of the determining factors in producing the total score. Since all the determining factors of the part are included within the determining factors of the whole, $r^2 = \frac{1}{5} = .20$ and $r = .447$. This much correlation might appear even though the part is actually unrelated to the remainder of the whole.[1] If all the parts had about equal importance in producing the total score, then one could still compare the correlations of parts with the whole in order to obtain a relative rating of the validity of the parts. The degree of spurious correlation would then be equalized for all the parts. Under these circumstances the correlation of part with whole can be used to find the relative validity of the parts.

Problems

1. Using the data given in Prob. 4 on page 69, or the data for Prob. 1 on page 325, construct a scatter diagram and compute a Pearson r; find the standard error of estimate and the two regression equations. Make the appropriate tests of reliability.

2. Find the rank difference coefficient of correlation, its equivalent Pearson r, and its probable error for the following data.[2] The ages of the individuals are to be correlated with an *Erlebnistypus* score on the Rorschach test. The score in each case is the ratio of the number of 'movement' responses to the number of 'color' responses. The ages are given to the nearest half year.

M/C	Age	M/C	Age	M/C	Age	M/C	Age
0.0	19.5	1.5	22.5	8.0	25.0	1.3	21.0
2.9	22.0	0.0	17.5	2.5	20.5	2.7	20.0
6.0	26.0	1.7	20.5	1.4	26.0	0.3	20.0
0.8	24.5	0.3	20.0	1.4	17.5	0.8	18.5
0.5	21.5	1.2	24.5	0.3	20.0	0.7	20.5

3. Using the data given for Prob. 1 on page 325, find a correlation ratio η_{yx}, using a coarse grouping in a few classes. Apply a test for linearity.

4. Find a biserial r for the following data, which give the distribution of scores in Army Alpha tests for those passing and those failing to pass a given test item. How significant is this biserial r?

[1] This statement is true if the whole and the part are perfectly reliable and if the dispersion of scores in the part is comparable with the dispersions in the other parts.

[2] Adapted from G. R. Thornton, *The Erlebnistypus Factors in the Rorschach Test*, 1935 (master's thesis on file in the University of Nebraska library).

Score	90	100	110	120	130	140	150	160	170	180	190
Passed			2	15	16	21	40	10	16	7	2
Failed	1	3	9	28	32	39	15	11			

5. From the following fourfold table, find:

  a. A coefficient of correlation assuming a point distribution.

  b. A coefficient of mean square contingency.

The data are the numbers of individuals, male and female, who report a moderate or very strong taste sensation from *PTC* (phenyl-thio-carbamide) and those of either sex who report either a slight sensation or none at all. The former groups are designated by the sign (+) and the latter by (?).

	?	+
Males	102	146
Females	44	98

6. From the following ninefold table find the correlation between color of eyes and color of hair in the following ways:

  a. A coefficient of mean square contingency.

  b. A coefficient of contingency, corrected for number of categories.

  c. A coefficient of contingency, corrected for class indexes (assuming a normal distribution for hair color and a rectangular distribution for eye color) and its standard error.

Eye color	Hair color		
	Blonde	Brown	Black or red
Blue	65	63	17
Gray, green, or hazel	38	67	14
Brown	21	74	31

7. Two tests have a correlation of .51 with one another. Their self-correlations are .82 and .74, respectively. What is their probable true correlation?

8. Two forms of two different tests have the four following intercorrelations: .38, .44, .50, and .55. Their respective self-correlations are .65 and .92. Find the most probable intrinsic correlation between the two tests, using two methods.

9. In the preceding problem, the intercorrelation of the sums of the scores in the one test with the sums of the scores in the other is .52. Find the most probable true correlation between the two tests.

10. Find the average correlation between the 20 sets of ranks given in the problem on page 261.

11. Find the correlation existing between siblings in a test of mechanical ability, the test scores for pairs of siblings being listed in the following table:[1]

1	2	1	2	1	2	1	2	1	2
167	140	160	150	136	139	161	155	129	137
129	134	154	142	153	161	157	175	124	130
117	125	169	166	148	171	200	170	155	159
136	153	134	150	173	114	155	162	78	71
146	136	122	168	165	168	136	143	163	161
150	140	158	180	145	160	196	190	144	132
155	143	178	197	113	105	168	164	151	163
159	129	148	144	126	148	104	126	142	185
127	159	161	191	141	139	152	128	163	170
150	163	213	197	139	125	138	130	142	154
139	147	120	158	157	130	161	143	111	104
126	126	192	131	201	180	130	124	142	206
153	154	126	114	122	128	146	148	126	133
138	137	129	138	168	144	119	144	184	148
158	127	136	161	131	134	134	131	197	135
154	167	143	160	130	136	209	169	185	206

12. Find the probable true correlation between the initial values and gains in the following cases. The notations are explained in connection with formula (167) on page 373.

Case	σ_x	σ_z	r_{xx}	r_{zz}	r_{xz}
a	8.5	7.0	.60	.60	− .40
b	8.5	7.0	.95	.95	− .40
c	8.5	7.0	.95	.95	− .80
d	7.0	8.5	.95	.95	− .80
e	7.0	8.5	.60	.60	− .80

REFERENCES

1. BROWN, WM., and G. H. THOMSON, "The Essentials of Mental Measurement," Cambridge University Press, London, 1925.
2. CURETON, E. E., Note on the computation of the rank difference correlation coefficient, *J. Educ. Psychol.*, 1927, **18**, 627–630.

[1] Adapted from E. K. Frye, *The Mechanical Abilities of Siblings*, 1934 (doctoral thesis on file in the University of Nebraska library).

3. CURETON, E. E., and J. W. DUNLAP, Spearman's correction for attenuation and its probable error, *Amer. J. Psychol.*, 1930, **42**, 235–245.

4. DUNLAP, J. W., and E. E. CURETON, The correlation corrected for attenuation in one variable and its standard error, *Amer. J. Psychol.*, 1930, **42**, 405–407.

5. DUNLAP, J. W., and A. K. KURTZ, "Handbook of Statistical Nomographs, Tables, and Formulas," World Book Company, Yonkers, 1932.

6. EDGERTON, H. A., and H. A. TOOPS, A formula for finding the average inter-correlation coefficient, *J. Educ. Psychol.*, 1928, **19**, 131–138.

7. EZEKIEL, M., "Methods of Correlation Analysis," John Wiley & Sons, Inc., New York, 1930.

8. FISHER, R. A., "Statistical Methods for Research Workers," 4th ed., Oliver & Boyd, Edinburgh, 1932.

9. FURFEY, P. H., A formula for correlating interchangeable variables, *J. Educ. Psychol.*, 1927, **18**, 122–124.

10. GARRETT, H. E., "Statistics in Psychology and Education," Longmans, Green & Company, New York, 1926.

11. GOODENOUGH, F. L., A short method for computing the correlation between interchangeable variables, *J. Educ. Psychol.*, 1929, **20**, 386.

12. HULL, C. L., "Aptitude Testing," World Book Company, Yonkers, 1928.

13. KELLEY, T. L., "Statistical Method," The Macmillan Company, New York, 1924.

14. MAY, M. A., A method of correcting coefficients of correlation for hetero-geneity in the data, *J. Educ. Psychol.*, 1929, **20**, 417–423.

15. NYGAARD, P. H., A percentage equivalent for the coefficient of correlation, *J. Educ. Psychol.*, 1926, **17**, 86–92.

16. SYMONDS, P. M., Variations of the product-moment (Pearson) coefficient of correlation, *J. Educ. Psychol.*, 1926, **17**, 458–469.

17. THOMSON, G. H., A formula to correct for the effect of errors of measurement on the correlation of initial values with gains, *J. Exper. Psychol.*, 1924, **7**, 321–324.

18. ———, An alternative formula for the true correlation of initial values with gains, *J. Exper. Psychol.*, 1925, **8**, 323–324.

19. THURSTONE, L. L., *et al.*, "Computing Diagrams for the Tetrachoric Corre-lation Coefficients," University of Chicago Bookstore, Chicago, 1933.

20. TOOPS, H. A., Plotting equations of three variables in mental measurements, *Psychol. Rev.*, 1919, **26**, 317–326.

21. TRYON, R. C., The interpretation of the correlation coefficient, *Psychol. Rev.*, 1929, **36**, 419–445.

22. WALKER, H. M., A note on the correlation of averages, *J. Educ. Psychol.*, 1928, **19**, 636–642.

23. WALLACE, H. A., and G. W. SNEDECOR, "Correlation and Machine Calcu-lation," Ames: Iowa State College Bulletin, 1931.

24. YULE, G. U., "Introduction to the Theory of Statistics," Charles Griffin & Company, Ltd., London, 1919.

CHAPTER XII

MULTIPLE AND PARTIAL CORRELATION

INTRODUCTION

In most statistical work, in psychology or elsewhere, we are constantly faced with the task of unraveling whole networks of relationships. Simple relationships between two isolated variables are the exception rather than the rule. Every effect is traceable to a number of causes, antecedents, or concomitants. Our task is that of determining to what extent the effect or dependent variable is determined by each one of the causal factors and to what extent the pool of causal factors acting jointly can account for the total result. When we find the *net* correlation between the dependent variable and one selected independent variable, with the effects of other independent variables eliminated from both of them, we call the result a **partial correlation**. When we find the correlation between the dependent variable and a pool of independent variables, we call the result a **multiple correlation**.

The Meaning of Partial Correlation.—It is customary, in dealing with more than two variables, to call the dependent variable X_1 and the independent variables $X_2, X_3, X_4, \ldots, X_n$. A coefficient of partial correlation written as $r_{12.3}$ refers to the net correlation between X_1 and X_2 with the influences of X_3 held constant. That is to say, we have a correlation between variables 1 and 2 in which all the influences of variable 3 have been ruled out. If X_1 were the measure of a student's scholastic record, X_2 his intelligence-test score, and X_3 the average number of hours he spends in preparation of school subjects, then the partial correlation $r_{12.3}$ would mean the correlation between school grades and intelligence-test scores which would have been found if all students in the group had studied the same number of hours.[1] In a similar manner, $r_{12.34}$ would mean the

---

[1] This does not mean that, to obtain the net amount of correlation between intelligence-test score and scholastic record only *one* time interval of study is supposed. If students were grouped into homogeneous categories as to hours of study, the average amount of correlation between intelligence and scholarship

379

net correlation between variables 1 and 2, with the effects of two other variables, 3 and 4, both nullified. The coefficient $r_{14 \cdot 235}$ means the net correlation between 1 and 4, with variables 2, 3, and 5 held constant.

The Multiple Regression Equation and the Multiple R.—The multiple correlation is expressed by capital R. $R_{1 \cdot 23}$ is the correlation between X_1 and the joint effect of X_2 and X_3. The general notation is $R_{1 \cdot 234 \ldots n}$, in which all the variables given following the period belong in the pool of independent variables. A multiple correlation is often interpreted as the correlation between the observed X_1 values and the X_1' values that are predicted from all the independent variables combined. This assumes that the independent variables are properly weighted, in a **multiple regression equation,** each with the appropriate regression coefficient. Such an equation would read

$$X_1 = a_{1 \cdot 234} + b_{12 \cdot 34} X_2 + b_{13 \cdot 24} X_3 + b_{14 \cdot 23} X_4$$

in the case of a four-variable problem. The subscript for the constant a is like that for the multiple R. The subscripts for the b coefficients are like those for partial correlation and they have similar meanings. The coefficient $b_{12 \cdot 34}$, for example, means the net weight to be assigned to variable X_2 in predicting X_1 when the simultaneous effects of X_3 and X_4 are held constant. The b coefficients are called the **partial regression coefficients.**

Multiple Correlation with Three Variables

In the next few pages let us take as an example a problem in affective psychology. The task is to find out what factors help to determine the affective value, *i.e.*, the degree of pleasantness or unpleasantness, of a combination of two colors. In the experiment, pairs of colored paper rectangles, 2 in. $\times$ 4 in., were exposed to O for judgment, juxtaposed upon a gray background. At another time the color samples were shown singly in the form of 4-in. squares. The same O judged the affective values of the colors when alone and when in combination five different times, using a rating scale of nine steps, 1 to 9, with a value of 5 at the indifference point. Our data consist of means of five judgments for a single O for 45 color combinations and for the single colors that made up the combinations.

---

in all the groups would be equivalent to the partial correlation obtained without the experimental control of subdividing the individuals into groups.

It has been shown before (8) that the affective value of a color pair (for which we shall use the symbol A) is definitely related to the affective values of the two color components. It is rather difficult in this problem to distinguish clearly between the two members of a color pair. We could separate them perhaps according to the more pleasing and the less pleasing members of the pairs. We could distinguish between the 'warmer' and the 'cooler' members, the 'lighter' and 'darker,' or the more and less saturated. None of these distinctions seems logically satisfactory. In this particular problem let us distinguish between the 'stronger' (S) and 'weaker' (W) members of the pairs. By a stronger member is meant the one farther from the indifference point in affective tone and by weaker is meant the one nearer the indifference point. We want an equation of the form $A = a_{a \cdot sw} + b_{as \cdot w}S + b_{aw \cdot s}W$, in which the b coefficients give the partial regression weights for the stronger and weaker members, respectively. We want also to find $R_{a \cdot ws}$, or the multiple correlation between the A' values predicted from the equation and the observed A values. The latter will tell us to what extent the affective value of the combination is determined by the affective values of the two components, when the latter are distinguished as stronger and weaker.

Solution of the Beta Coefficients.—The solution of the multiple regression equation and the multiple R for three variables is relatively simple. The most direct approach is that suggested by Wallace and Snedecor (13, p. 21). This involves the finding of the beta coefficients, or the **standard partial regression coefficients.** Beta coefficients were defined in the preceding chapter (page 337). The standard regression coefficients, it will be recalled, may be used in place of the b coefficients if the variables are given in terms of standard measurements. The b coefficients are readily obtainable from the beta coefficients through the use of formula (128), for, in a two-variable problem, $r_{12} = \beta_{12}$. In the present problem we have to deal with *partial* standard regression coefficients. They are computed from the formulas

$$\beta_{12 \cdot 3} = \frac{r_{12} - r_{13}r_{23}}{1 - r_{23}^2} \tag{169a}$$

$$\beta_{13 \cdot 2} = \frac{r_{13} - r_{12}r_{23}}{1 - r_{23}^2} \tag{169b}$$

It is obvious that all one needs thus far are the three intercorrelations between X_1, X_2, and X_3. Letting X_1 be the affective value of the color combination A, X_2 the value of the stronger component S, and X_3 the value of the weaker component W, the required raw or **zero-order coefficients** are $+.414$, $+.452$, and $+.390$, for r_{12}, r_{13} and r_{23}, respectively (see Table 76). Applying formulas (169a) and (169b),

$$\beta_{12.3} = \frac{.414 - (.452)(.390)}{1 - .1521} = \frac{.238}{.8479} = .280.$$

$$\beta_{13.2} = \frac{.452 - (.414)(.390)}{1 - .1521} = \frac{.291}{.8479} = .343.$$

A simple check upon the computation of the beta coefficients is

$$r_{13} = \beta_{12.3}r_{23} + \beta_{13.2}.$$

In other words,

$$.452 = (.280)(.390) + .343$$
$$= .109 + .343$$
$$= .452.$$

Interpreted, the beta coefficients tell us the relative importance of the two independent variables. If measurements in both are given in terms of standard measures, then the prediction of X_1 depends upon X_2 to the extent of .280 and upon X_3 to the extent of .343. As it happens, the 'stronger' color component, in the sense that it is farther from the indifference point, has only about 82 per cent as much influence upon the combination as the 'weaker' component has.

A further interpretation may be made as follows: The sum of the betas is .623, which may be taken to represent the total variation of X_1 that is accounted for by X_2 and X_3 combined. Of this total variation .280/.623 or 45 per cent is accounted for by variations in X_2, and .343/.623 or 55 per cent is accounted for by X_3. The beta coefficients thus prove their worth in making direct comparisons between the causal factors as to relative importance. The b coefficients cannot be so used since their size depends upon the measuring scales that are employed.

Finding the b Coefficients.—The b coefficients may be obtained directly from the beta coefficients by the relations

$$b_{12.3} = \beta_{12.3}\left(\frac{\sigma_1}{\sigma_2}\right) \quad \text{and} \quad b_{13.2} = \beta_{13.2}\left(\frac{\sigma_1}{\sigma_3}\right).$$

In general,

$$b_{12 \cdot 345 \ldots n} = \beta_{12 \cdot 345 \ldots n} \left(\frac{\sigma_1}{\sigma_2} \right) \tag{170}$$

Here we need to know the standard deviations of the three variables. In our color-preference problem they are 1.54, 1.38, and .87, for variables X_1, X_2, and X_3, respectively (see Table 76). Applying formula (170),

$$b_{12 \cdot 3} = .280 \frac{1.54}{1.38} = (.280)(1.116) = .312.$$

$$b_{13 \cdot 2} = .343 \frac{1.54}{.87} = (.343)(1.770) = .607.$$

The Multiple Regression Equation.—Once the b coefficients are determined, the only thing lacking for the complete multiple regression equation is the constant $a_{1 \cdot 23 \ldots n}$. This constant can be computed from the general equation[1]

$$a_{1 \cdot 234 \ldots n} = M_1 - b_2 M_2 - b_3 M_3 - \cdots - b_n M_n \tag{171}$$

In our example, the three means are 5.43, 6.43, and 5.76, respectively, so

$$\begin{aligned}
a_{1 \cdot 23} &= 5.43 - (6.43)(.312) - (5.76)(.607) \\
&= 5.43 - 2.006 - 3.496 \\
&= -.072.
\end{aligned}$$

The entire equation then becomes $X_1 = -.072 + .312 X_2 + .607 X_3$, or, in terms of the original symbols, $A = -.072 + .312 S + .607 W$. From this formula the affective value of a color combination may be predicted from the affective values of the two components. This regression equation may be interpreted in the same manner as any regression equation. The value of a color combination increases .312 units for every unit of increase in the stronger component, and it increases .607 units for every unit of increase in the weaker component. One cannot justly say from this that the weaker component has about twice the influence of the stronger component, as a direct comparison of the b coefficients would seem to show. That com-

---

[1] In this equation the subscripts have been abbreviated for the sake of brevity and clarity. The expression b_2 when written out in full would be $b_{12 \cdot 345 \ldots n}$, and the others follow the same system.

parison, as was said before, is rather to be made with the beta coefficients.

The Coefficients of Multiple Correlation.—How much can we depend upon the predictions from the given regression equation? The multiple R will indicate the answer. So would a standard error of estimate. We could proceed from this point to make all the predictions and correlate these predictions with the observed A values. We could compute the residuals and their standard error, which would be the familiar standard error of the estimate. The most direct way of finding R and the sigma of the estimate, however, is to use the constants we already have. Unless there is some special interest in the residuals, there is no point in making the predictions and calculating their deviations from the observed values. The multiple R for a three-variable problem is given by the simple formula

$$R_{1 \cdot 23} = \sqrt{\beta_{12 \cdot 3} r_{12} + \beta_{13 \cdot 2} r_{13}}.$$

Generalized, the formula is[1]

$$R_{1 \cdot 234 \dots n} = \sqrt{\beta_{12} r_{12} + \beta_{13} r_{13} + \cdots + \beta_{1n} r_{1n}} \tag{172}$$

Substituting the necessary constants,

$$\begin{aligned}
R_{1 \cdot 23} &= \sqrt{(.280)(.414) + (.343)(.452)} \\
&= \sqrt{.115920 + .155036} \\
&= \sqrt{.270956} \\
&= .521
\end{aligned}$$

Such an R applies to the set of data from which it is obtained. In order to estimate the probable correlation for the universe from which the data were drawn, the correction of Ezekiel (3, p. 177) is in order. The correction for the limited number of cases and for the number of variables is the same as that used in Chapter X [formula (117)]. To repeat that correction as applied to a multiple R,

$$_cR^2 = 1 - (1 - R^2)\left(\frac{N - 1}{N - m}\right) \tag{173}$$

In the illustrative problem,

[1] The subscripts of the betas have been abbreviated for convenience, for example, $\beta_{13} = \beta_{13 \cdot 245 \dots n}$.

$$_cR^2 = 1 - (1 - .270956)\left(\frac{44}{42}\right)$$
$$= 1 - (.729044)(1.048)$$
$$= .235962.$$
$$_cR = .486.$$

If merely the multiple R is wanted in a three-variable problem, there being no special interest in obtaining a regression equation, or even in finding the beta coefficients, this may be found directly from the zero-order coefficients by means of the formula

$$R_{1\cdot23}^2 = \frac{r_{12}^2 - 2r_{12}r_{13}r_{23} + r_{13}^2}{1 - r_{23}^2} \tag{174}$$

In the given example,

$$R_{1\cdot23}^2 = \frac{.171396 - .145960 + .204304}{.8479}$$
$$= \frac{.229740}{.8479}$$
$$= .270952.$$
$$R_{1\cdot23} = .521.$$

The Standard Error of the Estimate.—The same relation holds between the multiple R and the corresponding standard error of the estimate as between an ordinary r and its corresponding error of estimate, as in formula (112), which, adapted to the multiple R, reads

$$\sigma_{1\cdot234\ldots n} = \sigma_1\sqrt{1 - R_{1\cdot234\ldots n}^2} \tag{175}$$

In the color-preference problem,

$$\sigma_{1\cdot23} = 1.54\sqrt{.729044}$$
$$= (1.54)(.8538)$$
$$= 1.315.$$

Thus two-thirds of the observed values should lie within 1.315 units of our predictions. This should hold true in the long run of the 45 samples we have. To embrace also all the similar cases in the universe from which the data came, Ezekiel's correction should be made in $\sigma_{1\cdot23}$. From formula (116a),

$$_c\sigma_{1\cdot23}^2 = \sigma_{1\cdot23}^2\left(\frac{N-1}{N-m}\right).$$

And so

$$c\sigma^2_{1\cdot 23} = 1.729225\left(\frac{44}{42}\right) = (1.729225)(1.048) = 1.812228.$$

$$c\sigma_{1\cdot 23} = 1.346.$$

A similarly adjusted sigma of the estimate may be obtained directly from $_cR$ if the latter is substituted for R in formula (175).

The Coefficient of Multiple Determination.—As in the case of simple correlation, if we can assume that all the factors in the independent variables are included within the determining factors of the dependent variable, R_2 measures the percentage of the determination of X_1 by X_2 and X_3 combined. Under such circumstances, R^2 can be called the **coefficient of multiple determination.** Using the square of the unadjusted R, we find that, in the samples represented in the data, X_1 is determined by the combined effects of X_2 and X_3 to the extent of 27.1 per cent. For the particular observer and for the color combinations so far sampled, the affective value of a combination is more than one-fourth a matter of the affective values of the two components. The remaining 72.9 per cent, or almost three-quarters, is due to something else. Using the square of the adjusted R, we find that X_1 is determined to the extent of 23.6 per cent by X_2 and X_3 when the latter are weighted as in the multiple regression equation. The remaining determination of X_1 is 76.4 per cent, or $1 - _cR^2$, which we can consistently call $_cK^2$, the **coefficient of multiple nondetermination.**

To find that the affective value of a pair of color patches is in general determined only to the extent of about 24 per cent for this particular observer leaves us with a search on our hands for the factor or factors that determine the remaining 76 per cent. To say that at least three-fourths of the preference for color combinations is due to caprice or chance is merely to shirk responsibility. The remaining factors may be numerous but they can be found and their relative merits evaluated in much the same manner as we have already done with the two factors already investigated.

A Search for Additional Factors.—Among other possible factors determining the pleasantness or unpleasantness of a color combination, the artists often mention contrast in brightness or tint and contrast in chroma. It is generally supposed that contrasting tints are preferred and that contrasting chromas are less pleasing. As for differences in hue, the consensus of opinion seems to be that either very great or very small differences are preferred to medium differences. In the two former cases, the relationship is thus assumed to be continuous, and perhaps linear. In the last case the relationship is assumed to be decidedly nonlinear.

TABLE 76.—INTERCORRELATIONS, MEANS, AND STANDARD DEVIATIONS OF THE DATA IN THE PROBLEM OF COLOR PREFERENCES

	X_3 (W)	X_4 (T)	X_5 (C)	X_1 (A)	M_x	σ_x
X_2 (S)	.390	−.075	−.025	.414	6.43	1.38
X_3 (W)	....	.000	.000	.452	5.76	.87
X_4 (T)	....	......	−.140	.318	2.08	1.73
X_5 (C)	....	......	......	−.246	3.18	2.27
X_1 (A)					5.43	1.54

$X_1 = A =$ the affective value of the color combination.
$X_2 = S =$ the affective value of the stronger component.
$X_3 = W =$ the affective value of the weaker component.
$X_4 = T =$ the difference in tint between the components.
$X_5 = C =$ the difference in chroma between the components.

The colors used in this experiment were evaluated for hue, tint, and chroma by the use of the "Munsell Book of Color."[1] Numerical evaluations are given to every color, and differences in hue, tint, and chroma therefore provide additional data in which to look for the determining factors for the agreeableness of the combinations. Are the artists correct? Will there be any correlation between differences in hue, tint, and chroma and the affective value of the color combination? Will the relationships be linear in form? In the previous correlations linearity was assumed because the plot of the points between A and either S or W was apparently linear. Whenever two almost equally strong independent variables are involved, however, one cannot always accept such plots at their face value. Certainly, when there are three or more independent factors, the plotted relation between X_1 and any one of the other variables may be distorted by the contaminating effects of those other variables. Ezekiel (3, Chap. 14) gives detailed instructions for discovering the shapes of the various *net* relationships, *i.e.*, relationships from which the influences of other variables have been removed.

[1] Published by the Munsell Color Company, Baltimore, Maryland.

Determining the Nature of Net Relationships.—Space does not permit a full account of Ezekiel's methods of analyzing data for net relationships. It may suffice to give a few general hints. After one has plotted each independent variable in turn against X_1, or after one has computed linear correlations of zero order, the variable having the closest apparent relation to X_1 may be dealt with first. If the relationship with this variable is not linear, then some curvilinear correlation coefficient should be computed or one should draw through the scatter diagram a freehand curve. Next, whether the first relation is linear or not, one should estimate the discrepancies of the X_1 values from the predicted X_1' values or from the freehand curve. It is in these discrepancies that the relationships between the other independent variables and X_1 are to be found. One can proceed, dealing with the next strongest variable and eliminating its influence in the same manner, only this time using the residuals in place of the original X_1 measurements. If all the relationships are found to be reasonably linear, then one may proceed as has already been described.

The Reliability of Multiple Correlation Constants.—We have just solved the data for a multiple R and for the partial regression coefficients, both β (the standard form) and b (the form used with original measurements). Like all statistical constants, these are subject to fluctuations due to sampling errors. Their reliabilities are indicated as usual by their standard errors. The standard error of a beta coefficient when there are three variables is given by the formula

$$\sigma^2_{\beta_{12.3}} = \frac{1 - R^2}{(1 - r^2_{23})(N - 3)} \tag{176}$$

The same formula holds for both beta coefficients in a three-variable problem. As applied to the illustrative problem,

$$\sigma^2_{\beta_{13.2}} = \sigma^2_{\beta_{12.3}} = \frac{1 - .270956}{(1 - .1521)(42)} = \frac{.729044}{(.8479)(42)} = .020472.$$

$$\sigma_{\beta_{13.2}} = \sigma_{\beta_{12.3}} = .143.$$

The two beta coefficients are .280 and .343, respectively. By finding the ratio of beta to its sigma, we can derive the probability that beta would not be zero or less. Such ratios are analogous to the familiar 'critical ratio,' or they are equivalent to Fisher's t coefficient. For the given data they are

$$t_{\beta_{12.3}} = \frac{\beta_{12.3}}{\sigma_\beta} = \frac{.280}{.143} = 1.96$$

and

$$t_{\beta_{13.2}} = \frac{13.2}{\sigma_\beta} = \frac{.343}{.143} = 2.40.$$

Assuming a very large number of observations, a critical ratio of 1.96 gives a probability of .975 that the obtained beta will always have the same algebraic sign, and a ratio of 2.40 gives a similar probability of .992. But since the number of observations is limited, it is safer to employ Fisher's test of significance of t by using Table K. The number of degrees of freedom is 42. By referring to the last column of Table K, we find opposite an $(N - m)$ of 40 that the first beta, $\beta_{12.3}$, is barely below the boundary line of significance, there being at least 5 chances in 100 that it could have arisen by chance. The other beta, $\beta_{13.2}$, is certainly significant, but lacks sufficient size to be regarded as highly significant.

If the standard error of the b coefficients is desired, since $b_{12.3}$ is equal to σ_1/σ_2 times $\beta_{12.3}$, the standard error of b is σ_1/σ_2 times as large as the standard error of β. In this problem,

$$\sigma_{b_{12.3}} = 1.54/1.38 \times \sigma_{\beta_{12.3}},$$

or $1.116 \times .143 = .160$. If the standard error of the b coefficients is wanted directly, without first computing σ_β, then formula (176) becomes transformed into

$$\sigma_{b_{12.3}} = \frac{\sigma_{1.23}}{\sigma_{2.3}\sqrt{N - 3}} \tag{177}$$

and the standard error of $b_{13.2}$ is found in a similar manner.

The standard error of the multiple R is similar to that for the simple coefficient of correlation, namely,

$$\sigma_R = \frac{1 - R^2}{\sqrt{N - m}} \tag{178}$$

In the problem above,

$$\sigma_R = \frac{1 - .270956}{6.48} = \frac{.729044}{6.48} = .113.$$

R was found to be .521, which is more than three times its standard error, and it is therefore to be regarded as reliable. Using Fisher's test of significance, it is found from Table K that, when $(N - m)$ is 40 and when the number of variables is 3, an R of .373 or higher is considered significant and one of .454 or higher is very significant. We are therefore sure of a positive correlation, and the chances are 2 to 1 that it lies within $\pm.113$ of .521.

MULTIPLE CORRELATION WITH FOUR VARIABLES

To the two independent determining factors already treated in the illustrative problem, let us add still a third supposed determiner of affective value of color combinations. Let that third factor be the difference in *tint* of the two component colors. In Table 76 it is designated by the symbol T, and also as X_4. Since this factor is uncorrelated with X_3 and practically uncorrelated with X_2, and yet correlates .318 with X_1, it should add something toward the prediction of X_1. It appears to be at least a small determining factor. The plot of the points X_1 against X_4 is apparently linear. Since X_4 is practically uncorrelated with both X_2 and X_3, this plot represents the *net* regression of X_1 upon X_4, and so we may proceed with linear correlation methods.

In order to make the work systematic, let us list first the information needed for the solution of a four-variable problem. That information is as follows:[1]

The Zero-order Data:

M_1	M_2	M_3	M_4	σ_1	σ_2	σ_3	σ_4
5.43	6.43	5.76	2.08	1.54	1.38	.87	1.73

r_{12}	r_{13}	r_{14}	r_{23}	r_{24}	r_{34}
.414	.452	.318	.390	$-.075$	.000

Next we list some constants computed from the zero-order data. The α constants are used in various connections and need to be computed only once. The α constant has no particular name or significance, except in the computation of the beta coefficients. The constant k, however, is the already well-known coefficient of alienation. The second list is as follows:

First-order Calculations:

$$\alpha_{13\cdot2} = r_{13} - r_{12}r_{23}. \qquad k_{23}^2 = 1 - r_{23}^2.$$
$$\alpha_{14\cdot2} = r_{14} - r_{12}r_{24}. \qquad k_{24}^2 = 1 - r_{24}^2.$$
$$\alpha_{43\cdot2} = r_{34} - r_{23}r_{24}. \qquad \beta_{13\cdot2} = \frac{\alpha_{13\cdot2}}{k_{23}^2}.$$
$$\beta_{43\cdot2} = \frac{\alpha_{43\cdot2}}{k_{23}^2}.$$

[1] This systematic plan is adapted from schema suggested by Griffin (7).

In the problem at hand,

$$\alpha_{13 \cdot 2} = .452 - (.414)(.390) = .452 - .161 = .291.$$
$$\alpha_{14 \cdot 2} = .318 - (.414)(-.075) = .318 + .031 = .349.$$
$$\alpha_{43 \cdot 2} = .000 - (.390)(-.075) = .000 + .029 = .029.$$

$$k_{23}^2 = 1 - (.390)^2 = 1 - .1521 = .8479.$$
$$k_{24}^2 = 1 - (-.075)^2 = 1 - .0056 = .9944.$$

$$\beta_{13 \cdot 2} = \frac{.291}{.8479} = .343.$$

$$\beta_{43 \cdot 2} = \frac{.029}{.8479} = .034.$$

The Beta Coefficients:

$$\beta_{14 \cdot 23} = \frac{\alpha_{14 \cdot 2} - \beta_{13 \cdot 2}\alpha_{43 \cdot 2}}{k_{24}^2 - \beta_{43 \cdot 2}\alpha_{43 \cdot 2}}.$$

$$\beta_{13 \cdot 24} = \beta_{13 \cdot 2} - \beta_{14 \cdot 23}\beta_{43 \cdot 2}.$$
$$\beta_{12 \cdot 34} = r_{12} - (\beta_{13 \cdot 24}r_{23} + \beta_{14 \cdot 23}r_{24}).$$

CHECK: $\qquad r_{13} = \beta_{12 \cdot 34}r_{23} + \beta_{13 \cdot 24} + \beta_{14 \cdot 23}r_{34}.$

$$\beta_{14 \cdot 23} = \frac{.349 - (.343)(.029)}{.9944 - (.034)(.029)} = \frac{.349 - .0099}{.9944 - .0010} = \frac{.3391}{.9934} = .341.$$

$$\beta_{13 \cdot 24} = .343 - (.341)(.034) = .343 - .012 = .331.$$
$$\beta_{12 \cdot 34} = .414 - (.331)(.390) + (.341)(-.075)$$
$$= .414 - (.1291 - .0256) = .414 - .103 = .311.$$

CHECK: $\quad .452 = (.311)(.390) + .331 + (.341)(.000)$
$$= .1213 + .331 = .4523.$$

The Solution of $R_{1 \cdot 234}$:

$$R_{1 \cdot 234}^2 = r_{12}\beta_{12 \cdot 34} + r_{13}\beta_{13 \cdot 24} + r_{14}\beta_{14 \cdot 23} \text{ [from formula (172)]}$$
$$= (.414)(.311) + (.452)(.331) + (.318)(.341)$$
$$= .128754 + .149612 + .108438$$
$$= .386804.$$

$$R_{1 \cdot 234} = .622.$$

$$\sigma_R = \frac{1 - .386804}{\sqrt{41}} = \frac{.613196}{6.40} = .096.$$

The Multiple Regression Equation:

$$b_{12 \cdot 34} = \beta_{12 \cdot 34}\frac{\sigma_1}{\sigma_2} = (.311)(1.116) = .347.$$

$$b_{13 \cdot 24} = \beta_{13 \cdot 24}\frac{\sigma_1}{\sigma_3} = (.331)(1.77) = .586.$$

$$b_{14 \cdot 23} = \beta_{14 \cdot 23}\frac{\sigma_1}{\sigma_4} = (.341)(.89) = .303.$$

$$a_{1 \cdot 234} = M_1 - b_2 M_2 - b_3 M_3 - b_4 M_4$$
$$= 5.43 - (.347)(6.43) - (5.86)(5.76) - (.303)(2.08)$$
$$= 5.43 - 2.231 - 3.375 - .630$$
$$= -.806.$$

The equation reads

$$X_1 = -.806 + .347 X_2 + .586 X_3 + .303 X_4.$$

The standard error of the predictions is

$$\sigma_{1 \cdot 234} = \sigma_1 \sqrt{1 - R^2_{1 \cdot 234}}$$
$$= 1.54 \sqrt{1 - .386804} = 1.54 \sqrt{.613196}$$
$$= (1.54)(.783) = 1.206.$$

The Reliability of the Regression Coefficients.—As before, we can find the standard errors of the regression coefficients. The standard error of a beta coefficient, generalized for any number of variables [from formula (176)], is given by the relation

$$\sigma^2_{\beta_{12 \cdot 345 \ldots n}} = \frac{1 - R^2_{1 \cdot 234 \ldots n}}{(1 - R^2_{2 \cdot 345 \ldots n})(N - m)} \tag{179}$$

It will be noticed that the denominator requires the computation of a multiple R between X_2 and all the variables except X_1. In like manner, every beta coefficient will have a different standard error, depending upon that new multiple R. The standard error of the b coefficients is similar, being related to σ_β through the ratio σ_1/σ_x, in which σ_x is the standard deviation of any one of the variables. Formula (177) may be modified to read

$$\sigma_{b_{123 \cdot 45 \ldots n}} = \frac{\sigma_{1 \cdot 2345 \ldots n}}{\sigma_{2 \cdot 345 \ldots n} \sqrt{N - m}} \tag{180}$$

It will be noted that for the use of formula (179) in the illustrative problem we need to know one new constant, namely, $R_{2 \cdot 34}$. This multiple R, found as in any three-variable problem, is .397. The solution of $\sigma_{\beta_{12 \cdot 34}}$ is then

$$\sigma^2_{\beta_{12 \cdot 34}} = \frac{1 - .386804}{(1 - .1576)(41)} = \frac{.613196}{34.5384} = .017754.$$
$$\sigma_{\beta_{12 \cdot 34}} = .133$$

and

$$t = \frac{.311}{.133} = 2.34.$$

From Table K we see that this t coefficient is significant but it is hardly to be regarded as very significant. The other beta coefficients may be tested for significance in a similar manner.

Interpretation of the Regression Equation.—As with the three-variable problem, the relative importance of the variables is best seen in the comparison of the beta coefficients. The three betas are .311, .331, and .341, for variables X_2, X_3, and X_4 respectively. They are very evenly matched for strength when standard measures are used. Their sum is .983. Of this amount, which may be taken to represent the total determination of X_1 by the three variables combined, the stronger color component X_2 has 31.7 per cent of the determining power; the weaker color component X_3 now has 33.6 per cent, and difference in tint X_4 has 34.7 per cent. The partial b coefficients again tell us how many units of change in X_1 accompany a unitary change in the other three variables, respectively. The coefficient of multiple determination, $R^2_{1 \cdot 234}$, is .386804. With the usual proper assumption, we can say that the three factors combined determine 38.68 per cent of the variation in the affective value of the color combinations. The nondetermination is 62.76 per cent.

MULTIPLE CORRELATION BY THE DOOLITTLE METHOD

The multiple correlation with more than four variables can be carried out by merely extending the scheme that was used with four variables. The necessary formulas for doing so are given by Griffin (7). Many investigators, however, make use of another routine procedure known as the Doolittle method. That method will now be explained and illustrated with a five-variable problem, although it is applicable to any number of variables. It may be applied with the information that is given in Table 76.

The Normal Equations.—The solution begins by solving four simultaneous equations to obtain the four beta coefficients. The normal equations are made up as follows:[1]

$$\beta_{12} + r_{23}\beta_{13} + r_{24}\beta_{14} + r_{25}\beta_{15} = r_{12}.$$
$$r_{23}\beta_{12} + \beta_{13} + r_{34}\beta_{14} + r_{35}\beta_{15} = r_{13}.$$
$$r_{24}\beta_{12} + r_{34}\beta_{13} + \beta_{14} + r_{45}\beta_{15} = r_{14}.$$
$$r_{25}\beta_{12} + r_{35}\beta_{13} + r_{45}\beta_{14} + \beta_{15} = r_{15}.$$

[1] The subscripts of the betas have been abbreviated in order to save space and to increase the clarity of the equations. For example, β_{13} always means $\beta_{13 \cdot 245}$, and so on.

Notice that the table of equations is very systematic. The four unknown betas appear in four columns. The known coefficients of the betas are the zero-order correlations, and these are also systematically arranged. In the first row and first column they correspond exactly. Any other corresponding row and column (second, third, and fourth) likewise have the same series of r coefficients. At the diagonal positions we should find, to complete the system, r_{22}, r_{33}, r_{44}, and r_{55}, in other words, the self-correlations. These are all assumed to be 1.00 and so they are not mentioned. Because the table is symmetrical, the upper right duplicating the lower left, we need to deal only with the upper right, plus the diagonal values, in the computations that follow.

Solution of the Beta Coefficients.—The steps in the solution of the standard partial regression coefficients are as follows (see Table 77):

1. Enter in row A the raw coefficients of correlation with X_2. These are designated at the left as r_{2k}. The variables come in order at the top of the table, except that X_1 is placed at the right. The very last column at the right is for the check sum, a very useful checking device which will expose any errors at almost every step of the way. The first sum is the Σr_{2k}.

2. In row B we have the result of dividing the first row through by -1.0000. The instruction in the table calls for $A \div (-A2)$, which means row A divided through by the value found at the intersection of row A and column 2, with the sign changed, including the check sum in row A.

3. In row C, the coefficients r_{3k} are entered, together with their check sum. Remember that not all the coefficients r_{3k} appear in row C. The missing one is r_{23} which appears at $A3$. This coefficient must be added to those in row C in order to obtain the check sum.

4. Row D calls for the values in row A to be multiplied by the value to be found at $B3$, namely, $-.3900$.

5. Row E is obtained by summing the two values in each of the columns for rows C and D.

6. To obtain row F, the values in row E are divided by the value at $E3$, with sign changed.

7. The remainder of the table is solved in much the same manner.

The instructions given at the left in each row are easily followed. A check should be made in rows B, F, K, and Q, in other words, at the end of each 'block' of the table. All calculations should be carried out to one or two decimal places beyond those in the original r coefficients, the additional places being dropped in the final results.

The Back Solution.—The beta coefficients have not yet been solved, except for $\beta_{15 \cdot 234}$, which is the last value in column 1 (with

TABLE 77.—SOLUTION OF THE FOUR NORMAL EQUATIONS

Column number		2	3	4	5	1	Check Σ
	Variable	X_2	X_3	X_4	X_5	X_1	
Row	Instruction:						
A	r_{2k}	1.0000	.3900	− .0750	− .0250	.4140	1.7040
B	$A \div (-A2)$	− 1.0000	− .3900	.0750	.0250	−.4140	− 1.7040
C	r_{3k}		1.0000	.0000	.0000	.4520	1.8420
D	$A \times B3$		− .1521	.0293	.0098	−.1615	− .6646
E	$C + D$		.8479	.0293	.0098	.2905	1.1774
F	$E \div (-E3)$		− 1.0000	− .0346	− .0116	−.3426	− 1.3893
G	r_{4k}			1.0000	− .1400	.3180	1.1030
H	$A \times B4$			− .0056	− .0019	.0311	.1278
I	$E \times F4$			− .0010	− .0003	−.0101	− .0407
J	$G + H + I$			.9934	− .1422	.3390	1.1901
K	$J \div (-J4)$			− 1.0000	.1431	−.3413	− 1.1980
L	r_{5k}				1.0000	−.2460	.5890
M	$A \times B5$				− .0006	.0104	.0426
N	$E \times F5$				− .0001	−.0034	− .0137
O	$J \times K5$				− .0203	.0485	.1703
P	$L + M + N + O$				.9790	−.1905	.7882
Q	$P \div (-P5)$				− 1.0000	.1946	− .8051

The Back Solution

$\beta_{15 \cdot 234}$					− .1946 =	− .1946	$(-Q1)$
$\beta_{14 \cdot 235}$				.3135 =	− .0278	+.3413	$(-K1)$
$\beta_{13 \cdot 245}$			.3341 =	− .0108	+ .0023	+.3426	$(-F1)$
$\beta_{12 \cdot 345}$		.3023 =	− .1303	+ .0235	− .0049	+.4140	$(-B1)$

sign reversed) namely, −.1946. The remaining betas are to be obtained from all the values in bold-faced type by employing what is called the *back solution*. The steps are as follows (see the bottom of Table 77):

1. Record in reverse order and with signs changed at the bottom of column 1 the four values at the end of each 'block.' These appear in rows Q, K, F, and B, respectively. As was just said, the value at the top of this set becomes $\beta_{15 \cdot 234}$.

2. At the lower end of column 5 record the products of the three values appearing in bold-faced type in that column times $\beta_{15 \cdot 234}$. Those three values are in rows K, F, and B, respectively. They are .1431, −.0116, and .0250, and they are to be multiplied by −.1946. The products are −.0049, +.0023, and −.0278, reading from below upward.

3. Now $\beta_{14 \cdot 235}$ may be computed by adding the second row of the back solution across, obtaining .3135.

4. Next, in column 4, the values in bold-faced type are multiplied by $\beta_{14 \cdot 235}$ and the products are recorded in reverse order in the last two rows of the table.

5. The sum of the third row of the back solution is now equal to $\beta_{13 \cdot 245}$, which is .3341.

6. Finally, the product of .3341 times −.3900 is recorded at the bottom of column 3, and the sum of the last row gives the remaining beta coefficient, $\beta_{12 \cdot 345}$.

As a check for the accuracy of the back solution, in fact, for the solution of the normal equations thus far, we may substitute the obtained betas in the last of the normal equations and see whether that equation is satisfied. The checking process is more conveniently done if tabulated, as in Table 78.

TABLE 78.—A CHECK OF THE SOLUTION OF THE NORMAL EQUATIONS

X_k	β_{1k}	r_{k5}	$\beta_{1k}r_{k5}$
X_2	.3023	− .025	− .0076
X_3	.3341	.000	.0000
X_4	.3135	− .140	− .0439
X_5	− .1946	1.000	− .1946
X_1		$r_{15} = -.246$ =	$-.2461 = \Sigma(\beta_{1k}r_{k5})$

The Solution of R and the Regression Equation.—The regression coefficients and the multiple R are next solved by means of a simple routine. Table 79 provides the form.

The regression equation reads

$$A = -.30 + .337S + .591W + .279T - .132C$$

to use the original notations of the five variables. The multiple R is very significant, since in Table K we find that an R of .526 or higher is considered so, with 40 degrees of freedom and five variables. The b coefficients can be tested for significance as usual by finding

TABLE 79.—SOLUTION OF R AND THE REGRESSION EQUATION WITH FIVE VARIABLES

	β_{1k}	r_{1k}	$\beta_{1k}r_{1k}$	σ_1/σ_k	(b_{1k}) $\beta_{1k}(\sigma_1/\sigma_k)$	M_k	$(-M_k)b_{1k}$
X_2	.3023	.414	.125152	1.116	.337	6.43	−2.167
X_3	.3341	.452	.151013	1.770	.591	5.76	−3.404
X_4	.3135	.318	.099693	.890	.279	2.08	− .580
X_5	− .1946	− .246	.047872	.678	− .132	3.18	.420

$$R^2 = .423730 \qquad\qquad M_1 = 5.43$$

$$R_{1\cdot2345} = .651 \qquad\qquad a_{1\cdot2345} = -.30$$
$$_cR_{1\cdot2345} = .605 \qquad _cR^2_{1\cdot2345} = .3661$$
$$\sigma_{1\cdot2345} = 1.169$$

their standard errors. This would require the solution of four new multiple R coefficients if formula (180) is to be used. Wallace and Snedecor (13, p. 45) illustrate a shorter systematic procedure for calculating these standard errors, and Ezekiel (3, p. 366) gives another.

Relative Importance of the Various Factors.—Since we have found the correlation between X_1 and one, two, three, and four other variables, we can survey the results to see what the addition of each new variable does. For convenience the data are assembled in Table 80, showing the increase in R and the decrease in the standard error of the estimate as each new variable is added. The correlation r_{13} is listed first, since that one was the highest of the zero-order coefficients. Each added variable contributed to the total correlation a small amount. The index of multiple determination R^2 also increased from .2043 to .4237, no variable failing to add something. The coefficients of alienation K are given to show the percentage of reduction in the standard error of estimate when predictions are made from one to four factors. The standard errors themselves are given to show how the scatter or errors of prediction will grow less as new variables are added. They are to be compared with an original standard deviation of 1.540.

To generalize our conclusions to include the 'universe' from which the limited data were drawn, however, we must deal with the adjusted coefficients. For this particular observer we have

TABLE 80.—COMPARISON OF MULTIPLE CORRELATIONS AS NEW VARIABLES ARE BROUGHT INTO ACCOUNT

Variables	R	R^2	K	$\sigma_{1 \cdot k}$	$_cR$	$_cR^2$	$_cK$	$_c\sigma_{1 \cdot k}$
1.3	.452	.2043	.892	1.374	.431	.1858	.902	1.389
1.23	.521	.2710	.854	1.315	.486	.2360	.874	1.346
1.234	.622	.3868	.783	1.206	.585	.3420	.811	1.249
1.2345	.651	.4237	.759	1.169	.605	.3661	.796	1.226

evidently found barely more than a third of the determining factors (36.6 per cent) of the affective value of color combinations. Were we to predict affective values of new color combinations for this observer on the basis of our multiple regression equation, the chances are two to one that our predictions would be within 1.23 units of the truth. Limiting ourselves to the nine-point scale that the observer used, it can readily be seen that the predictions would be relatively wide of the mark. For the practical purposes of prediction then, a multiple R (uncorrected) of .651 is not of great significance, and yet that is about the level of validity of our best batteries of mental tests. In the present problem the interest is confined to the theoretical question of the factors influencing the agreeableness of colors and their relative strengths. We have reached a fairly satisfactory answer to this question in the case of one observer.

Solution of Multiple Correlations without Computing Raw Coefficients.—In some problems it may be desirable to proceed very directly to the computation of the multiple R and the regression equation without having any special interest in the zero-order coefficients. This can be done with a saving in labor by following a routine solution of normal equations in which the 'product-sums' (Σx_2^2, $\Sigma x_2 x_3$, $\Sigma x_2 x_4$, and the like) are used in place of the r coefficients. A routine for this procedure is described by Ezekiel (3, pp. 357 ff.). The normal equations in the case of a four-variable problem are:

$$\Sigma(x_2^2)b_{12 \cdot 34} + \Sigma(x_2 x_3)b_{13 \cdot 24} + \Sigma(x_2 x_4)b_{14 \cdot 23} = \Sigma(x_1 x_2).$$
$$\Sigma(x_2 x_3)b_{12 \cdot 34} + \Sigma(x_3^2)b_{13 \cdot 24} + \Sigma(x_3 x_4)b_{14 \cdot 23} = \Sigma(x_1 x_3).$$
$$\Sigma(x_2 x_4)b_{12 \cdot 34} + \Sigma(x_3 x_4)b_{13 \cdot 24} + \Sigma(x_4^2)b_{14 \cdot 23} = \Sigma(x_1 x_4).$$

Notice that deviation scores are used. They are found from the sums and the means of the original measurements. For example, $\Sigma(x_2^2) = [\Sigma(X_2^2) - N(M_2^2)]$ and $\Sigma(x_2x_3) = [\Sigma(X_2X_3) - N(M_2)(M_3)]$ and so on. The long method, with cross-products of the original measurements, is thus employed. In addition to dispensing with the calculation of the r's the calculation of the beta coefficients is also unnecessary, the b's being found directly from the solution of the normal equations. Higher order partial correlations may also be derived through this process without the use of raw r's. With a limited number of cases and with machine calculation this method probably takes less time than the procedures already described. Ordinarily in psychological problems we wish to know the zero-order r's, however, and for that reason space is not used here to describe in full this alternative procedure.

PARTIAL CORRELATIONS

The meaning of partial correlation has already been discussed. It is the *net* correlation between two variables when the influence of one or more other variables upon both of them is nullified. When only one factor is 'held constant' we speak of a **first-order partial correlation.** When two are held constant, we speak of **second-order partials,** and so on.

First-order Partial Correlations.—The general formula for a first-order partial correlation is

$$r_{12\cdot3} = \frac{r_{12} - r_{13}r_{23}}{\sqrt{1 - r_{13}^2}\sqrt{1 - r_{23}^2}} \qquad (181)$$

Notice the make-up of the formula. Its intent is to nullify the effects of the correlation of X_3 with both X_1 and X_2. So the product of r_{13} times r_{23} is deducted from r_{12} and the difference is divided by the product k_{13} times k_{23}. Notice also the similarity to formula (169a), the formula for $\beta_{12\cdot3}$. The numerators are just the same, but the denominator in the former is $k_{13}k_{23}$, whereas in the latter it is k_{23}^2. Because of this relationship, however, the partial $r_{12\cdot3}$ can be calculated from beta by means of the following relationship:

$$r_{12\cdot3} = \sqrt{\beta_{12\cdot3}\beta_{21\cdot3}}.$$

This formula can be generalized to read

$$r_{12\cdot34\ldots n} = \sqrt{\beta_{12\cdot34\ldots n}\beta_{21\cdot34\ldots n}} \qquad (182a)$$

$$r_{12\cdot34\ldots n} = \sqrt{b_{12\cdot34\ldots n}b_{21\cdot34\ldots n}} \qquad (182b)$$

In other words, $r_{12\cdot3}$ is the geometric mean of $\beta_{12\cdot3}$ and $\beta_{21\cdot3}$ or of $b_{12\cdot3}$ and $b_{21\cdot3}$.   Remember that these two betas are not the same. The former is a coefficient for predicting X_1 from X_2 and the latter is a coefficient for predicting X_2 from X_1, when the effects of X_3 upon X_1 are nullified in either case.   One might say that the beta coefficient indicates the amount of relationship when there is only a one-way nullification of X_3, while the partial r indicates the amount of relationship when the effects of X_3 upon both X_1 and X_2 are simultaneously nullified.

To apply formula (181), let us return to our color-preference problem.   The first-order partial is

$$r_{12\cdot3} = \frac{.414 - (.452)(.390)}{(.892)(.921)} = \frac{.2377}{.8215} = .289.$$

To apply formula (182) when $\beta_{21\cdot3}$ equals .299 and $\beta_{12\cdot3}$ is .280,

$$r_{12\cdot3} = \sqrt{(.299)(.280)} = \sqrt{.0837} = .289.$$

The Significance of a Partial Correlation Coefficient.—The significance of a partial r is estimated in just the same way as for any correlation coefficient, by its standard error.   Using Table K and letting $(N - m)$ be 42 and the number of variables be two, we find that, even if $(N - m)$ were 45, it would require an r of .288 to be significant (19 chances to 1); if $(N - m)$ is 40, the least significant r is .304.   Our partial coefficient just fails to pass the test of significance.

Second-order Partial Correlations.—For a second-order partial coefficient of correlation the general formula is

$$r_{12\cdot34} = \frac{r_{12\cdot3} - r_{14\cdot3}r_{24\cdot3}}{\sqrt{1 - r_{14\cdot3}^2}\sqrt{1 - r_{24\cdot3}^2}} \tag{183}$$

In the solution of this formula three first-order partials must be obtained.   We already know $r_{12\cdot3}$, which is .289.   The others are $r_{14\cdot3} = .357$ and $r_{24\cdot3} = -.081$.   The solution is

$$r_{12\cdot34} = \frac{.290 - (.357)(-.081)}{(.934)(.997)} = \frac{.290 + .0289}{.9311} = .342.$$

Reference to Table K will show that this is a significant coefficient although not highly significant.   In this case the number of degrees of freedom is 41 and the number of variables is taken as two.   As compared with the partial $r_{12\cdot3}$, the last-obtained partial is somewhat higher. Nullifying the combined effects of X_3 and X_4 shows a significant correlation between factors 1 and 2 which did not appear when only the effects of factor 3 were nullified.[1] Suppose the effects of X_5 are also nullified; will the net correlation between X_1 and X_2 be any greater? This requires a partial coefficient of the third order for an answer.

Third-order Partials.—The general formula is given by Garrett (6, p. 242) as

$$r_{12\cdot453} = \frac{r_{12\cdot45} - r_{13\cdot45}r_{23\cdot45}}{\sqrt{1 - r_{13\cdot45}^2}\sqrt{1 - r_{23\cdot45}^2}} \tag{184}$$

Such a formula, however, requires numerous computations of lower order partials before it can be applied and so it is probably used but little. There are other more convenient ways of computing higher order partials from multiple R's, ways which are relatively simple when the necessary multiple R's are known.

Partial Correlations Derived from Multiple R's.—The partial $r_{12\cdot34\ldots n}$ can be derived from the general formula

$$r_{12\cdot34\ldots n}^2 = 1 - \frac{1 - R_{1\cdot234\ldots n}^2}{1 - R_{1\cdot34\ldots n}^2} \tag{185}$$

Notice that the only difference between numerator and denominator of the fraction at the right is that variable X_2 has been omitted in the latter. The numerator will be recognized as $K_{1\cdot234\ldots n}^2$ or the coefficient of nondetermination when all the variables are included. The denominator is the similar coefficient when variable X_2 is omitted. The fraction is the ratio of the nondetermined variance, after all variables are accounted for, to the nondetermined variance when all variables except X_2 are accounted for. This same ratio is equivalent to $k_{12\cdot34\ldots n}^2$, since any r^2 equals $1 - k^2$. The ratio is then the nondetermined variance (X_1 nondetermined by X_2) when the effects of other factors are nullified.

We may apply this formula to the calculation of $r_{12\cdot34}$ in our color-preference problem in which $R_{1\cdot234}$ and $R_{1\cdot34}$ are .622 and .553, respectively.

---

[1] This illustrates the importance of being cautious in interpreting the lower order partial correlations. Unless additional factors are accounted for, we are not sure that a low-order partial gives the true correlation.

$$r_{12\cdot34}^2 = 1 - \frac{1 - R_{1\cdot234}^2}{1 - R_{1\cdot34}^2}$$

$$= 1 - \frac{1 - .3868}{1 - .3054}$$

$$= 1 - .8828 = .1172.$$

$$r_{12\cdot34} = .342.$$

If many of the partials are wanted among a set of variables, this method is time consuming, for as many multiple R's must be computed as there are variables, and more. This can be reduced to a routine in which a table like Table 77 above is merely rearranged (see Wallace and Snedecor, 13, p. 52).

The Coefficient of Part Correlation.—A relatively new constant, the coefficient of **part correlation,** may prove to be even more useful than the partial correlation, and it is usually much easier to compute. It is the correlation between one of the independent variables, X_2, for example, and the variations in X_1 after the part of X_1 that is related to the other variables has been removed. In a four-variable equation,

$$X_1 = a + b_{12\cdot34}X_2 + b_{13\cdot24}X_3 + b_{14\cdot23}X_4.$$

Suppose that we had removed the effects of variables 3 and 4 by means of the adjustment $X_1 - (b_{13\cdot24}X_3 + b_{14\cdot23}X_4)$. We should have then a new adjusted variable X_1'' from which the influences of X_3 and X_4 have been removed. The part correlation is between X_2 and the adjusted X'' values. For this particular problem, the formula is

$$_{12}r_{34}^2 = \frac{1}{1 + \dfrac{\sigma_1^2(1 - R_{1\cdot234}^2)}{b_{12\cdot34}^2\sigma_2^2}} = \frac{1}{1 + \dfrac{(1 - R_{1\cdot234}^2)}{\beta_{12\cdot34}^2}}.$$

In generalized form,

$$_{12}r_{34\ldots n}^2 = \frac{1}{1 + \dfrac{\sigma_1^2(1 - R_{1\cdot234\ldots n}^2)}{b_{12\cdot34\ldots n}^2\sigma_2^2}}$$

$$= \frac{1}{1 + \dfrac{(1 - R_{1\cdot234\ldots n}^2)}{\beta_{12\cdot34\ldots n}^2}} \tag{186}$$

From the illustrative data, $R_{1\cdot234} = .622$ and $\beta_{12\cdot34} = .311$.

Therefore

$$_{12}r^2_{34} = \cfrac{1}{1 + \cfrac{1 - .386804}{.096721}} = \frac{1}{7.340} = .13624$$

and

$$_{12}r_{34} = .369.$$

As compared with $r_{12\cdot34}$, which is .343, the part correlation is slightly higher, and it is undoubtedly significant, although not highly significant, as Table K will indicate.

Some Variations in the Partial Correlation Technique.—Considerable caution should be observed in dealing with partial correlations, especially when causal relationships are supposed to be involved. First of all, the fact that we 'hold constant' the effects of a third, or a third and a fourth, variable while correlating X_1 and X_2 is no sign that we have the true correlation between those two variables. There may be a fifth and a sixth or a seventh variable which should also be held constant in finding the true net correlation between X_1 and X_2. If we use $r^2_{12\cdot34\ldots n}$ as the coefficient of partial determination, we may justly conclude that this is the amount of net determination of X_1 by X_2, provided there are no other factors simultaneously affecting X_1 and X_2 so as to change the apparent correlation between them. It is not even safe to say that the coefficient of partial determination indicates the *maximum* causal relationship, since a partial r may be either raised or lowered by holding constant additional factors.

It has been pointed out (2) that there are problems in which the true amount of correlation is not best indicated by means of the usual partial correlation formula. For example, suppose that we want to know the probable true correlation between midparent and child for intelligence, with the factor of cultural level of the home nullified. There will undoubtedly be some correlation between both midparent intelligence and the child's intelligence and the cultural level of the home. But in the former case the intelligence of the parents is the cause in part for the culture of the home, whereas the latter is a causal factor in the variation of intelligence in children. Therefore, to find a partial correlation between intelligence of parent and child with home culture nullified for both those factors gives a distorted picture of the true relation between intelligence of parent and offspring. In so doing, we partial out too much. Intelligence of parent as expressed in cultural level of the home is only a part of that factor of parental intelligence which is related to or which is a causal factor of the intelligence of the child.

To meet just such problems as this one, Franzen proposes (4) some modified partial correlation formulas. In the case of three variables,

$$r_{(1 \cdot 3) 2} = \frac{r_{12} - r_{13} r_{23}}{\sqrt{1 - r_{13}^2}} \tag{187}$$

in which $r_{(1 \cdot 3) 2}$ is the correlation between factors 1 and 2, with the effects of factor 3 eliminated from 1 but not from 2. In a four-variable problem, the formula reads

$$r_{(1 \cdot 3)(2 \cdot 4)} = \frac{r_{12} - r_{14} r_{24} - r_{13} r_{23} + r_{34} r_{13} r_{24}}{\sqrt{1 - r_{13}^2} \sqrt{1 - r_{24}^2}} \tag{188}$$

In the latter case, we have the correlation between factors 1 and 2 when the influence of 3 is removed from 1 and when that of 4 is removed from 2. At the same time, the influence of factor 4 is not removed from 1, nor is the influence of 3 removed from 2.

A Brief History of Correlation Methods

It may be of interest to sketch at this point some of the important landmarks in the history of correlation methods. A rather full account of this history is given by Walker (12). Only the outstanding names and dates that are associated with the major concepts of correlation will be mentioned here.

Origin of the Concept and Method of Correlation.—Undoubtedly, if any one man deserves credit for the first fundamental insight into the meaning of correlation it is Galton. A number of others, among them the mathematicians, Bravais, Laplace, Gauss, and Adrian, and the physiologist Bowditch, almost made the discovery. In his "Memories" (5) Galton tells how in the late seventies while taking a walk he was caught in a sudden shower and took shelter among some rocks. There the idea of correlation flashed upon him, and he was able in 1877 to publish in rough form his ideas of the regression lines, the concept of the standard error of regression, and the expression of measurements in terms of standard measures. He came to use the letter r to stand for the slope of the regression line, the selection of 'r' coming from the terms 'reversion' and 'regression.' By 1888 the term 'correlation' appeared in print. From that time on the name of Pearson dominates the scene although Edgworth and Weldon made a number of contributions. During the early nineties it was they who introduced the term 'coefficient of correlation,' laid the basis for multiple correlation, and suggested the concept of 'regression coefficient' for the expression $r\sigma_1/\sigma_2$.

The first application of the correlation method to a psychological problem may be credited to Bryan (1) in 1892 when, with the cooperation of Boas, he used it in his classical studies of motor learning. The first serious application to mental-test results was made by Wissler (14) when in 1901 he applied a number of tests to 200 college students. No doubt the greatest stimulus to the correlation of mental tests and to the ultimate factor analysis methods was given by Spearman's introduction of his formula for the correction for attenuation, which was published for the first time in 1904. Up to that date the results with tests had been very discouraging. In that same year Thorndike (11) published his first edition of "Theory of Mental and Social Measurements," which no doubt gave added impetus to the use of correlation methods, particularly in education. Today it might well be said that the educational psychologists have taken over the leadership in the development of new correlation methods and their application.

The Introduction of Some Important Correlation Methods.— For the sake of brevity, we may merely list alphabetically a number of the more prominent correlational concepts, together with the names of their authors and the dates of origin (12, pp. 175 *ff*.):

Beta coefficient, Kelley, 1924.

Biserial r, Pearson, 1907.

Coefficient of alienation, named by Kelley, 1924.

Coefficient of contingency, Pearson, 1904.

Correction for attenuation, Spearman, 1904.

Correlation ratio, Pearson, 1905.

Mean square contingency, Pearson, 1904.

Partial correlation, Pearson, 1897.

Reliability coefficient, Spearman, 1910.

Tetrachoric correlation, Everitt, 1910.

Problems

The following intercorrelations are rather typical of the relations found between general athletic ability and such factors as height, weight, and strength. The five variables are: (1) age (with a range from twelve to nineteen years); (2) height, in inches; (3) weight, in pounds; (4) strength (a pool of various measures); (5) ability in track and field events (a weighted pool of scores).

Variables

	1	2	3	4	5	Mean	σ
1	. . .	.52	.54	.56	.50	15.8	1.4
2	.52	. . .	.78	.58	.46	65.2	2.8
3	.54	.78	. . .	.72	.41	121.5	12.0
4	.56	.58	.72	. . .	.65	246.0	35.2
5	.50	.46	.41	.65	. . .	165.0	18.0

1. Find the multiple regression equations predicting athletic score from height and weight and also from age and strength. Find an equation for predicting strength from height and weight. Compute all the pertinent statistical constants that should go with these equations. N equals 175.

2. Find equations for estimating athletic score from height, weight, and strength combined and from age, height, and weight combined. Compute all appropriate constants.

3. Find an equation for estimating athletic score from all other variables combined, with all other appropriate computations being made.

4. Compute a number of the more illuminating partial and part coefficients of correlation which you think should be found from the above data. Interpret your results.

REFERENCES

1. BRYAN, W. L., On the development of voluntary motor ability, *Amer. J. Psychol.*, 1892, **5**, 125–204.

2. BURKS, B. S., On the inadequacy of the partial and multiple correlation technique, *J. Educ. Psychol.*, 1926, **17**, 532–540.

3. EZEKIEL, M., "Methods of Correlation Analysis," John Wiley & Sons, Inc., New York, 1930.

4. FRANZEN, R., A comment on partial correlation, *J. Educ. Psychol.*, 1928, **19**, 194–197.

5. GALTON, F., "Memories of My Life," Methuen & Co., Ltd., London, 1908.

6. GARRETT, H. E., "Statistics in Psychology and Education," Longmans, Green & Company, New York, 1926.

7. GRIFFIN, H. D., Simplified schemas for multiple linear correlation, *J. Exper. Educ.*, 1933, **1**, 239–254.

8. GUILFORD, J. P., The prediction of affective values, *Amer. J. Psychol.*, 1931, **43**, 469–478.

9. KELLEY, T. L., "Statistical Method," The Macmillan Company, New York, 1924.

10. SPEARMAN, C., The proof and measurement of association between two things, *Amer. J. Psychol.*, 1904, **15**, 72–101.

11. THORNDIKE, E. L., "An Introduction to the Theory of Mental and Social Measurements," Teachers College, Columbia University, New York, 1904.
12. WALKER, H. M., "Studies in the History of Statistical Method," Williams & Wilkins Company, Baltimore, 1929.
13. WALLACE, H. A., and G. W. SNEDECOR, "Correlation and Machine Calculation," Iowa State College, Ames, 1931.
14. WISSLER, C., The correlation of mental and physical tests, *Psychol. Rev. Mon. Suppl.*, 1901, **3**, no. 16.

CHAPTER XIII

MENTAL-TEST METHODS

Of all the psychometric methods, those coming under the heading of mental tests have overshadowed all others in application and in significance. Unfortunately, mental tests grew up quite apart from the development of the psychophysical methods, in spite of the fact that both have depended upon the same fundamental statistical tools. Both would have benefited from a closer coordination from time to time. No rift in psychology is more eloquent of diverging points of view than that between psychophysics and test methods. The one developed within the narrow limits of a general, sensational psychology of the Fechner-Wundt-Titchener lineage, whereas the other grew out of biological stock, emphasizing functions and individual differences, and boasts of a Darwin-Galton-Cattell-Binet pedigree. From the functional point of view, psychophysics is concerned with the measurement of powers of sensory discrimination and the psychophysical methods are conceived as species of tests of ability. This view brings a consistency and unity into the psychometric methods. This possible unity was insufficient, however, to make effective any extensive beneficial traffic between the two great wings of psychometrics. Only within the last decade have mental testers felt any serious urge to submit their tests to the microscopic examination, item by item, which would have been the natural thing for one of psychophysical temper and training to do at a very early stage of the test movement. Even today the mental tester who is unschooled in psychophysics and its methods invents anew the tools for dissecting his tests—tools which might readily have been borrowed directly from psychophysics.

THE HISTORY OF MENTAL TESTS

Every student knows the bare outlines of the development of mental tests. Space does not permit an adequate account of even the more significant details of that history here. The reader who wishes to know those details is referred to an excellent account given by Peterson (36). It is sufficient to remind the reader how Galton, inspired by the evolutionary doctrine of Darwin, made the first serious attempts to measure individual differences in physical and mental traits; how, after a certain amount of groundwork in France and in Germany, Binet developed his mental-age scale; how the concepts of mental age and *IQ* arose; and how with the Army Alpha examination the group test was launched on a truly grand scale.

The Statistical Aspect of Tests.—It is more pertinent to the content of this chapter to review briefly the statistical aspect of mental testing, for that is the phase of mental tests that is emphasized here. The early tests of Galton, being of the simple sensory or motor type, were readily scored in physical units. For sensory tests, the stimuli that could be discriminated were readily calibrated in terms of physical units. In motor tests, standard performances could be scored in terms of work units per time interval or in terms of time required for a given quantum of work accomplished. This applied to such tests as reaction-time, color-naming, addition, and association tests. Binet, who wanted to measure more complex hypothetical mental functions such as reasoning, comprehension, memory, and suggestibility, could not always resort to physical scales. The level of performance in a test had to be given in other terms.

Because intelligence is something that was thought to increase with the age of a child, and because, according to all preliminary scoring standards, the older the child, the better his performance in almost any single mental test, the natural procedure was to adopt age as the psychological yardstick for intelligence. Any test that could be passed with a certain standard of excellence by about 70 per cent of the seven-year-old children was established as a seven-year-old test. Other tests were calibrated at fixed age levels in a similar manner. It has already been suggested (page 210) that a proportion of 50 per cent would have been a better criterion of age level. A knowledge of psychophysical procedure, as in the constant methods, would have suggested this criterion. However, Binet's criterion did not at all invalidate his age scale with the year as the unit of mental development.

The *IQ* is said to be an invention of Stern. Since it is a ratio of mental age to chronological age, it is therefore not a measure of amount but an index—an index of brightness. Since it has been found that the *IQ*, although relatively constant for normal children, is inclined to increase with supernormal children and to decrease with subnormal children, Heinis (17) has introduced his *personal constant* as an improved index of brightness.

Aside from individual tests like Binet's and its various revisions which adopt age as the measuring scale, most group tests, whose applications are far more extensive, employ the test item as the unit of measurement. The test score is the number of items, weighted or unweighted, which the individual passes, with some correction being made for chance successes whenever that is felt necessary. Tests are typically composed of a large number of heterogeneous items varying in difficulty from very easy to very difficult, with some items highly diagnostic of the trait to be measured and others absolutely worthless for diagnostic purposes. Such a situation has challenged some of the more scientifically minded mental testers to resort to various methods of item analysis in order to calibrate items for difficulty and to weed out the 'dead timber' from their tests. Among those who have taken the lead in this phase of the test movement are Thorndike and his students. As another outcome of this careful study of difficulty and validity of test items, we have what is perhaps the crowning achievement in mental testing; that is the attainment of a rationalized absolute scale for measuring ability, a scale with equal units throughout and perhaps even with an absolute zero point (57). For all this we are indebted chiefly to Woody (65), McCall (32), Otis (34), and Thurstone (53–56).

The Reliability and Validity of Tests.—Not the least important in the history of testing are the various improved methods for checking the reliability and validity of tests. The former, as is well known, is given by the correlation of a test with itself. The latter is given by the correlation of the test with some accepted outside criterion. Of special interest and importance in connection with the reliability of tests is the Spearman-Brown prophecy formula. This formula, which was suggested at the same time by Spearman and Brown, enables us to estimate the self-correlation of the whole of a homogeneous test from the known reliability of a fraction of the test. Much practical experience with tests has brought forth many other devices and techniques for dealing with reliability and validity of tests and of test items. These topics will be dealt with in turn with all other statistical aspects of testing, which have only been suggested in the preceding paragraphs.

The Reliability of Tests

The Meaning of Reliability.—It is unnecessary to repeat the statement already made more than once that measurements in psychology are subject to a multitude of variable factors and that errors of measurement are to be expected under the best experimental conditions. So with test scores; standardize the examiner, the test, the instructions, the immediate surroundings of the individual, his physical and mental condition, his motivation, and his set of the moment, and yet we cannot be sure that the obtained test score would be the same were the test to be repeated under the same set of known conditions. We could not be sure that a score of 50 points represents the individual's true ability or that he would obtain a score of 50 on comparable occasions.

Let us represent the *true* score of an individual on a test by X_∞. Let X_1 stand for an actual score made by that individual in taking that test. Let e_1 represent the deviation of the actual score from the true score. In other words, $X_1 = X_\infty + e_1$. We can transpose the equation to read $X_\infty = X_1 - e_1$. Let us assume that the true score, X_∞, can be predicted from X_1. The reliability of the actual test scores is proportional to the correlation between X_∞ and X_1, the true scores and the actual scores. It is inversely related to the size of the discrepancies, e_1. Since we can never know the true scores, we can never calculate the correlation $r_{\infty 1}$. But fortunately we can estimate that correlation. We can use a comparable test whose test scores can be assumed to measure X_∞ with no greater error. Its test score for the same individual may be designated as X_I, and we may set an equation $X_\infty = X_\mathrm{I} - e_\mathrm{I}$ similar to that for the first test. We may now find the correlation between the two sets of fallible scores, in other words, $r_{1\mathrm{I}}$, and from that correlation we may estimate $r_{\infty 1}$ and also $r_{\infty \mathrm{I}}$. The amount of correlation between the two forms of the test will depend entirely upon the amount of the true score (X_∞) that is common to both, assuming that the errors of measurement are entirely independent and hence uncorrelated.

The Coefficient of Reliability.—There are three ways of finding a self-correlation of a test: (1) repetition of the same test on different occasions; (2) the use of two parallel forms of the test; and (3) the split-half method of dividing a test into two comparable halves. These three methods are actually different, involving different assumptions and giving different results.

The first method is almost out of the question for the majority of tests.   If the test is repeated at too short an interval, the memory factor is important and it tends to make the self-correlation higher than it should be.   If repeated at greater intervals apart, factors of growth, intervening learning, and other causes tend to reduce the self-correlation to a point below what it should be.   The second procedure has the advantage that the second form can be given on the same occasion as the first, taking advantage of a more uniform set of personal conditions.   The memory factor is also excluded, except as certain general habits of test taking learned in the first form transfer to the second.   It has the disadvantage that twice as much material must be prepared as may be needed for any purpose other than that of finding reliability.   Many testers demand that more than one form of a test shall be prepared in case the test needs to be repeated with the same subjects and in case there is danger of coaching new subjects by practiced ones.

The third procedure, the split-half method, avoids most of the disadvantages of the other two and is the one most generally used. In order to obtain comparable halves of a test, it is divided by pooling the odd-numbered items in one half and the even-numbered items in the other, unless it is known that for some reason the 'odds' and 'evens' so pooled are not equivalent.   The division into a first and last half is not wise, since there may be continuous shifts in such general factors as set, practice, fatigue, boredom, or confidence from the first to the last of the test.   Tests are customarily arranged with the items in order of difficulty, which again precludes the use of first and last halves.   The use of a time-limit test also makes the score of the last half more variable than that of the first since some individuals complete the second half and some do not, whereas all complete the first.

The only disadvantage of the split-half method as compared with the others is that the true reliability of a test is directly related to its length.   The reliability of a half-test is lower than that of the whole test.   Fortunately, the Spearman-Brown formula enables us to estimate the reliability of the whole from the calculated reliability of the half, so that this handicap of the split-half method is not at all serious.   It must be remembered in the use of these three methods that different conditions apply and that the resulting estimates of reliability have different meanings.   The split-half method probably gives the coefficient of reliability that is nearest the true reliability, but from the standpoint of mental-test practice it gives an estimate of reliability that is probably too high. It does not take account of changes in individuals from day to day or from month to month.

The Index of Reliability.—As was intimated before, we can estimate the correlation between a set of fallible test scores and the true scores, in other words, $r_{\infty 1}$, from the self-correlation of a test, r_{11}. The formula is

$$r_{\infty 1} = \sqrt{r_{11}} \tag{189}$$

The square root of the coefficient of reliability becomes the **index of reliability.** To reverse the formula, $r_{11} = r_{\infty 1}^2$. In other words, the coefficient of reliability is the coefficient of determination of X_1 by X_∞. The remaining determination of X_1 is due to e_1. The coefficient of reliability may therefore be treated as a percentage.[1] To say that the reliability coefficient of a test is .95 enables us to conclude that 95 per cent of the test score represents the ability measured by the test and 5 per cent represents the proportion of the test score attributable to errors of measurement. Figure 39 may help to clarify this point. One rectangle represents the fallible test scores X_1 and the other the fallible test scores X_I.

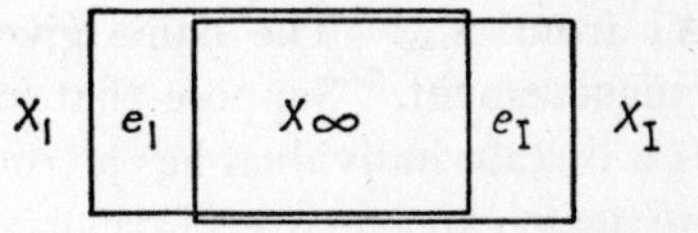

$$r_{11} = r_{\infty 1}^2 = r_{\infty I}^2 = \frac{X_\infty}{X_\infty + e_1} = \frac{X_\infty}{X_\infty + e_I}$$

Fig. 39.—Common factors in the self-correlation of a test.

The common territory represents that portion of both sets of scores which is due to the true measurements of the ability. This common territory is called X_∞. With either $r_{\infty 1}$ or $r_{\infty I}$, it can be seen that the conditions are fulfilled for using r^2 as the coefficient of determination. $r_{\infty 1}^2 = r_{\infty I}^2 = r_{11}$, as we see from formula (189). Unlike previous correlation problems in which r is found first and r^2 later, in dealing with reliability and self-correlations, r^2 is obtainable first and r later.

It will be recalled that, from formula (110), $r_{yx} = \sigma_{y'}/\sigma_y$, the ratio of the standard deviation of the predicted measurements to the observed measurements, and that $r_{yx}^2 = \sigma_{y'}^2/\sigma_y^2$, the ratio of the *variance* of the predicted values to the *variance* of the observed values, so that $r_{\infty 1}^2 = r_{11} = \sigma_\infty^2/\sigma_1^2$, the ratio of the true variance to the observed variance. This is another definition of reliability.

[1] For additional proof of this, see Tryon's discussion (61).

One may, with strong justification, use the index of reliability rather than the coefficient of reliability. This tells us directly how well the obtained scores correlate with the true scores. It is the true scores that we are attempting to predict, so naturally we may use the customary test of accuracy of our predictions. Since the coefficient of reliability is the square of the index, it is always smaller, and it tells us what proportion of the test scores is attributable to the actual abilities being measured.

The Standard Error of Measurement.—Besides using coefficients of correlation to indicate the closeness of predictions, we also employ the standard error of estimate, which has the general formula $\sigma_{yx} = \sigma_y\sqrt{1 - r_{yx}^2}$. The same sort of standard error can be applied when we are dealing with X_∞ and X_1. In predicting X_1 from X_∞, the formula becomes[1]

$$\sigma_{1\infty} = \sigma_1\sqrt{1 - r_{11}} \qquad (190)$$

In this form of the equation, we are dealing with predictions of X_1 from X_∞. The name given to $\sigma_{1\infty}$ is the **standard error of measurement.** Suppose that for a given set of test scores $\sigma_{1\infty}$ is 4. If a certain individual has a true score of 50 points in the test, then we may expect two-thirds of all his actual scores to lie between 46 and 54.[2] If we wish to turn the prediction about and estimate X_∞ from X_1, then the standard error of estimate becomes

$$\sigma_{\infty 1} = \sigma_\infty\sqrt{1 - r_{11}}.$$

This is not a serviceable formula, however, since we do not know the true standard deviation σ_∞. The latter may be estimated from known data, however. Consider that

$$r_{11} = \frac{\sigma_\infty^2}{\sigma_1^2} \qquad \text{and} \qquad \sqrt{r_{11}} = \frac{\sigma_\infty}{\sigma_1}.$$

Therefore,

$$\sigma_\infty = \sigma_1\sqrt{r_{11}} \qquad (191)$$

[1] The notation of $\sigma_{1\infty}$ is often given as $\sigma_{(M)}$. It goes without saying that $PE_{1\infty} = .6745\sigma_{1\infty}$.

[2] Too often one finds the interpretation of a $\sigma_{1\infty}$ misstated. For a given score of 50, when $\sigma_{1\infty}$ is 4, one is likely to read the interpretation that "the probability is two-thirds that the true score lies between 46 and 54." The latter statement implies the prediction of X_∞ from X_1.

Since σ_∞ can be thus estimated, the standard error of estimate of a true score becomes

$$\sigma_{\infty 1} = \sigma_1 \sqrt{r_{11}(1 - r_{11})} \tag{192}$$

Assuming that r_{11} is .81 and that $\sigma_{1\infty}$ is 4, then $\sigma_{\infty 1}$ would be .9 $\times$ 4, or 3.6. For an individual score of 50, we would be justified in saying that the probability is two-thirds that the true score lies between 46.4 and 53.6. It is correct practice to speak of $\sigma_{1\infty}$ as the **standard error of a raw score** and of $\sigma_{\infty 1}$ as the **standard error of a true score.** The former is the one more often used.

The chief advantage of using the standard error of measurement to indicate the reliability of a test is that it is independent of the range of talent. The coefficient of reliability, r_{11}, is very dependent upon the range of talent represented in the group tested, as will now be shown.

Reliability in Different Ranges of Ability.—As a rule, the wider the range of talent represented in the test group, the higher the self-correlation will be. This is clearly demonstrated by the scatter diagrams in Fig. 40. In the large square we have to deal with an extreme range. This scatter diagram might, for instance, represent the self-correlation of scores in Army Alpha for individuals ranging

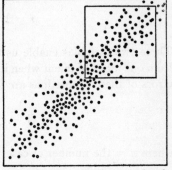

Fig. 40.—Scatter diagrams for the self-correlation of a test in both a short and a long range of talent in the test group.

from the lowest literates to college graduates. Suppose we were to confine our group to college students. This group may be supposed to fall within the small square at the upper right corner of the correlation diagram. Notice how the points now scatter rather widely over the correlation surface. To indicate just how serious this is, in a single school grade a test may give an r_{11} equal to .40, whereas in a group of individuals ranging from grades 2 to 12 the corresponding r_{11} is .90. Now *the* reliability of the test is surely the same no matter to what range of talent it is applied, provided of course that the test is an appropriate one for the entire range. While r_{11} may thus vary considerably with the range of ability, the standard error of measurement will not do so, for the σ_1 of the group normally increases in proportion to the range of ability and so the standard error of the estimate that is based upon it remains constant. If we let R_{1I} be the coefficient of reliability for a group with the large range of ability and let Σ_1 be the standard error of that group, then Kelley (24, p. 222) has shown that

$$\frac{\sigma_1}{\Sigma_1} = \sqrt{\frac{1 - R_{1I}}{1 - r_{11}}} \tag{193}$$

if we can assume that the test is equally effective (the standard error of measurement remaining constant) in both ranges. Solving for one r in terms of the other,

$$R = 1 - \frac{\sigma^2(1 - r)}{\Sigma^2} \tag{194a}$$

$$r = 1 - \frac{\Sigma^2(1 - R)}{\sigma^2} \tag{194b}$$

These two formulas enable us to estimate the reliability coefficient from one range of talent when it is known in another. The standard errors of these estimations are found from the formula (15)

$$\sigma_r = (1 - r)\left[\frac{2}{n} + \frac{3 - R^2}{N}\right]^{1/2} \tag{195}$$

where n = the number of cases in the distribution with the smaller range.

N = the number of cases in the corresponding distribution of larger range.

The solution of σ_R is readily found by the same formula except that the use of r and R and also of n and N is reversed throughout.[1]

There is no standard range of talent that is generally recognized, in terms of which all reliability coefficients should be translated. For this reason, whenever one presents any coefficient of reliability, one should always mention the range of talent from which it is derived. For practical purposes, whether the reliability of a test is acceptably high will be determined by the type of groups with which the test is going to be used. No hard and fast rules can be laid down as to the minimum reliability required for a practical test. For measuring individual scores it seems to be the general

---

[1] Alternative formulas for (193), (194), and (195) are given by Dickey (11); they are said to be more reliable than those of Kelley.

opinion that r_{11} should be at least .90, preferably above .94. For measuring groups of individuals the minimum reliability coefficient may be lower. The factor of validity, however, complicates the picture. A test with a validity of .70 and reliability of .75 is better than a test whose validity is only .50 and whose reliability may be .90. It depends also upon the purposes for which the test is intended. The tester must use his own good judgment when making a final decision about the reliability of a particular test.

Factors Influencing Reliability.—Much experience in mental testing has led to rather definite conclusions as to what factors raise or lower the reliability of a test and also as to the relative importance of those factors. This experience has been summarized by Symonds (47, 48), whose conclusions are briefly listed here:

1. The greater the number of items, the more reliable the test.

2. On the whole, the longer the test time, the greater the reliability. This is due primarily to the fact that time is correlated with the number of items. Lindquist and Cook (30) have shown that for a test of a given length there is an optimal length of time for reliability; times longer than this decrease the reliability.

3. The narrower the range of difficulty of items, the greater the reliability. Items so easy that all individuals can pass them, or so difficult that none can pass them, obviously add nothing to the discrimination of individual differences. An exception to the rule is when a too narrow range of difficulty is applied to a too homogeneous group. In the latter case nearly all individuals will obtain approximately the same score.

4. Interdependent items tend to reduce the reliability. Such items are passed or failed together and this has the equivalent result of reducing the length of the test.

5. The more objective the scoring, the greater the reliability. The subjective judgments of the scorer obviously introduce more chance variations.

6. Inaccuracy in scoring may be an important factor, but this is readily controllable.

7. The chance factor in answering test items is important; the greater the probability of success by chance, the lower the reliability. In a two-response test, like the true-false test, the reliability for a test of 100 items was found to be about .84. When the number of alternative responses was increased to 3, 5, and 7, the reliability increased to .89, .88, and .91, respectively. In a recall test, in which

success by chance is infinitely small, the reliability was .95 [see Symonds (48)].

8. The more homogeneous the material, the greater the reliability.

9. The more common the experiences of the individuals tested, the greater the reliability.

10. Catch questions lower the reliability.

11. Various subtle factors which lead to misinterpretation of the item lead to unreliability:

 a. The emotional coloring of words used.

 b. Length of the test item.   Short items are generally better than long ones.

 c. Choice of words.

 d. Poor sentence construction.

 e. Inadequate or faulty directions.

 f. Misleading intent of the question.

12. Speed of work on a test.   Some individuals are set for speed and some are not.   Some distribute their time properly; some do not.

13. The mental set for accuracy is important for reliability.

14. Variations in incentive or effort are important.

15. Perseverations from previous mental or emotional experiences are important.

16. Distractions have some effect, although they can be overrated.

17. Accidents, like breaking a pencil or finding a defective test blank, are incidental factors.

18. Illness, worry, or excitement are often suggested as important factors, but they have been very much overrated.

19. Time interval between tests.   This is relatively unimportant up to a year for tests of ability, but reliability generally decreases with intervening time.

20. Cheating may be a factor for unreliability.

21. Position of the individual on the learning curve for the tasks of the test may be important, but not always so.

22. Failure of the individual to grasp the proper mental set and to hold it throughout the test is important.

THE SPEARMAN-BROWN PROPHECY FORMULA

The Estimated Reliability of a Test Doubled in Length.—By means of the Spearman-Brown (S-B) prophecy formula we can estimate the reliability of a long test from the known reliability of a shorter test. The vital assumption that must be satisfied if the estimate is to be valid is that the entire test is homogeneous; the long test must be comparable in every way to the shorter test. The formula is especially useful when we have employed the split-half method of finding r_{11} and when we wish to know the corresponding r for the full length. This is a matter of doubling the length, and for this special though most common case the formula is

$$r_{2\text{II}} = \frac{2r_{11}}{1 + r_{11}} \tag{196}$$

where $r_{2\text{II}}$ = the reliability of a test doubled in length.

$r_{2\text{I}}$ = as usual, the reliability of the single length.

For example, if r_{11} is .60, then $r_{2\text{II}}$ = 1.20/1.60, which is .75. Doubling the length of test again, $r_{4\text{IV}}$ would be 1.50/1.75, which is .857. We could go on, increasing the reliability to any desired degree by increasing the length of test. As a reliability of 1.00 is approached, however, the increase in the coefficient becomes smaller and smaller. A law of diminishing returns applies, and there is a limit beyond which practical returns in higher reliability no longer pay for the labor of extra length of test.

The Estimated Reliability of a Test of Any Length.—The general S-B formula which applies to any amount of increase in test length is given as follows:

$$r_{AA} = \frac{Ar_{11}}{1 + (A - 1)r_{11}} \tag{197}$$

in which A is the number of times the test is lengthened. With an r_{11} of .60, if the test is lengthened four times,

$$r_{4\text{IV}} = \frac{2.40}{2.80} = .857$$

which agrees with the result of twice doubling a similar test in the preceding paragraph. The value of A need not be unitary. A test may be increased 60 per cent in length, in which case $A = 1.6$ and the formula may be used accordingly. In fact one may estimate the reliability of a test of reduced length. Suppose a test has a reliability coefficient of .75; what would be the reliability of a test half as long? A then equals .5 and the formula gives the result

$$\frac{.375}{(1 - .375)} = \frac{.375}{.625} = .60.$$

The Reliability of Estimated Test Reliabilities.—The standard error of r_{AA} has been provided by Shen (41) as[1]

$$\sigma_{r_{AA}} = \frac{A(1 - r_{11}^2)}{\sqrt{N}[1 + (A - 1)r_{11}]^2} = \frac{A\sigma_{r_{11}}}{[1 + (A - 1)r_1]^2} \quad (198)$$

When $A = 2$, in other words, for a test of doubled length, formula (198) reduces to

$$\sigma_{r_{2II}} = \frac{2(1 - r_{11}^2)}{\sqrt{N}(1 + r_{11})^2} \quad (199)$$

The Required Length of Test for a Given Reliability.—It is often desirable, knowing the reliability of a test, to find out how much longer the test must be in order to attain a reliability of a stated amount. Suppose that the reliability of a test is found to be .85. We want to know how many times as long the test should be in order to obtain a reliability of .95. By solving formula (197) for A, we obtain

$$A = \frac{r_{AA}(1 - r_{11})}{r_{11}(1 - r_{AA})} \quad (200)$$

In the problem just mentioned,

$$A = \frac{.95(1 - .85)}{.85(1 - .95)} = \frac{(.95)(.15)}{(.85)(.05)} = 3.35.$$

The test would have to be at least three and one-third times as long to attain a reliability of .95, and then only if the lengthened material were psychologically equivalent to the material already used.

The standard error of A is given by Cureton (10) as

$$\sigma_A = \frac{A(1 + r_{11})}{r_{11}\sqrt{N}} \quad (201)$$

Empirical Tests of the Spearman-Brown Formula.—Not content with the theoretical assumptions that would make the results with the S-B formula valid, a number of investigators have tested the matter experimentally. In practically every case the experimental

---

[1] Douglass (12) presents what is claimed to be a more accurate estimate of $\sigma_{r_{AA}}$.

results were in line with the predictions expected from the formula
(40, 58). This held true for tests of intelligence, spelling, achievement, and personality. It held true when the test was increased to
10 times its original length. We may therefore regard the estimates
made by the formula as highly valid, provided it is wisely applied.

The Spearman-Brown Formula Applied to Ratings.—We reach
now a very crucial question which was postponed from the chapter
on rating-scale methods. The problem arose there as to whether
the pooling of similar ratings would increase the reliabilities of the
ratings in proportion as the S-B formula would lead us to expect.
The results of Remmers and others (37, 38) lead rather definitely
to the conclusion that, if the judges are comparable, the reliability
of pooled judgments increases directly with the number of judges
according to the S-B formula. However, the correspondence
between prediction and fact is not so close as in the case of reliabilities of tests. But the difference between predicted and computed
reliabilities was never greater than 2.3 times the *PE* of the difference
(37). Kelley (26) found that, for ranked judgments of lifted weights,
the reliabilities for pools of 5, 10, and 20 judges could be predicted
very closely from the S-B formula, the greatest discrepancy being
only two times its *PE*. We may say, tentatively at least, that the
reliabilities of pooled judgments tend to increase according to the S-B
formula.

The Validity of Tests

Types of Criteria.—The validity of a test always demands some
outside criterion with which to correlate the test scores of a group.
Such criteria may be of various kinds. According to Hull (23,
p. 375), they belong to one of three classes: (1) *product criteria*, (2)
action criteria, and (3) *subjective judgment criteria*.

Product criteria are the result of some specific type of activity,
for example, the number of bricks laid by a mason, the number of
words typed by a typist, the number of boxes inspected by a worker,
or the number of shirts completed by a seamstress. If no tangible
product is left as a result of the activity, then the activity itself may
be measured while it takes place and we have an action criterion.
Such a criterion is illustrated by the speed of a runner, the errors
in juggling balls, or the height of a pole vault. Aside from these
objective measures of performance, we are compelled to depend upon
the subjective judgments of observers who know the subjects well.

To make such judgments as accurate as possible, we may resort to any one of the scaling methods, equal-appearing intervals, paired comparisons, ranking, or rating-scale methods. No matter what the type of criterion, its reliability should be established by any of the means used in determining the reliability of tests. Correction for attenuation in the criterion alone is then in order. This procedure was discussed in an earlier chapter (page 368).

The Relation of Validity to the Length of a Test.—The validity of a test will depend upon errors of attenuation in the test itself as well as upon errors in the criterion; the more reliable the test, the smaller the influence of these errors, and the longer the test, the more reliable it is. Then it follows that longer tests will be more valid than shorter ones. The increase in validity to be expected from lengthening a test A times is estimated by the formula (24, p. 200)[1]

$$r_{y(Ax)} = \frac{r_{xy}}{\sqrt{\dfrac{1 - r_{xx}}{A} + r_{xx}}} \qquad (202)$$

where $r_{y(Ax)}$ = the correlation between a criterion Y and a test X that has been increased A times in length.

r_{xy} = the original correlation between Y and X.

r_{xx} = the self-correlation of X.

A = the number of times the test is lengthened.

In case one wishes to know the number of times a test must be lengthened in order to attain a given validity coefficient, this can be found by solving formula (202) for A.

$$A = \frac{1 - r_{xx}}{\dfrac{r_{xy}^2}{r_{y(Ax)}^2} - r_{xx}} \qquad (203)$$

If one wants to know the highest limit of validity attainable by a test of a certain type—and this would be reached when the test is made infinitely long—it may be estimated by substituting ∞ for A in formula (202), which then becomes

$$r_{y\omega} = \frac{r_{xy}}{\sqrt{r_{xx}}} \qquad (204)$$

[1] It is assumed in this that the time granted to the subjects is increased in proportion to the increase in test content.

This may also be interpreted as the *correlation between a fallible criterion and a true test score*. By analogy, the *correlation between a true criterion and a fallible test score is*

$$r_{\infty x} = \frac{r_{xy}}{\sqrt{r_{yy}}} \qquad (205)$$

Equation (205) enables us to estimate the limit in validity of a test when its criterion is made perfectly reliable. This formula is really identical with formula (159) of Chapter XI. The latter derives $r_{\infty x}$ when the split-half method of finding r_{yy} has been employed. Formula (205) is a more general one.

The Relation between Validity and Reliability.—Since reliability depends directly upon the length of a test, the remarks just made and the formulas introduced apply to the relation between validity and reliability. A close study of the preceding formulas, particularly of formula (204), will show that, for a given validity r_{xy}, the smaller the reliability r_{xx} of the test, the higher will be the upper limit of validity when a test is lengthened. In other words, an unreliable test gains proportionately more in validity by lengthening than does a test that is already very reliable. Recall that the increase of reliability with length obeys a law of diminishing returns. So it is that the errors of measurement are reduced very slowly by lengthening a highly reliable test. The validity increases correspondingly very slowly. Paradoxical as it may seem, of two short tests having the same validity coefficients, the less reliable of the two is the one to cultivate and lengthen when the greatest possible increase in validity is wanted.

The Relation of Validity to the Time of the Test.—In time-limit tests there is likely to be an inverse relation between reliability and validity. As the length of time is increased the test usually becomes more valid, but the reliability becomes lower. Lindquist and Cook (30) show how this may be true in a spelling test of 60 items which is applied for 3, 4, 5, and 6 min. in different trials. The reliability coefficients may decrease in the order .91, .87, .84, and .82 for the four time intervals, respectively. The validity coefficients may increase in the order .58, .69, .74, and .75, respectively. Both the reliability and the validity approach certain limits beyond which they do not change.

From a practical standpoint, if the test time is to be lengthened, the question arises as to whether the additional time should be spent upon the same material or whether additional material should be included. There is, in other words, for a given amount of material an optimal time which makes for maximum reliability and validity. This optimal time has been defined as "the shortest time at which a greater increase in the validity of the obtained scores can be secured through the addition of more (homogeneous) material with a proportionate increase of time than by permitting more time to be spent on the same material" (30, p. 164).

The solution of the question of optimal time rests on the use of formula (202), in which both the validity and reliability coefficients appear. Having found these coefficients for a given amount of material, as in the four pairs mentioned in the discussion above, assume that A is an increase in length proportional to a chosen hypothetical increase in time. For example, with 60 items in the test and 3 min. alloted time, $r_{xy} = .58$ and $r_{xx} = .91$. Let us assume an increase in time of 1 min., or 33.3 per cent. A corresponding increase in material would make 80 items, or $A = 1.33$. Applying formula (202), we have

$$r_{y(1.33x)} = \frac{.58}{\sqrt{\dfrac{1 - .91}{1.33} + .91}} = \frac{.58}{\sqrt{.9777}} = .587.$$

From this it may be seen that the addition of items would make no appreciable increase in validity, whereas, if the additional minute had been spent on the 60 items, the validity would have increased to .69, as indicated by the list of validities given above. Let us solve the same equation when the time is 5 min., to be increased to 6 min. In this case the increase in validity by adding time alone was actually from .74 to .75. Suppose we add 20 per cent more items; what would the increase theoretically become?

$$r_{y(1.2x)} = \frac{.74}{\sqrt{\dfrac{1 - .84}{1.2} + .84}} = \frac{.74}{\sqrt{.9733}} = .750.$$

Here the increase from additional test material is identical with that from additional time; therefore we may conclude that without a longer test the optimal time for a 60-item test has been reached. The optimal time is probably not greater than 5 min., but it is certainly greater than 3 min. Thus the optimal time for almost any test can be empirically determined when maximal validity is wanted for the best use of the time allowed.

The Validity of Batteries of Tests.—Tests are ordinarily not given singly but in teams or batteries. Some parts of a battery are more reliable than others and some are more valid than others. The battery as a whole almost invariably has a higher validity than any one test taken alone. The selection of tests which will be retained in a battery is an important matter, for some tests, which as single tests have a high validity, add little or nothing to the validity of a battery, whereas other tests, which taken alone correlate very little or not at all with the criterion, may add something to the predictive value of the battery. It all depends upon the intercorrelations of the tests themselves. Certain principles have been found to operate in the pooling of tests in batteries. These principles are admirably summarized by Hull (23, p. 449).

In general, the practice is to select for a battery tests that correlate high with the criterion but low with one another. This rule has been observed for a long time. But there are various exceptions to the rule. In this discussion we speak of a 'high' correlation as one that is in the upper part of the range, which extends from −1.00 to +1.00, and a 'low' correlation as one in the lower part of that range; the more negative it is, the lower it is. We shall speak of a 'large' correlation as one distant from .00 and a 'small' correlation as one approaching .00, either negative or positive. Hull (23) presents four cases, which we shall illustrate in Table 81.

TABLE 81.—THE VALIDITY COEFFICIENTS OF TEST BATTERIES FOR DIFFERENT VALIDITIES AND INTERCORRELATIONS OF PARTS

r_{12}	r_{13}	Intercorrelations (r_{23})										
		−.70	−.40	−.20	−.10	−.05	.00	+.05	+.10	+.20	+.40	+.70
+.50	+.40	....	.82	.71	.67	.66	.64	.63	.61	.59	.55	.50
−.50	−.40	....	.82	.71	.67	.66	.64	.63	.61	.59	.55	.50
±.50	∓.40	.50	.55	.59	.61	.63	.64	.66	.67	.71	.82	....
±.50	.00	.70	.55	.51	....	....	.50	....	....	.51	.55	.70

Case I.—Correlations with the criterion positive and large. The lower the intercorrelations, the higher the validity of the battery. This is illustrated in the first line of Table 81.[1]

[1] Two tests that correlate strongly and in the same direction, either positively or negatively, with a criterion will ordinarily correlate positively with one another. Negative correlations between human abilities are extremely rare and

Case II.—Correlations with the criterion negative and large. The lower the intercorrelations, the higher the validity of the battery.

Case III.—Correlations with the criterion large but reversed in sign. The higher the intercorrelations, the higher the validity of the battery.

Case IV.—Validity of one test high, either positive or negative, and the validity of the other zero. The greater the intercorrelations, either positive or negative, the higher the validity of the battery. Thus a test that does not correlate at all with the criterion may add to the validity of the battery if it correlates strongly enough with a test that does correlate with the criterion.

The four rules just listed are naturally only rough guiding principles. In order to get the maximum forecasting value from a battery of tests, the thing to do is to apply the methods of multiple correlation, finding a multiple regression equation and weighting the tests accordingly. This gives the maximum validity to be obtained from a test battery. Those tests that are found to have very slight regression weights may be eliminated and a new multiple R may be computed with those remaining. It should be pointed out, however, that the validity as indicated by a multiple R applies strictly to the group of subjects from which the regression equation was obtained. When the test battery is applied to a new group, there is typically a *shrinkage* in the size of R and the regression weights may vary from those obtained earlier. This shrinkage becomes greater as the number of tests in the battery increases and as the number of subjects in the first criterion group decreases.

The Validity of Test Items

Discrimination Value versus Difficulty of a Test Item.—It is important at the beginning of this discussion to make clear the distinction in meaning between the difficulty of a test item and its diagnostic value. The two factors are not practically independent, as we shall see, but logically they are different. An item is highly diagnostic or has high discriminating power if it can be passed

---

probably nonexistent. Negative correlations are likely to occur only because two measuring scales are reversed as to direction. A time-limit test gives high scores for greater ability whereas a work-limit test gives low scores for greater ability. The correlation between two such tests would probably be negative although the abilities measured are in reality positively correlated.

successfully by almost all individuals who have abilities that lie above the amount required to respond correctly to the item and if it is failed by most of those with abilities below that point. An item that can be passed equally often by individuals of all levels of ability obviously has no discriminating power. An item that can be passed by no one likewise has no discriminating power. Thus items that are entirely too easy or entirely too difficult are not diagnostic of differences of ability. But some items that are of medium difficulty can be passed by too many of low ability and are

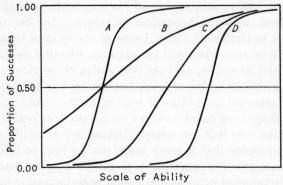

Fig. 41.—Four ogives showing the increase in the probability of success in test items with increase in the ability of the individual.

failed by too many of high ability. They, likewise, are not very diagnostic.

Theoretically, every test item can be passed by more and more individuals as the level of ability increases from group to group. Figure 41 illustrates these relationships between level of ability and proportions of successes. The increase in probability of success with increase in ability is assumed to be of the familiar ogive form. The ogives drawn in Fig. 41 represent four test items. The level of difficulty of the item is the median of the ogive. Thus, items *A* and *B* have identical levels of difficulty, whereas *C* and *D* are of greater difficulty. The diagnostic value of the item is represented by the slope of the ogive. Items *A* and *D* have the steepest slope and they are equally diagnostic, although *D* is a more difficult item. Item *C* is one of medium difficulty and medium discriminatory power. Item *B* has the poorest diagnostic value of the four. If one could establish a scale of difficulty in psychological units, it would be possible to identify any test item whatsoever by giving its median value and its 'precision' value in terms of h as in the method of constant stimuli. This is an ideal toward which testers have been working in recent years and already the various tools for approaching that goal are being refined. It is to those devices that we now direct our attention.

A Classification of Methods of Item Analysis.—While the straight-forward constant process, as outlined in the preceding discussion, would seem to fit the situation, the application of the constant methods to the problem of item analysis has not been the typical approach. One reason, as was said before, is the unfamiliarity of most testers with psychophysical technique. Another reason is the failure to establish a rational scale of ability or of level of difficulty. To be sure, Binet and his followers, adopting mental age as the yardstick of ability, used the proportions of individuals passing an item as the indicator of level, but mental age has never been seriously regarded as a rational scale of ability. Any substitutes for mental age were based upon raw scores, decile or centile ratings, and the like. So it is not strange, lacking any generally accepted guiding principles, that so many varied devices have been suggested for evaluating test items. Most of the devices for determining diagnostic values of items merely assume some increasing functional relationship between level of ability and the proportion of successes.

In attempting to classify the validating methods for items, one has to be rather arbitrary. In the classification to follow, it has been assumed that there are six possible classes of devices. This is based upon the fact that the criterion scores can be treated in three different ways. The subjects can be divided into two extreme categories; they can be separated into a number of classes greater than two; or they can be treated as a continuous distribution. The test item can be scored in one of two dichotomous categories or in a greater number of classes. As a matter of fact, the devices fall into only four groups. If the scoring of the items is dichotomous, the criterion scoring may likewise be dichotomous, it may be in groups, or it may be continuous. Although from the procedure of the constant method the division of criterion individuals into several equidistant groups as to ability would be the most natural thing to do, very few have followed that procedure. With multiple scoring of items, as in multiple-choice tests, the criterion scoring is almost universally kept in terms of a continuous variable.

Dichotomous Scoring and Multiple Criterion Groups. 1. *The Precision Method.*—This method is best illustrated by the work of Paterson (35) and of Uhrbrock and Richardson (62). In general, the criterion subjects are classified in thirds, in quartiles, or in any other groupings that contain equal numbers. This gives a base line of units that corresponds with percentile measures rather than units of raw scores. The unit will vary, of course, from group to group. It is not an absolute scale of ability. This is unimportant practically, unless the items are to be scaled for difficulty. For every test item the proportion of each group passing the item is determined. The diagnostic value of the item is indicated by the steepness of the curve. Where no accurate computation of h (the precision) is wanted, graphic solutions or mere inspections of the proportions are sufficient to tell which items are the most discriminative. To show how important the result can be, we may cite the work of Uhrbrock and Richardson (62). Starting with a battery of tests containing 820 items, they eliminated all but 85 of the most diagnostic items. A test of 400 items containing the original 'dead wood' had a validity coefficient of only .49, whereas the final test of 85 items had a validity of .71 for the forecasting of supervisory ability.

Multiple Scoring and a Continuous Criterion. 2. *The Correlation Ratio* (Eta).—In this method, the subjects making each response to the item, or receiving the same scoring weight, are segregated. The solution of eta is then the same as that described in Chapter XI (pages 343 *ff.*).

3. *The McCall Method.*—This method is described by Barthelmess (2), who gives the following formula

$$AD_{y''} = \frac{\Sigma[n|Y'' - M_y|]}{N} \tag{206}$$

where Y'' = the mean criterion score of a particular response group.

M_y = the mean criterion score of the total group.

n = the number of individuals in a particular response group.

N = the total number of individuals.

A comparison of this formula with formula (133) will show that it is in reality a species of correlation ratio. It is based upon the average deviation rather than the standard deviation and lacks merely the AD of the total distribution (AD_y) in the denominator of being comparable directly with eta. Since for any test AD_y is identical for all items, for comparative purposes it is omitted.

4. *The Long Method.*—The formula for this is also given by Barthelmess (2).

$$L = \frac{(m_1 - m_2)f_1f_2 + (m_1 - m_3)f_1f_3 + \cdots (m_{n-1} - m_n)f_{n-1}f_n}{(\sigma_y)N} \quad (207)$$

where m = the mean of the criterion scores of individuals making a certain response.

f = the corresponding number of individuals making that response.

σ_y = the sigma of the entire criterion group.

N = the total number of individuals.

It should be stated that the means are arranged in the order of size, m_1 being the largest and m_n the smallest.

**Dichotomous Scoring with a Continuous Variable. 5. *The Vincent Overlapping Method.*—This method, suggested by Vincent (63), has also been credited to Thorndike. For every item the criterion group is divided into two parts, those passing and those failing. The median score of the passing group is established. The percentage of the failing group who exceed the median of the passing group is taken as the measure of validity. In this method, unlike most others, a high coefficient (coefficient of overlapping) indicates low validity and vice versa. In terms of a formula, we may say that

$$VO = p_{f > Mdn_p} \quad (208)$$

where VO = the Vincent coefficient of overlapping.

$p_{f > Mdn_p}$ = the proportion of the failing group exceeding the median of the passing group.

6. *Modified Vincent Method.*—Barthelmess (2) improved upon the Vincent overlapping method by including also the proportion of those passing the item who fall below the median of the failing group. The coefficient of overlapping then becomes the mean of the two proportions. In terms of a formula,

$$BO = \frac{p_{f > Mdn_p} + p_{p > Mdn_f}}{2} \quad (209)$$

7. *Long's Overlapping Method.*—Long (31) proposes an overlapping method which he claims to be superior to that of Vincent. It is given briefly by the formula

$$LO = 1 - \frac{2\Sigma \ (\text{``passes'' below ``fails''})}{PF} \qquad (210)$$

where LO = the Long coefficient of overlapping.

P = the total number of passes.

F = the total number of failures.

To illustrate the method, consider the following list of criterion scores, arranged in rank order; for each score P or F will indicate whether the item in question was passed or failed.

Criterion scores	92	87	86	81	75	72	69	68	62	60	54	53	46
Passes...................	P	P		P	P	P		P			P	P	
Failures................			F				F		F	F			F
"Passes" below "fails"....			6				3		2	2			0

There are 8 passes and 5 failures. The sum of the "passes below fails" is 13. Therefore,

$$LO = 1 - \frac{(2)(13)}{(8)(5)} = 1 - .65 = .35.$$

8. *Long's Weighted Overlapping Method.*—Long (31) also provides a device for including the factor of difficulty of the item in his indicator of diagnostic power. The discriminatory power of an item is dependent upon its relative difficulty for the group to which it is applied. The formula then becomes

$$LWO = \frac{PF - 2\Sigma \ (\text{``passes'' below ``fails''})}{\left(\dfrac{n^2}{2}\right)} \qquad (211)$$

in which n is the number of items.

9. *The Biserial r Method.*—Since the test scores divide the group into two categories and the criterion measurements may still be continuous, the familiar biserial r may be obtained. Many investigators have used the biserial r in this connection and there has been a distinct tendency to set it up as the standard against which to check all other devices.

10. *The Summation of Agreement Method.*—Lentz and others (29) propose a novel method that is especially applicable with personality tests of the questionnaire type in which the subject replies to a question with "Yes" or "No." Each item is weighted

for validity according to the frequency with which all other items are marked in the same direction. In a questionnaire purporting to measure conservatism, for example, if item 1 is under inspection, each paper is examined in turn. If a subject gave the conservative reply to item 1, then the number of other items answered conservatively is recorded. When a subject gives a radical answer, the sum of all radical answers is recorded. The coefficient of agreement for the item is then

$$CAg = \frac{a_1 + a_2 + a_3 + \cdots + a_n}{N} \qquad (212)$$

where CAg = the coefficient agreement.

a_1 = the total number of responses by the first subject that agree with that subject's response to the item being considered.

a_2 = the same for the second subject and a_3 for the third.

N = the total number of subjects.

11. *The Method of Successive Pools.*—This method, which has been attributed to Toops (21), is a very elaborate one. First, the item with the highest validity is selected. It is paired with every other item in turn and the scores of the pool of two items are correlated with the criterion until the most valid pair is found. Then the most valid trio, quadruplet, quintuplet, etc., are found in turn, thus building up the most valid pool of items.

12. *The Method of Successive Residuals.*—This method, which is probably the most promising of any considered thus far, was developed by Horst (21). He points out that, in the selection of test items, it is not merely a matter of choosing items that are highly valid. In the composition of test batteries it was shown that the individual tests must correlate low with one another if we are to gain the benefit of pooling the tests. So, in pooling test items, if we disregard the intercorrelation of the items themselves, we may gain little by pooling them to form a test. The ideal procedure, as in the formation of test batteries, would be to use the multiple correlation technique. The work involved with a large number of test items would, however, be prohibitive.

Horst proposes the following short cut: First one selects that item which has the highest correlation with the criterion. One then finds that part of the original criterion which is *not* predicted by the best test item. This is the first residual, and it becomes the new criterion. The next step is to correlate every remaining item with this residual to find which single one predicts it best. Next the residual not predicted by the two items combined is found and the process is repeated again. The task is a lengthy one, but it may be carried out until most of the original criterion is accounted for. The whole process may then be repeated, giving a new set of items that predict a very large part of the criterion. The addition of other sets in this way will improve the reliability of the test. The procedures are so involved and the formulas so lengthy that they are not given space here. The reader who wishes to use the method will find a full account in Horst's report (21). To indicate the worth of the method, Horst (20) was able by means of it to develop a test for salesmen, composed of 117 of an original collection of 405 items, which had a validity coefficient of .975 and a reliability of .93.

Dichotomous Scoring and Dichotomous Criterion Groups. 13. *Difference between High and Low Groups.*—When test items are scored as either right or wrong, or according to any two other categories, and when criterion groups are divided into two parts, a high group and a low, the simplest and most direct indicator of validity is to find a simple difference in the number of successes in the upper and the lower group. The two groups may be the highest and the lowest thirds or fourths of the total population tested, or the extreme 27 per cent at either end of the range, or the highest and lowest 20 individuals. These various divisions of criterion groups have been used. The indicator of validity is the difference between the proportion (or number) of the high group passing the item and the proportion (or number) of the low group. The results are often in surprisingly good agreement with those from methods that require much more time.

14. *The Critical-ratio Method.*—This method has been a favorite with many. When the two extreme criterion groups are established, the proportions of successes in the two are found, with their standard errors or their probable errors. Next the differences between the proportions and the σ or the PE of the difference are found by formulas already well known to the reader. The size of the critical ratio that is regarded necessary for a significant item is somewhat arbitrary, but a d/σ_d of 2.00 or a d/PE_d of 3.00 is quite commonly used as the minimum criterion of significance for a test item. Since the size of σ_p or of PE_p depends upon N, it can be seen that the required standard of significance can be easily attained if one uses a large number of cases, whereas with a small N the same items might not reach the same standard of significance. In contrast with this method, the overlapping methods are independent of N. The amount of faith to be placed in any test of validity should, of course, increase inversely as the square root of N. But for practical purposes, the amount of overlapping of high and low groups, regardless of the number, gives a truer picture of discriminatory power. Graphic methods for using the critical-ratio test of validity have been described by Votaw (64).

15. *Clark's Index of Validity.*—Clark (5) proposes an index of validity given by the formula

$$IV = \frac{P - D}{1 - D} \tag{213}$$

where IV = the index of validity.

D = the proportion of all individuals who fail to pass the item.

P = the proportion of the low-criterion group who fail.

For example, if 40 per cent of all the subjects fail to pass an item, then, if the item were a perfect one, we should expect that 40 per cent would be made up of the lowest 40 per cent of the group in the ability being measured. Accordingly, the lowest 40 per cent of the group, according to the criterion measures, is separated from the highest 60 per cent. But the item is probably not perfectly valid. Not all of the low group fail to pass it. Suppose that 90 per cent of the low group did fail to pass the item, P then equals .90 and D equals .40. The formula gives

$$IV = \frac{.90 - .40}{1.00 - .40} = \frac{.50}{.60} = .833.$$

Had the item been perfectly valid, then the numerator would have been .60 and the IV equal to 1.00. Had P been equal to .40, IV would have been zero.

16. *Cook's Index of Discrimination* (A).—Cook (7) presents a number of original indexes of validity. These were originally used in the validation of spelling-test items, but they may be generally applied. Index A uses data similar to those of Clark's method. It consists in finding "the percentage of pupils misspelling the word in that group which consists of all those pupils who would misspell it if the word were perfect in discriminating power" (7, p. 43). The formula is

$$ID_a = \frac{F}{E'},\tag{214}$$

where E' = the lowest part of the criterion group, equal in number to E, when E is the total number who failed with the item.

F = the number of group E' who actually failed with the item.

Index A is therefore the percentage of those who are expected to fail who actually do fail, assuming a perfectly discriminating item.

17. *Cook's Index of Discrimination* (B).—This index is defined as "the percentage of pupils misspelling the word in that group which consists of all those pupils who would misspell it if the word were perfect in discriminating power, after those pupils who would misspell the word in a normal group of that size have been subtracted" (7, p. 44). The formula is

$$ID_b = \frac{FN - E^2}{EN - E^2}\tag{215}$$

where E = the number in the total group failing with the item.

F = the number of those in group E' (the group expected to fail if the item were perfect) failing with the item.

N = the number of individuals.

18. *Cook's Index of Discrimination* (C).—This is given by the formula

$$ID_c = \frac{p_1 - p_4}{75}\tag{216}$$

where p_1 = the proportion passing an item among those in the highest quartile.

p_4 = the proportion passing it in the lowest quartile.

75 = the number of percentiles of ability between the lowest and highest quartiles.

Index C is the slope of the line connecting the percentages of the lower and higher quarters of ability when the units of percentage of accuracy and units of ability are assumed to be equal (7, p. 46).

19. *Cook's Index of Discrimination* (D).—This is given by the "ratio of the per cent of accuracy with which the upper one-fourth of spelling ability spells a word to the per cent of accuracy for the lower one-fourth" (7, p. 48). The formula is

$$ID_d = \frac{p_1}{p_4} \tag{217}$$

where p_1 = the proportion of those in the highest quartile who
pass the item.

p_4 = the proportion of those in the lowest quartile who
pass it.

General Evaluation of the Validating Methods.—More than a
dozen distinct devices were mentioned for the selection of diagnostic
items and for the weeding out of nondiagnostic items. What is
their general value, their relative usefulness and efficiency in general
practice? These are important questions, and unfortunately the
answers can be given only with hesitation.

It might be expected that the selection of only valid items would
increase the validity of the test as a whole. But, unless the dependence of one item upon another is taken into account, as Horst
has shown, this hope is bound to be disappointed. It might be
expected that items can be weighted according to their validity and
that this will improve the test as a whole. The question of weighted
scoring is to be taken up in some detail later. Suffice it to say here
that all such attempts have not given results that live up to expecta-
tions. It is not true that tests made up only of the items of highest
validity make the most desirable tests. The addition of items of
moderate validity increases the worth of the test (43). But the
elimination of 'dead wood' not only increases the validity of the test
as a whole but obviously reduces the testing time. Thorndike
proposes the rule that no item having a validity coefficient (based
upon biserial r) lower than .30 shall be included in a test designed
for the type of group from which that index of validity was found
(52, p. 129). Others seem to concur in the opinion that the chief use
of studies of item validity is to eliminate the worthless material.
If a method like that of *successive residuals* is used in addition, then
the maximum validity for a test as a whole can be obtained.

Concerning the relative worth of the various devices, little can be
said. One criticism often brought out concerning several of them
is that they do not use all the available data. The selection of two
extreme groups, for example, leaving out of account the average
individuals, reduces the numbers of cases available and so reduces
the reliability of proportions obtained from them. A number of
methods are of the empirical, rough-and-ready sort, without the
customary respectable mathematical rationalizing that one would

like to see. Against this criticism the reply may be made that they work, and, since usually we expect to base upon them only the rejection of worthless items and since we use unweighted scoring for those that remain, nothing better is needed. The last statement being true, those devices which demand the least time are to be preferred on practical grounds. Another general criticism offered is that some indexes are too much influenced by the difficulty of an item. But since the diagnostic value of an item is dependent upon its relative difficulty for the group to which it is applied, this criticism is again of practical unimportance. For advice applying to particular devices, the reader is referred to reports of those who have had the most experience with them (2, 7, 29, 31, 43, and 52).

The Difficulty of Test Items

Perhaps the most adequate hypothetical analysis of measured intelligence is that which was made explicit by Thorndike (52), who points out the variables of *altitude*, *breadth* or *extent*, and *speed*. An individual's intelligence, he postulated, can be measured in terms of the level of difficulty with which he can succeed half the time. It is measurable, other things being equal, by the proportion of items of a given degree of difficulty which the individual can pass. It is also measurable, other things being equal, by the number of solutions per unit of time. The Binet tests are obviously 'altitude' tests, although the factor of breadth enters in. The typical group test, if it is a time-limit test, measures all three aspects simultaneously, although no one knows to what degree. In the latter, to the extent that variations in altitude play a role, the difficulty of an item is important.

In the construction of group tests care has usually been taken to place the test items in order of difficulty with the easiest first, although this order has usually been determined by inspection and subjective judgment. When a test is to be applied to groups varying greatly in ability, naturally there must be some items so easy that the lowest can master them and some so difficult that even the ablest sometimes fail. But in any group, no matter how wide the scatter of ability, an item that can be passed by all has no discriminating value. An item that is passed by 99 and failed by 1 out of 100 makes only 99 discriminations and one that is passed by 98 and failed by 2 makes only 2×98 or 196 discriminations. It is evident, then, that the difficulty of an item is a very important factor in the reliability and validity of a test. It is important that we have devices for establishing the relative difficulty of items, not only that they may be used, as in the Binet tests, to measure altitude, or that we may arrange test items in order of difficulty, but also that the maximum discriminating power of the test may be assured.

Evaluation of Difficulty by Expert Opinion.—It might be supposed that, as an improvement on a mere inspection of test items, the more accurate and controlled scaling methods, such as paired comparisons, ranking method, equal-appearing intervals, and the like, could be employed for evaluating the difficulty of test items. This has not proved to be the case. Says Thorndike (52, p. 156), "We cannot trust any consensus of present opinion to provide an accurate measure of the difficulty or of the intellectual difficulty of a single brief task." The reasons given are that no one, not even a psychologist, yet knows enough about intelligence to render valid judgments. Constant errors creep in, such as the overestimation of easy tasks and underestimation of difficult ones. For any task it is hard to judge to what extent intelligence is involved and what nonintellectual factors may aid or hinder in the solution. On the other hand, such estimates agree well with one another and correlate highly with objective experimental results. They may not be used to replace experimental evaluations of difficulty, but they may certainly be used as preliminary estimates or rough approximations.

The Relation of Difficulty to the Proportion of Successes.—It goes without saying that, the greater the proportion of individuals passing an item, the easier the item. With a group of individuals homogeneous as to ability, we may assume that the relationship is a normal ogive function. This ogive is *not* the same as that pictured in Fig. 41. In that case the X-axis was a scale of ability and each ogive represented a constant degree of difficulty. In Fig. 42 we have a variable scale of difficulty, and each ogive represents a constant degree of ability. The ogives are descending because, naturally, the more difficult the item, the *smaller* the proportion of the homogeneous group passing it. If we assume that the group represented in Fig. 42 is one of twelve-year-old children and that 90 per cent of them passed a particular problem A, then, by going to the tables and finding the corresponding value of x/σ, we know that the X value of the test item is -1.28σ in terms of standard measures. Another item that was passed by only 20 per cent of the children has a scale value of $.84\sigma$. In order to make all the scale values positive, we may assume an arbitrary zero point at -3σ. In that case, the first problem would have a scale value of 1.72 and the second a scale value of 3.84.

Ayres (1) was probably the first to employ this principle in the construction of his standard measuring scale of spelling ability. Woody (65) followed with a scale for arithmetic ability with problems evaluated for level of difficulty. The important advance in this

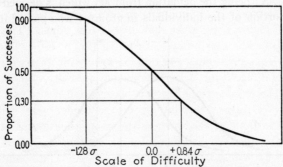

Fig. 42.—The scale values of test items evaluated as to difficulty as a function of the proportions of successes in a homogeneous group of individuals.

development is the use of the standard error of a distribution as the unit of mental ability.

The standard deviation was also used, though in a somewhat different fashion, by McCall (32) in his well known T-scale. He used the standard deviation of a group of twelve-year-old children as the unit, not of difficulty, but of ability. A child's test score was translated into a standard score on the twelve-year-old distribution. He assumed a distribution ranging from -5σ to $+5\sigma$. Each sigma unit was subdivided into 10 parts of $.1\sigma$ each, so that the total scale had 100 points in all. The twelve-year-old group was thought to be a happy choice, for the scale could be extended, as needed, either above or below that range, and the scores from all tests and all age groups would thus have the same zero point and the same unit. The plan was followed, also, in using the twelve-year-old group as the typical, homogeneous one for determining the scale values for difficulty of test items. Unfortunately it was shown that the real variabilities of different age groups differ and that, to develop a scale for intelligence which could be called an absolute scale, with the same unit throughout, this change in variability from group to group must be taken into account.

Thurstone's Absolute Scaling Methods.—In the presentation of Thurstone's absolute scaling methods, his own accounts (53, 55, 56) will be followed very closely. In Fig. 43 we have represented two normal distributions for two groups of individuals of adjacent age levels, whose averages, M_1 and M_2, are not far apart on the scale of ability and whose standard deviations, σ_1 and σ_2, are assumed not to be equal. Let X represent the position of a certain test item on the scale, X_1 being the deviation from M_1 which is derived from p_1, the proportion of the individuals in group A who passed it. Simi-

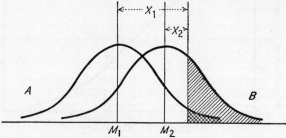

Fig. 43.—The scale separations of a test item from the means of two different groups of individuals.

larly, X_2 represents the sigma distance of the same test item from M_2 as determined by p_2, the proportion of group B that passed it. The shaded areas under the two curves represent p_1 and p_2, respectively. From Fig. 43 it can be seen that $M_1 + X_1\sigma_1 = M_2 + X_2\sigma_2$. Dividing through by σ_2,

$$\frac{M_1}{\sigma_2} + X_1\frac{\sigma_1}{\sigma_2} = \frac{M_2}{\sigma_2} + X_2.$$

Solving for X_2,

$$X_2 = X_1\left(\frac{\sigma_1}{\sigma_2}\right) + \left(\frac{M_1 - M_2}{\sigma_2}\right)$$

which is the equation of a straight line with a slope of σ_1/σ_2 and an X_2-intercept of $(M_1 - M_2)/\sigma_2$. Thus, if enough of the values in the above equation can be assumed or known, we can translate the scale values of an item from one distribution into the terms of another. This is the fundamental secret of absolute scaling.

The various steps required in the solution of scale values for test items will be illustrated by a problem given by Thurstone (53). The problem concerns the evaluation of items of the Binet scale as applied to seven- and eight-year-old groups. Table 82 gives a small portion of the necessary data, originally based upon 53 items. The routine steps are as follows:

1. Find the proportion of the individuals of each group who pass each item. In Table 82 we have those proportions in the seven- and eight-year groups for 11 of the items selected at random. These are designated as p_7 and p_8, respectively.

2. Translate the proportions into scale separations, X_7 and X_8, in the illustrative problem. These are the X-distances of the items from the means of the respective age groups in terms of the standard errors of those age groups.

3. Find the means of the X values for each group, in this case m_7 and m_8. The means given in Table 82 are based upon 50 items as presented in Thurstone's article.

TABLE 82.—THE COMPUTATION OF UNWEIGHTED SCALE VALUES FOR TEST ITEMS BY MEANS OF THURSTONE'S ABSOLUTE SCALING METHOD

Test item	p_7	p_8	X_7	X_8	X_7^2	X_8^2
10	.992	.996	− 2.41	− 2.65	5.81	7.02
15	.973	.990	− 1.93	− 2.33	3.72	5.43
20	.953	.986	− 1.67	− 2.20	2.79	4.84
25	.940	.972	− 1.55	− 1.91	2.40	3.65
30	.853	.952	− 1.05	− 1.66	1.10	2.76
35	.673	.872	− .45	− 1.14	.20	1.30
40	.391	.682	+ .28	− .47	.08	.22
41	.425	.602	+ .19	− .26	.04	.07
50	.063	.131	+ 1.53	+ 1.12	2.34	1.25
55	.009	.153	+ 2.37	+ 1.02	5.62	1.04
59	.018	.043	+ 2.10	+ 1.72	4.41	2.96
		Σ	−14.64	−40.27	113.55	119.32
		m	− .293	− .805		
					s 1.478	1.318

4. Find the standard deviations of the two distributions of X values. These are called s_7 and s_8 to distinguish them from σ_7 and σ_8, which belong to the absolute scale and not to the raw X values.

5. Find σ_8 in terms of σ_7, assuming that σ_7 is already known. In Thurstone's illustrative problem, σ_3, or the standard error of the

three-year-old group, was arbitrarily adopted as the unit of the entire scale, and M_3, the mean of the three-year-old group, was adopted as the zero point, age three being the lowest age group used. By comparing successive pairs of age groups it had been previously found that σ_7 was equal to 1.33, in other words, it was a third larger than σ_3. M_7 was found to be 4.06, or that many σ_3 units above M_3. Knowing values for M_7 and σ_7, we can now proceed to determine M_8 and σ_8 also in terms of the adopted unit and zero point. The formula for finding σ_2 from a known σ_1 is

$$\sigma_2 = \sigma_1\left(\frac{s_1}{s_2}\right) \tag{218}$$

In the given problem,

$$\sigma_8 = 1.33\frac{1.478}{1.318} = 1.491.$$

6. Find M_8 from the formula

$$M_2 = \sigma_1 m_1 - \sigma_2 m_2 + M_1 \tag{219}$$

Applied to the given problem,

$$M_8 = (1.33)(-.293) - (1.491)(-.805) + 4.06 = 4.87.$$

7. Find the scale values of the test items. For this purpose Thurstone uses the two proportions for each test item that are nearest .50, with one on either side of .50. For example in Table 82, item 40 was passed by .391 of the seven-year group and by .682 of the eight-year group. The formula to be applied is

$$S = .5[(M_1 + X_1\sigma_1) + (M_2 + X_2\sigma_2)] \tag{220}$$

In this case,
$$S_{40} = .5[4.06 + (.28)(1.33) + 4.87 + (-.47)(1.491)]$$
$$= .5(8.60)$$
$$= 4.30.$$

The result, 4.30, is in terms of three-year intelligence as the zero point and in terms of the sigma of the distribution of three-year intelligence.[1]

---

[1] Thomson (51) proposes a very simple device for evaluating the scale value of an item in terms of age level. Unlike Thurstone's proposal, it uses *all* the proportions given for the item. The method assumes that the age group next below the one having any passes has a proportion of 0.00 and the group next

8. Test the validity of the scale value of an item by means of the following device (57). Draw a vertical line at the point on the base line corresponding to the scale value of the item. Draw the ogive distributions of the different age groups. Do the proportions of the various age groups exceeding this scale value coincide with the observed proportions? This is a graphic test. The test may be made arithmetically, computing the expected proportions and finding the discrepancies between them and the experimental proportions.

Where the greatest accuracy is desired in absolute scaling, the observations should be weighted. As in the constant method and as in paired comparisons, the proportions are of unequal reliability and the X values that are derived from them should be weighted according to Urban's weights. The procedure to be followed when Urban's weights are used may be found in another article by Thurstone (56).

A few fundamental results obtained from absolute scaling deserve to be mentioned. Whereas in earlier scaling methods it was assumed that the dispersions for ability, when measured in sigma units, were all equal, regardless of age, Thurstone found in the Binet test that the dispersion actually increases with age, with $\sigma = 1.00$ at the age of 3.5 (three-year-old group) and 1.792 at the age of 14.5 years (53). The Woody arithmetic tests have an absolute dispersion of 1.00 (arbitrary) at the level of grade 2; they have a dispersion of 4.5 at grade 8 (56). In Trabue's language scale the absolute variability increased from a sigma of 1.00 for grade 2 to a sigma of 2.12 for grade 12 (55). These results make it necessary to consider changes in

---

above the one with the highest has a proportion of 1.00, as in the following list:

Age	Proportion
4.5	.095
5.5	.340
6.5	.653
7.5	.873
8.5	.956
9.5	.986
	= 3.903

The median is $10.0 - 3.903 = 6.097$, which is the age level sought. Spearman's method for finding the arithmetic mean (see page 169) is also adaptable, as in fact are any of the constant processes.

variability from one level of ability to another when attempting to establish the scale values for difficulty of test items.

Another important result following from these facts is Thurstone's estimation of the absolute zero point for intelligence (57). The change in variability was found to have a linear relationship with mean test performance for a number of tests. A law of variability could be stated (57, p. 187) as follows: "With uniform conditions of selection, the relative variability of absolute test intelligence of different age groups is constant." Absolute zero was assumed to be at the point where the variability equalled zero. In general, the absolute zero for any age group was -5σ in terms of the distribution of that age group. In terms of age, absolute zero for a test could be found by extrapolation, and most of the tests rate intelligence at zero just about the time of birth or a few weeks before. The absolute scale also enables us to obtain a more accurate notion of the growth curve for intelligence. Instead of the curve of negative acceleration, which corresponds to the increase in raw test scores in early childhood, test intelligence probably increases with a positive acceleration at first, with an inflection point near the age of ten and negative acceleration thereafter (59).

The Optimal Difficulty of a Test Item.—Concerning the difficulty of a test item that will give the greatest reliability and validity, Symonds (49) draws several pertinent conclusions based upon theoretical considerations. The single item that will indicate best the level of ability of an individual is one for which his probability of passing is .50. The most accurate test for such an individual would be made up of items of the same degree of difficulty. For discriminating between the abilities of two different individuals, the best item is one that lies midway between two items that could be passed 50 per cent of the time by the two. The best test for the two individuals, likewise, would be one made up of average level of difficulty. The best test for a typical school grade is one whose items could be passed 50 per cent of the time by the average child in that grade. The best test for a number of grades would be made up of items ranging in difficulty from those that could be passed by 50 per cent of those in the lowest grade to items that could be passed by 50 per cent of those in the highest grade.

Empirical tests seem to bear out Symonds's conclusions. With spelling tests, T. G. Thurstone (60) found that the maximum validity was attained by using words that could be spelled by 30 to 70 per cent of the sixth-grade children, the highest validity being reached by items passable by 45 to 55 per cent. Tests of uniform difficulty, she concluded, are probably better for a homogeneous group than are tests with a range of difficulty. Cleeton (6) found that the best test items lie between those passable by only 30 per cent and those passable by as many as 80 per cent. In applying these principles, however, it is well to remember the caution expressed by McCall (32, p. 275) that the difficulty of an item is partly a function of some preceding item in the test, which may have induced a right or wrong mental set or which may have developed a new insight that transfers; and it is also a function of the distance from the first item, and perhaps of other factors as well.

Weighted Scoring of Ability

Practically all group tests of ability are scored according to the number of items passed, with some correction being made for possible chance successes when the number of alternative answers is limited. The items are known to vary in validity as well as in difficulty. When the validity and difficulty of an item are known, would it not be wise to weight the scoring of the item accordingly? Do the customary corrections for chance, like the familiar "rights minus wrongs" for true-false tests, give the expected improvement? Shall errors be neglected entirely in scoring, or shall they be given some weight? These are the questions that hold our attention next.

Corrections for Chance Success.—It has been assumed in multiple-response tests that the individual has a gambling chance of passing items whether he knows anything about them or not. When there are two alternative items he has one chance in two; with four, he has one chance in four, and so on. The customary correction for chance success is given by the formula

$$S = R - \frac{W}{n-1} \tag{221}$$

where S = the test score, corrected for chance success.

R = the number of right responses.

W = the number of wrong responses.

n = the number of alternative responses per item.

Whatever may be said in theoretical defense of this formula, the probability of a chance success, upon which it is based, is not just $1/2$, or $1/3$, or $1/4$, or $1/n$.   As in guessing which of two weights is the heavier, although even the subject maintains that he is making a pure guess and is sincere in saying so, he is more likely to be right than pure chance would lead us to expect, if there is any actual difference in the weights at all.   Even though he does not know the answer in a four-choice test, the four alternatives have by no means the same value for him.   He is very often prejudiced for or against several of them.   Certainly, when the test is a work-limit test in which all subjects attempt all items, there is nothing to be gained by applying the correction formula (18), since the number of 'wrongs' is a function of the number of 'rights,' in that $W = T - R$, where T stands for the total number of items.   When instructions "not to guess" are given, the theory underlying corrections for chance is less clear.   Ruch concludes (39, p. 356) that the correction formula probably overpenalizes and that experimental results leave the question still debatable as to whether it raises or lowers the reliability of a test; but the evidence is quite clear that the correction raises the validity of it.   There is evidence that the best practice is to give instructions against guessing and to correct for chance, especially in two- and three-answer tests.

Weighted Scoring for Errors.—The question of how much weight to give the errors is after all an empirical one, and it must be decided for every particular test.   In formula (221), which applies to multiple-response tests, the weight is $\dfrac{-1}{(n-1)}$, which is based upon the theory of probability.   In a two-response test this weight is -1; in a three-response test, it is $-.5$; and in a five-response test, it is $-.25$.   The weight to be assigned to the number of 'wrongs' can be determined experimentally for any test, and it may pay to do so (1) if there is a reasonably large range of errors for different individuals and (2) if the test is a time-limit test.   The problem is one in multiple correlation, of finding a multiple regression equation for getting the best predictions of ability with 'rights' and 'wrongs' properly weighted.   In this case, however, we arbitrarily choose a weight of $+1$ for the 'rights' and find the corresponding relative weight for the 'wrongs.'   This weight, which we shall call E (for errors), would naturally be expected to have a negative sign, but as a matter of fact it may actually be positive, and indeed it may sometimes have a stronger positive weight than that for 'rights.'

Fortunately, we can estimate the amount of correlation that would be attained between a weighted scoring and a criterion before the task of deriving the weight E is carried out. If the multiple R, ($R_{C \cdot RW}$), is appreciably higher than the correlation r_{CR}, in which C stands for a criterion and R for the 'rights,' then the further work of finding E is justified. The formula for R is given by Thurstone (58, p. 80) as

$$R^2_{C \cdot RW} = \frac{r^2_{CR} + r^2_{CW} - 2r_{CR}r_{CW}r_{RW}}{1 - r^2_{RW}} \tag{222}$$

The optimal weight for the 'wrongs' is given by (58, p. 78)

$$E = \frac{\sigma_R(r_{CR}r_{RW} - r_{CW})}{\sigma_W(r_{CW}r_{RW} - r_{CR})} \tag{223}$$

When in addition to a relatively large number of errors in the test results there are also many omissions, it may pay to score each paper for the number of omissions and to establish a scoring weight for them as well as for the errors (44). This would make a multiple-correlation problem with four variables. This procedure would apply to a work-limit test as well as to a time-limit test. Scoring weights for either errors or omissions should never be undertaken seriously unless a large number of subjects have been employed. Even then, for the sake of convenience in scoring, it is unnecessary to carry the solution of the weight beyond the first decimal place.

Tests Weighted According to Their Dispersions.—When tests are combined to form a battery and a total score is wanted, in order that every test will have an equal voice in determining the battery score, certain adjustments must be made. A test that has a mean score of 35 points, let us say, with a relatively wide range, will have much more to do with variations in the total scores than will a test that has a mean score of 10 and a correspondingly narrow range. The ideal way of combining test scores in a battery would be to reduce all scores to standard form. The labor would be prohibitive. The same end may be accomplished by weighting the raw scores of the various tests by the reciprocal of their standard deviation. That is to say, we use X_1/σ_1 rather than x_1/σ_1, for it can be shown that the two are comparable (58, p. 84).

Assume five tests, A, B, C, D, and E, whose means and sigmas are given in Table 83. The first step is to find the reciprocals, $1/\sigma$. They appear in the third row of Table 83. To be rid of decimal places, we multiply them by a constant, for example, 20. From these we adopt the nearest whole number as the approximate weight that we want.

TABLE 83.—WEIGHTING TESTS ACCORDING TO THEIR DISPERSIONS

	A	B	C	D	E
Means.................	20	15	35	12	24
σ.....................	12	8	16	5	10
$1/\sigma$....................	.083	.125	.063	.20	.10
$20/\sigma$..................	1.7	2.5	1.3	4.0	2.0
Weight................	2	2.5	1	4	2
Augmented weight......	2	5	4	4	2

If in addition to an adjustment for varying dispersions we also have definite reasons for favoring one or more of the tests, we can multiply some of the weights by arbitrary amounts. In this case it was deemed wise to double the importance of test B and to triple the weight of test C. The augmented weights in the last row of Table 83 show that this has been done.

Weighting Test Items for Validity.—The experience with weighting test items according to their validity has been limited as yet, but what few results we have point definitely to the inference that such weighting is not worth the trouble. The correlations between weighted and unweighted scores are almost perfect and they are generally higher than reliability coefficients for the same tests.

Scoring Based upon Items Scaled for Difficulty.—There have been some attempts to take into account the difficulty of items in weighting the scoring of tests. The scoring of items scaled for difficulty is best carried out by the use of median scale values or similar devices for estimating the altitude of ability (4, 54). Any of the ways of finding a median that were used in connection with the constant methods would apply here. When items of a group test are pooled to give a composite score, the factor of difficulty is not so easy to manage if one wishes a cumulative or total score rather than a median. It is reasonable, naturally, that an individual who passes a more difficult item should receive more toward his final score than one who passes an easier item. This will not work, however, unless individuals are also penalized for failing to pass easy items. It is more significant of stupidity to fail on an easy item that it is to fail on a difficult one. Thus failures must be weighted as well as passes. These considerations must be ironed out before weighted scoring based on difficulty promises any real gain over previous practice with cumulative scores. Culler (9) has shown that the unweighted scoring of items varying in difficulty is not a serious source of errors when the number of items is large.

WEIGHTED SCORING IN PERSONALITY TESTS

The remarks of this chapter have so far been directed almost exclusively to tests of ability. This does not mean that tests of personality traits and scales for measurement of interests, attitudes, and adjustments cannot be subjected to the same statistical treatments. As a general rule, they can be so treated and they are. The same tests of reliability and validity may be applied, provided, *always*, that the proper assumptions may be made. It is sometimes very doubtful, for example, whether the assumption of homogeneity which underlies the use of the Spearman-Brown formula can be made with tests of personality. Wherever possible, empirical proof for its use should accompany any logical assumptions that are made. All the various devices for estimating the validity of test items probably apply with personality tests. They are all the more necessary in the latter case, for we have even less a priori notions of the appropriateness of an item for the diagnosis of a given trait than we have in the case of tests of ability. Furthermore, the direction indicated by a certain response to an item is often in doubt until some test of validity is applied.

Tests of ability measure something that is assumed to extend from zero to something very large. A test of personality, on the other hand, usually assumes a trait that has two opposite poles. Another complication found in some personality tests is that *every* response of the individual is taken to mean something as regards the trait in question. An item in a test of ability is typically scored as right or wrong and, except in the rare cases where errors are scored, only one response to the item is scored. In a personality test, of the questionnaire type, for example, there are typically three alternative responses, "Yes," "?," and "No." In the better tests, each response receives its appropriate weight, positive or negative, high or low. In the latter case, we must know not only whether an item is diagnostic but also how to weight the alternative responses. At present we are in a rather primitive stage in the history of personality tests.   One or two devices for deriving scoring weights will now be reviewed.

The Kelley-Cowdery Scoring Weights.—The question of weighting scores for responses first arose in connection with vocational-interest questionnaires (8).   An individual may be asked concerning his likes or dislikes for various occupations, sports, magazines, types of people, and the like, and he responds by encircling *L* (like), ?, and *D* (dislike).   The development of a scale for interest in being a personnel manager, let us say, involved finding the proportions of the personnel managers who presumably liked their occupation, who responded in each way, *L*, ?, or *D*, to every test item. Similar proportions were derived from groups of people who were not personnel managers.   Let us suppose the item called for a response concerning interest in being an actor.   The personnel managers gave proportions of .49, .38, and .13 for the responses *L*, ?, and *D*, respectively.   All other occupational groups combined gave corresponding proportions of .38, .35, and .27, respectively.   Kelley proposed a scoring weight given by the formula

$$b = \frac{\phi}{(1 - \phi^2)\sigma}$$

in which ϕ is the coefficient of correlation as obtained by formula (142) for a fourfold point surface.[1]   The fourfold table in this case is presumably set up by combining the proportions of *L* and ?, or of ? and *D*, or of *L* and *D* while categories *D*, *L*, and ?, respectively, are being treated.   It can be seen that the procedure is very detailed, but it has given excellent results in discriminating between every occupational group so treated and people in general.

Strong's Scoring Weights.—Strong (45) found that there is in reality an almost linear relationship between the *b* weight of Kelley and Cowdery and the difference in proportion of the two criterion groups in a response to any item.   For example, to use the same proportions as were given above, in response to the item 'actor':

	L	?	*D*
Personnel manager......................	.49	.38	.13
Others..............................	.38	.35	.27
Difference............................	+.11	+.03	−.14

[1] Kelley (27) has recently proposed another formula for this purpose.

In order to reduce the weight to small integers, Strong used the following scheme. If the two proportions between which the difference was found are both between .08 and .92, differences from 0 to 2 are weighted 0; 3 to 7 are weighted 1; 8 to 11, 2; 12 to 15, 3; 16 to 20, 4; and so on, in a linear relation. When either proportion is .00 to .02 or .98 to 1.00 inclusive, the weights are: for differences 0, 0; 1, 1; 2 to 3, 2; 4 to 6, 3; 7 to 10, 4; 11 to 14, 5; 15 to 18, 6; and so on. If either proportion is between .03 and .07 or between .93 and .97, an intermediate set of weights is used. From this scheme, the three given differences, $+.11$, $+.03$, and $-.14$, should become $+2$, $+1$, and -3, for the responses L, $?$, and D, respectively.[1]

Scoring Personality Tests and Factor Analysis.—The determination of the validity of test items and, in addition, the use of differential scoring weights may be carried out without the use of an outside criterion, which has been implied in all the discussion so far. Especially with personality tests, for which it is difficult to find a valid objective criterion, it has been customary to let the test become its own criterion. For example, after one has begun with a priori scoring for a questionnaire on introversion-extroversion, in which the responses are first given either a $+1$ or -1, criterion groups consisting of highest and lowest quartiles may be selected and every item examined as to the proportions of these two groups that respond in a given manner. The diagnostic items may be selected, according to any of the appropriate methods discussed earlier in the chapter, and they may be differentially weighted or not. The fate of an item is therefore determined by its degree of internal consistency with all the others.

The chief criticism to be offered against this procedure is that we do not yet know what the real dimensions or variables of personality are. It would be possible, according to the tests of internal consistency, to choose, or even to invent, any trait whatsoever. One could select items that seemed logically consistent with the supposed trait and the statistical tests of internal consistency might even bear out the fallacious conviction that a real trait is being measured. The correct approach would be to insert into the procedure a factor analysis of the test items. From their intercorrelations it is possible to determine the least number of real, independent dimensions or variables of personality represented in the items. Once these are

---

[1] A recent device for weighting responses based upon a fourfold correlation of the response with a dichotomous criterion group is proposed by Flanagan (16).

established, the diagnostic value of any item for any factor can be determined and the responses to that item may be weighted accordingly. To these questions we turn in the next and last chapter.

Problems

1. The coefficient of reliability of a test is .92 and the standard deviation is 15. Find:
   a. The index of reliability.
   b. The standard error of a true score.
   c. The standard error of an obtained score.
   d. The correlation between the obtained scores and the true scores.
   e. The standard error of measurement. Interpret each result.

2. In a test of 40 items the coefficient of reliability is .83. What is the most probable reliability of a test having 80 comparable items? Of a test having 200 such items? Of one with 140 such items? Find the reliability of each answer when N equals 120.

3. In the previous problem, how many items would be required to attain a reliability coefficient of .90? A reliability of .95? What is the margin of error of these estimates?

4. A test was given to 300 individuals with the result that the standard deviation was 11.5 and the coefficient of reliability was .88. In a selected group of 50 subjects the standard error was 9.6. What is the probable coefficient of reliability in the latter group, assuming that the test is equally effective in both groups? What is the margin of error of this estimate?

5. Pool the rank-order evaluations in the problem on page 261 into four sets of five judges each and find four sets of scale values for the 12 stimuli. Intercorrelate the four sets. Estimate the probable correlation of scale values based upon pools of 10 comparable judges. Obtain two such pools and find an actual correlation. Was your prediction within the error of sampling?

6. A test has a validity coefficient of .50 and a reliability coefficient of .70. Estimate the validity that should be expected if the reliability were .90. If the reliability were 1.00.

7. A test in mathematics has a reliability of .85 and a test in English has a reliability of .75. The intercorrelation of the two tests is .45. Estimate the degree of intercorrelation if:
   a. The mathematics test alone is made perfectly reliable.
   b. The English test alone is made perfectly reliable.
   c. The maximum amount of correlation is made possible.
   d. The intrinsic relation between the two abilities is to be known.

8. A certain intelligence test of 75 items has a validity coefficient of .68 and a reliability coefficient of .95. Estimate the validity if the test were doubled in length. If the test were made up of 200 comparable items. Make the same two estimates, assuming that the reliability is now .70 instead of .95.

9. How many items must the test of the preceding problem have in order to attain a validity of .80? A validity of .90? (Assume in turn reliabilities of .70 and .50.)

10. A certain item in the Army Alpha test was passed by 77.1 per cent of the highest 50 individuals in a group of 200 and by 39.3 per cent of the lowest 50. Find an index of validity according to each of several appropriate methods described in this chapter. Another item was passed by 96.0 per cent of the high group and by 80.6 per cent of the low group. A third was passed by 27.7 per cent and 12.5 per cent of the two groups, respectively. A fourth was passed by 59.0 per cent and 45.6 per cent, respectively. Draw conclusions as to the relative merits of these items, both as regards the diagnostic value and relative difficulty.

11. Using the data of Prob. 4 on page 376, find one or more measures of diagnostic value other than the biserial r.

12. For a problem in absolute scaling of test items, assume the following facts: Two adjacent groups of subjects are known as K and L. p_k is the proportion of group K which passes an item and p_l is the corresponding proportion for group L. For test item 25, $p_k = .825$ and $p_l = .945$. For item 42, $p_k = .076$ and $p_l = .202$. $m_k = -.185$ and $m_l = -.765$. $s_k = 1.54$ and $s_l = 1.36$. $\sigma_k = 1.50$ and $M_k = 5.70$. From these known facts, compute σ_l, M_l, S_{25}, and S_{42}. S_{25} is the absolute scale value of item 25 and S_{42} has a similar meaning.

13. Let R stand for the number of right answers to a test, W for the number of wrong answers, and C for a criterion score. Given the following information concerning a time-limit test:

$$r_{CR} = .50 \qquad r_{CW} = -.30 \qquad r_{RW} = -.80$$
$$\sigma_R = 12 \qquad \sigma_W = 3 \qquad \sigma_C = 8$$

Estimate: (*a*) The maximum validity of the test when the errors are given an optimal weight in scoring; (*b*) the optimal weight for the errors, the 'rights' being weighted 1.00.

14. A certain test item in a questionnaire on introversion-extroversion was answered by 800 individuals. Of the highest quarter (those judged most introverted by a preliminary scoring), the numbers of those responding "Yes," "?," and "No" were 61, 6, and 133, respectively. Of the 200 most extroverted, the corresponding numbers were 142, 8, and 50. Find scoring weights for the three responses by using Kelley's original method and also the Cowdery-Strong approximation method. Do the same for the numbers 189, 6, and 5; and 62, 24, and 114.

REFERENCES

1. AYERS, L. P., "A Measuring Scale for Ability in Spelling," Russell Sage Foundation, New York, 1915.
2. BARTHELMESS, H. M., The validity of intelligence test elements, *Teach. Coll. Contrib. Educ.*, no. 505, 1931.
3. BROTEMARKLE, R. A., and S. W. FERNBERGER, A method for investigating the validity of the categories of a judgment test, *J. Educ. Psychol.*, 1934, **25**, 579–584.
4. BROWN, C. W., P. BARTELME, and G. M. COX, The scoring of individual performance on tests scaled according to the theory of absolute scaling, *J. Educ. Psychol.*, 1933, **24**, 654–662.

5. CLARK, E. L., A method of evaluating the units of a test, *J. Educ. Psychol.*, 1928, **19**, 263–265.

6. CLEETON, G. U., The optimum difficulty of group test elements, *J. Appl. Psychol.*, 1926, **10**, 327–340.

7. COOK, W. W., The measurement of general spelling ability involving controlled comparisons between techniques, *Univ. Iowa Stud. Educ.*, 1932, **6**, no. 6, 38–59.

8. COWDERY, K. M., Measurement of professional attitudes, *J. Person. Res.*, 1926, **5**, 131–141.

9. CULLER, E., Studies in psychometric theory, *J. Exper. Psychol.*, 1926, **9**, 271–279.

10. CURETON, E. E., The standard error of the Spearman-Brown formula when used to estimate the length of a test necessary to achieve a given reliability, *J. Educ. Psychol.*, 1933, **24**, 305–306.

11. DICKEY, J. W., On estimating the reliability coefficient, *J. Appl. Psychol.*, 1934, **18**, 103–115.

12. DOUGLASS, H. R., A note on the correctness of certain error formulas, *J. Educ. Psychol.*, 1929, **20**, 434–437.

13. ———, and F. W. COZENS, On formula for estimating the reliability of test batteries, *J. Educ. Psychol.*, 1929, **20**, 369–377.

14. DUNLAP, J. W., Comparable tests and reliability, *J. Educ. Psychol.*, 1933, **24**, 422–453.

15. ———, and E. E. CURETON, Note on the standard error of a reliability coefficient, *J. Educ. Psychol.*, 1929, **20**, 705–706.

16. FLANAGAN, J. C., "Factor Analysis in the Study of Personality," Stanford University Press, Stanford, 1935.

17. HEINIS, H., A personal constant, *J. Educ. Psychol.*, 1926, **17**, 163–186.

18. HOLZINGER, K. J., On scoring multiple response tests, *J. Educ. Psychol.*, 1924, **15**, 445–447.

19. ———, and B. CLAYTON, Further experiments in the application of Spearman's prophecy formula, *J. Educ. Psychol.*, 1925, **16**, 289–299.

20. HORST, P., Increasing the efficiency of selection tests, *Person. J.*, 1934, **12**, 254–259.

21. ———, Item analysis by the method of successive residuals, *J. Exper. Educ.*, 1934, **2**, 254–263.

22. HUFFAKER, C. L., and H. R. DOUGLASS, On the standard errors of the mean due to sampling and to measurement, *J. Educ. Psychol.*, 1928, **19**, 643–649.

23. HULL, C. L., "Aptitude Testing," World Book Company, Yonkers, 1928.

24. KELLEY, T. L., "Statistical Method," The Macmillan Company, New York, 1924.

25. ———, "Interpretation of Educational Measurements," World Book Company, Yonkers, 1927.

26. ———, The applicability of the Spearman-Brown formula for the measurement of reliability, *J. Educ. Psychol.*, 1925, **16**, 300–303.

27. ———, The scoring of alternative responses with reference to some criterion, *J. Educ. Psychol.*, 1934, **25**, 504–510.

28. ———, and A. C. KREY, "Tests and Measurements in the Social Sciences," Charles Scribner's Sons, New York, 1934.

29. LENTZ, T. F., B. HIRSHSTEIN, and F. H. FINCH, Evaluation of methods of evaluating test items, *J. Educ. Psychol.*, 1932, **23**, 344–350.

30. LINDQUIST, E. F., and W. W. COOK, Experimental procedures in test evaluation, *J. Exper. Educ.*, 1933, **1**, 163–185.

31. LONG, J. A., Improved overlapping methods for determining validities of test items, *J. Exper. Educ.*, 1934, **2**, 264–267.

32. MCCALL, W. A., "How to Measure in Education," The Macmillan Company, New York, 1922.

33. MILLER, G. F., Formulas for scoring tests in which the maximum amount of chance is determined, *J. Educ. Psychol.*, 1925, **16**, 304–315.

34. OTIS, A. S., Some logical aspects of the Binet scale, *Psychol. Rev.*, 1916, **23**, 129–152, 165–179.

35. PATERSON, D. G., "Preparation and Use of New-type Examinations," World Book Company, Yonkers, 1926.

36. PETERSON, J., "Early Conceptions and Tests of Intelligence," World Book Company, Yonkers, 1925.

37. REMMERS, H. H., The equivalence of judgments to test items in the sense of the Spearman-Brown formula, *J. Educ. Psychol.*, 1931, **22**, 66–71.

38. ———, and N. W. SHOCK, and E. L. KELLY, An empirical study of the validity of the Spearman-Brown formula as applied to the Purdue rating scale, *J. Educ. Psychol.*, 1927, **18**, 187–195.

39. RUCH, G. M., "The Objective or New-type Examination," World Book Company, Yonkers, 1929.

40. ———, L. ACKERSON, and J. D. JACKSON, An empirical study of the Spearman-Brown formula as applied to educational test material, *J. Educ. Psychol.*, 1926, **17**, 309–313.

41. SHEN, E., The standard error of certain estimated coefficients of correlation, *J. Educ. Psychol.*, 1924, **15**, 462–465.

42. ———, The reliability coefficient of personal ratings, *J. Educ. Psychol.*, 1925, **16**, 232–236.

43. SMITH, M., The relationship between item validity and test validity, *Teach. Coll. Contrib. Educ.*, 1934, no. 621.

44. STAFFELBACH, E. H., Weighting responses in true-false examinations, *J. Educ. Psychol.*, 1930, **21**, 136–139.

45. STRONG, E. K., An interest test for personnel managers, *J. Person. Res.*, 1927, **5**, 194–203.

46. ———, Procedure for scoring an interest test, *Psychol. Clinic*, 1930, **19**, 63–72.

47. SYMONDS, P. M., A study of extreme cases of unreliability, *J. Educ. Psychol.*, 1924, **15**, 99–106.

48. ———, Factors influencing test reliability, *J. Educ. Psychol.*, 1928, **19**, 73–87.

49. ———, Choice of items for a test on the basis of difficulty, *J. Educ. Psychol.*, 1929, **20**, 481–493.

50. ———, "Diagnosing Personality and Conduct," D. Appleton-Century Company, Inc., New York, 1931.

51. THOMSON, G. H., A note on scaling tests, *J. Educ. Psychol.*, 1926, **17**, 551–553.

52. THORNDIKE, E. L., *et al.*, "The Measurement of Intelligence," Bureau of Publications, Teach. College, Columbia University, New York, 1927.

53. THURSTONE, L. L., A method of scaling psychological and educational tests, *J. Educ. Psychol.*, 1925, **16**, 433–451.

54. ———, The scoring of individual performance, *J. Educ. Psychol.*, 1926, **17**, 446–457.

55. ———, The unit of measurement in educational scales, *J. Educ. Psychol.*, 1927, **18**, 505–524.

56. ———, Scale construction with weighted observations, *J. Educ. Psychol.*, 1928, **19**, 441–453.

57. ———, The absolute zero in intelligence measurement, *Psychol. Rev.*, 1928, **35**, 175–197.

58. ———, "The Reliability and Validity of Tests," Edwards Brothers, Ann Arbor, 1931.

59. ———, and L. ACKERSON, The mental growth curve for the Binet tests, *J. Educ. Psychol.*, 1929, **20**, 569–583.

60. THURSTONE, T. G., The difficulty of a test and its diagnostic value, *J. Educ. Psychol.*, 1932, **23**, 335–343.

61. TRYON, R. C., The reliability coefficient as a per cent, *Psychol. Rev.*, 1930, **37**, 140–157.

62. UHRBROCK, R. S., and M. W. RICHARDSON, Item analysis, *Person. J.*, 1933, **12**, 141–154.

63. VINCENT, L., A study of intelligence test elements, *Teach. Coll. Contrib. Educ.*, 1924, no. 152.

64. VOTAW, D. F., Graphical determination of probable error in validation of test items, *J. Educ. Psychol.*, 1933, **24**, 682–686.

65. WOODY, C., Measurement of some achievements in arithmetic, *Teach. Coll. Contrib. Educ.*, 1916, no. 80.

CHAPTER XIV

FACTOR ANALYSIS

Probably no movement in psychology has been so significant in its social consequences as the mental-test movement. This can still be said of mental testing after we acknowledge that for the most part we have had only vague ideas as to what it is that psychological tests actually measure. The plea is frequently offered in defense of the tests that, by analogy, we do not know the whole truth about electricity and yet we do not question the right of the physicist or the engineer to measure it. Let us be ready to recognize that, although the full nature of electricity is not known, some of the independent real variables of electricity, such as potential, resistance, and inductance, have been singled out and laws of their interrelationships have been stated. The fundamental variables or dimensions of human ability are still very much within the unexplored territory reserved for psychologists. To meet the challenge of this situation, a few of our number have stepped forward with statistical instruments whereby we may discover the fundamental unitary abilities— instruments with which any unitary traits of personality can be isolated from the intricate web of mental life. I refer to the various devices now known as methods of factor analysis.

If one were to consult an unabridged dictionary in order to find all the terms that are used to describe human personality and human ability and the terms that stand for observable traits, one would find perhaps several thousand such concepts. Science, wishing to describe human nature, has at its disposal all these concepts. But to use all of them is very poor economy. Many are synonyms; others overlap to various degrees; others express opposite characteristics. Science, forever motivated to bring order out of chaos, to reduce to the simple that which is complex, wants to know what is the least possible number of concepts with which one can order and describe adequately the multiplicity of phenomena that come under its scrutiny. From the quantitative aspect, what is the least number of variables or dimensions of personality that will be ade-

457

quate to the task? Wundt saw this problem in connection with feeling and proposed his famous tridimensional theory. The existential psychologists have seen the problem in connection with sensory phenomena, and attributes of colors, of sounds, and of experience in general are the result. The task of isolating the independent aspects of experience has been a difficult one. The task of isolating independent variables in personality is even more difficult. Armchair methods dominated by deductive logic rather than by observation led to the faculty psychologies, traditionally unacceptable to modern psychology. Direct observation has likewise failed to arrive at any set of unitary traits which even approach a universal acceptance. Factor analysis or some similar objective process had to be brought into the search for the unitary traits of personality. Factor analysis may also unravel some of the intricate interplay of variables which we find in problems of strictly experimental psychology. It will undoubtedly find a fruitful field of application in the social sciences, and probably also in biology. It is not inconceivable that it may yet be required to solve some of the remaining mysteries in the field of atomic physics.

HISTORY OF FACTOR THEORY AND FACTOR METHODS

Early Conceptions of Mental Ability.—Probably the first conception of mental ability is that handed down from the faculty psychologies which regarded mind as having a limited number of distinct and unitary powers. Although very old, this idea has been assumed, at least implicitly, by those who have constructed mental tests. Binet, rejecting the simple sensory and motor tests of Galton and Cattell, proposed to measure the higher functions of memory, imagination, judgment, and the like. Kraepelin, likewise, proposed tests to measure varying losses of the important functions in the insane and in individuals under the influence of drugs and fatigue. Whipple's classical manual of tests presented a classification under the categories long made familiar as separate functions, or, by implication, faculties. The implication carried the further idea that a memory test measured memory and nothing else and that an association test measured the power of association and nothing else. We know from the way in which tests intercorrelate that this part of the implication is quite untrue. According to this theory two tests of memory should correlate perfectly with each other, allowing for errors of measurement, and a test of memory should correlate zero with a test of judgment or of attention or of perception. This is decidedly not the case. Most tests of mental ability exhibit some degree of positive correlation; often two tests that are classified under the same name exhibit no more correlation than do two other tests supposedly belonging to two different categories of ability. The notion of separate and unitary powers which operate singly and in an isolated manner must therefore be discarded.

Even more untenable is the idea that mental ability may be summed up under the one category of "intelligence." This conception is perhaps common to the unobserving layman, who regards individuals as equally bright or dull in everything they do, provided that emotion or some other nonintellectual factor does not enter in. The conception of intelligence as a unitary entity was a gift to psychology from biology through the instrumentality of Herbert Spencer. Were this theory true, any two tests of intelligence should correlate perfectly with one another, allowing for errors of observation. Attempts to define this supposed unitary ability have signally failed to satisfy. Whether it is defined as the power to adapt to novel situations, as the power to learn, or as the power to solve the problems of life, the way is left open to analyze intelligence into a number of abilities which, working together, accomplish the result. If it is defined as the ability to do abstract thinking or as the ability to combine experiences, it becomes a more unitary affair, but then many factors admittedly belonging under the category of mental ability are clearly ignored. Thus all **unifactor theories** fail to meet the test of accounting for the known facts and the test of universal agreement.

Spearman's Two-factor Theory.—No single event in the history of mental testing has proved to be of such momentous importance as Spearman's proposal of his famous two-factor theory in 1904 (26). His logic at that time ran somewhat as follows: First, we may assume that any correlation between two tests implies a factor common to both, plus two specific factors, as indicated in Fig. 44A. Let the two tests be called a and b, the common factor g, and the two specific factors s_a and s_b, as shown in the diagram. We may then regard tests a and b as two measures of the common element g, with the random errors s_a and s_b. Since a and b are measures of the same ability, we may look upon the correlation r_{ab} as a coefficient of reliability. Now let p and q be two other tests with g' as the common element, as in Fig. 44*B*. As before, we may regard r_{pq} as a coefficient of reliability of a measure of g'. Using the formula for the correction for attenuation, we may now estimate the correlation between g and g', since we have two independent measures of each. Applying formula (156) we have

(1)
$$r_{gg'} = \frac{\sqrt[4]{r_{ap}r_{aq}r_{bp}r_{bq}}}{\sqrt{r_{ab}r_{pq}}}.$$

From some experiments which Spearman reports, $r_{gg'}$, so computed, was found to approximate a value of 1.00. This meant that g and g' were practically identical. The factor pattern could be more

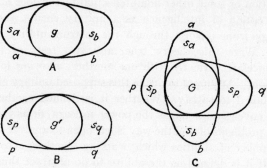

Fɪɢ. 44.—Graphic representation of the common element in correlated tests in relation to the Spearman two-factor theory.

appropriately sketched as in Fig. 44*C*. In a similar manner we can test whether or not the common factor in one pair of tests is identical with the common factor in any other pair of tests. Spearman was willing to draw the far-reaching conclusion that the common element is identical in all tests involving the process of cognition. Every test, then, is thought to be composed of the g-factor, which is universal, plus a specific factor that is found in each test alone. We may state Spearman's two-factor pattern in algebraic terms as follows:

(2)
$$\begin{cases} x_1 = m_1g + n_1s_1, \\ x_2 = m_2g + n_2s_2, \\ x_3 = m_3g + n_3s_3, \\ \ldots\ldots\ldots\ldots \\ x_n = m_ng + n_ns_n, \end{cases}$$

where $x_1, x_2, x_3, \ldots, x_n$ = test scores in deviation form

g = the universal, common factor which accounts for all correlation between tests.

$s_1, s_2, s_3, \ldots, s_n$ = the abilities specific to the various tests.

m's and n's = regression coefficients as in the ordinary regression equation.

The Criterion of Proportionality.—From equation (1) it can be shown that, in order to assume the two-factor pattern in a set of tests for which the intercorrelations are known, any two columns of coefficients must be in direct proportion. Consider a general set of intercorrelations given in Table 84. Let us consider first columns 1 and 2. The criterion of proportionality requires that

$$\frac{r_{13}}{r_{23}} = \frac{r_{14}}{r_{24}} = \frac{r_{15}}{r_{25}} = \frac{r_{16}}{r_{26}}.$$

The same would necessarily be true of the rows, since the table is symmetrical about the principal diagonal which contains the self-correlations. Let us confine our interest to the first two ratios, namely,

$$\frac{r_{13}}{r_{23}} = \frac{r_{14}}{r_{24}}.$$

TABLE 84

	1	2	3	4	5	6
1	..	r_{12}	r_{13}	r_{14}	r_{15}	r_{16}
2	r_{12}	..	r_{23}	r_{24}	r_{25}	r_{26}
3	r_{13}	r_{23}	..	r_{34}	r_{35}	r_{36}
4	r_{14}	r_{24}	r_{34}	..	r_{45}	r_{46}
5	r_{15}	r_{25}	r_{35}	r_{45}	..	r_{56}
6	r_{16}	r_{26}	r_{36}	r_{46}	r_{56}	..

Multiplying the extremes by the means in this proportion, we have $r_{13}r_{24} = r_{23}r_{14}$. Transposing, $r_{13}r_{24} - r_{23}r_{14} = 0$.

The Tetrad Difference.—This is Spearman's famous **tetrad difference,** which became the most acceptable criterion of the two-factor pattern. It can be written for any combination of four tests at a time. By rearranging the four coefficients involved, three tetrad differences (or **tetrads,** as they are economically called) can be written for every combination of four tests. The following equations give the three tetrads for tests 1, 2, 3, and 4, with the notations as they were systematized by Kelley.

$$\left.\begin{aligned} t_{1234} &= r_{12}r_{34} - r_{13}r_{24} \\ t_{1243} &= r_{12}r_{34} - r_{14}r_{23} \\ t_{1342} &= r_{13}r_{24} - r_{14}r_{23} \end{aligned}\right\} \tag{224}$$

in which t stands for the tetrad difference. Notice that the subscript of t designates one particular tetrad. t_{1234} is the product of r_{12} (the first two subscripts) and r_{34} (the last two subscripts) minus the product of r_{13} (first and third subscripts) and r_{24} (second and fourth subscripts).

As examples of tetrads, let us examine two of the cases selected at random in a table of intercorrelations,[1] in which the two-factor pattern holds. From that table,

$$\begin{aligned} t_{1234} &= (.58)(.51) - (.58)(.50) \\ &= .2958 - .2900 = .0058. \\ t_{2378} &= (.47)(.31) - (.44)(.38) \\ &= .1457 - .1672 = .0215. \end{aligned}$$

In these two cases the tetrads are so close to zero that one could say that the criterion is satisfied. Not so, however, for two similar cases selected from Table 87, in which it is known that Spearman's two-factor pattern does not hold. Here

$$\begin{aligned} t_{1234} &= (.47)(.72) - (.65)(.64) \\ &= .3384 - .4160 = -.0776. \\ t_{2378} &= (.64)(.72) - (.40)(.27) \\ &= .4607 - .1080 = .3528. \end{aligned}$$

In the last examples one tetrad is fairly close to zero but the other obviously is not. Because of sampling errors in the data the coefficients of correlation are not perfectly reliable and so the tetrads that are computed from them are unreliable. A tetrad may deviate from zero to a small extent and still the criterion of proportionality may be regarded as satisfied. A probable error of the tetrad may be calculated by means of formulas now provided for that purpose. By comparing a tetrad with its PE one can decide whether it deviates significantly from zero. Since the tetrad now has limited usefulness, even for Spearman and his followers, the writer does not present

[1] From data attributed to Stead by Kelley (18, p. 209).

this formula. It may be found in Holzinger's *Resumé* (11). The use of the tetrad is a laborious procedure except when one is dealing with a small number of tests. The number of tetrads increases enormously as the number of tests increases. With 10 tests there are 630 tetrads and with 20 tests there are 14,535. More effective

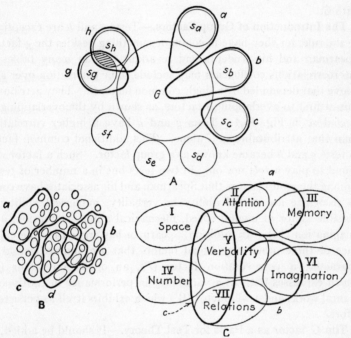

Fig. 45.—Graphic representation of Spearman's two-factor theory (*A*), of the sampling theory (*B*), and of the weighted group-factor theory (*C*), showing correlated tests.

and economical methods are now available; hence tetrads have little more than historical importance.

Graphic Illustration of *G* and *S*.—The two-factor pattern is illustrated graphically in Fig. 45*A*, Spearman's *g*-factor being shown as the large central circle and the specifics as small circles grouped about *G*. Each ellipse stands for a mental test, whether it is a cancellation test, opposites test, number-completion test, or vocabulary test. The ellipses are permitted to overlap *G* to different extents in order to indicate the fact that some tests are more heavily 'loaded' with *G* than others. Spearman's methods enable us to determine the extent to which a test measures G and the extent to which it measures the specific factor. The amount of correlation between any two tests is determined by the extent to which the two tests are loaded with G. Thus, tests a and b will have a relatively high correlation, since they have much in common in G. Tests a and c will be scarcely correlated at all, since both have small loadings with G.

The Introduction of Group Factors.—Tests g and h are exceptions to the rule, for they have in common something besides the g-factor. Spearman and his students had to admit that in many tables of intercorrelations coefficients may include some correlation over and above that demanded by a single common factor G. They attributed this at first to overlapping s-factors, as shown by the overlapping of s_g and s_h in Fig. 45A. Tests g and h have a higher correlation than that attributable to G alone. This additional common factor in tests g and h became known as a **group factor.** Such a factor was found to play a role not only in two tests but in a number of tests. Among the group factors that Spearman and his associates have come to recognize are verbal ability or verbality, numerical ability, a possible factor of mental speed, mechanical ability, attention, and imagination (12). In addition, Spearman has argued for the existence of three other very broad factors that are nonintellectual in character, a perseveration factor (P), an oscillation factor (O) which expresses itself as a variability in performance in continuous mental work, and a will factor (W) which exhibits itself as persistent effort.

The G-factor as a Basis for Test Theory.—It should be added, in passing, that the two-factor pattern is able to account for the known facts of correlations between tests and for some of the common procedures found to work in test practice. In the first place the almost universal positive correlation among tests of mental ability is accounted for by the notion that every test is to some extent saturated with G. The practice of pooling in test batteries a large variety of tasks Spearman regards as sound, for in that way we approach a pure measure of G. In a variety of tests the s-factors are all different, except for possible cases of overlapping among them. Each individual possesses the s-factors to varying degrees. Since the s-factors are uncorrelated, by chance one S can be possessed to a high degree and another to a low degree by the same individual. The test score of a battery is a sum or mean of the scores of the parts. The parts of the total score contributed by the *s*-factors will constitute a negligible component since in pooling them the chance combinations tend to cancel one another; what is left measures G. The two-factor pattern does not, however, explain why it is that the best batteries of tests are those in which the parts intercorrelate low with one another although each correlates high with the criterion. If one wishes to pool tests, each of which is highly saturated with G, one would necessarily have to choose tests that have high intercorrelations. Their intercorrelations must be in proportion to their saturation with G.

The Sampling Theory of Mental Ability.—Perhaps the severest critic of the two-factor theory has been G. H. Thomson (4), who has proposed in its place a sampling theory which makes the group factors of greater importance than either G or S of Spearman's theory. Thomson was able to show by means of artificial 'mental tests,' in the form of dice or of playing cards selected at random, that, when the experimental plan involved the presence of many group factors with no *g*-factor, the table of intercorrelations approached the 'hierarchial' order demanded by the two-factor theory. In fact, Spearman's criterion of proportionality could be completely satisfied, justifying the assumption of a two-factor pattern when by the nature of the experiment none really existed. He concluded that the hierarchial order is the natural one to expect among coefficients of correlation when they are the result of a chance sampling of numerous independent abilities entering into chance combinations in the various tests. This theory is shown graphically in Fig. 45B. Each small circle represents an independent ability, which, though limited in scope, may enter into a great variety of tasks. Test a may be assumed to draw upon 8 of those abilities, test b upon 10, test c upon 11, and test d upon 9. The degree of correlation between any two tests will depend upon the number of abilities they have in common. The correlation between test a and the others would be zero, a rare event indeed. The correlation r_{bc} would equal the number of elements in common divided by the geometric mean of the total numbers of elements in tests b and c, or

$$\frac{4}{\sqrt{10 \times 11}} = \frac{4}{10.488} = .38.$$

The correlation r_{cd}, likewise, is .60, and $r_{bd} = .32$.

Every test thus samples a certain range of human abilities; some sample a wide range and some a narrow range.   Thomson does not deny the possible existence of something that can be called 'general ability.'   If several tests are very extensive in the number of elementary abilities upon which they draw, all these tests may have in common a certain collection of those elements.   This collection which enters into all the tests may therefore constitute a general factor or a *G* for that group of tests.   But it is by nature a composite. The sampling theory does not deny the existence of specific factors, for any elementary ability appearing in one test and in no other in the group is specific for that test.   What the theory does maintain is that *there are group factors* and that, when Spearman's criterion of proportionality is completely satisfied, a number of the group factors may be acting as a universal factor.   But when the criterion is known not to be satisfied, it is possible to dispense entirely with a general factor, and group factors *must* be assumed.   General and specific factors are to be regarded as special cases of group factors.

The Sampling Theory as a Basis for Test Theory and Practice.— The sampling theory explains many known facts of test experience much better than does the two-factor theory.   Both theories explain equally well the fact that most tests correlate positively with one another.   In the two-factor theory the common element is identical for every pair of tests whereas for the sampling theory the common element or elements may or may not be identical.   The sampling theory accounts for the fact that the parts of a test battery should correlate low with one another and high with the criterion in order to obtain the maximum validity.   When the parts correlate too high with one another, they are sampling too much the same elementary group factors.   When they correlate little with one another, the range of abilities sampled is extended.   The criterion will have more in common with a battery that samples a wider range of abilities. Pooling varieties of tests differing in content and in type of activity demanded, as in the Binet scale, led to satisfactory results because that procedure also touched upon a large number of elementary abilities.   The total score in the Binet test or in a test battery is regarded as a sum total or average of all the abilities, neglecting few if any, whereas in the two-factor theory, as was said before, the total score is thought to measure *G* by canceling out the effects of the *s*-factors. Another universal fact readily explainable by the sampling theory is the significant tendency for complex tests to correlate higher with all other tests than do simple tests. Complex tests, on the basis of this theory, draw upon a larger number of elementary factors. The two-factor theory would perhaps apply here if we find that, the more complex the test, the greater its saturation with G.

Hull has pointed out (15, p. 201) that the two-factor theory makes impossible any program of aptitude testing, whereas a sampling theory lends to aptitude tests a good theoretical basis. In the first place, if Spearman's s-factors are really confined to one task alone, as he insists, there is no way of predicting from tests an individual's standing in his s-factors for various occupations. It is likely, since many occupational activities have a low correlation with tests that measure G, that occupational tasks depend largely upon their own s-factors, which could not be measured without asking an applicant to perform the tasks themselves. Otherwise any prediction of success in an occupation would rest entirely upon the extent to which the occupational task depends upon G. Since G is universal, every test would correlate at least to some degree with every occupation. But since each individual possesses a constant amount of G, and if all the information which we can obtain about him from tests is his amount of G, we could not tell him which of several occupations equally saturated with G would be best for him. Vocational guidance would thus be next to impossible without allowing the individual to try out the different alternatives. On the basis of the sampling theory, however, both vocational selection and vocational guidance become logically possible.

Implications of Sampling Theory for Genetics.—The implications of the sampling theory for genetics are interesting. Thomson draws an analogy between the independent group factors and the Mendelian unitary factors in heredity which, acting together in chance combinations, give rise to personal characteristics. In fact there is more than an analogy in Thomson's conception for he suggests that any activity carried out by an individual may be regarded as a sample of these unitary Mendelian qualities (4, p. 190). If, then, by any process of factor analysis we can single out the unitary abilities, many genetic problems may be solved.

A Weighted Group-factor Theory.—Many of those who have lent much thought to factor theory and practice seem inclined to think that some group-factor theory will serve as a most convenient working hypothesis and will eventually be found to fit most of the facts.

They are inclined to differ with Thomson's theory in one or two respects. In the first place, they regard his assumption of a great many independent factors (Thomson is not very clear as to how many must be postulated) as not simple enough for a working basis and unnecessarily intricate to take care of the facts. Sometimes it is hinted even by those who hold to the sampling theory that the simplest unitary ability is the stimulus-response bond. The behavioristic notion that ability is a composite of learned connections would bring one logically to that extreme position. Recent writers on factor theory seem inclined to reduce human ability to a rather limited number of important factors or determiners of performance. Among these writers may be mentioned Hull, Thurstone, and Kelley. The factors are conceived as broad group factors, in the sense that they enter into a great variety of human tasks. According to this conception *there are no specific factors*. A group factor may appear to be specific to one test alone when that test in the list of tests intercorrelated is the only one containing that group factor. Had other tests been added to the investigation, that factor would disappear as a specific; and if all possible tasks were included in the investigation, no specific factor would appear. The elements measured by every test would consist of group factors plus observational errors.

The proponents of this theory are also likely not to expect a universal factor in the sense of Spearman's G, although all are probably open-minded and are willing that G make its appearance if their methods bring it to the surface. If Spearman's criterion of proportionality holds for any set of tests, indicating a g-factor, they are likely to question whether this G is identical with that which is similarly found in another set of tests.[1] There is nothing in the theory under present discussion that makes a universal factor impossible. It could exist alongside the other factors as the followers of Spearman now believe.

The sampling theory of Thomson carries the implicit assumption that every unitary ability operates on an all-or-none principle. Each element is either present or absent in a given mental task. That conception is tenable if one wishes to postulate a very large number of such determiners of performance. The weighted group-

---

[1] Thurstone has also shown (39, p. 141) that it is possible for two or more common factors in a group of tests to give the appearance of a single common factor if their loadings in the various tests are directly proportional.

factor theory, however, makes a different assumption. It probably agrees with the sampling theory in assuming that each unitary ability is present to different degrees in different individuals. But it makes the further assumption that each unit of ability enters into different tasks in varying degrees, just as Spearman's *G* was said to be present in varying degrees in different tasks (28). It may have to be admitted that the same factor does not carry the same relative weight for a task in different individuals or in the same individual at different times. The loadings of each test with the various factors that enter into it may be regarded as average or typical loadings for human nature of given age, sex, race, social culture, and present mental set. It may even be true that the same test does not draw upon the same abilities when it is relatively easy for a population and when it is relatively difficult. Thomson held similar views when he pointed out that the same task did not always call upon the same set of factors in the same individual at different times, or in different individuals at the same time. These are experimental problems toward whose solution the factor-analysis methods can well be directed.

Some Concrete Examples of the Weighted Group Factors.— The differences between the sampling theory and the weighted group-factor theory are brought out in Fig. 45*C*. Only seven hypothetical factors of an intellectual nature are illustrated. There are probably as many more. Three hypothetical tests are superimposed upon the factors. Test *a* depends upon factors II, III, and V; it draws rather heavily upon II and III but very little upon V. Test *b* draws upon factors V, VI, and VII; test *c* draws upon factors II, IV, V, and VII. The amount of correlation between tests *a* and *b* will be very slight; between *a* and *c* it will be larger, but still slight, and r_{bc} will be of significant size. The vacant spaces in the test ellipses may be assumed to comprise other group factors not shown, unique to each test and hence behaving like one of Spearman's specifics; they may be assumed to contain also whatever errors of measurement there may be. All intercorrelations will depend upon the weighting of the factors in common. But note that the common territory between pairs of tests may involve one, two, or more factors, and the degree of correlation will depend upon the loading of the two tests with those common factors. The factor pattern may be tabulated somewhat as follows, attempting to give for every test the proportion that is determined by each factor.

TABLE 85.—THE HYPOTHETICAL FACTOR LOADINGS OF THE THREE TESTS WITH THE SEVEN FACTORS IN FIG. 45C

Test	Factor						
	I	II	III	IV	V	VI	VII
a	..	.5	.5	..	.2	..	..
b	..	..	..	..	.4	.6	.2
c	.2	.1	..	.3	.5	..	.4

Equations for a Multiple-factor Pattern.—In algebraic form we may state an equation for test scores in tests a, b, or c, as follows:

$$s_a = a_2x_2 + a_3x_3 + a_5x_5 + a_ss_a + e_a,$$
$$s_b = b_5x_5 + b_6x_6 + b_7x_7 + b_ss_b + e_b,$$

and

$$s_c = c_1x_1 + c_2x_2 + c_4x_4 + c_5x_5 + c_7x_7 + c_ss_c + e_c$$

where s_a, s_b, and s_c = standard scores in tests a, b, and c, respectively.

a_2, a_3, and a_5 = the regression weights for unitary abilities II, III, and V in test a.

b_5, b_6, and b_7 = similarly, the weights for abilities V, VI, and VII in test b.

c_1, c_2, c_4, c_6, and c_7 = similar weights in test c.

x_1, x_2, x_3, $\ldots$, x_7 = standard scores in the seven unitary abilities.

a_s, b_s, and c_s = the regression weights for the factor or factors specific to tests a, b, and c, respectively.

s_a, s_b, and s_c = standard scores in the specific abilities in the three tests, respectively.

e_a, e_b, and e_c = the proportions of the scores attributable to errors of measurement.

A similar equation can be written for any test for which we know the unitary traits contributing to the test score and the extent to which each trait contributes. Since the specific factor s_n is really an additional unknown factor or factors, further knowledge of its composition would enable us to expand the equation to include additional terms, and with complete knowledge even the last term could perhaps be replaced with known factors.

The Factor-analysis Methods.—Since Spearman proposed his criterion of proportionality and the use of tetrad differences, a number of procedures of factor analysis have been invented. Among these may be mentioned the methods of Thurstone (39), of Hotelling (13), and of Kelley (19). Spearman and Holzinger (12) have an improved method for locating the group factors in addition to the *g*-factor, in which the tests represented in a table of intercorrelations are grouped and regrouped in various ways until those containing each group factor are isolated. The loadings of each test with *G* and with the group factors that it contains can be computed. By this method one can be guided constantly by one's knowledge of the nature of the tests, and the factors that arise as a result are readily interpretable. Holzinger's most recent assumption is that of the "hollow-staircase" pattern, in which every test contains *G* plus only *one* group factor plus a specific. In keeping with Spearman's terminology, this might be properly called a *three-factor theory*. Results from the other methods indicate, however, that a test is likely to have in it more than two factors common to others. The methods of Kelley and Hotelling are mathematically and statistically rigorous, but they frequently lead to unitary abilities that are difficult to interpret. It would be impossible to describe all the alternative methods in useful detail in the space of one chapter. The writer is compelled to depart from the previous custom of presenting alternative procedures. The choice in this case falls upon Thurstone's methods. These methods have been supplied with a very complete rational basis in the mathematics of matrix theory and they can be made to lead to significant, meaningful variables. There are one or two undesirable weaknesses in the methods, which will be pointed out later, but further developments will probably overcome all except inconsequential defects.

Thurstone's Factor Theory

Statement of the Problem.—The data with which we begin our task of factor analysis consist of a table of intercorrelations, such as Table 84 or Table 87. We could be content to assume as many variables as there are tests and to let the question of abilities rest just there. That is what testers have had to do in the past. But there is an infinite number of possible tests, and to assume an infinite number of abilities is poor scientific economy. We frequently find that a criterion may be predicted by means of a regression equation that involves a number of test variables. This is wasteful procedure. The test variables are correlated with one another and hence to that extent duplicate our work. To get the best prediction we have to include so large a number of test variables into our regression equation that the task becomes prohibitive. By factor analysis we can accomplish three ends: (1) we can determine the smallest number of independent abilities that must be postulated in order to account for the table of intercorrelations; (2) we can determine how much of each independent ability is represented by each test; (3) we can set up regression equations by which an individual's amount of any primary ability can be estimated from tests that depend upon that ability.

The Case of Two Common Factors.—Let us assume that among a certain group of tests there are two independent abilities or factors and that the tests are perfectly reliable, having no errors of measurement.[1] Let us assume further that there are no specific factors. The intercorrelations between tests are entirely determined by the two unitary abilities and the variance in test scores is also entirely due to those two factors. We make the additional assumptions that each factor bears a linear relation to the test scores and that their effects are additive. For these particular conditions we may write the equations

$$s_a = a_1 x_1 + a_2 x_2,$$
$$s_b = b_1 x_1 + b_2 x_2,$$

and

$$s_c = c_1 x_1 + c_2 x_2$$

where s_a, s_b, and s_c = standard scores in tests a, b, and c.

a_1, b_1, and c_1 = the factor loadings of factor I in tests a, b, and c.

a_2, b_2, and c_2 = the corresponding factor loadings of factor II.

x_1 and x_2 = standard scores in abilities I and II.

An individual might make a high score in test a either by having much of ability I or of ability II or by having a fair amount of both. If a_1 is much greater than a_2, then it matters much more for an individual's score in test a whether ability I is good or poor than whether ability II is good or poor. A high score in test a does not tell us whether ability I or II is responsible, unless the loading of the test with the one factor far outweighs the loading of the test with the other.

---

[1] The two factors here are not to be confused with Spearman's G and S. Here they are two *group* factors held in common by a number of tests. From this point of view, Spearman's is a *one*-factor theory since it postulates only one common factor.

The Communality of a Test.—Under the conditions imposed in the preceding discussion, it can be shown (34, p. 3) that

$$a_1^2 + a_2^2 = 1.$$
$$b_1^2 + b_2^2 = 1.$$
$$c_1^2 + c_2^2 = 1.$$

This principle can be extended to any number of variables. *The sum of the squares of the factor loadings for any test is equal to unity.* This is true only for perfect tests with no specific factors. The sum of the squares of the factor loadings is given the technical name of **communality,** for which the symbol h^2 stands. In terms of a general equation,

$$a_1^2 + a_2^2 + a_3^2 + \cdots + a_n^2 = h^2 \tag{225}$$

in which $a_1, a_2, \ldots, a_n$ are the factor loadings in test a with factors I, II, III, . . . , N.

A Geometric Interpretation of Factors.—Observe Fig. 46. In this illustration factor I is represented as the horizontal axis of the coordinate system and factor II as the vertical axis **orthogonal** (at right angles) to factor I. The independence of factors I and II is guaranteed by this orthogonality, since one may move along axis I, or in a line parallel to it without at all introducing any change along axis II, and vice versa. The circle in Fig. 46 is drawn with a radius of unity. Let us represent the positions of tests a, b, and c as points on the circumference of this circle. Let us drop perpendiculars from points a, b, and c to axis I. The projections of points a, b, and c upon axis I are a_1, b_1, and c_1, respectively; in other words, they are the factor loadings of tests a, b, and c with factor I. Test a has a relatively large loading with ability I; test b has much less, and test c has a slightly negative loading. A negative loading of a factor in a test would seem to mean that the ability is a handicap to the individual in that test. This is hardly true to the facts as we know them. What is done with negative factor loadings will soon be made clear. The lengths of the perpendiculars a_2, b_2, and c_2 give the factor loadings of tests a, b, and c for factor II. In this case all three loadings are positive, test a having the least and test c having the greatest amount of factor II. Line Oa with lines a_1 and a_2 form a right triangle. From an old familiar principle in geometry, $a_1^2 + a_2^2 = Oa^2 = 1$ and $b_1^2 + b_2^2 = Ob^2 = 1$, which are precisely the equations that appear above for the communality.

The correlation between tests *a* and *b* can also be interpreted on the basis of Fig. 46.   It is the cosine of the angle ϕ, or the angle formed at the origin between lines *Oa* and *Ob*.   The cosine of an angle is given by the ratio of the adjacent side of the right triangle in which the angle appears to the hypothenuse.   In Fig. 46 a line *bp* is drawn at right angles to the line *Oa*, forming the right triangle *bpO*. The cosine of ϕ is therefore the ratio m/n, where *n* is equal to *Ob*. But the line *Ob* is equal to unity; therefore the $\cos \phi = m$.   This is a reasonable interpretation of the Pearson *r* if we remember that *r*

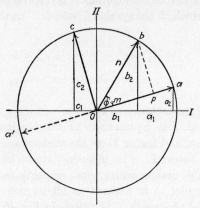

Fig. 46.—Geometric representation of three tests in a two-common-factor system. Axes I and II stand for the two independent common factors, and points *a*, *b*, and *c* represent the location of the three tests with reference to the coordinate system.

varies between -1.00 and $+1.00$, as also does $\cos \phi$. Let *b* and *a* approach one another in Fig. 46 and the line *m* grows larger, approaching $+1.00$ as its limit when *a* and *b* become identical. Let *b* depart farther and farther from *a*; then ϕ becomes larger and $\cos \phi$ becomes smaller, approaching a value of zero when *b* reaches a position at right angles to *a*.   This agrees with the fact that cos 90 deg. is zero.   In Fig. 46 the correlation between tests *a* and *c* is zero.   A test lying farther to the left of *c* would have a *negative* correlation with *a*.   When point *a'* is reached, at a point 180 deg. from *a*, the correlation becomes -1.00.   It follows that in a two-dimensional factor pattern all the tests under investigation may be represented as points on the periphery of a circle and that the correlation between any two tests is the cosine of the central angle which the test vectors form at the origin.

This line of thought gives us further illumination as to the nature of the factor loading. Factor loading a_1 is the cosine of the angle IOa and is therefore the correlation between test a and factor I. Likewise, a_2 is the cosine of the angle aOII, and is therefore the correlation between test a and factor II. *Any factor loading represents the correlation between a test and one of the reference abilities.* A *reference ability* is represented by a coordinate such as OI or OII in Fig. 46.

It has been shown algebraically (34, p. 4) that the correlation between tests a and b can be derived from the factor loadings common to the two tests. In this instance,

$$r_{ab} = a_1b_1 + a_2b_2.$$

Likewise,

$$r_{ac} = a_1c_1 + a_2c_2,$$

and

$$r_{bc} = b_1c_1 + b_2c_2.$$

In other words, the correlation between two tests is equal to the cross-products of the factor loadings in the corresponding abilities held in common by the two tests. In general terms,

$$r_{ab} = a_1b_1 + a_2b_2 + a_3b_3 + \cdots + a_nb_n \qquad (226)$$

where $a_1, a_2, a_3, \ldots, a_n =$ the factor loadings of factors I, II, III, $\ldots$, N in test a.

$b_1, b_2, b_3, \ldots, b_n =$ the corresponding factor loadings in test b.

Locating the Meaningful Axes: The Problem of Rotation.—In the typical factor-analysis problem we do not know at the beginning the values of $a_1, a_2, a_3, \ldots, a_n$ or of $b_1, b_2, b_3, \ldots, b_n$. All we know is the intercorrelations between tests. We know only the cosines of the central angles between *test vectors* (such as Oa, Ob, Oc, $\ldots$, On). These relationships would hold no matter where the reference axes were drawn. This is the most serious problem of the factor-analysis methods—where to locate reference axes that have psychological meaning. An infinite number of solutions are possible. We could arbitrarily locate them anywhere we pleased. What principles or criteria shall guide us and how shall the position of the **ability vectors** (such as axes I and II in Fig. 46) be determined?

The solution of this problem is based upon two principles: (1) That all factor loadings should be positive within the limits of sampling errors and (2) that there should be as many zero loadings as the configurations of points will permit. It can be seen in Fig. 46 that axes I and II may be rotated into any position and that the relative positions of points a, b, and c will remain the same. Following the principles just enunciated, it is obvious that a rotation of the axes should be made slightly counterclockwise so that axis I coincides with the line Oa and axis II coincides with the line Oc. Point c would then have a zero loading for factor I, losing its negative

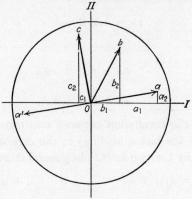

Fig. 47.—A geometric representation of tests whose variances are not wholly accounted for by the two common factors I and II.

loading, and point a would lose all its loading with factor II. Test b would retain factor loadings with both abilities, but it would gain slightly in factor I as it lost in factor II. The case of test a' in Fig. 46 very rarely occurs in practice; if it does, the direction of the scoring may be reversed so as to bring it into the positive quadrant of the coordinate system.

Factor Theory for the General Case.—The preceding discussion applies only to the case where there are two primary abilities and where the tests containing them are perfectly reliable. What will happen if the tests are not perfectly reliable? We must then represent the tests as in Fig. 47, with the lengths of the test vectors something short of unity. The directions of the test points from the origin remain the same and their central angles likewise. It will be noted that the factor loadings are now smaller than before but that they retain their correct proportions, since the right triangles in Fig. 47 are similar to the corresponding right triangles in Fig. 46. But now the hypothenuse of each right triangle is less than 1, and so $a_1^2 + a_2^2$ is less than 1; this is also true of $b_1^2 + b_2^2$ and $c_1^2 + c_2^2$. The differences between these sums and unity can be designated by $1 - h^2$, or one minus the communality. This quantity, $1 - h^2$, Thurstone calls the **uniqueness** of the test. It includes all that variance in the test which is due to a specific factor or factors and to errors of sampling. For test a, let a_s^2 denote that portion of the variance due to specific factors and a_e^2 that variance attributable to unreliability of the test. We now have a number of concepts defined:

$$\text{Total variance} = \sigma_a^2 = a_1^2 + a_2^2 + a_3^2 + \cdots + a_n^2 + a_s^2 + a_e^2 \quad (227)$$
$$\begin{aligned} \text{Reliability} = r_{aa} &= a_1^2 + a_2^2 + a_3^2 + \cdots + a_n^2 + a_s^2 \\ &= h_a^2 + a_s^2 = 1 - a_e^2 \end{aligned} \quad (228)$$
$$\begin{aligned} \text{Communality} = h_a^2 &= a_1^2 + a_2^2 + a_3^2 + \cdots + a_n^2 \\ &= 1 - a_s^2 - a_e^2 = 1 - a_u^2 \end{aligned} \quad (229)$$
$$\text{Specificity} = a_s^2 = r_{aa} - h_a^2 \quad (230)$$
$$\text{Uniqueness} = a_u^2 = a_s^2 + a_e^2 = 1 - h_a^2 \quad (231)$$

When there are other than two common factors, the geometric representation differs from that already used. With only one common factor, which is Spearman's special case, the factor loadings would be represented along a straight line. One dimension is all that is necessary. With three factors there are three dimensions. Every test vector is represented as lying somewhere within a sphere. If the tests are perfectly reliable and their communalities equal unity, or if a correction for uniqueness has been made, the points representing the tests lie on the surface of a sphere with radius equal to unity. With a fourth dimension one has to imagine an additional axis drawn at right angles to all three axes already present. A fifth factor requires a new axis at right angles to the four, and so on. One could add as many new axes in this conceptual common factor space as one desires. The problems of computation naturally become more complex and the task of rotation becomes more difficult, but the reasoning about the factors is in every way comparable to that in the case of the two-dimensional system already described. We shall now proceed to demonstrate the operation of the centroid method, first with a two-dimensional problem, then with a three-dimensional problem.

The Centroid Method: Solution of a Two-factor Problem

A Fictitious Two-factor Problem.—Let us take as our first example a fictitious problem in which there are two common factors. The reasons for using a fictitious problem are as follows: With as many as 10 tests one rarely finds just two common factors. In a problem invented for the occasion we can start with assumed factor loadings chosen to illustrate a simplified ideal case and we can see how well the factor analysis gives in the end the known factor loadings with which we started. Table 86 gives the assumed factor loadings in the 10 hypothetical tests. A table of factor loadings will be known hereafter as a **factor matrix.**

TABLE 86.—THE ASSUMED FACTOR LOADINGS FOR TWO COMMON FACTORS IN 10 HYPOTHETICAL TESTS

Test	Factor loadings		Communality h_k^2
	k_1	k_2	
1	.7	.1	.50
2	.6	.5	.61
3	.9	.2	.85
4	.8	.0	.64
5	.2	.8	.68
6	.5	.7	.74
7	.0	.8	.64
8	.1	.9	.82
9	.8	.1	.65
10	.3	.7	.58

The Correlation Matrix.—From the factor loadings in Table 86 we can compute the various intercorrelations by means of formula (226). For example, $r_{12} = a_1b_1 + a_2b_2 = (.7)(.6) + (.1)(.5) = .47$; $r_{13} = (.7)(.9) + (.1)(.2) = .65$; and $r_{23} = (.6)(.9) + (.5)(.2) = .64$; and so on. These intercorrelations such as Table 87 we shall call a **correlation matrix.**

Estimation of the Communalities.—The diagonal values in a correlation matrix as set up for the centroid method should be the communalities of the tests. These are generally unknown and have to be estimated. This is one serious weakness of the centroid method as it is now used, but it is certainly not a fatal weakness. Thurstone recommends that the communality (h^2) for each test be

TABLE 87.—INTERCORRELATIONS OF THE 10 TESTS AS OBTAINED FROM THE FACTOR PATTERN GIVEN IN TABLE 86 AND THE COMPUTATION OF THE FIRST FACTOR LOADINGS

	1	2	3	4	5	6	7	8	9	10	Σr_{ak}
1	**.65**	.47	.65	.56	.22	.49	.08	.16	.57	.28	4.13
2	.47	**.65**	.64	.48	.52	.65	.40	.51	.53	.53	5.38
3	.65	.64	**.74**	.72	.34	.59	.16	.27	.74	.41	5.26
4	.56	.48	.72	**.72**	.16	.40	.00	.08	.64	.24	4.00
5	.22	.52	.34	.16	**.74**	.66	.64	.74	.24	.62	4.88
6	.49	.65	.59	.40	.66	**.68**	.56	.68	.47	.64	5.82
7	.08	.40	.16	.00	.64	.56	**.72**	.72	.08	.56	3.92
8	.16	.51	.27	.08	.74	.68	.72	**.74**	.17	.66	4.73
9	.57	.53	.74	.64	.24	.47	.08	.17	**.74**	.31	4.49
10	.28	.53	.41	.24	.62	.64	.56	.66	.31	**.66**	4.91
Σr_{ka}	4.13	5.38	5.26	4.00	4.88	5.82	3.92	4.73	4.49	4.91	
k_1	.599	.780	.763	.580	.708	.844	.569	.686	.651	.712	
k_1^2	.3588	.6084	.5822	.3364	.5013	.7123	.3238	.4706	.4238	.5069	

$$47.52 = \Sigma r$$
$$\sqrt{\Sigma r} = 6.893475$$
$$1/\sqrt{\Sigma r} = .145064$$
$$\text{CHECK: } \Sigma k_1 = 6.892$$

estimated as equal to the highest correlation in the column for that test. The reason for this is that the communality should usually be as high as the highest correlation of a test with any other single test, barring errors of sampling in the latter. It is never so high as the coefficient of reliability whenever there is a specific variance, as there usually is, so the reliability coefficient should *not* be used as an estimate of h^2.

In the first column of Table 87 the highest r is .65; in the second column it is .65; in the third column it is .74; and so on. These will differ from the actual communalities, as one can see by comparing them with the known communalities in this fictitious problem. The first three communalities in Table 86 are .50, .61, and .74. In the solution of this problem we could make use of the known communalities. But for illustrative purposes it is better to proceed as if the communalities were unknown and then see how serious is the error in following Thurstone's assumption. Thurstone maintains that, when the number of tests is 20 or more, the error involved in guessing the communality as equal to the highest r in each column is negligible. But when there are fewer than 10 tests, a method of successive approximations should be introduced. With between 10 and 20 tests the investigator may use his own judgment as to this step.

Computation of the First Factor Loadings.—The first factor loadings for the tests are given by the general formula

$$a_1 = \frac{\Sigma r_{ka}}{\sqrt{\Sigma r}} \qquad (232)$$

where a_1 = the factor loading in test a.

Σr_{ka} = the sum of the coefficients in the column for test a.[1]

Σr = the sum of all the values of r in the table.

The solution of the first factor loadings is most simply carried out by means of the following steps:

1. Place in the diagonal position in each column the highest r in that column. This is assumed to be the best estimate of the unknown communality for the test represented by that column.

---

[1] The subscript ka is interpreted as follows: The first letter k is a general notation and stands for the row in which the r appears. The second letter indicates the column in which r appears. Σr_{ka} then means the sum of the r's in the column for test a, or in this case column 1.

2. Find the sums of the columns and also of the rows as a check upon the addition. If there should be a few scattered negative coefficients, the algebraic sum is the one to use, not the absolute sum. If there should be a sufficient number of negative signs in any column to give a negative sum (this is highly unlikely in the analysis of the first factor, when dealing with tests of ability and when the scoring scales give larger scores for greater ability), a process of reflection of one or more tests may be necessary. The process of reflection is described in steps 11 through 15 below.

3. Find the total for the entire table, or Σr. For Table 87 this is 47.52.

4. Find the square root of this total, or $\sqrt{\Sigma r}$. In this problem it is 6.893475.

5. Find the reciprocal of $\sqrt{\Sigma r}$, or $1/\sqrt{\Sigma r}$. In the present problem this value is .145064. As a check of this value, find the product of Σr times $1/\sqrt{\Sigma r}$, which should give $\sqrt{\Sigma r}$ if the work has been correct. In the illustrative problem, the product

$$47.52 \times .145064 = 6.893488,$$

which is accurate to four decimal places.

6. Multiply the sum of each column, Σr_{ka}, by $1/\sqrt{\Sigma r}$. This gives the first factor loading, k_1, for every test. As a check at this point, the sum of the factor loadings should equal $\sqrt{\Sigma r}$. In the example above $\Sigma k_1 = 6.892$.

7. The factor loadings are squared, as in the last row of Table 87. This gives for every test that portion of the communality which may be accounted for by the first factor loading.

Computation of the First Factor Residuals.—Having computed the first factor loadings, we next proceed to find the first factor residuals, or that part of the original correlations which cannot be attributed to the first centroid factor. The next steps are described in consecutive order:

8. The first factor residuals are given by formulas of the type

$$\rho_{ab} = r_{ab} - a_1 b_1 \tag{233}$$

where $a_1 = $ the first factor loading for test a.

$b_1 = $ the first factor loading for test b.

In column 1 of the illustrative problem,

$$\rho_{11} = .65 - (.599)(.599) = \quad .291.$$
$$\rho_{21} = .47 - (.599)(.780) = \quad .003.$$

$$\rho_{31} = .65 - (.599)(.763) = .193.$$
$$\rho_{41} = .56 - (.599)(.580) = .213.$$
$$\rho_{51} = .22 - (.599)(.708) = -.204.$$

$$. \quad . \quad . \quad . \quad . \quad .$$

$$\rho_{10\,1} = .28 - (.599)(.712) = -.146.$$

The first factor residuals are given in full in Table 88, each one with its proper algebraic sign recorded in the upper left part of its cell in a narrow strip provided for it. It will be noticed that the residuals range from $-.330$ to $+.384$. On the face of it we can see that there is something still common to the tests in addition to the one factor already removed.

9. Check the accuracy of the residuals by finding algebraic sums of the columns. These are recorded as Σ_0 at the bottom of Table 88. If the work has been accurate no Σ_0 should exceed .010. In this example none is greater than .006.

10. Replace each *diagonal* residual with the highest value in that column. Make the algebraic sign of this value positive regardless of what its sign originally was and leave it positive no matter what other changes may be made in signs.

The Second Factor Loadings and the Reflection of Test Vectors.— The computation of the second and succeeding factor loadings always involves the reflection of some of the test vectors as described in the next steps:

11. Whenever there are a large number of negative signs in some of the columns, we must proceed to *reflect* some of the test variables. By this we mean changing signs throughout some of the columns (and throughout the corresponding rows) so as to maximize the number of plus signs in the new correlation matrix. (We may regard a table of residuals as a correlation matrix after a common factor or factors have been removed.) The geometric interpretation of a reflection of a test would mean that we change the axis of the test vector end for end. In Fig. 46, for example, test a' as it stands would correlate negatively with all the other tests; the angle of separation between a' and the others is 90 deg. or more. By placing a' at the opposite end of its axis it would coincide with a and it would then have no negative correlations with the other tests. The process of reflection has been reduced to a routine process by Thurstone (39, p. 238). Prepare a table like Table 89, with the numbers of the tests along the top and in the first row place the number of

TABLE 88.—FIRST FACTOR RESIDUALS IN THE TWO-FACTOR PROBLEM AND THE COMPUTATION OF THE SECOND FACTOR LOADINGS

	+1	+2	+3	+4	-5	-6	-7	-8	+9	-10	Σrₐₖ
+1	+.291 +.261	+.003	+.193	+.213	+.204	+.016	+.261	+.251	+.180	+.146	1.728
+2	+.003	.042 +.045	+.045	+.028	+.032	+.008	+.044	+.025	+.022	+.025	.277
+3	+.193	+.045	.158 +.277	+.277	+.200	+.054	+.274	+.253	+.243	+.133	1.949
+4	+.213	+.028	+.277	.384 +.330	+.251	+.090	+.330	+.253	+.243	+.173	2.272
-5	+.204	+.032	+.200	+.251	.239 +.254	+.062	+.237	+.254	+.221	+.116	1.831
-6	+.016	+.008	+.054	+.090	+.062	.032 +.101	+.080	+.101	+.079	+.039	.630
-7	+.261	+.044	+.274	+.330	+.237	+.080	.396 +.330	+.330	+.290	+.155	2.331
-8	+.251	+.025	+.253	+.318	+.254	+.101	+.330	.269 +.318	+.277	+.172	2.299
+9	+.180	+.022	+.243	+.262	+.271	+.079	+.290	+.277	.316 +.290	+.054	2.018
-10	+.146	+.025	+.133	+.173	+.116	+.039	+.155	+.172	+.154	.153 +.173	1.286
Σ_0	+.002	+.006	+.002	+.002	.000	+.003	-.001	+.002	+.002	+.004	
Σr_{ka}	1.728	.277	1.949	2.272	1.831	.630	2.331	2.299	2.018	1.286	
k_2	+.424	+.068	+.478	+.557	-.449	-.155	-.572	-.564	+.495	-.315	
k_2^2	.1798	.0046	.2285	.3102	.2016	.0240	.3272	.3181	.2450	.0992	

$$\Sigma r = 16.621$$
$$\sqrt{\Sigma r} = 4.076886$$
$$1/\sqrt{\Sigma r} = .245285$$
CHECK: $\Sigma k_2 = 4.077$

negative signs in the various columns of Table 88, excluding diagonal values. The next to the last column is labeled "Check." It is to contain the sums of the numbers in the rows. The last column, headed V_k, stands for the number of the variable to be reflected.

TABLE 89.—SUCCESSIVE REFLECTIONS OF TEST VARIABLES

Test	1	2	3	4	x 5	x 6	x 7	x 8	9	x 10	Check	V_k
	5	5	5	5	5	5	5	5	5	5	50	7
	4	4	4	4	6	6	4	6	4	6	48	8
	3	3	3	3	7	7	3	3	3	7	42	5
	2	2	2	2	2	8	2	2	2	8	32	10
	1	1	1	1	1	9	1	1	1	1	18	6
	0	0	0	0	0	0	0	0	0	0	0	

12. It happens that all 10 tests are alike in having exactly five negative signs, excluding diagonal values, in their columns. The check sum is 50. One should begin by reflecting the test having the maximum number of negative signs. Since all have five, by inspection we may note which test has the largest negative residuals, or, more accurately, we may note which of those tests with an equal number of negative signs has the greatest absolute sum. This is variable 7 in Table 88. Its absolute sum is 2.331. We therefore reflect test 7 first. We place an x above the 7 in Table 89 and also record a 7 in the last column.

13. We want to know next how many negative signs will be left in each column after reflecting test 7. We do not actually change the signs yet, but use the following process. In this we disregard entirely the diagonal values. They will remain positive no matter what else we do. As for column 7, it has nine coefficients, not counting the diagonal. Five were negative. A complete change of signs in that column would give $9 - 5$, or 4 negative signs remaining. Record a 4 in column 7 and row 2 of Table 89. As for the other columns of Table 88, we examine the row of coefficients for test 7. If in any column the sign of the residual is negative, we deduct one negative sign in that column; if the sign is positive, we add one to the number of negative signs. In row 7, columns 1, 2, 3, 4, and 9 have negative signs. For these columns we therefore deduct one, which gives us 4 to record in row 2 of Table 89. For tests 5, 6, 8,

and 10 the signs in row 7 are positive, so we must add one in each case and record a 6 for each of those tests in Table 89.

14. The check upon our work thus far in Table 89 is obtained as follows: The sum of row 2 is 48. This is a reduction of two points from the corresponding sum in row 1. This total reduction should equal two times the reduction in negative signs in the column reflected. In column 7 there was a reduction of only one negative sign, hence the check is satisfied.

15. Now tests 5, 6, 8, and 10 are rivals for the next reflection with six negative signs each. Of these we choose to reflect test 8 since it has the highest absolute sum. The number of negative signs in column 8 will be $9 - 6 = 3$. All other columns are treated exactly as in step 13, *except column 7, which was reflected before.* Here an original plus sign has been made negative by the first reflection and so column 7 has one less negative again. The *total* reduction, in the check, should be $2 \times 3 = 6$, which equals $48 - 42$, and the check is satisfied.

16. We proceed now with columns 5, 10, and 6 in the same manner, until there are no negatives left in the matrix. This is a rather exceptional case. In general one carries the reflections on until every column has less than $n/2$ negative signs, where n is the number of tests. It may be found occasionally that a test already reflected may have to be reflected back again. It also sometimes happens that a column has a negative algebraic sum even after the number of negative signs has been minimized. That column should be reflected again.

17. The actual changes in signs may now be made in Table 88. First we change signs by rows. At the extreme left of the table are plus signs at the upper left of each test number. These indicate that the test variables have come through thus far without reflection. Beginning with row 5, we place a negative sign below and to the right of the plus sign. Proceeding along the row, place the changed sign just below the original sign. Do the same for rows 6, 7, 8, and 10.

18. At the top of Table 88 plus signs also appear before all the test numbers, indicating again that they were not reflected before this point. In column 1, in which the test is not to be reflected, bring down the plus sign and attach it to number 1. In each cell of that column copy just before each residual the *last sign* appearing in the space at the left. Do likewise for every column in which

no reflection is to be made. This applies to columns 2, 3, 4, and 9 in addition to column 1.

19. In the columns to be reflected, for example in column 5, *reverse all the last given signs* appearing at the left and place these reversed signs just before the residuals. Do likewise for columns 6, 7, 8, and 10. It so happens in this table that now all signs are positive. This was forecasted by the work in Table 89.

Computation of the Second Factor Loadings and Second Factor Residuals.—20. Compute the second factor loadings by following out steps 1 to 7 as before.

21. Attach to each second factor loading, k_2, its proper sign, positive if the test has not been reflected (or has been reflected an even number of times), negative if it has been reflected once (or any odd number of times). The signs of k_2 will coincide with those last attached to the numbers of the test variables at the top

TABLE 90.—SECOND FACTOR RESIDUALS IN THE TWO-FACTOR PROBLEM

	1	2	3	4	5	6	7	8	9	10
1	.081	−.026	−.010	−.023	+.014	+.050	+.018	+.012	−.030	+.012
2		+.040	+.012	−.010	+.001	−.003	+.005	−.013	−.012	+.004
3			+.049	+.011	−.015	−.020	+.001	−.017	+.006	−.018
4				+.020	+.001	+.004	+.011	+.004	−.014	−.002
5					+.052	−.008	−.020	+.001	−.001	−.025
6						+.077	−.009	+.014	+.002	−.010
7							−.003	+.007	+.007	−.025
8								.000	−.002	−.006
9									+.045	−.002
10										+.074
Σ_0	−.002	−.002	−.001	+.002	.000	−.003	−.002	.000	−.001	+.002

of Table 88. They are positive for tests 1, 2, 3, 4, and 9, and negative for tests 5, 6, 7, 8, and 10.

22. Compute the second factor residuals as in step 8 above. This time, naturally, one deducts the product of a_2b_2 from ρ_{ab}. In this and successive sets of residuals, algebraic signs must be considered. In determining the cross-products, a_2b_2, a_2c_2, . . . , a_2n_2, etc., the signs of the factor loadings are regarded as positive, and so the cross-products are positive. But the first factor residuals from which the products are deducted are given the same algebraic sign they had *after reflection* of the tests as in Table 88. In this problem it hap-

pened that all the signs after reflection were positive. The second factor residuals are given in Table 90. Except for the diagonal residuals they are all negligibly small. We have twice estimated the communalities. Were a third factor to be determined, we should discard these high diagonal residuals, so they are not to be taken seriously as indicators of our 'goodness of fit.' Had we used the exact known communalities at the beginning, the second factor residuals should have vanished completely. We may see now how much harm was done by assuming that the highest correlation in each column is the most probable value of the communality. In estimating the goodness of fit, more attention should be given to the nondiagonal residuals. Among these, the maximum value is .030.[1]

The Factor Matrix.—It is desirable next to collect all the factor loadings in a single table and to compute the communalities. For our fictitious two-factor problem these appear in Table 91. The communalities have been computed to two decimal places here to compare with the original known communalities. A comparison

TABLE 91.—FACTOR LOADINGS, COMMUNALITIES, RELIABILITIES, UNIQUENESS' AND SPECIFICITY, AS COMPUTED BY THE CENTROID METHOD IN THE TWO-FACTOR PROBLEM

Test	k_1	k_2	h_k^2	r_{kk}	k_u^2	k_s^2	k_e^2
1	.599	.424	.54	.85	.46	.31	.15
2	.780	.068	.61	.91	.39	.30	.09
3	.763	.478	.81	.87	.19	.06	.13
4	.580	.557	.65	.94	.35	.29	.06
5	.708	−.449	.70	.82	.30	.12	.18
6	.844	−.155	.74	.90	.26	.16	.10
7	.569	−.572	.65	.93	.35	.28	.07
8	.686	−.564	.79	.84	.21	.05	.16
9	.651	.495	.67	.78	.33	.11	.22
10	.712	−.315	.61	.89	.39	.28	.11

of the computed and known communalities (see Table 86) will show that the maximum error is .04. In a problem with unknown communalities, if we wish to obtain a more accurate set of factor

[1] In Table 90 only half of the residuals are given. The lower left part of the table would duplicate the upper right part. The sums Σ_0 are based upon the complete table.

loadings, we can begin over again, substituting in the original correlation matrix the computed communalities of Table 91, and solve again for the factor loadings k_1 and k_2. The second set of computed communalities would approximate the true ones more closely. A third as well as additional successive approximations could be made until the obtained h^2's coincide with the guessed h^2's. This should be done when the number of tests is less than 10 and sometimes when there are more than 10. A comparison of the assumed communalities with the final computed ones will indicate whether this is necessary.

Accounting for the Total Variances of the Tests.—From formulas (227) to (231), if we know the communalities and the reliabilities of the tests, it is possible to estimate that part of the variance of each test which is unique and also those parts due to specific elements and to errors of measurement. In our problem of fictitious tests we may assume some reliabilities. These are given in the column headed r_{kk} in Table 91. The variance due to uniqueness is

$$1 - h_k^2 = k_u^2,$$

and this value for each test is given in the fifth column. The uniqueness is subdivided into specific factors, k_s^2, and error factors, k_e^2, which appear in the last two columns of Table 91. The total variance of each test is thus accounted for.

ROTATION OF THE REFERENCE AXES

Centroid Axes Usually Lack Psychological Meaning.—As we have indicated before, we do not know directly from the intercorrelations just where the ability axes should be placed. The centroid method merely gives us two or more orthogonal reference axes and the factor loadings are the projections of the test vectors upon those axes. It would be gratuitous to attempt to give psychological meaning or significance to a centroid axis. It probably does not correspond to any real variable in human nature. It will be obvious, too, in comparing the assumed factor loadings in Table 86 with the centroid factor loadings in Table 91, that something is decidedly amiss. The two sets of factor loadings do not coincide in the least. Can we, by rotation of the axes, reproduce exactly the original or 'true' factor loadings?

A centroid is a center of gravity or a kind of average. In Fig. 48 are shown the two centroid axes (I and II) with the tests plotted as points in the plane formed by those two axes. The first factor loadings are the projections of these points upon axis I and the second factor loadings are the projections of the points upon axis II. Axis I obviously projects through the center of the configuration of points. Five of the points lie above axis I and five below it. Furthermore the positive and negative factor loadings for factor II are almost exactly numerically balanced. The sum of the k_2's is $-.033$.

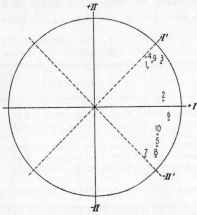

Fig. 48.—A plot of the ten test vectors in the two-factor problem on the centroid axes (I and II), showing the positions of the same test vectors with reference to the new axes (I' and II') after a rotation of 45 deg.

Were there more than two common factors, the sum of the factor loadings beyond those for factor I would be approximately zero. This location of the centroid axes is therefore a characteristic of the method rather than of the factor pattern.

Computation of the New Factor Loadings.—Following the principles of rotation laid down earlier, attempting to make all factor loadings positive and to make as many zeros as possible, it is quite clear in Fig. 48 that a rotation of about 45 deg. is called for. We shall make the rotation in the counterclockwise direction. Graphically this is very simple. However, we want to find the new factor loadings or coordinates in relation to the new set of reference axes, for it is assumed that these axes represent the real unitary abilities we are seeking. The general formulas for computing the new coordinates are

$$k'_1 = k_1\cos \phi + k_2\sin \phi$$
$$k'_2 = k_2\cos \phi - k_1\sin \phi$$

(234)

where k_1 and k_2 = the original centroid factor loadings for factors I and II.

k_1' and k_2' = the new factor loadings after rotation of the centroid axes.

ϕ = the angle of rotation.

The values of sin ϕ and of cos ϕ are to be found from trigonometric tables. For an angle of 45 deg., sin ϕ = cos ϕ = .7071. It is convenient, in applying formulas (234) to set up a work sheet like Table 92. The new factor loadings k_2' all have negative signs.

TABLE 92.—COMPUTATION OF THE FACTOR LOADINGS AFTER A ROTATION OF 45 DEG.

Test	1	2	3	4	5	6	7	8	9	10
$k_1 \cos \phi$	.4236	.5515	.5395	.4101	.5006	.5968	.4023	.4851	.4603	.5035
$k_2 \sin \phi$	.2998	.0481	.3380	.3939	−.3175	−.1096	−.4045	−.3988	.3500	−.2227
k_1'	.7234	.5996	.8775	.8040	.1831	.4872	−.0022	.0863	.8103	.2808
$k_2 \cos \phi$	.2998	.0481	.3380	.3939	−.3175	−.1096	−.4045	−.3988	.3500	−.2227
$-k_1 \sin \phi$	−.4236	−.5515	−.5395	−.4101	−.5006	−.5968	−.4023	−.4851	−.4603	−.5035
k_2'	−.1238	−.5034	−.2015	−.0162	−.8181	−.7064	−.8068	−.8839	−.1103	−.7262

Reference to Fig. 48 will show why this is so. It is the negative pole of axis II that carries the projections of the points. We can

TABLE 93.—FACTOR LOADINGS IN THE TWO-FACTOR PROBLEM AFTER A ROTATION OF 45 DEG.

Test	k_1'	k_2'	h_k^2
1	.72	.12	.54
2	.60	.50	.61
3	.88	.20	.81
4	.80	.02	.65
5	.18	.82	.70
6	.49	.71	.74
7	.00	.81	.65
8	.09	.88	.79
9	.81	.11	.67
10	.28	.73	.61

change sign throughout, which is equivalent to reflecting trait vector II, making the second factor loadings all positive. In Table

93 the new coordinates are listed, rounded to two decimal places, with the communalities. The communalities remain the same regardless of the rotation. Their computation from the rotated coordinates serves as a numerical check upon the process of rotation. It will now be noticed that the factor loadings almost exactly coincide with those in Table 86. The largest discrepancy is only .03.

The Solution of a Three-factor Problem

A Factor Analysis of the Army Alpha Examination.—Let us take for our next illustration data obtained from the intercorrelation of the parts of the Army Alpha examination. The eight parts of that battery of tests are designated as follows: (1) directions, (2)

TABLE 94.—Correlation Matrix for the Parts of the Army Alpha Examination with the Solution of the First Factor Loadings by the Centroid Method

	1	2	3	4	5	6	7	8	Σr_{ak}
1	**.409**	.352	.289	.206	.126	.387	.409	.107	2.285
2	.352	**.494**	.474	.372	.346	.494	.091	.310	2.933
3	.289	.474	**.474**	.435	.329	.364	.440	.426	3.231
4	.206	.372	.435	**.568**	.568	.324	.531	.453	3.457
5	.126	.346	.329	.568	**.568**	.134	.385	.410	2.866
6	.387	.494	.364	.324	.134	**.494**	.397	.157	2.751
7	.409	.091	.440	.531	.385	.397	**.531**	.288	3.072
8	.107	.310	.426	.453	.410	.157	.288	**.453**	2.604
Σr_{ka}	2.285	2.933	3.231	3.457	2.866	2.751	3.072	2.604	$\Sigma r = 23.199$
k_1	.474	.609	.671	.718	.595	.571	.638	.541	$\sqrt{\Sigma r} = 4.81654$
k_1^2	.2247	.3709	.4502	.5154	.3540	.3260	.4070	.2927	$1/\sqrt{\Sigma r} = .20761$
									CHECK: $\Sigma k_1 = 4.817$

arithmetic, (3) common sense, (4) synonym-antonym, (5) mixed sentences, (6) number completion, (7) word analogies, and (8) information. The data to be used were obtained from 108 university freshmen who were entering a college of engineering. They were homogeneous as to sex and age, and fairly homogeneous as to education. A group of subjects used in a factor-analysis problem should be fairly homogeneous except for the test variables in question. The correlation matrix is given in Table 94, with the solution of the first factor loadings according to the procedures described in connection with the two-factor problem.

TABLE 95.—FIRST FACTOR RESIDUALS AND THE COMPUTATION OF THE SECOND FACTOR LOADINGS IN THE ARMY ALPHA PROBLEM

	-1	-2	$+3$	$+4$	$+5$	-6	$+7$	$+8$	Σr_{ak}
-1	+.184 / **+.156**	+.063	+.029	+.134	+.156	+.116	-.107	+.149	.696
-2	+.063	.123 / **+.298**	-.065	+.065	+.016	+.146	+.298	+.019	.840
$+3$	+.029	-.065	.024 / **+.070**	-.047	-.070	+.019	+.012	+.063	.011
$+4$	+.134	+.065	-.047	.052 / **+.141**	+.141	+.086	+.073	+.065	.658
$+5$	+.156	+.016	-.070	+.141	.214 / **+.206**	+.206	+.005	+.088	.748
-6	+.116	+.146	+.019	+.086	+.206	.168 / **+.206**	-.033	+.152	.898
$+7$	-.107	+.298	+.012	+.073	+.005	-.033	.124 / **+.298**	-.057	.489
$+8$	+.149	+.019	+.063	+.065	+.088	+.152	-.057	.160 / **+.152**	.631
Σ_0	+.002	-.001	-.001	-.001	.000	.000	-.001	-.001	
Σr_{ka}	.696	.840	.011	.658	.748	.898	.489	.631	
k_2	-.312	-.377	+.005	+.295	+.335	-.403	+.219	+.283	
k_2^2	.0973	.1421	.0000	.0870	.1122	.1624	.0480	.0801	

$$\Sigma r = 4.971$$
$$\sqrt{\Sigma r} = 2.22958$$
$$1/\sqrt{\Sigma r} = .44851$$
$$\text{CHECK: } \Sigma k_2 = 2.229$$

TABLE 96.—SECOND FACTOR RESIDUALS AND THE COMPUTATION OF THE THIRD FACTOR LOADINGS IN THE ARMY ALPHA PROBLEM

	-1	+2	+3	+4	+5	-6	-7	+8	Σr_{ak}
-1	.059 / +.175	+.055	+.027	+.042	+.051	-.010	+.175	+.061	.576
+2	+.055	.156 / +.215	+.067	+.046	+.110	+.006	+.215	+.088	.802
+3	+.055	+.067	.070 / +.072	-.048	-.072	+.017	-.011	+.062	.114
+4	+.027	+.046	-.048	.054 / +.048	+.042	-.033	-.008	-.018	.071
+5	+.042	+.110	-.072	+.042	.094 / +.110	+.071	+.068	-.007	.373
-6	+.051	+.006	+.017	-.033	+.071	.044 / +.121	+.121	+.038	.331
-7	-.010	+.215	-.011	-.008	+.068	+.121	.250 / +.215	+.119	.894
+8	+.175	+.088	+.062	-.018	-.007	-.038	+.119	.072 / +.119	.462
Σ_0	.000	+.001	.000	+.001	+.001	.000	+.005	+.001	
Σr_{ka}	.576	.802	.114	.071	.373	.331	.894	.462	
k_3	-.303	+.421	+.060	+.037	+.196	-.174	-.470	+.243	
k_3^2	.0918	.1772	.0036	.0014	.0384	.0303	.2209	.0590	

$$\Sigma r = 3.623$$
$$\sqrt{\Sigma r} = 1.90342$$
$$1/\sqrt{\Sigma r} = .52537 \quad \text{CHECK: } \Sigma k_3 = 1.904$$

The first factor residuals with the solution of the second factor loadings are presented in Table 95. Tests 1, 2, and 6 had to be reflected according to the process already described. The second factor residuals are given in Table 96 and also the solution for the third factor loadings. In this table it was found necessary to reflect tests 2 and 7. Test 2 had been reflected once before, so its third factor loading has a positive sign. Tests 1 and 6 were previously reflected and retain their negative signs for factor three. Test 7 gains a negative sign for the first time. We find the next residuals in Table 97.

TABLE 97.—THIRD FACTOR RESIDUALS IN THE ARMY ALPHA PROBLEM

	1	2	3	4	5	6	7	8
1	+.083	−.073	+.009	+.031	−.008	−.063	+.033	−.013
2		+.038	+.042	+.030	+.027	−.067	+.017	−.014
3			+.068	−.050	−.084	+.007	−.039	+.047
4				+.047	+.035	−.039	−.025	−.027
5					+.072	+.037	−.024	−.055
6						+.091	+.039	−.004
7							−.006	+.005
8								+.060
Σ_0	−.001	.000	.000	+.002	.000	+.001	.000	−.001

How Far to Continue the Factor Analysis.—The question naturally arises as to how many factors one should extract from the correlation matrix. One could of course continue until as many factors are extracted as there are test variables. We set out, in the factor methods, to reduce the number of variables as much as we could and still account for all the real correlations. It should also be remembered that the original correlations are fallible. Were we to continue to extract factors beyond a legitimate limit, we would simply be playing with sampling errors and deriving artifacts from the data. This gives us a clue. We should stop when practically all the residuals are within the errors of sampling.

One criterion for the stopping place is to find the standard error of the distribution of residuals in the table and to compare it with the standard deviation of the average r in the original correlation matrix. In the Army Alpha problem the average r is .343 and its σ_r is .085. According to this criterion we should have stopped after extracting two factors, for the σ of the second factor residuals is .082. The writer is inclined to believe that this criterion is too crude. Notice that in the table of second factor residuals there are values of .175 and .215, involving tests 1, 2, and 7, or three out of the eight tests in the battery. These values should be compared with the σ_r's of the corresponding original coefficients of correlation. $\sigma_{r_{17}} = .080$ and $\sigma_{r_{27}} = .095$. The two residuals, .175 and .215, are more than twice their corresponding σ_r's. When $N = 108$ these ratios would be regarded as significant, but not very significant, according to the standards of Fisher's table (see Appendix, Table K).

When we carry through the analysis for the third factor, we find three factor loadings of reasonable size, two of which contribute more than .100 to the communality. Were there only one significant factor loading here, we should be skeptical of the reality of the third dimension. But when at least three of the eight tests have so much in common over and above the communality involving factors one and two, then we feel justified in adopting the third factor as real. By contrast, note that no third-factor residual, aside from the diagonal values, is greater than .073. The σ of the residuals is .039, which is less than half the σ of the average original r. We should certainly end the search for factors at this point.

Recalculation with Successive Approximations.—It was said earlier that, when the number of test variables is less than 10, the guessed communalities, if erroneous, will lead to inaccurate estimates of the factor loadings. We may compare the computed communalities with the guessed communalities to see how serious this matter is, as in Table 98. Four of the guessed communalities

TABLE 98.—COMPARISON OF GUESSED COMMUNALITIES WITH COMPUTED COMMUNALITIES, FIRST APPROXIMATIONS, IN THE ARMY ALPHA PROBLEM

	1	2	3	4	5	6	7	8
Guessed	.409	.494	.474	.568	.568	.494	.531	.453
Computed	.322	.513	.478	.602	.466	.488	.455	.373
Discrepancies	+.087	−.019	−.004	−.034	+.102	+.006	+.076	+.080

are seriously in error as compared with the communalities that were computed on the basis of them. As a consequence of these findings, the analysis of the Army Alpha data was made completely twice more, using as the guessed communalities each time those values which were computed by the previous analysis. The results of the third analysis were taken as satisfactory since by that time the factor loadings and the communalities became rather stabilized, indicating that further approximations would change them very little. The results of the third analysis are summarized in Table 99.

TABLE 99.—FACTOR LOADINGS AND COMMUNALITIES AS FOUND BY THE THIRD APPROXIMATION FOR THE ARMY ALPHA PROBLEM

	k_1	k_2	k_3	h_k^2
1	.465	−.293	−.271	.3754
2	.675	−.475	.434	.8696
3	.656	.000	.042	.4321
4	.720	.287	.058	.6042
5	.572	.325	.207	.4756
6	.566	−.371	−.151	.4808
7	.686	.247	−.538	.8210
8	.530	.288	.243	.4228

ROTATION OF AXES WITH THREE OR MORE FACTORS

Two Methods of Rotation in Three Dimensions.—When there are three common factors, there are two methods by which the positions of the real axes may be located.[1]   One way is to plot the points representing the tests on the surface of a sphere, locate the new axes graphically, make one rotation of all axes simultaneously, and then compute the new coordinates. The other way is to deal with only two factors at a time, rotating them about the third axis as a pivot, computing new factor loadings after each rotation, and repeating the process as many times as is necessary. This method is the more general one and it is applicable to cases with more than three dimensions. The first method is limited to the three-factor situation, but it will be described here because in doing so the whole process of rotation may be made clearer. This method will be treated first.

Correction for Uniqueness: Augmenting the Coordinates.—As was pointed out earlier in connection with the two-factor problem, because tests are unreliable and because they contain variances that are unique, h^2 rarely equals unity. Therefore, if we wish to plot

[1] Thurstone describes additional procedures of rotation (39). The ones described here are perhaps the simplest and most easily applied.

the tests as points on the surface of a sphere of a radius equal to unity, we shall have to lengthen each test vector from its actual terminus inside the sphere to its extended position on the surface. In so doing, the test vector retains its original direction from the origin but its coordinates or projections upon the three centroid axes will all be enlarged. We must enlarge the three coordinates of a point until the sum of the squares of the coordinates equals 1.00. This is accomplished by dividing every coordinate by h, the square root of its communality. The square root of the communality is the length of the test vector, or the linear distance of a point from the origin. In Table 100 are given the square roots of the communalities (h_k) and the reciprocals ($1/h_k$), which are to be the common multipliers for the three original coordinates of each test (k_1, k_2, and k_3); finally, as a check upon the arithmetic, in the last column are given the new augmented communalities, which should equal approximately 1. They do so to the third decimal place.

Plotting the Points on a Sphere.—The augmented factor loadings may now be used in plotting the points on the surface of a sphere.

TABLE 100.—WORK SHEET FOR AUGMENTING THE FACTOR LOADINGS TO BE PLOTTED ON THE SURFACE OF A SPHERE

Test	h_k^2	h_k	$1/h_k$	k_1''	k_2''	k_3''	$h_k''^2$
1	.3754	.6127	1.6321	.759	−.478	−.442	1.0000
2	.8696	.9325	1.0724	.724	−.509	.465	.9995
3	.4321	.6573	1.5214	.998	.000	.064	1.0001
4	.6042	.7773	1.2865	.926	.369	.075	.9993
5	.4756	.6896	1.4501	.829	.471	.300	.9990
6	.4808	.6934	1.4422	.816	−.535	−.218	.9996
7	.8210	.9061	1.1036	.757	.273	−.594	1.0003
8	.4228	.6502	1.5380	.815	.443	.374	1.0003

A sphere having a diameter of 8 or 10 in. is convenient. It should be covered with a black paint that will permit writing upon it with chalk. Such spheres are used by geography teachers. First, locate three points, I, II, and III, to represent the three centroid vectors at right angles to one another. Thurstone describes the plotting of the points very concisely as follows (39, pp. 164 *f.*):

Mark off on a narrow strip of paper the distance $\pi D/4$, where D is the diameter of the sphere. This is also the surface distance between any two of the orthogonal reference points. Divide this distance into 90 parts in any convenient units to represent 90 deg. On the same strip of paper mark off the cosines of the angles with any convenient unit such as .00, .05, .10, etc. In doing this, look up $\cos^{-1}$ .05* $\cos^{-1}$ .10, and mark .05, .10 on the strip at the appropriate angles. The strip is then ready for use. In locating a point on the sphere, use the arithmetical check which is provided by the fact that the position of each point is determined by the angular separation from two reference points. The angular separation from the third reference point constitutes an arithmetical check.

Locating the New Reference Axes.—When the points are plotted, the next thing is to look for what Thurstone calls **simple structure.**

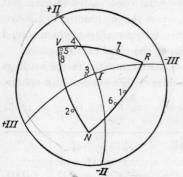

FIG. 49.—The factor loadings of the Army Alpha tests plotted on the surface of a sphere, demonstrating a positive manifold and new reference axes.

In the case of three dimensions, simple structure obtains when we can extend three planes at right angles to one another through the origin and when in doing so the planes cut through, or near, all the points. For our illustrative problem, Fig. 49 shows the side of the sphere that contains all eight test vectors. The positive poles of all the centroid axes are labeled and also the negative poles of axes II and III. Simple structure is observable on the surface when all the points come close to the sides of a right spherical triangle.

It is naturally unsatisfactory to attempt to locate a right spherical triangle by means of only eight points. It requires at least two points (in addition to the origin) to locate each one of the planes. That leaves only two degrees of freedom, and if the points happen to be poorly distributed the task is impossible. But in this particular configuration of points, fortunately, three sides of a right spherical triangle are rather clearly determined as shown in Fig. 49. To place the triangle so that all the points are inside the triangle follows a principle mentioned in connection with the two-factor problem; it makes all the factor loadings positive. It gives what Thurstone calls a **positive manifold.** This condition is

* The expression $\cos^{-1}$ .05 means the angle whose cosine is .05.

demanded by tests of ability, except that there may be permitted a few small negative factor loadings which can be explained on the basis of sampling errors.   Furthermore, the three lines as drawn in Fig. 49 make the maximum number of zero factor loadings.   Only one test, test 3, lacks even one zero loading, but tests 5 and 8 have two zero loadings each.

Interpretation of the Primary Factors.—We are aided somewhat in this problem by the knowledge of the composition of the tests.   We ordinarily let the configuration of points determine the positions of the new axes and then lend psychological meaning to the result. If it is an easy matter to interpret the new axes, we have additional support for the choice of their positions.   In this problem, test 5 is one involving disarranged sentences which the testee must put in meaningful order and state whether they are true or false.   Test 8 is an information test, depending primarily upon vocabulary, school training, and general reading.   Test 4 is the synonym-antonym test. For each pair of words given, the testee states whether they mean the same or the opposite.   It is clear enough that these three tests lean heavily upon verbal knowledge or ability, a unitary trait that is almost universally found in factor analysis.   The factor whose pole is at this apex of the triangle we shall call V.   Near the lower apex are tests 2 and 6.   Test 2 is on arithmetic and test 6 is the number-completion test; both involve number.   We designate this corner of the triangle N, for numerical ability, another trait commonly obtained.

The third apex is less easy to interpret.   Tests 7 and 1 come nearest to it, test 7 being the word-analogies test and test 1 the directions test.   I have designated this trait R because the use of simple relationships seems to be the most obvious characteristic common to the two tests, in test 7 especially.   This conclusion is further supported by the fact that test 6, a number-relation test, has a significant weight in R; this is also true of test 4 (same-opposites test) to a slight extent.   The designation *simple* relationships is emphasized because test 2 (arithmetic) involves relationships, as does test 5, but more intricate and involved relationships.   It is reasonable that test 2 (arithmetic) should involve some verbal ability whereas test 6 (numerical relations) does not.

It is striking that tests 4, 5, 7, and 8 involve no arithmetical computation whatever and none is weighted at all with the N-factor, whereas test 1 (directions) involves a slight amount of use of num-

bers. Test 3 is a poser. It is placed in the configuration so as to
carry weight in all three traits, R, N, and V. It clearly involves
verbality, and it is nearest the V-pole. It does not involve the
simpler relationships that were postulated for factor R, nor does it
involve the slightest amount of number work. It is a very complex
test, however, and so may touch upon R and N in some obscure
manner. It is the shortest of the Alpha tests and it may be the least
reliable. Its apparent relationships with factors N and R may be
artifacts. Had there been many more tests in the battery, a better
interpretation of factor R might have been made to account for its
presence in test 3. Or, had a fourth or a fifth factor been introduced,
with more tests, the more exact placing of test 3 in the system might
have resulted. With only eight points, we cannot push the interpretation too far or too positively. The preceding discussion has merely
been illustrative of the final task of interpretation. This, after all,
is the important psychological excuse for the factor methods.

The Computation of New Factor Loadings in the Rotated System.
The three-factor pattern is met commonly enough in dealing with
limited numbers of tests to make it worth while to present briefly the
procedure for computing new factor loadings after rotation. Having
located the three points of the right spherical triangle, as in Fig. 49,
one makes sure by measurements that points such as R, V, and N
are exactly 90 deg. from one another. The surface distance on the
sphere should be one-fourth the circumference. The positions
of these points with respect to the original reference axes I, II, and
III may be determined by measurement with the same strip of paper
by which one locates the points· in plotting them on the sphere.
These measurements are the coordinates of the three points, R, V,
and N, or the so-called **direction cosines.** The direction cosine is
the cosine of the central angle made with a reference axis, and it is
also the coordinate of the point on that axis when the length of the
test vector, or hypothenuse, is unity. The direction cosines of
points R, V, and N are given in Table 101, just as they were determined graphically by measurements on the sphere.

The graphic coordinates are only approximately correct. Before
going further it is necessary to make certain readjustments in them.
Two conditions must be satisfied in such a table of coordinates.
The sums of the squares of the columns and of the rows must equal
unity. Furthermore, the sums of the cross-products of any pair of
rows or columns must equal zero. The sum of the cross-products

of any pair of columns or rows gives the correlation between the two variables. The traits being orthogonal, there should be no correla-

TABLE 101.—COORDINATES OF THE NEW REFERENCE AXES IN TERMS OF THE ORIGINAL CENTROID AXES

	Graphic coordinates			Adjusted coordinates		
	R	N	V	R	N	V
I	+.485	+.420	+.760	+.4850	+.4200	+.7671
II	.000	−.880	+.505	.0000	−.8771	+.4802
III	−.890	+.310	+.370	−.8745	+.2329	+.4254

tion between them. The adjusted coordinates are given also in Table 101.

The new factor loadings may be obtained in a systematic manner. Let the letter λ stand for any one of the coordinates in Table 101. Let us designate by subscripts the number of the row and column from which λ comes. For example, λ_{11} is the value in the first row and first column, namely, .4850; λ_{21} is from the second row and first column, namely, .0000; and λ_{32} is from the third row and second column, or .2329. For any test, k, the factor loadings in R, N, and V are given by the formulas

$$\left.\begin{aligned} k_1' &= k_1\lambda_{11} + k_2\lambda_{21} + k_3\lambda_{31} \\ k_2' &= k_1\lambda_{12} + k_2\lambda_{22} + k_3\lambda_{32} \\ k_3' &= k_1\lambda_{13} + k_3\lambda_{23} + k_3\lambda_{33} \end{aligned}\right\} \tag{235}$$

where k_1', k_2', and k_3' = the new factor loadings after rotation.

k_1, k_2, and k_3 = the original, unaugmented factor loadings obtained by the centroid method.

$\lambda_{11}, \lambda_{21}, \ldots, \lambda_{33}$ = the direction cosines of the new orthogonal axes in terms of the centroid reference axes.

It will be noticed that for the first factor loadings the multipliers of k_1, k_2, and k_3 are the λ's in the first column of Table 101; for the second factor, the multipliers of k_1, k_2, and k_3 are the corresponding λ's in the second column of Table 101; and for the third factors the multipliers are the three λ's in the third column. The work is capable of arrangement in a work sheet similar to Table 92. The new factor loadings for the Army Alpha problem are given in Table 102. The communalities are computed as a check upon the arithmetical work. It is of interest now to note the squares of the new factor loadings which are also given in the table. These indicate the amount of the total variance of each test that may be attributed to each one of the factors, R, N, and V. The uniqueness

TABLE 102.—IMPORTANCE OF THE FACTORS R, N, AND V, IN THE EIGHT PARTS OF THE ARMY ALPHA EXAMINATION

Test	Factor loadings			Communality, h^2	Variances			Uniqueness
	R	N	V		R^2	N^2	V^2	U^2
1	.462	.389	.101	.3754	.21	.15	.01	.62
2	−.052	.801	.474	.8690	.00	.64	.22	.13
3	.282	.285	.521	.4318	.08	.08	.27	.57
4	.298	.064	.715	.6044	.09	.00	.51	.40
5	.096	.003	.683	.4757	.01	.00	.47	.52
6	.406	.528	.192	.4809	.17	.28	.04	.52
7	.803	−.054	.416	.8208	.64	.00	.17	.18
8	.044	.027	.648	.4225	.00	.00	.42	.58

of each test is given under U^2 in Table 102. In five of the eight tests, more than half the variance is due to factors other than R, N, and V.

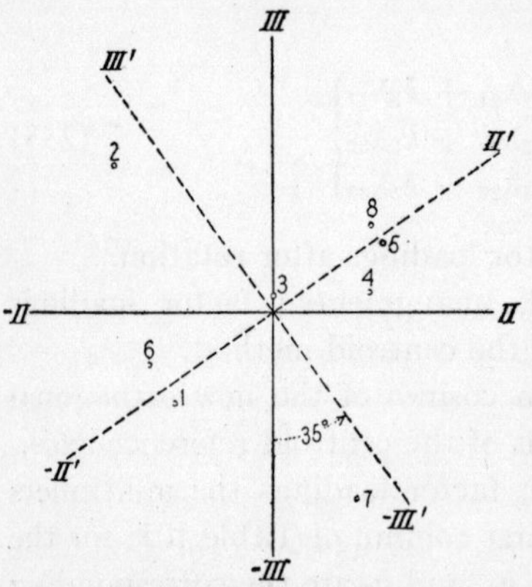

Rotation of Axes in One Plane at a Time.—In this method, we begin with the centroid factor loadings of Table 99. If we plot the values k_3 and k_2 in a two-dimensional system, it is as if we are looking at the configuration from the direction of axis I. The distribution of the points from that direction will appear as in Fig. 50. Here we have the projection of the three-dimensional system on a plane, just as the configuration of stars in the big dipper seems to make a flat picture although some of the stars are nearer and some farther away. In this approach to the problem of rotation it is well to plot the values of k_2 against k_1 and also k_3 against k_1 as well as k_3 against k_2

FIG. 50.—Projection of the eight test vectors of Army Alpha upon the plane, II–III, with a rotation of 35 deg. about axis I indicated.

(Fig. 50), in order to see in which plane the most obvious rotation appears.

Rotation about Axis I.—In this problem it seemed that a rotation in the plane II-III was most reasonable, or could be made with greatest accuracy. The dotted lines in Fig. 50 show the position of the rotated axes that would best meet our principles. It was impossible to make all the factor loadings positive, but it was possible to extend lines (which are really planes, for they extend above and below the plane of the page) through in the neighborhood of a large number of points. We draw the two lines, II′ and III′, and measure the angle of rotation by means of a quadrant. It is 35 deg. in the counterclockwise direction. We immediately find the new coordinates for factors II and III, applying formulas (234). The value of sin 35° is .5736; for cos 35°, it is .8192. The factor loadings for ability I will not be changed by this rotation, for axis I was the pivot about which the rotation took place. Our coordinates are now those given in Table 103.

TABLE 103.—FACTOR LOADINGS IN THE ARMY ALPHA PROBLEM AFTER A ROTA-TION OF 35 DEG. ABOUT AXIS I

	I	II′	III′
1	.465	− .395	− .054
2	.675	− .140	.628
3	.656	.024	.034
4	.720	.268	− .117
5	.572	.385	− .016
6	.566	− .390	.089
7	.686	− .106	− .582
8	530	.375	.034

Rotation about Axis III′.—Factor II′ now has a greater weighting among the negative loadings than does any other factor. Axis I has not yet been rotated. Therefore, it seems that a rotation about axis III′ is next in order. The plot on plane I-II′ is to be seen in Fig. 51. Here it is obvious what general change should be made. There are a number of choices, however. One should make axis II′ touch points 5 and 8, or one could make axis I pass near point 1. As a first guess we shall let those two axes come about equally near to the two pairs of points, 5 and 8, and 1 and 6. Measuring the angle of rotation, we find that a change of 50 deg. in the clockwise direction is called for. This is equivalent to a rotation of 40 deg. in the counterclockwise direction, except that the axes will be interchanged, II′ for I and I for −II′. The naming of the axes is arbitrary, so we may rename them if necessary after rotation. Cos 40° is .7660 and sin 40° is .6428. Applying formulas (234) find we the new factor loadings which are given in Table 104.

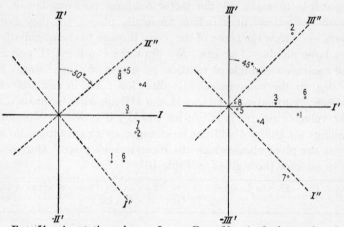

FIG. 51.—A rotation of axes I and II′ 50 deg. about axis III′ as a pivot.

FIG. 52.—A final rotation in the plane I′–III′ of 45 deg. about axis II″.

Final Rotation about Axis II″.—In Table 104 all negative coordinates are now eliminated from the first two factors, but four of them remain for factor III′. We could perhaps eliminate these by rotation in plane I′-III′ or in the plane II″-III′. We have already made one rotation in the plane II-III. Let us make the next rotation in the plane I′-III′, about axis II″. Figure 52 shows the plot of the points. Now it appears that a rotation of 45 deg. will make all loadings positive, except for tests 2 and 7. No matter what the rotation here, one or both of those tests will retain a negative value. Slight negative factor loadings not greater than −.10 are to be tolerated as due to sampling errors. Let us be impartial and rotate the axes so as to give both tests 2 and 7 small negative loadings. It is possible that further rotations would remove even these two small negative loadings. It may be seen in Fig. 49 that the whole triangle might have been shifted upward and to the left, thus reducing the loadings of the *V*-factor in tests 1 and 6 to zero and also reducing the negative loadings in tests 2 and 7. This change, however, would have enlarged the positive loadings of the *N*-factor in tests 4, 5, and 8, which by their nature should be regarded as free from any numerical ability requirement. Computing the new coordinates in the usual manner, we find that the factor loadings are now as given in Table 105.

TABLE 104.—FACTOR LOADINGS AFTER A SECOND ROTATION OF 50 DEG. ABOUT AXIS III′

	I′	II″	III′
1	.602	.102	− .154
2	.541	.428	.628
3	.403	.518	.034
4	.258	.724	− .117
5	.073	.686	− .016
6	.663	.183	.089
7	.522	.457	− .582
8	.054	.647	.034

TABLE 105.—FINAL FACTOR LOADINGS FOR THE THREE UNITARY ABILITIES IN THE ARMY ALPHA TESTS, WITH THEIR COMMUNALITIES

	R	V	N	h^2
1	.464	.102	.388	.3762
2	− .062	.428	.827	.8709
3	.261	.518	.309	.4319
4	.265	.724	.100	.6044
5	.063	.686	.040	.4762
6	.406	.183	.532	.4813
7	.781	.457	− .042	.8206
8	.014	.647	.062	.4226

It is rather doubtful, if our rotation has been even approximately correct, that there is a universal factor in the sense of Spearman's *G* in these tests. Factor *R* has three tests with zero weight; factor *V* has two very weak loadings in tests 1 and 6; and factor *N* has three, or perhaps four, tests with negligible weights. Factor *V* comes closest to being a *g*-factor, but it is more readily identifiable as verbal in character.

The communalities were computed for the new factor loadings, and they check very closely with the original unrotated communalities as they should. A comparison of the values in Table 105 with those in Table 102 will show that the two methods of rotation have led to essentially the same results. Two methods that are based upon the graphic location of the new axes could hardly be expected to agree more closely.

The configuration of the eight test vectors in three-dimensional space is now shown graphically in Fig. 53. The three orthogonal

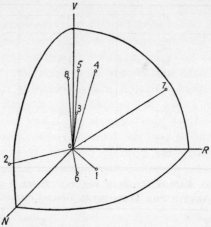

FIG. 53.—Geometric representation of the eight test vectors of Army Alpha in the three-dimensional common factor space.

planes, *VOR*, *VON*, and *NOR*, are shown with axes cut off at a value of unity. Remembering that the correlation between any pair of tests is proportional to the cosine of the central angle between the two test vectors after allowance for uniqueness has been made, some interesting interpretations may be made of Fig. 53. The figure is three dimensional and so the sizes of the angles are not exactly in strict proportion as they appear in Fig. 53, but it is clear that tests 4, 5, and 8 are in a cluster and form small central angles. We should expect the highest raw correlations among these three. In Table 94 it will be seen that $r_{45} = .568$, the highest in the table; r_{48} is .453 and r_{58} is .410, not among the next highest, but still relatively high. The first centroid axis was projected through nearest test 4, which had the highest factor loading, but it also came near tests 3 and 7. The lowest raw correlation might be expected between tests 2 and 7; they lie almost on orthogonal planes. In Table 94 we find $r_{27} = .091$, the lowest in the table. The correlations r_{18} and r_{68} would be expected to be low; they are .107 and

.157, respectively. Test 3 appears to lie in a cluster and might be expected to have relatively high correlations with tests 4, 5, and 8. The closest affinity to test 3, as indicated in Table 94, however, is test 2; r_{23} is .474. In other words, test vector 3 comes forward off the plane *VOR* in Fig. 53.

It can be seen also in Fig. 53 how all the tests fall short of reaching the surface of the sphere because their communalities are less than unity. Tests 2 and 7 are clearly nearer the surface than any others, and tests 1, 3, and 6 seem farthest from the surface. Allowances must be made for foreshortening in the figure, however, for in Table 105 test 8 has a lower communality than either test 3 or 6.

Rotation of Axes with Four or More Variables.—When there are four or more common factors, the procedure of rotating the axes in one plane at a time may be applied just as it was for the case of three factors. If all axes are orthogonal, any two may be rotated about the remaining ones simultaneously as the pivot. It is best to begin by plotting all possible pairs of axes which will give $n(n - 1)/2$ plots, where n is the number of factors. Note which plot gives the most obvious rotation. After this rotation, and every other rotation, compute the new factor loadings and make a new set of plottings wherever these new loadings are involved. Repeat the process as many times as is necessary. It is convenient in this connection to use a sheet of engineer's tracing paper upon which two orthogonal axes are drawn with two parallel lines on either side of each axis at distances of $\pm.10$. These extra lines show the limits within which points may vary from the new axes and still be regarded as having zero loadings for a factor. They also help to locate the new axes by showing for any possible rotation the total number of points that would be embraced within the limits of $\pm.10$.

The Question of Oblique Axes.—It may happen that in the projections of the points upon one or more of the planes two very distinct clusters of points appear. In addition, it may be that the tests belonging to each group are very similar in some respect and seem to be relatively pure measures of one trait. In such a case one feels impelled to extend the new axes directly through the centroid of each cluster and to name the variables, even though the new axes are not orthogonal; they are oblique. This means that the two unitary traits are not statistically independent of each other; so long as the angle of separation of the two axes is not exactly 90 deg., there will be some correlation between them. Such cases have been known in practice. New factor loadings in terms of the new oblique axes can be computed (39, pp. 171 *ff.*). Oblique axes are rather awkward to deal with, but, if mental organization is actually of such a nature that some of the primary traits are *not* independent, then we must be willing to face the fact and be prepared to deal with them statistically. It would be a much neater solution, naturally, to assume only orthogonal axes, with only independent primary abilities. But we may have a situation among the primary abilities similar to that among the hereditary unit characters in which linkages occur among the genes. Such linkages correspond to the correlations we may find among the primary abilities.

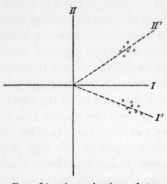

Fig. 54.—A projection of two clusters of test vectors on a plane, demonstrating two primary abilities which are probably correlated. A case of oblique axes.

The writer is inclined to the opinion that some cases of oblique axes, such as that in Fig. 54, could be eliminated by the inclusion of another dimension. Axes I′ and II′ in this diagram might be regarded as the projection of two orthogonal axes upon a plane. Had the analysis of the group of tests been carried a step farther, another real orthogonal dimension might have appeared to take care of the apparently oblique axes. In Fig. 51, for example, although the number of tests is too limited to give us real clusters of points, yet one might regard tests 4, 5, and 8 as forming one constellation and tests 1 and 6 as forming another; without any further knowledge, oblique axes might be extended through those clusters. But with the inclusion of a third dimension we have seen how those same clusters actually lie in orthogonal planes. More extensive experience with factor methods will be required before we can answer the question as to whether or not there are correlations between the unitary abilities and whether oblique axes will be required to take care of them.

MEASURING PRIMARY ABILITIES

The Practical Problem.—Thus far in the development of the factor methods the interest has been in theoretical questions, which

is quite as it should be.   Before we attempt to measure the degree
to which each individual possesses any primary ability, we must
know with some assurance that such an ability exists.   Knowing
what the real variables in human ability are will probably take us a
long way along the road to a really scientific approach to vocational
guidance and vocational selection and kindred applications.   There
are at least two possible approaches to vocational problems.   We
may take a measure of vocational success as one test variable, put
it into the battery of tests, subject the whole to factor analysis, and
thus determine the primary abilities represented and their degree in
each occupational task.   Or, having established batteries of tests
for the measurement of each primary ability in its purest form, with
appropriate scoring weights, we may then adopt the older approach
of using vocational success as the criterion and of writing regression
equations for the abilities which best predict that criterion.   It
may be that from a practical standpoint not much can be gained in
this way.   The predictions of the criterion scores directly from the
raw test scores may yet be the most feasible practical approach.   It
would be of considerable theoretical interest, however, to have the
occupational tasks analyzed in order to determine the primary
abilities upon which they draw.   Knowing these facts, we would
then be in a better position to predict which tests out of the multitude would most likely lead to success.   As it stands now, we must
adopt a trial-and-error method of selection of tests, or else make use
of our limited powers of job analysis and from this guess which tests
will be most adequate.   It would seem a very important step to
make the job analysis a real scientific process by conducting it in
the form of a factor analysis.

Measuring a Primary Ability with a Battery of Tests.—As a rule
no single test can be taken as a pure measuring stick for any one
primary ability.   In Table 105, for example, it will be seen that,
although test 7 is highly correlated with the R-factor, tests 4, 5, and
8 with the V-factor, and tests 2 and 6 with the N-factor, those tests
also contain variances due to one or more of the other two factors
represented in that table, besides factors not represented.   Tests
5 and 8 come nearest to being pure measures of V among the eight
tests here represented, but their relatively low communalities (.4762
and .4226) show that they are undoubtedly weighted with common
factors other than R, V, and N.   It is highly unlikely that their
reliabilities would be as low as these figures.   As usual, a combina-

tion of tests in a battery gives a better prediction of some single criterion than does any one test taken alone. Suppose, too, that test 2 were to be taken alone as a measure of the N-factor. This test also correlates .428 with the V-factor, and hence a test score would be influenced not only by an individual's ability in the N-factor but also to an appreciable extent by his ability in the V-factor. For this reason, the problem of appraisal of the N-factor, or of any single factor, is a rather complicated one. Were there a relatively large number of tests in the battery, enough so that we might assume, as Spearman did with his g-factor, that the other factors in the test, being uncorrelated, would tend to cancel one another in the final score, leaving the total score as a measure of the factor common to all of them, the task would be somewhat simplified.

The appraisal of unitary abilities from tests is primarily a problem in multiple correlation. Using the primary factor that we wish to measure as the criterion to be predicted from the combined effect of a number of test variables, we can set up the necessary equations as in Chapter XII and solve for the regression weights to be attached to the tests. A solution of the problem in matrix form is briefly described by Thurstone (39, pp. 226 ff.).

Applications of Factor Analysis

Primary Abilities Already Indicated.—In its first and most general field of application, factor analysis has already indicated many of the unitary abilities. Factors to which many already agree are verbal ability, numerical ability, spatial ability, mechanical ability, memory (probably immediate memory), and mental speed. Other intellectual factors often mentioned are attention, imagination, and a possible logical or reasoning ability. Among the nonintellectual abilities mentioned are motor speed, oscillation, and musical ability.

Factor Analysis of Personality.—Among the nonintellectual characteristics of human nature are those called 'traits of personality,' although personality in its properly broad sense would include the intellectual abilities as well. Here the task of unraveling the unitary aspects of man is even more baffling, even more in need of a helping device like factor analysis. Spearman's suggestions of the general, if not universal, perseveration factor and of the also general W-factor are first in this field. Thurstone's analysis of vocational interests into the *social, language, people,* and *business* groups is an early example of what might be done toward bringing simplicity and order into that field (36).   His analysis of some of the social attitudes into their fundamental variables is another type of application (37).   The writer was the first to attempt a factor analysis of a questionnaire on personality (10), and Flanagan (8) has made a similar study.   This approach has limited though important possibilities.   It would seem that certain types of men, such as Spranger's, should also be subjected to the techniques of analysis now available in order to see whether armchair analysis of fundamental interests—*theoretical, economic, aesthetic, social, political*, and *religious*—can be upheld after rigid scientific examination has been applied.

Personality traits, unlike abilities, present the problem of negative values.   All abilities are thought of as extending from zero to a maximum.   A personality trait as a rule has an opposite quality.   Introversion-extroversion, optimism-pessimism, tactfulness-tactless-ness, honesty-dishonesty—contrasting terms like these describe countless aspects of personality.   The problem presented to the factor methods by this situation is not a serious one.   There will naturally be many negative raw coefficients of correlation.   The process of reflection takes care of these.   There will be negative factor loadings in the factor matrix.   This is nothing new, except that now the first column may also contain negative values.   It will probably facilitate the process of rotating axes to eliminate all negative signs from the first column.   If the sign of any loading in that column is reversed, we must also reverse the other signs in that row of the factor matrix.   This means that the test vector for this row has had its polarity reversed in the common factor space.   We may then proceed to find a positive manifold and simple structure. It may be found that these criteria are inadequate when dealing with personality tests.

The writer is not so sure that we shall always find a positive manifold for traits of personality.   We may have to depend mostly upon the tendency for the configuration to fall into lines and planes, paying most attention to those test vectors having the greatest communalities and to the meanings of constellations of points in the common factor space.   Certain it is, that, when independent real traits of personality can be established, their correlations with gland-ular and other aspects of the individual will be most illuminating.

Traits of character are customarily set aside from other personality traits although this distinction is more practical and ethical than scientific. Traits of character are recognized as more generally attributable to habit formation and conditioning than are abilities and traits of temperament. Can we postulate in character formation any real, extensive unitary structures which may be uncovered by factor analysis? The writer believes so. These broad factors, if they possess any degree of isolation or separateness, may not be independent, they may call for the liberal use of oblique axes and of dichotomies if the analytical methods are applied. The many questions of transfer of training and of generality of habit may be cleared up to some extent if the procedures of this chapter can be made to apply.

Factor Analysis in Experimental Psychology.—It was announced early in the chapter that factor analysis might be applicable to problems in experimental psychology. This is especially true where other means of discovering the fundamental variables have so far failed. We still do not know what the attributes of odors or of the somesthetic senses are. It is possible that here is a place for factor methods. Wundt's theory of feelings attempted to give the basic dimensions of affective experience, and yet few psychologists are satisfied with it. If there are any real independent variables in feelings or in the emotions, why not determine them by use of the factor methods? In the field of psychophysical judgment the applications seem almost unlimited. We know that every psychophysical judgment is determined by a number of criteria, perhaps mutually independent. By setting up the proper experimental conditions it is highly probable that these criteria can be singled out and that their relative importance in different individuals and in the same individual at different times can be estimated. Indeed, the range of usefulness of the factor methods is so extensive that another generation of psychologists may well devote its time to their exploitation.

If psychology has been held back from either a strong theoretical foundation or from fruitful application because it does not know its own real variables, and if the present methods of analysis can demonstrably accomplish those ends, we would do well to stop now and develop the foundation we so badly need. If to some individuals the factor loadings and their geometrical representations seem just so much more statistical hocus-pocus or merely abstract representations, let us be reminded that abstraction is the key to scientific or philosophical advance and that any science is ultimately useful to the extent that it becomes abstract and mathematical in its conceptions.

Factor Analysis Is Needed to Save the Mental-test Program.—Not all the criticisms leveled at the mental-test movement by the supposedly uninformed layman are without point or significance. Many generalizations about age differences, sex differences, and racial differences are as conflicting as they are unjust because no one knows just what abilities his tests are sampling. There can no longer be any excuse for basing conclusions about mental growth and decline upon tests of 'general intelligence' and upon one battery of tests in one population and upon another battery in another population. There may be a different curve of growth and decline for every one of the primary abilities and no one will be justified hereafter in presenting growth curves without specifying the function or functions of which he speaks. The problem is further complicated by the question of how the abilities are organized at different ages, in the two sexes, in different races, and in tests of different levels of difficulty.

In the same class is the great question of the extent to which ability can be improved by training. This much debated problem breaks up when we apply factor analysis. It is then a question of which primary abilities can be improved and to what extent. The many conflicting answers we have had to this question in the past may readily find reconciliation when the problem of nature versus nurture is recast in this form. Let us attempt to answer these more fundamental questions before we launch into the more complicated but more socially vital problems. Our answers will gain far more respect and lead to far greater social consequences and our efforts in human engineering will at last be placed upon a firm scientific basis.

Problems

The correlation matrix on page 514 was obtained from the test scores made by 70 students in general psychology in 10 tests from the Woodworth and Wells series of association tests. The tests were given individually as time-limit tests, the scores being the length of time required to finish the test plus a small amount of time for occasional errors. Test 11 was the simple reaction time to an auditory stimulus. The names of the tests are as follows: (1) number checking (a cancellation test); (2) directions (the harder form); (3) addition; (4) color naming; (5) substitution (digit for symbol); (6) opposites; (7) supraordinate; (8) part-whole; (9) action-agent; (10) mixed relations; and (11) simple auditory reaction time.

1. Apply the centroid method of factor analysis and determine how many factors are needed for their relative weights in the different tests.

2. Rotate the centroid axes using any method described in the chapter and attempt to name the factors.

	1	2	3	4	5	6	7	8	9	10	11
1		.140	.267	.144	.233	.312	.162	.104	.351	.073	−.317
2			.150	.497	.299	.408	.255	.134	.275	.368	−.224
3				.055	.078	.147	.072	.298	.285	.103	+.091
4					.418	.246	.259	.216	.213	.150	−.178
5						.367	.188	.163	.222	.238	−.050
6							.452	.388	.332	.339	−.120
7								.414	.328	.290	−.027
8									.491	.358	−.026
9										.338	−.270
10											−.112

REFERENCES

1. ADAMS, H. F., The theory of two factors: an alternative explanation, *J. Appl. Psychol.*, 1931, **15**, 16–34.

2. ANASTASI, A., A group factor in immediate memory, *Arch. Psychol.*, 1930, no. 120.

3. BROWN, WM., The mathematical and experimental evidence for the existence of a central intellective factor (g), *Brit. J. Psychol.*, 1932, **23**, 171–179.

4. ——, and G. H. THOMSON, "The Essentials of Mental Measurement," Cambridge University Press, London, 1925.

5. CURETON, E. E., and J. W. DUNLAP, Some effects of heterogeneity on the theory of factors, *Amer. J. Psychol.*, 1930, **42**, 608–620.

6. DODD, S. C., The coefficient of equiproportion as a criterion of hierarchy, *J. Educ. Psychol.*, 1928, **19**, 217–229.

7. ——, The theory of factors, *Psychol. Rev.*, 1928, **35**, 211–234.

8. FLANAGAN, J. C., "Factor Analysis in the Study of Personality," Stanford University Press, Stanford, 1935.

9. GARNETT, J. C. M., On certain independent factors in mental measurements, *Proc. Royal Soc.*, series A, 1919, **96.**

10. GUILFORD, J. P., and R. B. GUILFORD, An analysis of the factors present in a typical test of introversion-extroversion, *J. Abn. and Soc. Psychol.*, 1934, **28**, 377–399.

11. HOLZINGER, K. J., "Statistical Resumé of the Spearman Two-factor Theory," University of Chicago Press, Chicago, 1930.

12. ——, "Preliminary Report on Spearman-Holzinger Unitary Trait Study," University of Chicago Press, Chicago, 1935, nos. 1–8.

13. HOTELLING, H., Analysis of a complex of statistical variables into principal components, *J. Educ. Psychol.*, 1933, **24**, 417–441.

14. ——, The most predictable criterion, *J. Educ. Psychol.*, 1933, **26**, 139–142.

15. HULL, C. L., "Aptitude Testing," World Book Company, Yonkers, 1928.

16. IRWIN, J. O., On the uniqueness of the factor *g* for general intelligence, *Brit. J. Psychol.*, 1932, **22**, 359–363.

17. JASPER, H. H., Is perseveration a functional unit participating in all behavior processes?, *J. Soc. Psychol.*, 1931, **2**, 28–51.

18. KELLEY, T. L., "Crossroads in the Mind of Man," Stanford University Press, Stanford, 1928.

19. ——, "Essential Traits of Mental Life," Harvard University Press, Cambridge, 1935.

20. LINE, W., and H. B. HEDMAN, A simplified statement of the two-factor theory, *J. Educ. Psychol.*, 1933, **24**, 195–220.

21. MOORE, T. V., The empirical determination of certain syndromes underlying praecox and manic depressive psychoses, *Amer. J. Psychiat.*, **9**, 719–738.

22. ——, Multiple correlation and the correlation between general factors, *Cath. Univ. Amer. Stud. Psychol. and Psychiat.*, 1931, **3**, no. 1.

23. ——, Formal causality and the analysis of mental life, *J. Educ. Psychol.*, 1934, **25**, 401–421.

24. REINHART, M., A scale for measuring the *g*-factors in intelligence, *Cath. Univ. Amer. Stud. Psychol. and Psychiat.*, 1931, **2**, 1–42.

25. SCHILLER, B., Verbal, numerical, and spatial abilities of young children, *Arch. Psychol.*, 1934, no. 161.

26. SPEARMAN, C., The proof and measurement of association between two things, *Amer. J. Psychol.*, 1904, **15**, 72–101.

27. ——, The theory of two factors, *Psychol. Rev.*, 1914, **21**, 101–115.

28. ——, "Abilities of Man," The Macmillan Company, New York, 1927.

29. ——, The factor theory and its troubles, *J. Educ. Psychol.*, 1934, **25**, 383–391.

30. STEPHENSON, WM., Tetrad-differences for verbal subtests relative to non-verbal subtests, *J. Educ. Psychol.*, 1931, **22**, 334–350.

31. SUTHERLAND, J. D., The speed factor in intelligent reactions, *Brit. J. Psychol.*, 1934, **24**, 276–294.

32. THOMSON, G. H., On complete families of correlation coefficients and their tendency to zero tetrad-differences, *Brit. J. Psychol.*, 1935, **26**, 63–92.

33. THURSTONE, L. L., Multiple factor analysis, *Psychol. Rev.*, 1931, **38**, 406–427.

34. ——, "The Theory of Multiple Factors," Edwards Brothers, Ann Arbor, 1932.

35. ——, "A Simplified Multiple Factor Method," University of Chicago Press, Chicago, 1933.

36. ——, A multiple factor study of vocational interests, *Person. J.*, 1931, **10**, 198–205.

37. ——, Vectors of mind, *Psychol. Rev.*, 1934, **41**, 1–32.

38. ——, Unitary abilities, *J. Gen. Psychol.*, 1934, **11**, 126–132.

39. ——, "The Vectors of Mind," University of Chicago Press, Chicago, 1935.

40. TRYON, R. C., Multiple factors versus two factors as determiners of ability, *Psychol. Rev.*, 1932, **39**, 324–351.

41. ———, So-called group factors as determiners of ability, *Psychol. Rev.*, 1932, **39,** 403–439.

42. Whisler, L. D., Multiple-factor analysis of generalized attitudes, *J. Soc. Psychol.*, 1934, **5,** 283–297.

43. Wishart, J., Sampling errors in the theory of two factors, *Brit. J. Psychol.*, 1928, **19,** 180–187.

APPENDIX

TABLE A.—Squares and Square Roots of Numbers from 1 to 1000[1]

Number	Square	Square root	Number	Square	Square root
1	1	1.0000	41	1681	6.4031
2	4	1.4142	42	1764	6.4807
3	9	1.7321	43	1849	6.5574
4	16	2.0000	44	1936	6.6332
5	25	2.2361	45	2025	6.7082
6	36	2.4495	46	2116	6.7823
7	49	2.6458	47	2209	6.8557
8	64	2.8284	48	2304	6.9282
9	81	3.0000	49	2401	7.0000
10	100	3.1623	50	2500	7.0711
11	121	3.3166	51	2601	7.1414
12	144	3.4641	52	2704	7.2111
13	169	3.6056	53	2809	7.2801
14	196	3.7417	54	2916	7.3485
15	225	3.8730	55	3025	7.4162
16	256	4.0000	56	3136	7.4833
17	289	4.1231	57	3249	7.5498
18	324	4.2426	58	3364	7.6158
19	361	4.3589	59	3481	7.6811
20	400	4.4721	60	3600	7.7460
21	441	4.5826	61	3721	7.8102
22	484	4.6904	62	3844	7.8740
23	529	4.7958	63	3969	7.9373
24	576	4.8990	64	4096	8.0000
25	625	5.0000	65	4225	8.0623
26	676	5.0990	66	4356	8.1240
27	729	5.1962	67	4489	8.1854
28	784	5.2915	68	4624	8.2462
29	841	5.3852	69	4761	8.3066
30	900	5.4772	70	4900	8.3666
31	961	5.5678	71	5041	8.4261
32	1024	5.6569	72	5184	8.4853
33	1089	5.7446	73	5329	8.5440
34	1156	5.8310	74	5476	8.6023
35	1225	5.9161	75	5625	8.6603
36	1296	6.0000	76	5776	8.7178
37	1369	6.0828	77	5929	8.7750
38	1444	6.1644	78	6084	8.8318
39	1521	6.2450	79	6241	8.8882
40	1600	6.3246	80	6400	8.9443

[1] From Sorenson, "Statistics for Students of Psychology and Education."

TABLE A.—SQUARES AND SQUARE ROOTS OF NUMBERS FROM 1 TO 1000.[1]—
(*Continued*)

Number	Square	Square root	Number	Square	Square root
81	6561	9.0000	121	14641	11.0000
82	6724	9.0554	122	14884	11.0454
83	6889	9.1104	123	15129	11.0905
84	7056	9.1652	124	15376	11.1355
85	7225	9.2195	125	15625	11.1803
86	7396	9.2736	126	15876	11.2250
87	7569	9.3274	127	16129	11.2694
88	7744	9.3808	128	16384	11.3137
89	7921	9.4340	129	16641	11.3578
90	8100	9.4868	130	16900	11.4018
91	8281	9.5394	131	17161	11.4455
92	8464	9.5917	132	17424	11.4891
93	8649	9.6437	133	17689	11.5326
94	8836	9.6954	134	17956	11.5758
95	9025	9.7468	135	18225	11.6190
96	9216	9.7980	136	18496	11.6619
97	9409	9.8489	137	18769	11.7047
98	9604	9.8995	138	19044	11.7473
99	9801	9.9499	139	19321	11.7898
100	10000	10.0000	140	19600	11.8322
101	10201	10.0499	141	19881	11.8743
102	10404	10.0995	142	20164	11.9164
103	10609	10.1489	143	20449	11.9583
104	10816	10.1980	144	20736	12.0000
105	11025	10.2470	145	21025	12.0416
106	11236	10.2956	146	21316	12.0830
107	11449	10.3441	147	21609	12.1244
108	11664	10.3923	148	21904	12.1655
109	11881	10.4403	149	22201	12.2066
110	12100	10.4881	150	22500	12.2474
111	12321	10.5357	151	22801	12.2882
112	12544	10.5830	152	23104	12.3288
113	12769	10.6301	153	23409	12.3693
114	12996	10.6771	154	23716	12.4097
115	13225	10.7238	155	24025	12.4499
116	13456	10.7703	156	24336	12.4900
117	13689	10.8167	157	24649	12.5300
118	13924	10.8628	158	24964	12.5698
119	14161	10.9087	159	25281	12.6095
120	14400	10.9545	160	25600	12.6491

[1] From Sorenson, "Statistics for Students of Psychology and Education."

TABLE A.—SQUARES AND SQUARE ROOTS OF NUMBERS FROM 1 TO 1000.[1]—
(*Continued*)

Number	Square	Square root	Number	Square	Square root
161	25921	12.6886	201	40401	14.1774
162	26244	12.7279	202	40804	14.2127
163	26569	12.7671	203	41209	14.2478
164	26896	12.8062	204	41616	14.2829
165	27225	12.8452	205	42025	14.3178
166	27556	12.8841	206	42436	14.3527
167	27889	12.9228	207	42849	14.3875
168	28224	12.9615	208	43264	14.4222
169	28561	13.0000	209	43681	14.4568
170	28900	13.0384	210	44100	14.4914
171	29241	13.0767	211	44521	14.5258
172	29584	13.1149	212	44944	14.5602
173	29929	13.1529	213	45369	14.5945
174	30276	13.1909	214	45796	14.6287
175	30625	13.2288	215	46225	14.6629
176	30976	13.2665	216	46656	14.6969
177	31329	13.3041	217	47089	14.7309
178	31684	13.3417	218	47524	14.7648
179	32041	13.3791	219	47961	14.7986
180	32400	13.4164	220	48400	14.8324
181	32761	13.4536	221	48841	14.8661
182	33124	13.4907	222	49284	14.8997
183	33489	13.5277	223	49729	14.9332
184	33856	13.5647	224	50176	14.9666
185	34225	13.6015	225	50625	15.0000
186	34596	13.6382	226	51076	15.0333
187	34969	13.6748	227	51529	15.0665
188	35344	13.7113	228	51984	15.0997
189	35721	13.7477	229	52441	15.1327
190	36100	13.7840	230	52900	15.1658
191	36481	13.8203	231	53361	15.1987
192	36864	13.8564	232	53824	15.2315
193	37249	13.8924	233	54289	15.2643
194	37636	13.9284	234	54756	15.2971
195	38025	13.9642	235	55225	15.3297
196	38416	14.0000	236	55696	15.3623
197	38809	14.0357	237	56169	15.3948
198	39204	14.0712	238	56644	15.4272
199	39601	14.1067	239	57121	15.4596
200	40000	14.1421	240	57600	15.4919

[1] From Sorenson, "Statistics for Students of Psychology and Education."

Table A.—Squares and Square Roots of Numbers from 1 to 1000.[1]—
(*Continued*)

Number	Square	Square root	Number	Square	Square root
241	58081	15.5242	281	78961	16.7631
242	58564	15.5563	282	79524	16.7929
243	59049	15.5885	283	80089	16.8226
244	59536	15.6205	284	80656	16.8523
245	60025	15.6525	285	81225	16.8819
246	60516	15.6844	286	81796	16.9115
247	61009	15.7162	287	82369	16.9411
248	61504	15.7480	288	82944	16.9706
249	62001	15.7797	289	83521	17.0000
250	62500	15.8114	290	84100	17.0294
251	63001	15.8430	291	84681	17.0587
252	63504	15.8745	292	85264	17.0880
253	64009	15.9060	293	85849	17.1172
254	64516	15.9374	294	86436	17.1464
255	65025	15.9687	295	87025	17.1756
256	65536	16.0000	296	87616	17.2047
257	66049	16.0312	297	88209	17.2337
258	66564	16.0624	298	88804	17.2627
259	67081	16.0935	299	89401	17.2916
260	67600	16.1245	300	90000	17.3205
261	68121	16.1555	301	90601	17.3494
262	68644	16.1864	302	91204	17.3781
263	69169	16.2173	303	91809	17.4069
264	69696	16.2481	304	92416	17.4356
265	70225	16.2788	305	93025	17.4642
266	70756	16.3095	306	93636	17.4929
267	71289	16.3401	307	94249	17.5214
268	71824	16.3707	308	94864	17.5499
269	72361	16.4012	309	95481	17.5784
270	72900	16.4317	310	96100	17.6068
271	73441	16.4621	311	96721	17.6352
272	73984	16.4924	312	97344	17.6635
273	74529	16.5227	313	97969	17.6918
274	75076	16.5529	314	98596	17.7200
275	75625	16.5831	315	99225	17.7482
276	76176	16.6132	316	99856	17.7764
277	76729	16.6433	317	100489	17.8045
278	77284	16.6733	318	101124	17.8326
279	77841	16.7033	319	101761	17.8606
280	78400	16.7332	320	102400	17.8885

[1] From Sorenson, "Statistics for Students of Psychology and Education."

TABLE A.—SQUARES AND SQUARE ROOTS OF NUMBERS FROM 1 TO 1000.[1]—
(*Continued*)

Number	Square	Square root	Number	Square	Square root
321	103041	17.9165	361	130321	19.0000
322	103684	17.9444	362	131044	19.0263
323	104329	17.9722	363	131769	19.0526
324	104976	18.0000	364	132496	19.0788
325	105625	18.0278	365	133225	19.1050
326	106276	18.0555	366	133956	19.1311
327	106929	18.0831	367	134689	19.1572
328	107584	18.1108	368	135424	19.1833
329	108241	18.1384	369	136161	19.2094
330	108900	18.1659	370	136900	19.2354
331	109561	18.1934	371	137641	19.2614
332	110224	18.2209	372	138384	19.2873
333	110889	18.2483	373	139129	19.3132
334	111556	18.2757	374	139876	19.3391
335	112225	18.3030	375	140625	19.3649
336	112896	18.3303	376	141376	19.3907
337	113569	18.3576	377	142129	19.4165
338	114244	18.3848	378	142884	19.4422
339	114921	18.4120	379	143641	19.4679
340	115600	18.4391	380	144400	19.4936
341	116281	18.4662	381	145161	19.5192
342	116964	18.4932	382	145924	19.5448
343	117649	18.5203	383	146689	19.5704
344	118336	18.5472	384	147456	19.5959
345	119025	18.5742	385	148225	19.6214
346	119716	18.6011	386	148996	19.6469
347	120409	18.6279	387	149769	19.6723
348	121104	18.6548	388	150544	19.6977
349	121801	18.6815	389	151321	19.7231
350	122500	18.7083	390	152100	19.7484
351	123201	18.7350	391	152881	19.7737
352	123904	18.7617	392	153664	19.7990
353	124609	18.7883	393	154449	19.8242
354	125316	18.8149	394	155236	19.8494
355	126025	18.8414	395	156025	19.8746
356	126736	18.8680	396	156816	19.8997
357	127449	18.8944	397	157609	19.9249
358	128164	18.9209	398	158404	19.9499
359	128881	18.9473	399	159201	19.9750
360	129600	18.9737	400	160000	20.0000

[1] From Sorenson, "Statistics for Students of Psychology and Education."

TABLE A.—Squares and Square Roots of Numbers from 1 to 1000.[1]—
(*Continued*)

Number	Square	Square root	Number	Square	Square root
401	160801	20.0250	441	194481	21.0000
402	161604	20.0499	442	195364	21.0238
403	162409	20.0749	443	196249	21.0476
404	163216	20.0998	444	197136	21.0713
405	164025	20.1246	445	198025	21.0950
406	164836	20.1494	446	198916	21.1187
407	165649	20.1742	447	199809	21.1424
408	166464	20.1990	448	200704	21.1660
409	167281	20.2237	449	201601	21.1896
410	168100	20.2485	450	202500	21.2132
411	168921	20.2731	451	203401	21.2368
412	169744	20.2978	452	204304	21.2603
413	170569	20.3224	453	205209	21.2838
414	171396	20.3470	454	206116	21.3073
415	172225	20.3715	455	207025	21.3307
416	173056	20.3961	456	207936	21.3542
417	173889	20.4206	457	208849	21.3776
418	174724	20.4450	458	209764	21.4009
419	175561	20.4695	459	210681	21.4243
420	176400	20.4939	460	211600	21.4476
421	177241	20.5183	461	212521	21.4709
422	178084	20.5426	462	213444	21.4942
423	178929	20.5670	463	214369	21.5174
424	179776	20.5913	464	215296	21.5407
425	180625	20.6155	465	216225	21.5639
426	181476	20.6398	466	217156	21.5870
427	182329	20.6640	467	218089	21.6102
428	183184	20.6882	468	219024	21.6333
429	184041	20.7123	469	219961	21.6564
430	184900	20.7364	470	220900	21.6795
431	185761	20.7605	471	221841	21.7025
432	186624	20.7846	472	222784	21.7256
433	187489	20.8087	473	223729	21.7486
434	188356	20.8327	474	224676	21.7715
435	189225	20.8567	475	225625	21.7945
436	190096	20.8806	476	226576	21.8174
437	190969	20.9045	477	227529	21.8403
438	191844	20.9284	478	228484	21.8632
439	192721	20.9523	479	229441	21.8861
440	193600	20.9762	480	230400	21.9089

[1] From Sorenson, "Statistics for Students of Psychology and Education."

TABLE A.—SQUARES AND SQUARE ROOTS OF NUMBERS FROM 1 TO 1000.[1]—
(*Continued*)

Number	Square	Square root	Number	Square	Square root
481	231361	21.9317	521	271441	22.8254
482	232324	21.9545	522	272484	22.8473
483	233289	21.9773	523	273529	22.8692
484	234256	22.0000	524	274576	22.8910
485	235225	22.0227	525	275625	22.9129
486	236196	22.0454	526	276676	22.9347
487	237169	22.0681	527	277729	22.9565
488	238144	22.0907	528	278784	22.9783
489	239121	22.1133	529	279841	23.0000
490	240100	22.1359	530	280900	23.0217
491	241081	22.1585	531	281961	23.0434
492	242064	22.1811	532	283024	23.0651
493	243049	22.2036	533	284089	23.0868
494	244036	22.2261	534	285156	23.1084
495	245025	22.2486	535	286225	23.1301
496	246016	22.2711	536	287296	23.1517
497	247009	22.2935	537	288369	23.1733
498	248004	22.3159	538	289444	23.1948
499	249001	22.3383	539	290521	23.2164
500	250000	22.3607	540	291600	23.2379
501	251001	22.3830	541	292681	23.2594
502	252004	22.4054	542	293764	23.2809
503	253009	22.4277	543	294849	23.3024
504	254016	22.4499	544	295936	23.3238
505	255025	22.4722	545	297025	23.3452
506	256036	22.4944	546	298116	23.3666
507	257049	22.5167	547	299209	23.3880
508	258064	22.5389	548	300304	23.4094
509	259081	22.5610	549	301401	23.4307
510	260100	22.5832	550	302500	23.4521
511	261121	22.6053	551	303601	23.4734
512	262144	22.6274	552	304704	23.4947
513	263169	22.6495	553	305809	23.5160
514	264196	22.6716	554	306916	23.5372
515	265225	22.6936	555	308025	23.5584
516	266256	22.7156	556	309136	23.5797
517	267289	22.7376	557	310249	23.6008
518	268324	22.7596	558	311364	23.6220
519	269361	22.7816	559	312481	23.6432
520	270400	22.8035	560	313600	23.6643

[1] From Sorenson, "Statistics for Students of Psychology and Education."

TABLE A.—SQUARES AND SQUARE ROOTS OF NUMBERS FROM 1 TO 1000.[1]—
(*Continued*)

Number	Square	Square root	Number	Square	Square root
561	314721	23.6854	601	361201	24.5153
562	315844	23.7065	602	362404	24.5357
563	316969	23.7276	603	363609	24.5561
564	318096	23.7487	604	364816	24.5764
565	319225	23.7697	605	366025	24.5967
566	320356	23.7908	606	367236	24.6171
567	321489	23.8118	607	368449	24.6374
568	322624	23.8328	608	369664	24.6577
569	323761	23.8537	609	370881	24.6779
570	324900	23.8747	610	372100	24.6982
571	326041	23.8956	611	373321	24.7184
572	327184	23.9165	612	374544	24.7385
573	328329	23.9374	613	375769	24.7588
574	329476	23.9583	614	376996	24.7790
575	330625	23.9792	615	378225	24.7992
576	331776	24.0000	616	379456	24.8193
577	332929	24.0208	617	380689	24.8395
578	334084	24.0416	618	381924	24.8596
579	335241	24.0624	619	383161	24.8797
580	336400	24.0832	620	384400	24.8998
581	337561	24.1039	621	385641	24.9199
582	338724	24.1247	622	386884	24.9399
583	339889	24.1454	623	388129	24.9600
584	341056	24.1661	624	389376	24.9800
585	342225	24.1868	625	390625	25.0000
586	343396	24.2074	626	391876	25.0200
587	344569	24.2281	627	393129	25.0400
588	345744	24.2487	628	394384	25.0599
589	346921	24.2693	629	395641	25.0799
590	348100	24.2899	630	396900	25.0998
591	349281	24.3105	631	398161	25.1197
592	350464	24.3311	632	399424	25.1396
593	351649	24.3516	633	400689	25.1595
594	352836	24.3721	634	401956	25.1794
595	354025	24.3926	635	403225	25.1992
596	355216	24.4131	636	404496	25.2190
597	356409	24.4336	637	405769	25.2389
598	357604	24.4540	638	407044	25.2587
599	358801	24.4745	639	408321	25.2784
600	360000	24.4949	640	409600	25.2982

[1] From Sorenson, "Statistics for Students of Psychology and Education."

TABLE A.—SQUARES AND SQUARE ROOTS OF NUMBERS FROM 1 TO 1000.[1]—
(*Continued*)

Number	Square	Square root	Number	Square	Square root
641	410881	25.3180	681	463761	26.0960
642	412164	25.3377	682	465124	26.1151
643	413449	25.3574	683	466489	26.1343
644	414736	25.3772	684	467856	26.1534
645	416025	25.3969	685	469225	26.1725
646	417316	25.4165	686	470596	26.1916
647	418609	25.4362	687	471969	26.2107
648	419904	25.4558	688	473344	26.2298
649	421201	25.4755	689	474721	26.2488
650	422500	25.4951	690	476100	26.2679
651	423801	25.5147	691	477481	26.2869
652	425104	25.5343	692	478864	26.3059
653	426409	25.5539	693	480249	26.3249
654	427716	25.5734	694	481636	26.3439
655	429025	25.5930	695	483025	26.3629
656	430336	25.6125	696	484416	26.3818
657	431649	25.6320	697	485809	26.4008
658	432964	25.6515	698	487204	26.4197
659	434281	25.6710	699	488601	26.4386
660	435600	25.6905	700	490000	26.4575
661	436921	25.7099	701	491401	26.4764
662	438244	25.7294	702	492804	26.4953
663	439569	25.7488	703	494209	26.5141
664	440896	25.7682	704	495616	26.5330
665	442225	25.7876	705	497025	26.5518
666	443556	25.8070	706	498436	26.5707
667	444889	25.8263	707	499849	26.5895
668	446224	25.8457	708	501264	26.6083
669	447561	25.8650	709	502681	26.6271
670	448900	25.8844	710	504100	26.6458
671	450241	25.9037	711	505521	26.6646
672	451584	25.9230	712	506944	26.6833
673	452929	25.9422	713	508369	26.7021
674	454276	25.9615	714	509796	26.7208
675	455625	25.9808	715	511225	26.7395
676	456976	26.0000	716	512656	26.7582
677	458329	26.0192	717	514089	26.7769
678	459684	26.0384	718	515524	26.7955
679	461041	26.0576	719	516961	26.8142
680	462400	26.0768	720	518400	26.8328

[1] From Sorenson, "Statistics for Students of Psychology and Education."

TABLE A.—Squares and Square Roots of Numbers from 1 to 1000.[1]—
(*Continued*)

Number	Square	Square root	Number	Square	Square root
721	519841	26.8514	761	579121	27.5862
722	521284	26.8701	762	580644	27.6043
723	522729	26.8887	763	582169	27.6225
724	524176	26.9072	764	583696	27.6405
725	525625	26.9258	765	585225	27.6586
726	527076	26.9444	766	586756	27.6767
727	528529	26.9629	767	588289	27.6948
728	529984	26.9815	768	589824	27.7128
729	531441	27.0000	769	591361	27.7308
730	532900	27.0185	770	592900	27.7489
731	534361	27.0370	771	594441	27.7669
732	535824	27.0555	772	595984	27.7849
733	537289	27.0740	773	597529	27.8029
734	538756	27.0924	774	599076	27.8209
735	540225	27.1109	775	600625	27.8388
736	541696	27.1293	776	602176	27.8568
737	543169	27.1477	777	603729	27.8747
738	544644	27.1662	778	605284	27.8927
739	546121	27.1846	779	606841	27.9106
740	547600	27.2029	780	608400	27.9285
741	549081	27.2213	781	609961	27.9464
742	550564	27.2397	782	611524	27.9643
743	552049	27.2580	783	613089	27.9821
744	553536	27.2764	784	614656	28.0000
745	555025	27.2947	785	616225	28.0179
746	556516	27.3130	786	617796	28.0357
747	558009	27.3313	787	619369	28.0535
748	559504	27.3496	788	620944	28.0713
749	561001	27.3679	789	622521	28.0891
750	562500	27.3861	790	624100	28.1069
751	564001	27.4044	791	625681	28.1247
752	565504	27.4226	792	627264	28.1425
753	567009	27.4408	793	628849	28.1603
754	568516	27.4591	794	630436	28.1780
755	570025	27.4773	795	632025	28.1957
756	571536	27.4955	796	633616	28.2135
757	573049	27.5136	797	635209	28.2312
758	574564	27.5318	798	636804	28.2489
759	576081	27.5500	799	638401	28.2666
760	577600	27.5681	800	640000	28.2843

[1] From Sorenson, "Statistics for Students of Psychology and Education."

Table A.—Squares and Square Roots of Numbers from 1 to 1000.[1]—
(*Continued*)

Number	Square	Square root	Number	Square	Square root
801	641601	28.3019	841	707281	29.0000
802	643204	28.3196	842	708964	29.0172
803	644809	28.3373	843	710649	29.0345
804	646416	28.3549	844	712336	29.0517
805	648025	28.3725	845	714025	29.0689
806	649636	28.3901	846	715716	29.0861
807	651249	28.4077	847	717409	29.1033
808	652864	28.4253	848	719104	29.1204
809	654481	28.4429	849	720801	29.1376
810	656100	28.4605	850	722500	29.1548
811	657721	28.4781	851	724201	29.1719
812	659344	28.4956	852	725904	29.1890
813	660969	28.5132	853	727609	29.2062
814	662596	28.5307	854	729316	29.2233
815	664225	28.5482	855	731025	29.2404
816	665856	28.5657	856	732736	29.2575
817	667489	28.5832	857	734449	29.2746
818	669124	28.6007	858	736164	29.2916
819	670761	28.6182	859	737881	29.3087
820	672400	28.6356	860	739600	29.3258
821	674041	28.6531	861	741321	29.3428
822	675684	28.6705	862	743044	29.3598
823	677329	28.6880	863	744769	29.3769
824	678976	28.7054	864	746496	29.3939
825	680625	28.7228	865	748225	29.4109
826	682276	28.7402	866	749956	29.4279
827	683929	28.7576	867	751689	29.4449
828	685584	28.7750	868	753424	29.4618
829	687241	28.7924	869	755161	29.4788
830	688900	28.8097	870	756900	29.4958
831	690561	28.8271	871	758641	29.5127
832	692224	28.8444	872	760384	29.5296
833	693889	28.8617	873	762129	29.5466
834	695556	28.8791	874	763876	29.5635
835	697225	28.8964	875	765625	29.5804
836	698896	28.9137	876	767376	29.5973
837	700569	28.9310	877	769129	29.6142
838	702244	28.9482	878	770884	29.6311
839	703921	28.9655	879	772641	29.6479
840	705600	28.9828	880	774400	29.6648

[1] From Sorenson, "Statistics for Students of Psychology and Education."

TABLE A.—SQUARES AND SQUARE ROOTS OF NUMBERS FROM 1 TO 1000.[1]—
(*Continued*)

Number	Square	Square root	Number	Square	Square root
881	776161	29.6816	921	848241	30.3480
882	777924	29.6985	922	850084	30.3645
883	779689	29.7153	923	851929	30.3809
884	781456	29.7321	924	853776	30.3974
885	783225	29.7489	925	855625	30.4138
886	784996	29.7658	926	857476	30.4302
887	786769	29.7825	927	859329	30.4467
888	788544	29.7993	928	861184	30.4631
889	790321	29.8161	929	863041	30.4795
890	792100	29.8329	930	864900	30.4959
891	793881	29.8496	931	866761	30.5123
892	795664	29.8664	932	868624	30.5287
893	797449	29.8831	933	870489	30.5450
894	799236	29.8998	934	872356	30.5614
895	801025	29.9166	935	874225	30.5778
896	802816	29.9333	936	876096	30.5941
897	804609	29.9500	937	877969	30.6105
898	806404	29.9666	938	879844	30.6268
899	808201	29.9833	939	881721	30.6431
900	810000	30.0000	940	883600	30.6594
901	811801	30.0167	941	885481	30.6757
902	813604	30.0333	942	887364	30.6920
903	815409	30.0500	943	889249	30.7083
904	817216	30.0666	944	891136	30.7246
905	819025	30.0832	945	893025	30.7409
906	820836	30.0998	946	894916	30.7571
907	822649	30.1164	947	896809	30.7734
908	824464	30.1330	948	898704	30.7896
909	826281	30.1496	949	900601	30.8058
910	828100	30.1662	950	902500	30.8221
911	829921	30.1828	951	904401	30.8383
912	831744	30.1993	952	906304	30.8545
913	833569	30.2159	953	908209	30.8707
914	835396	30.2324	954	910116	30.8869
915	837225	30.2490	955	912025	30.9031
916	839056	30.2655	956	913936	30.9192
917	840889	30.2820	957	915849	30.9354
918	842724	30.2985	958	917764	30.9516
919	844561	30.3150	959	919681	30.9677
920	846400	30.3315	960	921600	30.9839

[1] From Sorenson, "Statistics for Students of Psychology and Education."

TABLE A.—SQUARES AND SQUARE ROOTS OF NUMBERS FROM 1 TO 1000.[1]—
(*Continued*)

Number	Square	Square root	Number	Square	Square root
961	923521	31.0000	981	962361	31.3209
962	925444	31.0161	982	964324	31.3369
963	927369	31.0322	983	966289	31.3528
964	929296	31.0483	984	968256	31.3688
965	931225	31.0644	985	970225	31.3847
966	933156	31.0805	986	972196	31.4006
967	935089	31.0966	987	974169	31.4166
968	937024	31.1127	988	976144	31.4325
969	938961	31.1288	989	978121	31.4484
970	940900	31.1448	990	980100	31.4643
971	942841	31.1609	991	982081	31.4802
972	944784	31.1769	992	984064	31.4960
973	946729	31.1929	993	986049	31.5119
974	948676	31.2090	994	988036	31.5278
975	950625	31.2250	995	990025	31.5436
976	952576	31.2410	996	992016	31.5595
977	954529	31.2570	997	994009	31.5753
978	956484	31.2730	998	996004	31.5911
979	958441	31.2890	999	998001	31.6070
980	960400	31.3050	1000	1000000	31.6228

[1] From Sorenson, "Statistics for Students of Psychology and Education."

TABLE B.—AREA AND ORDINATE OF THE NORMAL CURVE IN TERMS OF x/σ[1]

x/σ	Area	Ordinate (y)	x/σ	Area	Ordinate (y)
.00	.0000000	.3989423	46	.1772419	.3588903
.01	.0039894	.3989223	.47	.1808225	.3572253
.02	.0079783	.3988625	.48	.1843863	.3555325
.03	.0119665	.3987628	.49	.1879331	.3538124
.04	.0159534	.3986233	.50	.1914625	.3520653
.05	.0199388	.3984439			
.06	.0239222	.3982248	.51	.1949743	.3502919
.07	.0279032	.3979661	.52	.1984682	.3484925
.08	.0318814	.3976677	.53	.2019440	.3466677
.09	.0358564	.3973298	.54	.2054015	.3448180
.10	.0398278	.3969525	.55	.2088403	.3429439
.11	.0437953	.3965360	.56	.2122603	.3410458
.12	.0477584	.3960802	.57	.2156612	.3391243
.13	.0517168	.3955854	.58	.2190427	.3371799
.14	.0556700	.3950517	.59	.2224047	.3352132
.15	.0596177	.3944793	.60	.2257469	.3332246
.16	.0635595	.3938684	.61	.2290691	.3312147
.17	.0674949	.3932190	.62	.2323711	.3291840
.18	.0714237	.3925315	.63	.2356527	.3271330
.19	.0753454	.3918060	.64	.2389137	.3250623
.20	.0792597	.3910427	.65	.2421539	.3229724
.21	.0831662	.3902419	.66	.2453731	.3208638
.22	.0870644	.3894038	.67	.2485711	.3187371
.23	.0909541	.3885286	.68	.2517478	.3165929
.24	.0948349	.3876166	.69	.2549029	.3144317
.25	.0987063	.3866681	.70	.2580363	.3122539
.26	.1025681	.3856834	.71	.2611479	.3100603
.27	.1064199	.3846627	.72	.2642375	.3078513
.28	.1102612	.3836063	.73	.2673049	.3056274
.29	.1140919	.3825146	.74	.2703500	.3033893
.30	.1179114	.3813878	.75	.2733726	.3011374
.31	.1217195	.3802264	.76	.2763727	.2988724
.32	.1255158	.3790305	.77	.2793501	.2965948
.33	.1293000	.3778007	.78	.2823046	.2943050
.34	.1330717	.3765372	.79	.2852361	.2920038
.35	.1368307	.3752403	.80	.2881446	.2896916
.36	.1405764	.3739106	.81	.2910299	.2873689
.37	.1443088	.3725483	.82	.2938919	.2850364
.38	.1480273	.3711539	.83	.2967306	.2826945
.39	.1517317	.3697277	.84	.2995458	.2803438
.40	.1555417	.3682707	.85	.3023375	.2779849
.41	.1590970	.3667817	.86	.3051055	.2756182
.42	.1627573	.3652627	.87	.3078498	.2732444
.43	.1664022	.3637136	.88	.2105703	.2708640
.44	.1700314	.3621349	.89	.3132671	.2684774
.45	.1736448	.3605270	.90	.3159399	.2660852

[1] From Kent, "The Elements of Statistics."

TABLE B.—AREA AND ORDINATE OF THE NORMAL CURVE IN TERMS OF x/σ.[1]—
(Continued)

x/σ	Area	Ordinate (y)	x/σ	Area	Ordinate (y)
.91	.3185887	.2636880	1.36	.4130850	.1582248
.92	.3212136	.2612863	1.37	.4146565	.1560797
.93	.3238145	.2588805	1.38	.4162067	.1539483
.94	.3263912	.2564713	1.39	.4177356	.1518308
.95	.3289439	.2540591	1.40	.4192433	.1497275
.96	.3314724	.2516443	1.41	.4207302	.1476385
.97	.3339768	.2492277	1.42	.4221962	.1455641
.98	.3364569	.2468095	1.43	.4236415	.1435046
.99	.3389129	.2443904	1.44	.4250663	.1414600
1.00	.3413447	.2419707	1.45	.4264707	.1394306
1.01	.3437524	.2395511	1.46	.4278550	.1374165
1.02	.3461358	.2371320	1.47	.4292191	.1354181
1.03	.3484950	.2347138	1.48	.4305634	.1334353
1.04	.3508300	.2322970	1.49	.4318879	.1314684
1.05	.3531409	.2298821	1.50	.4331928	.1295176
1.06	.3554277	.2274696	1.51	.4344783	.1275830
1.07	.3576903	.2250599	1.52	.4357445	.1256646
1.08	.3599289	.2226535	1.53	.4369916	.1237628
1.09	.3621434	.2202508	1.54	.4382198	.1218775
1.10	.3643339	.2178522	1.55	.4394292	.1200090
1.11	.3665005	.2154582	1.56	.4406201	.1181573
1.12	.3686431	.2130691	1.57	.4417924	.1163225
1.13	.3707619	.2106856	1.58	.4429466	.1145048
1.14	.3728568	.2083078	1.59	.4440826	.1127042
1.15	.3749281	.2059363	1.60	.4452007	.1109208
1.16	.3769756	.2035714	1.61	.4463011	.1091548
1.17	.3789995	.2012135	1.62	.4473839	.1074061
1.18	.3809999	.1988631	1.63	.4484493	.1056748
1.19	.3829768	.1965205	1.64	.4494974	.1039611
1.20	.3849303	.1941861	1.65	.4505285	.1022649
1.21	.3868606	.1918602	1.66	.4515428	.1005864
1.22	.3887676	.1895432	1.67	.4525403	.0989255
1.23	.3906514	.1872354	1.68	.4535213	.0972823
1.24	.3925123	.1849373	1.69	.4544860	.0956568
1.25	.3943502	.1826491	1.70	.4554345	.0940491
1.26	.3961653	.1803712	1.71	.4563671	.0924591
1.27	.3979577	.1781038	1.72	.4572838	.0908870
1.28	.3997274	.1758474	1.73	.4581849	.0893326
1.29	.4014747	.1736022	1.74	.4590705	.0877961
1.30	.4031995	.1713686	1.75	.4599408	.0862773
1.31	.4049021	.1691468	1.76	.4607961	.0847764
1.32	.4065825	.1669370	1.77	.4616364	.0832932
1.33	.4082409	.1647397	1.78	.4624620	.0818278
1.34	.4098773	.1625551	1.79	.4632730	.0803801
1.35	.4114920	.1603833	1.80	.4640697	.0789502

[1] From Kent. "The Elements of Statistics."

TABLE B.—AREA AND ORDINATE OF THE NORMAL CURVE IN TERMS OF x/σ.[1]—
(*Continued*)

x/σ	Area	Ordinate (y)	x/σ	Area	Ordinate (y)
1.81	.4648521	.0775379	2.26	.4880894	.0310319
1.82	.4656205	.0761433	2.27	.4883962	.0303370
1.83	.4663750	.0747663	2.28	.4886962	.0296546
1.84	.4671159	.0734068	2.29	.4889893	.0289847
1.85	.4678432	.0720649	2.30	.4892759	.0283270
1.86	.4685572	.0707404	2.31	.4895559	.0276816
1.87	.4692581	.0694333	2.32	.4898296	.0270481
1.88	.4699460	.0681436	2.33	.4900969	.0264265
1.89	.4706210	.0668711	2.34	.4903581	.0258166
1.90	.4712834	.0656158	2.35	.4906133	.0252182
1.91	.4719334	.0643777	2.36	.4908625	.0246313
1.92	.4725711	.0631566	2.37	.4911060	.0240556
1.93	.4731966	.0619524	2.38	.4913437	.0234910
1.94	.4738102	.0607652	2.39	.4915758	.0229374
1.95	.4744119	.0595947	2.40	.4918025	.0223945
1.96	.4750021	.0584409	2.41	.4920237	.0218624
1.97	.4755808	.0573038	2.42	.4922397	.0213407
1.98	.4761482	.0561831	2.43	.4924506	.0208294
1.99	.4767045	.0550789	2.44	.4926564	.0203284
2.00	.4772499	.0539910	2.45	.4928572	.0198374
2.01	.4777844	.0529192	2.46	.4930531	.0193563
2.02	.4783083	.0518636	2.47	.4932443	.0188850
2.03	.4788217	.0508239	2.48	.4934309	.0184233
2.04	.4793248	.0498001	2.49	.4936128	.0179711
2.05	.4798178	.0487920	2.50	.4937903	.0175283
2.06	.4803007	.0477996	2.51	.4939634	.0170947
2.07	.4807738	.0468226	2.52	.4941323	.0166701
2.08	.4812372	.0458611	2.53	.4943001	.0162452
2.09	.4816911	.0449148	2.54	.4944574	.0158476
2.10	.4821356	.0439836	2.55	.4946139	.0154493
2.11	.4825708	.0430674	2.56	.4947664	.0150596
2.12	.4829970	.0421661	2.57	.4949151	.0146782
2.13	.4834142	.0412795	2.58	.4950600	.0143051
2.14	.4838226	.0404076	2.59	.4952012	.0139401
2.15	.4842224	.0395500	2.60	.4953388	.0135830
2.16	.4846137	.0387069	2.61	.4954729	.0132337
2.17	.4849966	.0378779	2.62	.4956035	.0128921
2.18	.4853713	.0370629	2.63	.4957308	.0125581
2.19	.4857379	.0362619	2.64	.4958547	.0122315
2.20	.4860966	.0354746	2.65	.4959754	.0119122
2.21	.4864474	.0347009	2.66	.4960930	.0116001
2.22	.4867906	.0339408	2.67	.4962074	.0112951
2.23	.4871263	.0331939	2.68	.4963189	.0109969
2.24	.4874545	.0324603	2.69	.4964274	.0107056
2.25	.4877755	.0317397	2.70	.4965330	.0104209

[1] From Kent, "The Elements of Statistics."

TABLE B.—AREA AND ORDINATE OF THE NORMAL CURVE IN TERMS OF x/σ.[1]—
(*Continued*)

x/σ	Area	Ordinate (y)	x/σ	Area	Ordinate (y)
2.71	.4966358	.0101428	3.16	.4992112	.0027075
2.72	.4967359	.0098712	3.17	.4992378	.0026231
2.73	.4968333	.0096058	3.18	.4992636	.0025412
2.74	.4969280	.0093466	3.19	.4992886	.0024615
2.75	.4970202	.0090936	3.20	.4993129	.0023841
2.76	.4971099	.0088465	3.21	.4993363	.0023089
2.77	.4971972	.0086052	3.22	.4993590	.0022358
2.78	.4972821	.0083697	3.23	.4993810	.0021649
2.79	.4973646	.0081398	3.24	.4994024	.0020960
2.80	.4974449	.0079155	3.25	.4994230	.0020290
2.81	.4975229	.0076965	3.26	.4994429	.0019641
2.82	.4975988	.0074829	3.27	.4994623	.0019010
2.83	.4976726	.0072744	3.28	.4994810	.0018397
2.84	.4977443	.0070711	3.29	.4994991	.0017803
2.85	.4978140	.0068728	3.30	.4995166	.0017226
2.86	.4978818	.0066793	3.31	.4995335	.0016666
2.87	.4979476	.0064907	3.32	.4995499	.0016122
2.88	.4980116	.0063067	3.33	.4995658	.0015595
2.89	.4980738	.0061274	3.34	.4995811	.0015084
2.90	.4981342	.0059525	3.35	.4995959	.0014587
2.91	.4981929	.0057821	3.36	.4996103	.0014106
2.92	.4982498	.0056160	3.37	.4996242	.0013639
2.93	.4983052	.0054541	3.38	.4996376	.0013187
2.94	.4983589	.0052963	3.39	.4996505	.0012748
2.95	.4984111	.0051426	3.40	.4996631	.0012322
2.96	.4984618	.0049929	3.41	.4996752	.0011910
2.97	.4985110	.0048470	3.42	.4996869	.0011510
2.98	.4985588	.0047050	3.43	.4996982	.0011122
2.99	.4986051	.0045666	3.44	.4997091	.0010747
3.00	.4986501	.0044318	3.45	.4997197	.0010383
3.01	.4986938	.0043007	3.46	.4997299	.0010030
3.02	.4987361	.0041729	3.47	.4997398	.0009689
3.03	.4987772	.0040486	3.48	.4997493	.0009358
3.04	.4988171	.0039276	3.49	.4997585	.0009037
3.05	.4988558	.0038098	3.50	.4997674	.0008727
3.06	.4988933	.0036951	3.51	.4997759	.0008426
3.07	.4989297	.0035836	3.52	.4997842	.0008135
3.08	.4989650	.0034751	3.53	.4997922	.0007853
3.09	.4989992	.0033695	3.54	.4997999	.0007581
3.10	.4990324	.0032668	3.55	.4998074	.0007317
3.11	.4990646	.0031669	3.56	.4998146	.0007061
3.12	.4990957	.0030698	3.57	.4998215	.0006814
3.13	.4991260	.0029754	3.58	.4998282	.0006575
3.14	.4991553	.0028835	3.59	.4998347	.0006343
3.15	.4991836	.0027943	3.60	.4998409	.0006119

[1] From Kent, "The Elements of Statistics."

TABLE B.—AREA AND ORDINATE OF THE NORMAL CURVE IN TERMS OF x/σ.[1]—
(*Continued*)

x/σ	Area	Ordinate (y)	x/σ	Area	Ordinate (y)
3.61	.4998469	.0005902	4.06	.4999755	.0001051
3.62	.4998527	.0005693	4.07	.4999765	.0001009
3.63	.4998583	.0005490	4.08	.4999775	.0000969
8.64	.4998637	.0005294	4.09	.4999784	.0000930
3.65	.4998689	.0005105	4.10	.4999793	.0000893
3.66	.4998739	.0004921	4.11	.4999802	.0000857
3.67	.4998787	.0004744	4.12	.4999811	.0000822
3.68	.4998834	.0004573	4.13	.4999819	.0000789
3.69	.4998879	.0004408	4.14	.4999826	.0000757
3.70	.4998922	.0004248	4.15	.4999834	.0000726
3.71	.4998964	.0004093	4.16	.4999841	.0000697
3.72	.4999004	.0003800	4.17	.4999848	.0000668
3.73	.4999043	.0003661	4.18	.4999854	.0000641
3.74	.4999080	.0003526	4.19	.4999861	.0000615
3.75	.4999116	.0003386	4.20	.4999867	.0000589
3.76	.4999150	.0003396	4.21	.4999872	.0000565
3.77	.4999184	.0003271	4.22	.4999878	.0000542
3.78	.4999216	.0003149	4.23	.4999883	.0000519
3.79	.4999247	.0003032	4.24	.4999888	.0000498
3.80	.4999277	.0002919	4.25	.4999893	.0000477
3.81	.4999305	.0002810	4.26	.4999898	.0000457
3.82	.4999333	.0002705	4.27	.4999902	.0000438
3.83	.4999359	.0002604	4.28	.4999907	.0000420
3.84	.4999385	.0002506	4.29	.4999911	.0000402
3.85	.4999409	.0002411	4.30	.4999915	.0000385
3.86	.4999433	.0002320	4.31	.4999918	.0000369
3.87	.4999456	.0002232	4.32	.4999922	.0000354
3.88	.4999478	.0002147	4.33	.4999925	.0000339
3.89	.4999499	.0002065	4.34	.4999929	.0000324
3.90	.4999519	.0001987	4.35	.4999932	.0000310
3.91	.4999539	.0001910	4.36	.4999935	.0000297
3.92	.4999557	.0001837	4.37	.4999938	.0000284
3.93	.4999575	.0001766	4.38	.4999941	.0000272
3.94	.4999593	.0001698	4.39	.4999943	.0000261
3.95	.4999609	.0001633	4.40	.4999946	.0000249
3.96	.4999625	.0001569	4.41	.4999948	.0000239
3.97	.4999641	.0001508	4.42	.4999951	.0000228
3.98	.4999655	.0001449	4.43	.4999953	.0000218
3.99	.4999670	.0001393	4.44	.4999955	.0000209
4.00	.4999683	.0001338	4.45	.4999957	.0000200
4.01	.4999696	.0001286	4.46	.4999959	.0000191
4.02	.4999709	.0001235	4.47	.4999961	.0000183
4.03	.4999721	.0001186	4.48	.4999963	.0000175
4.04	.4999733	.0001140	4.49	.4999964	.0000167
4.05	.4999744	.0001094	4.50	.4999966	.0000160

[1] From Kent, "The Elements of Statistics."

TABLE C.—PROPORTIONS OF THE TOTAL AREA UNDER THE NORMAL PROBABILITY
CURVE CORRESPONDING TO DISTANCES ON THE ABSCISSA GIVEN IN
TERMS OF $1PE$ AS THE UNIT[1]

x/PE	.00	.05	x/PE	.00	.05
.0	.0000	.0135	3.0	.4785	.4802
.1	.0269	.0403	3.1	.4817	.4831
.2	.0536	.0670	3.2	.4845	.4858
.3	.0802	.0933	3.3	.4870	.4881
.4	.1063	.1193	3.4	.4891	.4900
.5	.1321	.1447	3.5	.4909	.4917
.6	.1571	.1695	3.6	.4924	.4931
.7	.1816	.1935	3.7	.4937	.4943
.8	.2053	.2168	3.8	.4948	.4953
.9	.2291	.2392	3.9	.4957	.4961
1.0	.2500	.2606	4.0	.4965	.4968
1.1	.2709	.2810	4.1	.4971	.4974
1.2	.2908	.3004	4.2	.4977	.4979
1.3	.3097	.3188	4.3	.4981	.4983
1.4	.3275	.3360	4.4	.4985	.4987
1.5	.3441	.3521	4.5	.4988	.4989
1.6	.3597	.3671	4.6	.4990	.4991
1.7	.3742	.3811	4.7	.4992	.4993
1.8	.3896	.3939	4.8	.4994	.4995
1.9	.4000	.4057	4.9	.4995	.4996
2.0	.4113	.4166	5.0	.4996	.4997
2.1	.4217	.4265	5.1	.49971	.49974
2.2	.4311	.4354	5.2	.49977	.49980
2.3	.4396	.4435	5.3	.49982	.49984
2.4	.4472	.4508	5.4	.49986	.49988
2.5	.4541	.4573	5.5	.49990	.49991
2.6	.4602	.4631	5.6	.49992	.49993
2.7	.4657	.4682	5.7	.49994	.49995
2.8	.4705	.4727	5.8	.499955	.49996
2.9	.4748	.4767	5.9	.499965	.49997

[1] Adapted from H. E. Garrett, "Statistics in Psychology and Education," by courtesy of
Longmans, Green & Company.

TABLE D.—TABLE OF χ^2*

n	P = .99	.98	.95	.90	.80	.70	.50	.30	.20	.10	.05	.02	.01
1	.000157	.000628	.00393	.0158	.0642	.148	.455	1.074	1.642	2.706	3.841	5.412	6.635
2	.0201	.0404	.103	.211	.446	.713	1.386	2.408	3.219	4.605	5.991	7.824	9.210
3	.115	.185	.352	.584	1.005	1.424	2.366	3.665	4.642	6.251	7.815	9.837	11.341
4	.297	.429	.711	1.064	1.649	2.195	3.357	4.878	5.989	7.779	9.488	11.668	13.277
5	.554	.752	1.145	1.610	2.343	3.000	4.351	6.064	7.289	9.236	11.070	13.388	15.086
6	.872	1.134	1.635	2.204	3.070	3.828	5.348	7.231	8.558	10.645	12.592	15.033	16.812
7	1.239	1.564	2.167	2.833	3.822	4.671	6.346	8.383	9.803	12.017	14.067	16.622	18.475
8	1.646	2.032	2.733	3.490	4.594	5.527	7.344	9.524	11.030	13.362	15.507	18.168	20.090
9	2.088	2.532	3.325	4.168	5.380	6.393	8.343	10.656	12.242	14.684	16.919	19.679	21.666
10	2.558	3.059	3.940	4.865	6.179	7.267	9.342	11.781	13.442	15.987	18.307	21.161	23.209
11	3.053	3.609	4.575	5.578	6.989	8.148	10.341	12.899	14.631	17.275	19.675	22.618	24.725
12	3.571	4.178	5.226	6.304	7.807	9.034	11.340	14.011	15.812	18.549	21.026	24.054	26.217
13	4.107	4.765	5.892	7.042	8.634	9.926	12.340	15.119	16.985	19.812	22.362	25.472	27.688
14	4.660	5.368	6.571	7.790	9.467	10.821	13.339	16.222	18.151	21.064	23.685	26.873	29.141
15	5.229	5.985	7.261	8.547	10.307	11.721	14.339	17.322	19.311	22.307	24.996	28.259	30.578
16	5.812	6.614	7.962	9.312	11.152	12.624	15.338	18.418	20.465	23.542	26.296	29.633	32.000
17	6.408	7.255	8.672	10.085	12.002	13.531	16.338	19.511	21.615	24.769	27.587	30.995	33.409
18	7.015	7.906	9.390	10.865	12.857	14.440	17.338	20.601	22.760	25.989	28.869	32.346	34.805
19	7.633	8.567	10.117	11.651	13.716	15.352	18.338	21.689	23.900	27.204	30.144	33.687	36.191
20	8.260	9.237	10.851	12.443	14.578	16.266	19.337	22.775	25.038	28.412	31.410	35.020	37.566
21	8.897	9.915	11.591	13.240	15.445	17.182	20.337	23.858	26.171	29.615	32.671	36.343	38.932
22	9.542	10.600	12.338	14.041	16.314	18.101	21.337	24.939	27.301	30.813	33.924	37.659	40.289
23	10.196	11.293	13.091	14.848	17.187	19.021	22.337	26.018	28.429	32.007	35.172	38.968	41.638
24	10.856	11.992	13.848	15.659	18.062	19.943	23.337	27.096	29.553	33.196	36.415	40.270	42.980
25	11.524	12.697	14.611	16.473	18.940	20.867	24.337	28.172	30.675	34.382	37.652	41.566	44.314
26	12.198	13.409	15.379	17.292	19.820	21.792	25.336	29.246	31.795	35.563	38.885	42.856	45.642
27	12.879	14.125	16.151	18.114	20.703	22.719	26.336	30.319	32.912	36.741	40.113	44.140	46.963
28	13.565	14.847	16.928	18.939	21.588	23.647	27.336	31.391	34.027	37.916	41.337	45.419	48.278
29	14.256	15.574	17.708	19.768	22.475	24.577	28.336	32.461	35.139	39.087	41.557	46.693	49.588
30	14.953	16.306	18.493	20.599	23.364	25.508	29.336	33.530	36.250	40.256	43.773	47.962	50.892

* Adapted from R. A. Fisher, "Statistical Methods for Research Workers," 4th ed., pp. 104 *f*; 1932, by courtesy of Oliver and Boyd, Ltd. For larger values of n, the expression $\sqrt{2\chi^2} - \sqrt{2n} - 1$ may be used as a normal deviate with unit standard error.

TABLE E.—DEVIATES AND ORDINATES FOR AREAS UNDER THE NORMAL CURVE[1]

Area from $x/\sigma = 0$	x/σ	Ordinate at x/σ	Area from $x/\sigma = 0$	x/σ	Ordinate at x/σ	Area from $x/\sigma = 0$	x/σ	Ordinate at x/σ
.000	0.0000	.3989	.040	0.1004	.3969	.080	0.2019	.3909
.001	0.0025	.3989	.041	0.1030	.3968	.081	0.2045	.3907
.002	0.0050	.3989	.042	0.1055	.3967	.082	0.2070	.3905
.003	0.0075	.3989	.043	0.1080	.3966	.083	0.2096	.3903
.004	0.0100	.3989	.044	0.1105	.3965	.084	0.2121	.3901
.005	0.0125	.3989	.045	0.1130	.3964	.085	0.2147	.3899
.006	0.0150	.3989	.046	0.1156	.3963	.086	0.2173	.3896
.007	0.0175	.3989	.047	0.1181	.3962	.087	0.2198	.3894
.008	0.0201	.3989	.048	0.1206	.3961	.088	0.2224	.3892
.009	0.0226	.3988	.049	0.1231	.3959	.089	0.2250	.3890
.010	0.0251	.3988	.050	0.1257	.3958	.090	0.2275	.3887
.011	0.0276	.3988	.051	0.1282	.3957	.091	0.2301	.3885
.012	0.0301	.3988	.052	0.1307	.3955	.092	0.2327	.3883
.013	0.0326	.3987	.053	0.1332	.3954	.093	0.2353	.3881
.014	0.0351	.3987	.054	0.1358	.3953	.094	0.2378	.3878
.015	0.0376	.3987	.055	0.1383	.3951	.095	0.2404	.3876
.016	0.0401	.3986	.056	0.1408	.3950	.096	0.2430	.3873
.017	0.0426	.3986	.057	0.1434	.3949	.097	0.2456	.3871
.018	0.0451	.3985	.058	0.1459	.3947	.098	0.2482	.3868
.019	0.0476	.3985	.059	0.1484	.3946	.099	0.2508	.3866
.020	0.0502	.3984	.060	0.1510	.3944	.100	0.2533	.3863
.021	0.0527	.3984	.061	0.1535	.3943	.101	0.2559	.3861
.022	0.0552	.3983	.062	0.1560	.3941	.102	0.2585	.3858
.023	0.0577	.3983	.063	0.1586	.3940	.103	0.2611	.3856
.024	0.0602	.3982	.064	0.1611	.3938	.104	0.2637	.3853
.025	0.0627	.3982	.065	0.1637	.3936	.105	0.2663	.3850
.026	0.0652	.3981	.066	0.1662	.3935	.106	0.2689	.3848
.027	0.0677	.3980	.067	0.1687	.3933	.107	0.2715	.3845
.028	0.0702	.3980	.068	0.1713	.3931	.108	0.2741	.3842
.029	0.0728	.3979	.069	0.1738	.3930	.109	0.2767	.3840
.030	0.0753	.3978	.070	0.1764	.3928	.110	0.2793	.3837
.031	0.0778	.3977	.071	0.1789	.3926	.111	0.2819	.3834
.032	0.0803	.3977	.072	0.1815	.3924	.112	0.2845	.3831
.033	0.0828	.3976	.073	0.1840	.3922	.113	0.2871	.3828
.034	0.0853	.3975	.074	0.1866	.3921	.114	0.2898	.3825
.035	0.0878	.3974	.075	0.1891	.3919	.115	0.2924	.3823
.036	0.0904	.3973	.076	0.1917	.3917	.116	0.2950	.3820
.037	0.0929	.3972	.077	0.1942	.3915	.117	0.2976	.3817
.038	0.0954	.3971	.078	0.1968	.3913	.118	0.3002	.3814
.039	0.0979	.3970	.079	0.1993	.3911	.119	0.3029	.3811

[1] Adapted from K. J. Holzinger, "Statistical Tables for Students in Education and Psychology," 1925, through the courtesy of the University of Chicago Press.

TABLE E.—Deviates and Ordinates for Areas under the Normal Curve[1]—
(*Continued*)

Area from $x/\sigma = 0$	x/σ	Ordinate at x/σ	Area from $x/\sigma = 0$	x/σ	Ordinate at x/σ	Area from $x/\sigma = 0$	x/σ	Ordinate at x/σ
.120	0.3055	.3808	.165	0.4261	.3643	.210	0.5534	.3423
.121	0.3081	.3804	.166	0.4289	.3639	.211	0.5563	.3417
.122	0.3107	.3801	.167	0.4316	.3635	.212	0.5592	.3412
.123	0.3134	.3798	.168	0.4344	.3630	.213	0.5622	.3406
.124	0.3160	.3795	.169	0.4372	.3626	.214	0.5651	.3401
.125	0.3186	.3792	.170	0.4399	.3621	.215	0.5681	.3395
.126	0.3213	.3789	.171	0.4427	.3617	.216	0.5710	.3389
.127	0.3239	.3786	.172	0.4454	.3613	.217	0.5740	.3384
.128	0.3266	.3782	.173	0.4482	.3608	.218	0.5769	.3378
.129	0.3292	.3779	.174	0.4510	.3604	.219	0.5799	.3372
.130	0.3319	.3776	.175	0.4538	.3599	.220	0.5828	.3366
.131	0.3345	.3772	.176	0.4565	.3595	.221	0.5858	.3360
.132	0.3372	.3769	.177	0.4593	.3590	.222	0.5888	.3354
.133	0.3398	.3766	.178	0.4621	.3585	.223	0.5918	.3349
.134	0.3425	.3762	.179	0.4649	.3581	.224	0.5948	.3343
.135	0.3451	.3759	.180	0.4677	.3576	.225	0.5978	.3337
.136	0.3478	.3755	.181	0.4705	.3571	.226	0.6008	.3331
.137	0.3505	.3752	.182	0.4733	.3567	.227	0.6038	.3325
.138	0.3531	.3748	.183	0.4761	.3562	.228	0.6068	.3319
.139	0.3558	.3745	.184	0.4789	.3557	.229	0.6098	.3313
.140	0.3585	.3741	.185	0.4817	.3552	.230	0.6128	.3306
.141	0.3611	.3738	.186	0.4845	.3548	.231	0.6158	.3300
.142	0.3638	.3734	.187	0.4874	.3543	.232	0.6189	.3294
.143	0.3665	.3730	.188	0.4902	.3538	.233	0.6219	.3288
.144	0.3692	.3727	.189	0.4930	.3533	.234	0.6250	.3282
.145	0.3719	.3723	.190	0.4959	.3528	.235	0.6280	.3275
.146	0.3745	.3719	.191	0.4987	.3523	.236	0.6311	.3269
.147	0.3772	.3715	.192	0.5015	.3518	.237	0.6341	.3263
.148	0.3799	.3712	.193	0.5044	.3513	.238	0.6372	.3256
.149	0.3826	.3708	.194	0.5072	.3508	.239	0.6403	.3250
.150	0.3853	.3704	.195	0.5101	.3503	.240	0.6433	.3244
.151	0.3880	.3700	.196	0.5129	.3498	.241	0.6464	.3237
.152	0.3907	.3696	.197	0.5158	.3493	.242	0.6495	.3231
.153	0.3934	.3692	.198	0.5187	.3487	.243	0.6526	.3224
.154	0.3961	.3688	.199	0.5215	.3482	.244	0.6557	.3218
.155	0.3989	.3684	.200	0.5244	.3477	.245	0.6588	.3211
.156	0.4016	.3680	.201	0.5273	.3472	.246	0.6620	.3204
.157	0.4043	.3676	.202	0.5302	.3466	.247	0.6651	.3198
.158	0.4070	.3672	.203	0.5330	.3461	.248	0.6682	.3191
.159	0.4097	.3668	.204	0.5359	.3456	.249	0.6713	.3184
.160	0.4125	.3664	.205	0.5388	.3450	.250	0.6745	.3178
.161	0.4152	.3660	.206	0.5417	.3445	.251	0.6776	.3171
.162	0.4179	.3656	.207	0.5446	.3440	.252	0.6808	.3164
.163	0.4207	.3652	.208	0.5476	.3434	.253	0.6840	.3157
.164	0.4234	.3647	.209	0.5505	.3429	.254	0.6871	.3151

TABLE E.—DEVIATES AND ORDINATES FOR AREAS UNDER THE NORMAL CURVE[1]—
(*Continued*)

Area from $x/\sigma = 0$	x/σ	Ordinate at x/σ	Area from $x/\sigma = 0$	x/σ	Ordinate at x/σ	Area from $x/\sigma = 0$	x/σ	Ordinate at x/σ
.255	0.6903	.3144	.300	0.8416	.2800	.345	1.0152	.2383
.256	0.6935	.3137	.301	0.8452	.2791	.346	1.0194	.2373
.257	0.6967	.3130	.302	0.8488	.2783	.347	1.0237	.2362
.258	0.6999	.3123	.303	0.8524	.2774	.348	1.0279	.2352
.259	0.7031	.3116	.304	0.8560	.2766	.349	1.0322	.2342
.260	0.7063	.3109	.305	0.8596	.2757	.350	1.0364	.2332
.261	0.7095	.3102	.306	0.8633	.2748	.351	1.0407	.2321
.262	0.7128	.3095	.307	0.8669	.2740	.352	1.0450	.2311
.263	0.7160	.3087	.308	0.8705	.2731	.353	1.0494	.2300
.264	0.7192	.3080	.309	0.8742	.2722	.354	1.0537	.2290
.265	0.7225	.3073	.310	0.8779	.2714	.355	1.0581	.2279
.266	0.7257	.3066	.311	0.8816	.2705	.356	1.0625	.2269
.267	0.7290	.3058	.312	0.8853	.2696	.357	1.0669	.2258
.268	0.7323	.3051	.313	0.8890	.2687	.358	1.0714	.2247
.269	0.7356	.3044	.314	0.8927	.2678	.359	1.0758	.2237
.270	0.7388	.3036	.315	0.8965	.2669	.360	1.0803	.2226
.271	0.7421	.3029	.316	0.9002	.2660	.361	1.0848	.2215
.272	0.7454	.3022	.317	0.9040	.2651	.362	1.0893	.2204
.273	0.7488	.3014	.318	0.9078	.2642	.363	1.0939	.2193
.274	0.7521	.3007	.319	0.9116	.2633	.364	1.0985	.2182
.275	0.7554	.2999	.320	0.9154	.2624	.365	1.1031	.2171
.276	0.7588	.2992	.321	0.9192	.2615	.366	1.1077	.2160
.277	0.7621	.2984	.322	0.9230	.2606	.367	1.1123	.2149
.278	0.7655	.2976	.323	0.9269	.2596	.368	1.1170	.2138
.279	0.7688	.2969	.324	0.9307	.2587	.369	1.1217	.2127
.280	0.7722	.2961	.325	0.9346	.2578	.370	1.1264	.2115
.281	0.7756	.2953	.326	0.9385	.2568	.371	1.1311	.2104
.282	0.7790	.2945	.327	0.9424	.2559	.372	1.1359	.2093
.283	0.7824	.2938	.328	0.9463	.2550	.273	1.1407	.2081
.284	0.7858	.2930	.329	0.9502	.2540	.374	1.1455	.2070
.285	0.7892	.2922	.330	0.9542	.2531	.375	1.1503	.2059
.286	0.7926	.2914	.331	0.9581	.2521	.376	1.1552	.2047
.287	0.7961	.2906	.332	0.9621	.2511	.377	1.1601	.2035
.288	0.7995	.2898	.333	0.9661	.2502	.378	1.1650	.2024
.289	0.8030	.2890	.334	0.9701	.2492	.379	1.1700	.2012
.290	0.8064	.2882	.335	0.9741	.2482	.380	1.1750	.2000
.291	0.8099	.2874	.336	0.9782	.2473	.381	1.1800	.1989
.292	0.8134	.2866	.337	0.9822	.2463	.382	1.1850	.1977
.293	0.8169	.2858	.338	0.9863	.2453	.383	1.1901	.1965
.294	0.8204	.2849	.339	0.9904	.2443	.384	1.1952	.1953
.295	0.8239	.2841	.340	0.9945	.2433	.385	1.2004	.1941
.296	0.8274	.2833	.341	0.9986	.2423	.386	1.2055	.1929
.297	0.8310	.2825	.342	1.0027	.2413	.387	1.2107	.1917
.298	0.8345	.2816	.343	1.0069	.2403	.388	1.2160	.1905
.299	0.8381	.2808	.344	1.0110	.2393	.389	1.2212	.1893

TABLE E.—Deviates and Ordinates for Areas under the Normal Curve[1]—
(*Concluded*)

Area from $x/\sigma = 0$	x/σ	Ordinate at x/σ	Area from $x/\sigma = 0$	x/σ	Ordinate at x/σ	Area from $x/\sigma = 0$	x/σ	Ordinate at x/σ
.390	1.2265	.1880	.430	1.4758	.1343	.470	1.8808	.0680
.391	1.2319	.1868	.431	1.4833	.1328	.471	1.8957	.0662
.392	1.2372	.1856	.432	1.4909	.1313	.472	1.9110	.0643
.393	1.2426	.1843	.433	1.4985	.1298	.473	1.9268	.0623
.394	1.2481	.1831	.434	1.5063	.1283	.474	1.9431	.0604
.395	1.2536	.1818	.435	1.5141	.1268	.475	1.9600	.0585
.396	1.2591	.1806	.436	1.5220	.1253	.476	1.9774	.0565
.397	1.2646	.1793	.437	1.5301	.1237	.477	1.9954	.0545
.398	1.2702	.1780	.438	1.5382	.1222	.478	2.0141	.0525
.399	1.2759	.1768	.439	1.5464	.1207	.479	2.0335	.0505
.400	1.2816	.1755	.440	1.5548	.1191	.480	2.0537	.0484
.401	1.2873	.1742	.441	1.5632	.1176	.481	2.0749	.0464
.402	1.2930	.1729	.442	1.5718	.1160	.482	2.0969	.0443
.403	1.2988	.1716	.443	1.5805	.1144	.483	2.1201	.0422
.404	1.3047	.1703	.444	1.5893	.1128	.484	2.1444	.0400
.405	1.3106	.1690	.445	1.5982	.1112	.485	2.1701	.0379
.406	1.3165	.1677	.446	1.6072	.1096	.486	2.1973	.0357
.407	1.3225	.1664	.447	1.6164	.1080	.487	2.2262	.0335
.408	1.3285	.1651	.448	1.6258	.1064	.488	2.2571	.0312
.409	1.3346	.1637	.449	1.6352	.1048	.489	2.2904	.0290
.410	1.3408	.1624	.450	1.6449	.1031	.490	2.3263	.0267
.411	1.3469	.1610	.451	1.6546	.1015	.491	2.3656	.0243
.412	1.3532	.1597	452	1.6646	.0998	.492	2.4089	.0219
.413	1.3595	.1583	.453	1.6747	.0982	.493	2.4573	.0195
.414	1.3658	.1570	.454	1.6849	.0965	.494	2.5121	.0170
.415	1.3722	.1556	.455	1.6954	.0948	.495	2.5758	.0145
.416	1.3787	.1542	.456	1.7060	.0931	.496	2.6521	.0118
.417	1.3852	.1529	.457	1.7169	.0914	.497	2.7478	.0091
.418	1.3917	.1515	.458	1.7279	.0897	.498	2.8782	.0063
.419	1.3984	.1501	.459	1.7392	.0879	.499	3.0902	.0034
.420	1.4051	.1487	.460	1.7507	.0862			
.421	1.4118	.1473	.461	1.7624	.0844			
.422	1.4187	.1458	.462	1.7744	.0826			
.423	1.4255	.1444	.463	1.7866	.0809			
.424	1.4325	.1430	.464	1.7991	.0791			
.425	1.4395	.1416	.465	1.8119	.0773			
.426	1.4466	.1401	.466	1.8250	.0755			
.427	1.4538	.1387	.467	1.8384	.0736			
.428	1.4611	.1372	.468	1.8522	.0718			
.429	1.4684	.1357	.469	1.8663	.0699			

TABLE F.—FOUR-PLACE LOGARITHMS OF NUMBERS[1]

N.	0	1	2	3	4	5	6	7	8	9
0	——	0000	3010	4771	6021	6990	7782	8451	9031	9542
1	0000	0414	0792	1139	1461	1761	2041	2304	2553	2788
2	3010	3222	3424	3617	3802	3979	4150	4314	4472	4624
3	4771	4914	5051	5185	5315	5441	5563	5682	5798	5911
4	6021	6128	6232	6335	6435	6532	6628	6721	6812	6902
5	6990	7076	7160	7243	7324	7404	7482	7559	7634	7709
6	7782	7853	7924	7993	8062	8129	8195	8261	8325	8388
7	8451	8513	8573	8633	8692	8751	8808	8865	8921	8976
8	9031	9085	9138	9191	9243	9294	9345	9395	9445	9494
9	9542	9590	9638	9685	9731	9777	9823	9868	9912	9956
10	0000	0043	0086	0128	0170	0212	0253	0294	0334	0374
11	0414	0453	0492	0531	0569	0607	0645	0682	0719	0755
12	0792	0828	0864	0899	0934	0969	1004	1038	1072	1106
13	1139	1173	1206	1239	1271	1303	1335	1367	1399	1430
14	1461	1492	1523	1553	1584	1614	1644	1673	1703	1732
15	1761	1790	1818	1847	1875	1903	1931	1959	1987	2014
16	2041	2068	2095	2122	2148	2175	2201	2227	2253	2279
17	2304	2330	2355	2380	2405	2430	2455	2480	2504	2529
18	2553	2577	2601	2625	2648	2672	2695	2718	2742	2765
19	2788	2810	2833	2856	2878	2900	2923	2945	2967	2989
20	3010	3032	3054	3075	3096	3118	3139	3160	3181	3201
21	3222	3243	3263	3284	3304	3324	3345	3365	3385	3404
22	3424	3444	3464	3483	3502	3522	3541	3560	3579	3598
23	3617	3636	3655	3674	3692	3711	3729	3747	3766	3784
24	3802	3820	3838	3856	3874	3892	3909	3927	3945	3962
25	3979	3997	4014	4031	4048	4065	4082	4099	4116	4133
26	4150	4166	4183	4200	4216	4232	4249	4265	4281	4298
27	4314	4330	4346	4362	4378	4393	4409	4425	4440	4456
28	4472	4487	4502	4518	4533	4548	4564	4579	4594	4609
29	4624	4639	4654	4669	4683	4698	4713	4728	4742	4757
30	4771	4786	4800	4814	4829	4843	4857	4871	4886	4900
31	4914	4928	4942	4955	4969	4983	4997	5011	5024	5038
32	5051	5065	5079	5092	5105	5119	5132	5145	5159	5172
33	5185	5198	5211	5224	5237	5250	5263	5276	5289	5302
34	5315	5328	5340	5353	5366	5378	5391	5403	5416	5428
35	5441	5453	5465	5478	5490	5502	5514	5527	5539	5551
36	5563	5575	5587	5599	5611	5623	5635	5647	5658	5670
37	5682	5694	5705	5717	5729	5740	5752	5763	5775	5786
38	5798	5809	5821	5832	5843	5855	5866	5877	5888	5899
39	5911	5922	5933	5944	5955	5966	5977	5988	5999	6010
40	6021	6031	6042	6053	6064	6075	6085	6096	6107	6117
41	6128	6138	6149	6160	6170	6180	6191	6201	6212	6222
42	6232	6243	6253	6263	6274	6284	6294	6304	6314	6325
43	6335	6345	6355	6365	6375	6385	6395	6405	6415	6425
44	6435	6444	6454	6464	6474	6484	6493	6503	6513	6522
45	6532	6542	6551	6561	6571	6580	6590	6599	6609	6618
46	6628	6637	6646	6656	6665	6675	6684	6693	6702	6712
47	6721	6730	6739	6749	6758	6767	6776	6785	6794	6803
48	6812	6821	6830	6839	6848	6857	6866	6875	6884	6893
49	6902	6911	6920	6928	6937	6946	6955	6964	6972	6981
50	6990	6998	7007	7016	7024	7033	7042	7050	7059	7067
N.	0	1	2	3	4	5	6	7	8	9

Prop. Parts

	22	21		20	19		18	17		16	15		14	13		12	11		9	8
1	2.2	2.1	1	2.0	1.9	1	1.8	1.7	1	1.6	1.5	1	1.4	1.3	1	1.2	1.1	1	0.9	0.8
2	4.4	4.2	2	4.0	3.8	2	3.6	3.4	2	3.2	3.0	2	2.8	2.6	2	2.4	2.2	2	1.8	1.6
3	6.6	6.3	3	6.0	5.7	3	5.4	5.1	3	4.8	4.5	3	4.2	3.9	3	3.6	3.3	3	2.7	2.4
4	8.8	8.4	4	8.0	7.6	4	7.2	6.8	4	6.4	6.0	4	5.6	5.2	4	4.8	4.4	4	3.6	3.2
5	11.0	10.5	5	10.0	9.5	5	9.0	8.5	5	8.0	7.5	5	7.0	6.5	5	6.0	5.5	5	4.5	4.0
6	13.2	12.6	6	12.0	11.4	6	10.8	10.2	6	9.6	9.0	6	8.4	7.8	6	7.2	6.6	6	5.4	4.8
7	15.4	14.7	7	14.0	13.3	7	12.6	11.9	7	11.2	10.5	7	9.8	9.1	7	8.4	7.7	7	6.3	5.6
8	17.6	16.8	8	16.0	15.2	8	14.4	13.6	8	12.8	12.0	8	11.2	10.4	8	9.6	8.8	8	7.2	6.4
9	19.8	18.9	9	18.0	17.1	9	16.2	15.3	9	14.4	13.5	9	12.6	11.7	9	10.8	9.9	9	8.1	7.2

[1] From Smail, "College Algebra."

TABLE F.—FOUR-PLACE LOGARITHMS OF NUMBERS.[1]—(*Continued*)

N.	0	1	2	3	4	5	6	7	8	9
50	6990	6998	7007	7016	7024	7033	7042	7050	7059	7067
51	7076	7084	7093	7101	7110	7118	7126	7135	7143	7152
52	7160	7168	7177	7185	7193	7202	7210	7218	7226	7235
53	7243	7251	7259	7267	7275	7284	7292	7300	7308	7316
54	7324	7332	7340	7348	7356	7364	7372	7380	7388	7396
55	7404	7412	7419	7427	7435	7443	7451	7459	7466	7474
56	7482	7490	7497	7505	7513	7520	7528	7536	7543	7551
57	7559	7566	7574	7582	7589	7597	7604	7612	7619	7627
58	7634	7642	7649	7657	7664	7672	7679	7686	7694	7701
59	7709	7716	7723	7731	7738	7745	7752	7760	7767	7774
60	7782	7789	7796	7803	7810	7818	7825	7832	7839	7846
61	7853	7860	7868	7875	7882	7889	7896	7903	7910	7917
62	7924	7931	7938	7945	7952	7959	7966	7973	7980	7987
63	7993	8000	8007	8014	8021	8028	8035	8041	8048	8055
64	8062	8069	8075	8082	8089	8096	8102	8109	8116	8122
65	8129	8136	8142	8149	8156	8162	8169	8176	8182	8189
66	8195	8202	8209	8215	8222	8228	8235	8241	8248	8254
67	8261	8267	8274	8280	8287	8293	8299	8306	8312	8319
68	8325	8331	8338	8344	8351	8357	8363	8370	8376	8382
69	8388	8395	8401	8407	8414	8420	8426	8432	8439	8445
70	8451	8457	8463	8470	8476	8482	8488	8494	8500	8506
71	8513	8519	8525	8531	8537	8543	8549	8555	8561	8567
72	8573	8579	8585	8591	8597	8603	8609	8615	8621	8627
73	8633	8639	8645	8651	8657	8663	8669	8675	8681	8686
74	8692	8698	8704	8710	8716	8722	8727	8733	8739	8745
75	8751	8756	8762	8768	8774	8779	8785	8791	8797	8802
76	8808	8814	8820	8825	8831	8837	8842	8848	8854	8859
77	8865	8871	8876	8882	8887	8893	8899	8904	8910	8915
78	8921	8927	8932	8938	8943	8949	8954	8960	8965	8971
79	8976	8982	8987	8993	8998	9004	9009	9015	9020	9025
80	9031	9036	9042	9047	9053	9058	9063	9069	9074	9079
81	9085	9090	9096	9101	9106	9112	9117	9122	9128	9133
82	9138	9143	9149	9154	9159	9165	9170	9175	9180	9186
83	9191	9196	9201	9206	9212	9217	9222	9227	9232	9238
84	9243	9248	9253	9258	9263	9269	9274	9279	9284	9289
85	9294	9299	9304	9309	9315	9320	9325	9330	9335	9340
86	9345	9350	9355	9360	9365	9370	9375	9380	9385	9390
87	9395	9400	9405	9410	9415	9420	9425	9430	9435	9440
88	9445	9450	9455	9460	9465	9469	9474	9479	9484	9489
89	9494	9499	9504	9509	9513	9518	9523	9528	9533	9538
90	9542	9547	9552	9557	9562	9566	9571	9576	9581	9586
91	9590	9595	9600	9605	9609	9614	9619	9624	9628	9633
92	9638	9643	9647	9652	9657	9661	9666	9671	9675	9680
93	9685	9689	9694	9699	9703	9708	9713	9717	9722	9727
94	9731	9736	9741	9745	9750	9754	9759	9763	9768	9773
95	9777	9782	9786	9791	9795	9800	9805	9809	9814	9818
96	9823	9827	9832	9836	9841	9845	9850	9854	9859	9863
97	9868	9872	9877	9881	9886	9890	9894	9899	9903	9908
98	9912	9917	9921	9926	9930	9934	9939	9943	9948	9952
99	9956	9961	9965	9969	9974	9978	9983	9987	9991	9996
100	0000	0004	0009	0013	0017	0022	0026	0030	0035	0039
N.	0	1	2	3	4	5	6	7	8	9

Prop. Parts

	9		**8**		**7**		**6**		**5**		**4**
1	0.9	1	0.8	1	0.7	1	0.6	1	0.5	1	0.4
2	1.8	2	1.6	2	1.4	2	1.2	2	1.0	2	0.8
3	2.7	3	2.4	3	2.1	3	1.8	3	1.5	3	1.2
4	3.6	4	3.2	4	2.8	4	2.4	4	2.0	4	1.6
5	4.5	5	4.0	5	3.5	5	3.0	5	2.5	5	2.0
6	5.4	6	4.8	6	4.2	6	3.6	6	3.0	6	2.4
7	6.3	7	5.6	7	4.9	7	4.2	7	3.5	7	2.8
8	7.2	8	6.4	8	5.6	8	4.8	8	4.0	8	3.2
9	8.1	9	7.2	9	6.3	9	5.4	9	4.5	9	3.6

[1] From Smail, "College Algebra."

Table G.—Urban's Tables for the Constant Process[1]

p	W	γW	$2W$	2^2W	$2\gamma W$	$3W$	3^2W	$3\gamma W$	$4W$	4^2W	$4\gamma W$
0.50	1.0000	0.0000	2.0000	4.0000	0.0000	3.0000	9.0000	0.0000	4.0000	16.0000	0.0000
0.51	0.9998	0.0177	1.9996	3.9991	0.0354	2.9993	8.9980	0.0531	3.9991	15.9965	0.0708
0.52	0.9991	0.0355	1.9982	3.9963	0.0709	2.9972	8.9917	0.1064	3.9963	15.9853	0.1419
0.53	0.9980	0.0531	1.9959	3.9918	0.1062	2.9938	8.9816	0.1593	3.9918	15.9672	0.2124
0.54	0.9964	0.0707	1.9928	3.9855	0.1415	2.9891	8.9674	0.2122	3.9855	15.9421	0.2830
0.55	0.9943	0.0883	1.9886	3.9772	0.1766	2.9829	8.9487	0.2649	3.9772	15.9088	0.3532
0.56	0.9918	0.1058	1.9836	3.9671	0.2116	2.9753	8.9260	0.3175	3.9671	15.8685	0.4233
0.57	0.9888	0.1233	1.9776	3.9551	0.2466	2.9663	8.8990	0.3699	3.9551	15.8205	0.4932
0.58	0.9853	0.1406	1.9706	3.9413	0.2812	2.9560	8.8679	0.4218	3.9413	15.7651	0.5624
0.59	0.9814	0.1579	1.9627	3.9254	0.3158	2.9441	8.8322	0.4737	3.9254	15.7018	0.6316
0.60	0.9768	0.1750	1.9537	3.9074	0.3501	2.9306	8.7916	0.5252	3.9074	15.6296	0.7002
0.61	0.9720	0.1920	1.9440	3.8881	0.3839	2.9161	8.7482	0.5759	3.8881	15.5523	0.7679
0.62	0.9666	0.2088	1.9332	3.8663	0.4176	2.8997	8.6992	0.6263	3.8663	15.4653	0.8351
0.63	0.9607	0.2254	1.9214	3.8429	0.4508	2.8822	8.6465	0.6762	3.8429	15.3715	0.9015
0.64	0.9542	0.2419	1.9084	3.8168	0.4838	2.8626	8.5878	0.7257	3.8168	15.2672	0.9676
0.65	0.9473	0.2581	1.8945	3.7890	0.5163	2.8418	8.5253	0.7744	3.7890	15.1562	1.0325
0.66	0.9398	0.2741	1.8797	3.7594	0.5481	2.8196	8.4586	0.8222	3.7594	15.0376	1.0962
0.67	0.9317	0.2899	1.8634	3.7268	0.5797	2.7951	8.3853	0.8696	3.7268	14.9072	1.1594
0.68	0.9232	0.3053	1.8464	3.6929	0.6106	2.7697	8.3090	0.9159	3.6929	14.7715	1.2212
0.69	0.9140	0.3205	1.8280	3.6561	0.6409	2.7421	8.2262	0.9614	3.6561	14.6243	1.2818
0.70	0.9043	0.3353	1.8085	3.6170	0.6706	2.7128	8.1383	1.0059	3.6170	14.4682	1.3412
0.71	0.8939	0.3498	1.7878	3.5755	0.6996	2.6816	8.0449	1.0493	3.5755	14.3021	1.3991
0.72	0.8830	0.3639	1.7659	3.5318	0.7277	2.6489	7.9466	1.0916	3.5318	14.1274	1.4555
0.73	0.8713	0.3775	1.7426	3.4852	0.7551	2.6139	7.8417	1.1326	3.4852	13.9408	1.5101
0.74	0.8590	0.3908	1.7180	3.4360	0.7815	2.5770	7.7310	1.1723	3.4360	13.7440	1.5630
0.75	0.8460	0.4035	1.6921	3.3842	0.8070	2.5381	7.6144	1.2104	3.3842	13.5366	1.6139
0.76	0.8323	0.4157	1.6646	3.3293	0.8313	2.4970	7.4909	1.2470	3.3293	13.3171	1.6626
0.77	0.8179	0.4273	1.6357	3.2714	0.8545	2.4536	7.3607	1.2818	3.2714	13.0858	1.7090
0.78	0.8025	0.4382	1.6051	3.2102	0.8764	2.4076	7.2229	1.3146	3.2102	12.8406	1.7527
0.79	0.7865	0.4484	1.5729	3.1459	0.8969	2.3594	7.0782	1.3453	3.1459	12.5835	1.7938
0.80	0.7695	0.4579	1.5390	3.0780	0.9159	2.3085	6.9255	1.3738	3.0780	12.3120	1.8317
0.81	0.7515	0.4665	1.5031	3.0061	0.9331	2.2546	6.7638	1.3996	3.0061	12.0245	1.8662
0.82	0.7327	0.4743	1.4653	2.9307	0.9485	2.1980	6.5940	1.4228	2.9307	11.7227	1.8970
0.83	0.7129	0.4810	1.4257	2.8515	0.9619	2.1386	6.4158	1.4429	2.8515	11.4059	1.9239
0.84	0.6921	0.4866	1.3842	2.7683	0.9732	2.0762	6.2287	1.4598	2.7683	11.0733	1.9464
0.85	0.6697	0.4908	1.3394	2.6788	0.9816	2.0091	6.0273	1.4725	2.6788	10.7152	1.9633
0.86	0.6463	0.4937	1.2927	2.5853	0.9875	1.9390	5.8170	1.4812	2.5853	10.3413	1.9749
0.87	0.6215	0.4950	1.2430	2.4860	0.9900	1.8645	5.5935	1.4851	2.4860	9.9440	1.9801
0.88	0.5953	0.4946	1.1907	2.3813	0.9892	1.7860	5.3580	1.4838	2.3813	9.5253	1.9784
0.89	0.5673	0.4920	1.1346	2.2692	0.9840	1.7019	5.1056	1.4760	2.2692	9.0766	1.9680
0.90	0.5376	0.4871	1.0751	2.1502	0.9743	1.6126	4.8380	1.4614	2.1502	8.6008	1.9485
0.91	0.5059	0.4796	1.0118	2.0236	0.9592	1.5177	4.5531	1.4388	2.0236	8.0944	1.9184
0.92	0.4718	0.4687	0.9435	1.8871	0.9374	1.4153	4.2459	1.4061	1.8871	7.5483	1.8748
0.93	0.4351	0.4540	0.8702	1.7403	0.9080	1.3052	3.9157	1.3620	1.7403	6.9613	1.8160
0.94	0.3954	0.4346	0.7907	1.5814	0.8692	1.1861	3.5582	1.3039	1.5814	6.3258	1.7385
0.95	0.3519	0.4093	0.7038	1.4076	0.8185	1.0557	3.1671	1.2278	1.4076	5.6304	1.6370
0.96	0.3036	0.3759	0.6073	1.2146	0.7518	0.9109	2.7328	1.1277	1.2146	4.8582	1.5036
0.97	0.2469	0.3282	0.4936	0.9871	0.6564	0.7403	2.2210	0.9847	0.9871	3.9485	1.3129
0.98	0.1881	0.2732	0.3762	0.7525	0.5463	0.5644	1.6931	0.8195	0.7525	3.0099	1.0926
0.99	0.1127	0.1854	0.2254	0.4508	0.3708	0.3381	1.0142	0.5561	0.4508	1.8030	0.7415

[1] Adapted from *Arch. ges. Psychol.*, 1912, **24**, 240–241, with corrections given by Wm. Brown and G. H. Thomson, "Essentials of Mental Measurement," pp. 202 f., 1925.

TABLE H.—Rich's Checking Tables for the Constant Method[1]

p	$x = -4$	$x = -3$	$x = -2$	$x = -1$	$x = 0$	$x = 1$	$x = 2$	$x = 3$	$x = 4$	p
.01	2.0210	1.1595	.5235	.1127	−.0727	−.0327	.2327	.7235	1.4396	.01
.02	3.2649	1.8631	.8375	.1881	−.0851	.0179	.4973	1.3529	2.5847	.02
.03	4.1930	2.3841	1.0686	.2469	−.0813	.0843	.7430	1.8953	3.5414	.03
.04	5.0749	2.8773	1.2868	.3036	−.0723	.1590	.9978	2.4437	4.4969	.04
.05	5.8024	3.2818	1.4649	.3519	−.0574	.2371	1.2355	2.9376	5.3436	.05
.06	6.4437	3.6368	1.6207	.3954	−.0392	.3170	1.4637	3.4012	6.1295	.06
.07	7.0181	3.9536	1.7592	.4351	−.0189	.3973	1.6836	3.8400	6.8667	.07
.08	7.5391	4.2398	1.8841	.4718	.0031	.4780	1.8963	4.2582	7.5637	.08
.09	8.0155	4.5005	1.9973	.5059	.0263	.5585	2.1025	4.6583	8.2259	.09
.10	8.4496	4.7373	2.0999	.5376	.0505	.6386	2.3015	5.0397	8.8530	.10
.11	8.8507	4.9550	2.1939	.5673	.0753	.7179	2.4951	5.4068	9.4531	.11
.12	9.2231	5.1565	2.2805	.5953	.1007	.7967	2.6835	5.7609	10.0289	.12
.13	9.5646	5.3406	2.3595	.6215	.1265	.8745	2.8655	6.0994	10.5764	.13
.14	9.8835	5.5118	2.4327	.6463	.1526	.9515	3.0431	6.4274	11.1043	.14
.15	10.1786	5.6696	2.4999	.6697	.1789	1.0275	3.2155	6.7428	11.6096	.15
.16	10.4569	5.8178	2.5628	.6921	.2055	1.1031	3.3848	7.0506	12.1007	.16
.17	10.7102	5.9520	2.6196	.7129	.2319	1.1767	3.5472	7.3434	12.5654	.17
.18	10.9474	6.0772	2.6723	.7327	.2584	1.2495	3.7059	7.6276	13.0148	.18
.19	11.1696	6.1938	2.7211	.7515	.2850	1.3215	3.8611	7.9038	13.4494	.19
.20	11.3773	6.3024	2.7665	.7695	.3116	1.3927	4.0127	8.1718	13.8699	.20
.21	11.5695	6.4022	2.8080	.7865	.3381	1.4627	4.1600	8.4304	14.2737	.21
.22	11.7474	6.4942	2.8458	.8025	.3643	1.5311	4.3032	8.6802	14.6624	.22
.23	11.9140	6.5795	2.8808	.8179	.3906	1.5991	4.4432	8.9231	15.0388	.23
.24	12.0670	6.6575	2.9126	.8323	.4166	1.6655	4.5792	9.1575	15.4004	.24
.25	12.2088	6.7292	2.9416	.8460	.4425	1.7310	4.7118	9.3846	15.7494	.25
.26	12.3392	6.7945	2.9677	.8590	.4682	1.7954	4.8407	9.6039	16.0852	.26
.27	12.4595	6.8542	2.9915	.8713	.4938	1.8589	4.9665	9.8168	16.4097	.27
.28	12.5702	6.9084	3.0127	.8830	.5191	1.9212	5.0891	10.0230	16.7228	.28
.29	12.6698	6.9567	3.0314	.8939	.5441	1.9821	5.2078	10.2213	17.0226	.29
.30	12.7614	7.0004	3.0481	.9043	.5690	2.0423	5.3239	10.4142	17.3130	.30
.31	12.8435	7.0390	3.0625	.9140	.5935	2.1010	5.4367	10.6004	17.5921	.31
.32	12.9177	7.0731	3.0750	.9232	.6179	2.1590	5.5466	10.7807	17.8611	.32
.33	12.9816	7.1016	3.0849	.9317	.6418	2.2153	5.6523	10.9526	18.1164	.33
.34	13.0401	7.1269	3.0935	.9398	.6657	2.2712	5.7567	11.1217	18.3665	.34
.35	13.0889	7.1471	3.1000	.9473	.6892	2.3257	5.8564	11.2819	18.6019	.35
.36	13.1303	7.1632	3.1045	.9542	.7123	2.3788	5.9537	11.4370	18.8287	.36
.37	13.1654	7.1758	3.1076	.9607	.7353	2.4313	6.0488	11.5878	19.0482	.37
.38	13.1919	7.1836	3.1085	.9666	.7578	2.4822	6.1397	11.7304	19.2543	.38
.39	13.2121	7.1880	3.1080	.9720	.7800	2.5320	6.2282	11.8684	19.4525	.39
.40	13.2242	7.1880	3.1056	.9768	.8018	2.5804	6.3128	11.9988	19.6386	.40
.41	13.2315	7.1853	3.1020	.9814	.8235	2.6284	6.3958	12.1261	19.8191	.41
.42	13.2309	7.1784	3.0966	.9853	.8447	2.6747	6.4754	12.2468	19.9887	.42
.43	13.2241	7.1681	3.0896	.9888	.8655	2.7198	6.5516	12.3609	20.1479	.43
.44	13.2107	7.1542	3.0811	.9918	.8860	2.7638	6.6251	12.4698	20.2983	.44
.45	13.1908	7.1367	3.0712	.9943	.9060	2.8063	6.6952	12.5727	20.4388	.45
.46	13.1653	7.1162	3.0599	.9964	.9257	2.8478	6.7625	12.6700	20.5703	.46
.47	13.1327	7.0920	3.0470	.9980	.9449	2.8878	6.8264	12.7610	20.6915	.47
.48	13.0945	7.0645	3.0326	.9991	.9636	2.9263	6.8872	12.8461	20.8033	.48
.49	13.0503	7.0339	3.0170	.9998	.9821	2.9640	6.9454	12.9263	20.9069	.49
.50	13.0000	7.0000	3.0000	1.0000	1.0000	3.0000	7.0000	13.0000	21.0000	.50

[1] Adapted from G. J. Rich, Checking tables, *Amer. J. Psychol.*, 1918, **29,** 120, through the courtesy of the editor and publisher.

TABLE H.—RICH'S CHECKING TABLES FOR THE CONSTANT METHOD[1]—
(*Concluded*)

p	$x = -4$	$x = -3$	$x = -2$	$x = -1$	$x = 0$	$x = 1$	$x = 2$	$x = 3$	$x = 4$	p
.51	12.9441	6.9631	2.9816	.9998	1.0175	3.0348	7.0516	13.0679	21.0839	.51
.52	12.8817	6.9227	2.9618	.9991	1.0346	3.0683	7.1000	13.1299	21.1581	.52
.53	12.8141	6.8796	2.9408	.9980	1.0511	3.1002	7.1450	13.1858	21.2225	.53
.54	12.7407	6.8332	2.9183	.9964	1.0671	3.1306	7.1869	13.2358	21.2777	.54
.55	12.6610	6.7835	2.8946	.9943	1.0826	3.1595	7.2250	13.2791	21.3218	.55
.56	12.5757	6.7308	2.8695	.9918	1.0976	3.1870	7.2599	13.3164	21.3565	.56
.57	12.4843	6.6749	2.8430	.9888	1.1121	3.2130	7.2914	13.3473	21.3809	.57
.58	12.3873	6.6160	2.8154	.9853	1.1259	3.2371	7.3190	13.3716	21.3947	.58
.59	12.2841	6.5537	2.7862	.9814	1.1393	3.2600	7.3432	13.3893	21.3981	.59
.60	12.1738	6.4876	2.7554	.9768	1.1518	3.2804	7.3630	13.3992	21.3890	.60
.61	12.0603	6.4202	2.7242	.9720	1.1640	3.3000	7.3800	13.4042	21.3723	.61
.62	11.9393	6.3486	2.6909	.9666	1.1754	3.3174	7.3925	13.4006	21.3421	.62
.63	11.8132	6.2742	2.6568	.9607	1.1861	3.3329	7.4012	13.3910	21.3020	.63
.64	11.6789	6.1956	2.6207	.9542	1.1961	3.3464	7.4051	13.3722	21.2477	.64
.65	11.5401	6.1145	2.5836	.9473	1.2054	3.3581	7.4052	13.3469	21.1831	.65
.66	11.3959	6.0307	2.5455	.9398	1.2139	3.3676	7.4011	13.3143	21.1071	.66
.67	11.2426	5.9422	2.5053	.9317	1.2216	3.3749	7.3915	13.2716	21.0150	.67
.68	11.0859	5.8519	2.4644	.9232	1.2285	3.3802	7.3784	13.2231	20.9141	.68
.69	10.9209	5.7572	2.4217	.9140	1.2345	3.3830	7.3595	13.1642	20.7967	.69
.70	10.7496	5.6592	2.3775	.9043	1.2396	3.3835	7.3357	13.0966	20.6660	.70
.71	10.5712	5.5577	2.3318	.8939	1.2437	3.3813	7.3066	13.0195	20.5204	.71
.72	10.3870	5.4530	2.2851	.8830	1.2469	3.3768	7.2723	12.9340	20.3616	.72
.73	10.1943	5.3440	2.2363	.8713	1.2488	3.3689	7.2317	12.8370	20.1849	.73
.74	9.9948	5.2315	2.1863	.8590	1.2498	3.3586	7.1853	12.7301	19.9928	.74
.75	9.7880	5.1154	2.1346	.8460	1.2495	3.3450	7.1328	12.6124	19.7842	.75
.76	9.5732	4.9949	2.0814	.8323	1.2480	3.3283	7.0732	12.4829	19.5570	.76
.77	9.3506	4.8705	2.0264	.8179	1.2452	3.3083	7.0068	12.3413	19.3114	.77
.78	9.1184	4.7414	1.9694	.8025	1.2407	3.2839	6.9324	12.1858	19.0442	.78
.79	8.8787	4.6084	1.9110	.7865	1.2349	3.2563	6.8506	12.0178	18.7581	.79
.80	8.6297	4.4706	1.8505	.7695	1.2274	3.2243	6.7603	11.8352	18.4491	.80
.81	8.3702	4.3276	1.7879	.7515	1.2180	3.1875	6.6603	11.6360	18.1148	.81
.82	8.1020	4.1802	1.7239	.7327	1.2070	3.1467	6.5515	11.4218	17.7574	.82
.83	7.8244	4.0282	1.6578	.7129	1.1939	3.1007	6.4330	11.1912	17.3752	.83
.84	7.5373	3.8714	1.5896	.6921	1.1787	3.0495	6.3044	10.9434	16.9667	.84
.85	7.2336	3.7062	1.5183	.6697	1.1605	2.9907	6.1603	10.6694	16.5178	.85
.86	6.9211	3.5368	1.4451	.6463	1.1400	2.9263	6.0055	10.3772	16.0415	.86
.87	6.5944	3.3604	1.3695	.6215	1.1165	2.8545	5.8355	10.0596	15.5266	.87
.88	6.2555	3.1781	1.2913	.5953	1.0899	2.7751	5.6511	9.7177	14.9749	.88
.89	5.8987	2.9870	1.2099	.5673	1.0593	2.6859	5.4471	9.3428	14.3731	.89
.90	5.5268	2.7887	1.1255	.5376	1.0247	2.5870	5.2243	8.9367	13.7242	.90
.91	5.1379	2.5821	1.0381	.5059	.9855	2.4769	4.9801	8.4951	13.0219	.91
.92	4.7269	2.3650	.9467	.4718	.9405	2.3528	4.7085	8.0078	12.2507	.92
.93	4.2941	2.1376	.8512	.4351	.8891	2.2133	4.4076	7.4720	11.4067	.93
.94	3.8359	1.8982	.7515	.3954	.8300	2.0554	4.0713	6.8782	10.4757	.94
.95	3.3470	1.6448	.6465	.3519	.7612	1.8743	3.6911	6.2118	9.4362	.95
.96	2.8195	1.3737	.5350	.3036	.6795	1.6626	3.2532	5.4509	8.2559	.96
.97	2.2236	1.0711	.4122	.2469	.5751	1.3971	2.7122	4.5211	6.8236	.97
.98	1.6261	.7705	.2913	.1881	.4613	1.1107	2.1363	3.5383	5.3163	.98
.99	.9088	.4181	.1527	.1127	.2981	.7089	1.3451	2.2065	3.2934	.99

Table I.—Hoisington's Table for Graphic Checking[1]

γ	p	γ	p	γ	p	γ	p
.00	.5000	.50	.7603	1.00	.9214	1.50	.9832
.01	.5057	.51	.7646	1.01	.9234	1.51	.9837
.02	.5113	.52	.7690	1.02	.9254	1.52	.9842
.03	.5169	.53	.7733	1.03	.9274	1.53	.9848
.04	.5226	.54	.7775	1.04	.9293	1.54	.9853
.05	.5282	.55	.7817	1.05	.9312	1.55	.9858
.06	.5338	.56	.7858	1.06	.9331	1.56	.9863
.07	.5395	.57	.7899	1.07	.9349	1.57	.9868
.08	.5451	.58	.7940	1.08	.9367	1.58	.9873
.09	.5508	.59	.7980	1.09	.9384	1.59	.9878
.10	.5563	.60	.8020	1.10	.9401	1.60	.9882
.11	.5618	.61	.8059	1.11	.9418	1.62	.9890
.12	.5674	.62	.8097	1.12	.9434	1.64	.9898
.13	.5730	.63	.8135	1.13	.9450	1.66	.9906
.14	.5785	.64	.8173	1.14	.9466	1.68	.9913
.15	.5840	.65	.8210	1.15	.9481	1.70	.9919
.16	.5895	.66	.8247	1.16	.9496	1.72	.9925
.17	.5950	.67	.8283	1.17	.9510	1.74	.9931
.18	.6005	.68	.8319	1.18	.9524	1.76	.9936
.19	.6059	.69	.8354	1.19	.9538	1.78	.9941
.20	.6114	.70	.8389	1.20	.9552	1.80	.9946
.21	.6168	.71	.8424	1.21	.9565	1.82	.9950
.22	.6222	.72	.8457	1.22	.9578	1.84	.9954
.23	.6275	.73	.8491	1.23	.9591	1.86	.9958
.24	.6329	.74	.8524	1.24	.9603	1.88	.9961
.25	.6382	.75	.8556	1.25	.9615	1.90	.9964
.26	.6435	.76	.8588	1.26	.9626	1.92	.9967
.27	.6487	.77	.8619	1.27	.9638	1.94	.9970
.28	.6540	.78	.8650	1.28	.9649	1.96	.9972
.29	.6592	.79	.8681	1.29	.9660	1.98	.9975
.30	.6643	.80	.8711	1.30	.9670	2.00	.9977
.31	.6695	.81	.8740	1.31	.9681	2.05	.9982
.32	.6746	.82	.8769	1.32	.9691	2.10	.9985
.33	.6797	.83	.8798	1.33	.9700	2.15	.9988
.34	.6847	.84	.8826	1.34	.9710	2.20	.9991
.35	.6897	.85	.8854	1.35	.9719	2.25	.9993
.36	.6947	.86	.8881	1.36	.9728	2.30	.9995
.37	.6996	.87	.8907	1.37	.9737	2.35	.9996
.38	.7045	.88	.8934	1.38	.9745		
.39	.7094	.89	.8959	1.39	.9754		
.40	.7142	.90	.8985	1.40	.9762	2.40	.9997
.41	.7190	.91	.9010	1.41	.9770	2.45	.9998
.42	.7238	.92	.9034	1.42	.9777	2.50	.9998
.43	.7285	.93	.9058	1.43	.9785	2.55	.9999
.44	.7331	.94	.9082	1.44	.9792	2.60	.9999
.45	.7378	.95	.9105	1.45	.9799	2.65	.9999
.46	.7424	.96	.9127	1.46	.9806	2.70	.9999
.47	.7469	.97	.9150	1.47	.9812	2.80	1.0000
.48	.7514	.98	.9171	1.48	.9819		
.49	.7559	.99	.9193	1.49	.9825		

[1] Adapted from the *Amer. J. Psychol.*, 1922, **33**, 245, by courtesy of the editor and publisher.

TABLE J.—RECIPROCALS OF pq, WHEN $p + q = 1.00$

p or q	$1/pq$	p or q	$1/pq$	p or q	$1/pq$
.50	4.0	.67	4.5	.84	7.5
.51	4.0	.68	4.6	.85	7.9
.52	4.0	.69	4.7	.86	8.3
.53	4.0	.70	4.8	.87	8.8
.54	4.0	.71	4.9	.88	9.4
.55	4.1	.72	5.0	.89	10.2
.56	4.1	.73	5.1	.90	11.1
.57	4.1	.74	5.2	.91	12.2
.58	4.1	.75	5.3	.92	13.6
.59	4.1	.76	5.4	.93	15.4
.60	4.2	.77	5.6	.94	17.7
.61	4.2	.78	5.8	.95	21.0
.62	4.3	.79	6.0	.96	26.0
.63	4.3	.80	6.2	.97	34.4
.64	4.4	.81	6.5	.98	51.0
.65	4.4	.82	6.8	.99	101.0
.66	4.5	.83	7.1	1.00	∞

APPENDIX

TABLE K.—SIGNIFICANT VALUES OF *r*, *R* AND *t**

Degrees of freedom	Number of variables									*t*
	2	3	4	5	6	7	9	13	25	
1	.997	.999	.999	.999	1.000	1.000	1.000	1.000	1.000	12.706
	1.000	**1.000**	**1.000**	**1.000**	**1.000**	**1.000**	**1.000**	**1.000**	**1.000**	**63.657**
2	.950	.975	.983	.987	.990	.992	.994	.996	.998	4.303
	.990	**.995**	**.997**	**.998**	**.998**	**.998**	**.999**	**.999**	**1.000**	**9.925**
3	.878	.930	.950	.961	.968	.973	.979	.986	.993	3.182
	.959	**.976**	**.983**	**.987**	**.990**	**.991**	**.993**	**.995**	**.998**	**5.841**
4	.811	.881	.912	.930	.942	.950	.961	.973	.986	2.776
	.917	**.949**	**.962**	**.970**	**.975**	**.979**	**.984**	**.989**	**.994**	**4.604**
5	.754	.836	.874	.898	.914	.925	.941	.958	.978	2.571
	.874	**.917**	**.937**	**.949**	**.957**	**.963**	**.971**	**.980**	**.989**	**4.032**
6	.707	.795	.839	.867	.886	.900	.920	.943	.969	2.447
	.834	**.886**	**.911**	**.927**	**.938**	**.946**	**.957**	**.969**	**.983**	**3.707**
7	.666	.758	.807	.838	.860	.876	.900	.927	.960	2.365
	.798	**.855**	**.885**	**.904**	**.918**	**.928**	**.942**	**.958**	**.977**	**3.499**
8	.632	.726	.777	.811	.835	.854	.880	.912	.950	2.306
	.765	**.827**	**.860**	**.882**	**.898**	**.909**	**.926**	**.946**	**.970**	**3.355**
9	.602	.697	.750	.786	.812	.832	.861	.897	.941	2.262
	.735	**.800**	**.836**	**.861**	**.878**	**.891**	**.911**	**.934**	**.963**	**3.250**
10	.576	.671	.726	.763	.790	.812	.843	.882	.932	2.228
	.708	**.776**	**.814**	**.840**	**.859**	**.874**	**.895**	**.922**	**.955**	**3.169**
11	.553	.648	.703	.741	.770	.792	.826	.868	.922	2.201
	.684	**.753**	**.793**	**.821**	**.841**	**.857**	**.880**	**.910**	**.948**	**3.106**
12	.532	.627	.683	.722	.751	.774	.809	.854	.913	2.179
	.661	**.732**	**.773**	**.802**	**.824**	**.841**	**.866**	**.898**	**.940**	**3.055**
13	.514	.608	.664	.703	.733	.757	.794	.840	.904	2.160
	.641	**.712**	**.755**	**.785**	**.807**	**.825**	**.852**	**.886**	**.932**	**3.012**
14	.497	.590	.646	.686	.717	.741	.779	.828	.895	2.145
	.623	**.694**	**.737**	**.768**	**.792**	**.810**	**.838**	**.875**	**.924**	**2.977**
15	.482	.574	.630	.670	.701	.726	.765	.815	.886	2.131
	.606	**.677**	**.721**	**.752**	**.776**	**.796**	**.825**	**.864**	**.917**	**2.947**
16	.468	.559	.615	.655	.686	.712	.751	.803	.878	2.120
	.590	**.662**	**.706**	**.738**	**.762**	**.782**	**.813**	**.853**	**.909**	**2.921**
17	.456	.545	.601	.641	.673	.698	.738	.792	.869	2.110
	.575	**.647**	**.691**	**.724**	**.749**	**.769**	**.800**	**.842**	**.902**	**2.898**
18	.444	.532	.587	.628	.660	.686	.726	.781	.861	2.101
	.561	**.633**	**.678**	**.710**	**.736**	**.756**	**.789**	**.832**	**.894**	**2.878**
19	.433	.520	.575	.615	.647	.674	.714	.770	.853	2.093
	.549	**.620**	**.665**	**.698**	**.723**	**.744**	**.778**	**.822**	**.887**	**2.861**
20	.423	.509	.563	.604	.636	.662	.703	.760	.845	2.086
	.537	**.608**	**.652**	**.685**	**.712**	**.733**	**.767**	**.812**	**.880**	**2.845**
21	.413	.498	.552	.592	.624	.651	.693	.750	.837	2.080
	.526	**.596**	**.641**	**.674**	**.700**	**.722**	**.756**	**.803**	**.873**	**2.831**
22	.404	.488	.542	.582	.614	.640	.682	.740	.830	2.074
	.515	**.585**	**.630**	**.663**	**.690**	**.712**	**.746**	**.794**	**.866**	**2.819**
23	.396	.479	.532	.572	.604	.630	.673	.731	.823	2.069
	.505	**.574**	**.619**	**.652**	**.679**	**.701**	**.736**	**.785**	**.859**	**2.807**

* Adapted from H. A. Wallace and G. W. Snedecor, "Correlation and Machine Calculation," 1931, by courtesy of the authors.

TABLE K.—SIGNIFICANT VALUES OF r, R AND t[1].—(*Continued*)

| Degrees of freedom | Number of variables | | | | | | | | | t |
	2	3	4	5	6	7	9	13	25	
24	.388 .496	.470 .565	.523 .609	.562 .642	.594 .669	.621 .692	.663 .727	.722 .776	.815 .852	2.064 2.797
25	.381 .487	.462 .555	.514 .600	.553 .633	.585 .660	.612 .682	.654 .718	.714 .768	.808 .846	2.060 2.787
26	.374 .478	.454 .546	.506 .590	.545 .624	.576 .651	.603 .673	.645 .709	.706 .760	.802 .839	2.056 2.779
27	.367 .470	.446 .538	.498 .582	.536 .615	.568 .642	.594 .664	.637 .701	.698 .752	.795 .833	2.052 2.771
28	.361 .463	.439 .530	.490 .573	.529 .606	.560 .634	.586 .656	.629 .692	.690 .744	.788 .827	2.048 2.763
29	.355 .456	.432 .522	.482 .565	.521 .598	.552 .625	.579 .648	.621 .685	.682 .737	.782 .821	2.045 2.756
30	.349 .449	.426 .514	.476 .558	.514 .591	.545 .618	.571 .640	.614 .677	.675 .729	.776 .815	2.042 2.750
35	.325 .418	.397 .481	.445 .523	.482 .556	.512 .582	.538 .605	.580 .642	.642 .696	.746 .786	2.030 2.724
40	.304 .393	.373 .454	.419 .494	.455 .526	.484 .552	.509 .575	.551 .612	.613 .667	.720 .761	2.021 2.704
45	.288 .372	.353 .430	.397 .470	.432 .501	.460 .527	.485 .549	.526 .586	.587 .640	.696 .737	2.014 2.690
50	.273 .354	.336 .410	.379 .449	.412 .479	.440 .504	.464 .526	.504 .562	.565 .617	.674 .715	2.008 2.678
60	.250 .325	.308 .377	.348 .414	.380 .442	.406 .466	.429 .488	.467 .523	.526 .577	.636 .677	2.000 2.660
70	.323 .302	.286 .351	.324 .386	.354 .413	.379 .436	.401 .456	.438 .491	.495 .544	.604 .644	1.994 2.648
80	.217 .283	.269 .330	.304 .362	.332 .389	.356 .411	.377 .431	.413 .464	.469 .516	.576 .615	1.990 2.638
90	.205 .267	.254 .312	.288 .343	.315 .368	.338 .390	.358 .409	.392 .441	.446 .492	.552 .590	1.987 2.632
100	.195 .254	.241 .297	.274 .327	.300 .351	.322 .372	.341 .330	.374 .421	.426 .470	.530 .568	1.984 2.626
125	.174 .228	.216 .266	.246 .294	.269 .316	.290 .335	.307 .352	.338 .381	.387 .428	.485 .521	1.979 2.616
150	.159 .208	.198 .244	.225 .270	.247 .290	.266 .308	.282 .324	.310 .351	.356 .395	.450 .484	1.976 2.609
200	.138 .181	.172 .212	.196 .234	.215 .253	.231 .269	.246 .283	.271 .307	.312 .347	.398 .430	1.972 2.601
300	.113 .148	.141 .174	.160 .192	.176 .208	.190 .221	.202 .233	.223 .253	.258 .287	.332 .359	1.968 2.592
400	.098 .128	.122 .151	.139 .167	.153 .180	.165 .192	.176 .202	.194 .220	.225 .250	.291 .315	1.966 2.588
500	.088 .115	.109 .135	.124 .150	.137 .162	.148 .172	.157 .182	.174 .198	.202 .225	.262 .284	1.965 2.586
1000	.062 .081	.077 .096	.088 .106	.097 .115	.105 .122	.112 .129	.124 .141	.144 .160	.188 .204	1.962 2.581
∞										1.960 2.576

Table L.—Values of $(1 - r^2)$ and $\sqrt{1 - r^2}$ for Given Values of r

r	$1 - r^2$	$\sqrt{1 - r^2}$	r	$1 - r^2$	$\sqrt{1 - r^2}$
.00	1.0000	1.0000	.25	.9375	.9682
.005	1.0000	1.0000	.255	.9350	.9670
.01	.9999	.9999	.26	.9324	.9656
.015	.9998	.9999	.265	.9298	.9643
.02	.9996	.9998	.27	.9271	.9629
.025	.9994	.9997	.275	.9244	.9615
.03	.9991	.9995	.28	.9216	.9600
.035	.9988	.9994	.285	.9188	.9585
.04	.9984	.9992	.29	.9159	.9570
.045	.9980	.9990	.295	.9130	.9555
.05	.9975	.9987	.30	.9100	.9539
.055	.9970	.9985	.305	.9070	.9524
.06	.9964	.9982	.31	.9039	.9507
.065	.9958	.9979	.315	.9008	.9491
.07	.9951	.9975	.32	.8976	.9474
.075	.9944	.9972	.325	.8944	.9457
.08	.9936	.9968	.33	.8911	.9440
.085	.9928	.9964	.335	.8878	.9422
.09	.9919	.9959	.34	.8844	.9404
.095	.9910	.9955	.345	.8810	.9386
.10	.9900	.9950	.35	.8775	.9367
.105	.9890	.9945	.355	.8740	.9349
.11	.9879	.9939	.36	.8704	.9330
.115	.9868	.9934	.365	.8668	.9310
.12	.9856	.9928	.37	.8631	.9290
.125	.9844	.9922	.375	.8594	.9270
.13	.9831	.9915	.38	.8556	.9250
.135	.9818	.9909	.385	.8518	.9229
.14	.9804	.9902	.39	.8479	.9208
.145	.9790	.9894	.395	.8440	.9187
.15	.9775	.9887	.40	.8400	.9165
.155	.9760	.9879	.405	.8360	.9143
.16	.9744	.9871	.41	.8319	.9121
.165	.9728	.9863	.415	.8278	.9098
.17	.9711	.9854	.42	.8236	.9075
.175	.9694	.9846	.425	.8194	.9052
.18	.9676	.9837	.43	.8151	.9028
.185	.9658	.9828	.435	.8108	.9004
.19	.9639	.9818	.44	.8064	.8980
.195	.9620	.9808	.445	.8020	.8955
.20	.9600	.9798	.45	.7975	.8930
.205	.9580	.9788	.455	.7930	.8905
.21	.9559	.9777	.46	.7884	.8879
.215	.9538	.9766	.465	.7838	.8853
.22	.9516	.9755	.47	.7791	.8827
.225	.9494	.9744	.475	.7744	.8800
.23	.9471	.9732	.48	.7696	.8773
.235	.9448	.9720	.485	.7648	.8745
.24	.9424	.9708	.49	.7599	.8717
.245	.9400	.9695	.495	.7550	.8689

TABLE L.—VALUES OF $(1 - r^2)$ AND $\sqrt{1 - r^2}$ FOR GIVEN VALUES OF r.— (*Continued*)

r	$1 - r^2$	$\sqrt{1 - r^2}$	r	$1 - r^2$	$\sqrt{1 - r^2}$
.50	.7500	.8660	.75	.4375	.6614
.505	.7450	.8631	.755	.4300	.6557
.51	.7399	.8617	.76	.4224	.6499
.515	.7348	.8572	.765	.4148	.6440
.52	.7296	.8542	.77	.4071	.6380
.525	.7244	.8511	.775	.3994	.6330
.53	.7191	.8480	.78	.3916	.6258
.535	.7138	.8449	.785	.3838	.6195
.54	.7084	.8417	.79	.3759	.6131
.545	.7030	.8385	.795	.3680	.6066
.55	.6975	.8352	.80	.3600	.6000
.555	.6920	.8319	.805	.3520	.5933
.56	.6864	.8285	.81	.3439	.5864
.565	.6808	.8251	.815	3358	.5795
.57	.6751	.8216	.82	.3276	.5724
.575	.6694	.8182	.825	.3194	.5652
.58	.6636	.8146	.83	.3111	.5578
.585	.6578	.8110	.835	.3028	.5503
.59	.6519	.8074	.84	.2944	.5426
.595	.6460	.8037	.845	.2860	.5348
.60	.6400	.8000	.85	.2775	.5268
.605	.6340	.7962	.855	.2690	.5187
.61	.6279	.7924	.86	.2604	.5103
.615	.6218	.7885	.865	.2518	.5018
.62	.6156	.7846	.87	.2431	.4931
.625	.6094	.7806	.875	.2344	.4841
.63	.6031	.7766	.88	.2256	.4750
.635	.5968	.7725	.885	.2168	.4656
.64	.5904	.7684	.89	.2079	.4560
.645	.5840	.7642	.895	.1990	.4461
.65	.5775	.7599	.90	.1900	.4359
.655	.5710	.7556	.905	.1810	.4254
.66	.5644	.7513	.91	.1719	.4146
.665	.5578	.7469	.915	.1628	.4035
.67	.5511	.7424	.92	.1536	.3919
.675	.5444	.7378	.925	.1444	.3800
.68	.5376	.7332	.93	.1351	.3676
.685	.5308	.7286	.935	.1258	.3547
.69	.5239	.7238	.94	.1164	.3412
.695	.5170	.7190	.945	.1070	.3271
.70	.5100	.7141	.95	.0975	.3122
.705	.5030	.7092	.955	.0880	.2966
.71	.4959	.7042	.96	.0784	.2800
.715	.4888	.6991	.965	.0688	.2623
.72	.4816	.6940	.97	.0591	.2431
.725	.4744	.6888	.975	.0494	.2223
.73	.4671	.6834	.98	.0396	.1990
.735	.4598	.6781	.985	.0298	.1726
.74	.4524	.6726	.99	.0199	.1411
.745	.4450	.6671	.995	.0100	.1000

APPENDIX

TABLE M.—TRIGONOMETRIC FUNCTIONS[1]

ANGLE	SIN	COS	TAN	ANGLE	SIN	COS	TAN
0°	.000	1.000	.000	45°	.707	.707	1.000
1°	.018	.999	.018	46°	.719	.695	1.036
2°	.035	.999	.035	47°	.731	.682	1.072
3°	.052	.998	.052	48°	.743	.669	1.111
4°	.070	.997	.070	49°	.755	.656	1.150
5°	.087	.996	.087	50°	.766	.643	1.192
6°	.105	.994	.105	51°	.777	.629	1.235
7°	.122	.992	.123	52°	.788	.616	1.280
8°	.139	.990	.141	53°	.799	.602	1.327
9°	.156	.988	.158	54°	.809	.588	1.376
10°	.174	.985	.176	55°	.819	.574	1.428
11°	.191	.982	.194	56°	.829	.559	1.483
12°	.208	.978	.213	57°	.839	.545	1.540
13°	.225	.974	.231	58°	.848	.530	1.600
14°	.242	.970	.249	59°	.857	.515	1.664
15°	.259	.966	.268	60°	.866	.500	1.732
16°	.276	.961	.287	61°	.875	.485	1.804
17°	.292	.956	.306	62°	.883	.469	1.881
18°	.309	.951	.325	63°	.891	.454	1.963
19°	.326	.946	.344	64°	.899	.438	2.050
20°	.342	.940	.364	65°	.906	.423	2.144
21°	.358	.934	.384	66°	.914	.407	2.246
22°	.375	.927	.404	67°	.921	.391	2.356
23°	.391	.921	.424	68°	.927	.375	2.475
24°	.407	.914	.445	69°	.934	.358	2.605
25°	.423	.906	.466	70°	.940	.342	2.747
26°	.438	.899	.488	71°	.946	.326	2.904
27°	.454	.891	.510	72°	.951	.309	3.078
28°	.469	.883	.532	73°	.956	.292	3.271
29°	.485	.875	.554	74°	.961	.276	3.487
30°	.500	.866	.577	75°	.966	.259	3.732
31°	.515	.857	.601	76°	.970	.242	4.011
32°	.530	.848	.625	77°	.974	.225	4.331
33°	.545	.839	.649	78°	.978	.208	4.705
34°	.559	.829	.675	79°	.982	.191	5.145
35°	.574	.819	.700	80°	.985	.174	5.671
36°	.588	.809	.727	81°	.988	.156	6.314
37°	.602	.799	.754	82°	.990	.139	7.115
38°	.616	.788	.781	83°	.992	.122	8.144
39°	.629	.777	.810	84°	.994	.105	9.514
40°	.643	.766	.839	85°	.996	.087	11.430
41°	.656	.755	.869	86°	.997	.070	14.300
42°	.669	.743	.900	87°	.998	.052	19.081
43°	.682	.731	.933	88°	.999	.035	28.636
44°	.695	.719	.966	89°	.999	.018	57.290

[1] From Smail, "College Algebra."

AUTHOR INDEX

A

Achilles, P. S., 108
Ackerson, L., 455
Adams, H. F., 276, 282, 514
Adrian, R., 404
Allen, J. F., 140
Allport, F. H., 106, 108
Ament, W., 163, 165
Anastasi, A., 514
Angell, F., 145
Appunn, A., 118
Arlett, A. H., 276, 282
Aubert, H., 136
Ayers, L. P., 439, 453

B

Barrett, M., 260 f.
Bartelme, P., 453
Barthelmess, H. M., 429 f., 453
Beebe-Center, J. G., 238, 242
Bernoulli, J., 6, 113n.
Binet, A., 3, 7, 10, 210, 408–410, 428, 437 f., 440, 443, 458, 466
Blakeman, J., 348
Boring, E. G., 18, 108, 117, 141, 154n., 165, 172 f., 176, 201, 210, 212
Bouguer, P., 113n., 115
Bousfield, W. A., 324, 326
Bowditch, H. P., 404
Boyce, A. C., 267, 282
Bradshaw, F. F., 279, 282
Bravais, A., 404
Bressler, J., 206n., 212
Brodhun, E., 136
Brogan, A. P., 245, 261
Brotemarkle, R. A., 453
Brown, C. W., 453
Brown, J. F., 18
Brown, W., 195, 202 f., 206, 208, 212, 410, 412, 418, 420 f., 449

C

Brown, Wm., 18, 66, 70, 141, 171n., 212, 368n., 377, 514, 543
Bryan, W. L., 405, 406
Bullough, E., 223, 242
Burks, B. S., 406

Cady, V. M., 277, 282
Camerer, W., 135
Cattell, J. McK., 7, 9 f., 64–66, 70, 113n., 136–139, 141, 151, 156, 165, 200 f., 206, 212, 217, 244 f., 261, 277, 282, 313, 408, 458
Clark, E. L., 434, 454
Clayton, B., 454
Cleeton, G. U., 445, 454
Clothier, R. C., 283
Cobb, P. W., 140, 141
Cohn, J., 223, 242
Conklin, E. S., 260 f., 265, 267, 280, 282
Conrad, H. S., 274, 276, 282
Cook, W. W., 417, 423, 434 f., 454 f.
Cowdery, K. M., 450, 453 f.
Cowdrick, M., 156, 165
Cox, C. M., 453
Cozens, F. W., 454
Crelle, A. L., 18
Culler, E., 4n., 9, 92 f., 108, 176n., 179, 179n., 180, 185, 192–194, 197, 199 f., 206, 212, 221, 449, 454
Cureton, E. E., 342, 367, 369, 377 f., 420, 454, 514
Czermak, J. N., 135

D

Dallenbach, K. M., 210–213, 282
Darwin, C., 408 f.
Delboeuf, J. R. L., 8, 145

553

SUBJECT INDEX

A

Ability, theories of, 458 *ff.*
Ability vectors, 475
Abscissa, 34
Absolute judgment, method of, 205
Absolute scaling methods, 440–444
Absolute test zero, 444
Aesthetic judgment, 223 *f.*
Alienation, coefficient of, 362
Appunn's lamella, 118
Aptitude testing, theory of, 467
Äquivalentswert, 128
Area, under normal curve, 93–99, 219
Arithmetic mean, 42–44, 169 *f.*, 189
Army Alpha, data on, 69, 376, 491
    factor analysis of, 491 *ff.*
Association tests, data on, 514
Associative limen, 210
Athletic ability, data on, 405 *f.*
Attenuation, correction for, 366–369
Attitudes, measurement of, 161–163
Augenmass, 65
Average deviation, formulas for, 46 *f.*
Average error, method of, 23–67
    criticisms of, 63–65
    history of, 25
Averages, method of curve fitting, 296 *f.*

B

Balanced values, method of, 239
Belief, experiment on, 265–267
Beta coefficient, 337 *f.*
    computation of, 394 *f.*
    formulas for, 381
Bimodal distribution, 36
Binomial expansion, 75 *f.*
Bisection, of sound interval, 147
    data for, 164

Biserial coefficient of correlation, 349–351
Biserial *r*, computation, 350
    method, 431
Blakeman's test, 348

C

Centesimal grades, 248*n.*
Central tendency, error of, 272
    law of, 255, 257
Centroid method, 478–488
Chi square, 356
    table for, 536
Chi square test, 92 *f.*, 180 *f.*
Clark's index of validity, 434
Class interval, 31
Coefficient, of alienation, 362
    tables of, 550 *f.*
    of contingency, 357
    of correlation, 301, 303–309
        interpretation of, 361–366
    of determination, 305
    of multiple determination, 386
    of multiple nondetermination, 386
    of nondetermination, 366
    of reliability, 411
    of variation, 49 *f.*
Color preferences, data on, 281, 387
Column diagram, 34
Communality, definition of, 473
    estimation of, 478 *f.*
Comparative judgment, law of, 217–221, 251 *f.*
Comparative judgments, applications of, 220 *f.*
Complete series, method of, 209
Composite standard, for ranked data, 250 *f.*
Computation, aids in, 18
Confidence, judgments of, 206

559